P9-CQI-671

MATHPOWER™10

ONTARIO EDITION

MATHPOWER™ 10

ONTARIO EDITION

**MATHPOWER™ 10,
Ontario Edition, Authors**

George Knill, B.Sc., M.S.Ed.

Eileen Collins, B.A., M.Ed.

Eleanor Conrad, B.Sc., M.Ed.

Fred Ferneyhough, B.Math.

Michael Hamilton, B.Sc., M.Sc.

Rosemary Miller, B.Math., M.Sc.(T)

Harold Wardrop, B.Sc.

Michael Webb, B.Sc., M.Sc., Ph.D.

**MATHPOWER™ 10, Ontario Edition,
Contributing Authors**

George Adams, B.Math, B.Ed., M.Math.
Head, Information Technology and
Technological Studies
Streetsville Secondary School
Mississauga, Ontario

Lynda Ferneyhough, B.Math.
Head, Mathematics Department
Chinguacousy Secondary School
Brampton, Ontario

**MATHPOWER™ 10, Ontario Edition,
Assessment Consultants**

Chris Dearling, B.Sc., M.Sc.
Mathematics Education Consultant
Burlington, Ontario

Lynda Ferneyhough, B.Math.
Head, Mathematics Department
Chinguacousy Secondary School
Brampton, Ontario

**MATHPOWER™ 10, Ontario Edition,
Technology Consultant**
Fred Ferneyhough, B.Math.
Head, Mathematics Department
Central Peel Secondary School
Brampton, Ontario

**McGraw-Hill
Ryerson**

Toronto Montréal New York Burr Ridge Bangkok Bogotá Caracas
Lisbon London Madrid Mexico City Milan New Delhi
Seoul Singapore Sydney Taipei

McGraw-Hill
Ryerson Limited
A Subsidiary of The **McGraw-Hill** Companies

MATHPOWER™ *10*
Ontario Edition

Copyright © 2000, McGraw-Hill Ryerson Limited, a Subsidiary of The McGraw-Hill Companies. All rights reserved. No part of this publication may be reproduced or transmitted in any form or by any means, or stored in a data base or retrieval system, without the prior written permission of McGraw-Hill Ryerson Limited, or, in the case of photocopying or other reprographic copying, a licence from CANCOPY (Canadian Copyright Licensing Agency), One Yonge Street, Suite 1900, Toronto, Ontario M5E 1E5.

Any request for photocopying, recording, taping, or information storage and retrieval of any part of this publication shall be directed in writing to CANCOPY.

ISBN 0-07-552908-4

http://www.mcgrawhill.ca

2 3 4 5 6 7 8 9 0 TRI 0 9 8 7 6 5 4 3 2 1 0

Printed and bound in Canada

Care has been taken to trace ownership of copyright material contained in this text. The publishers will gladly take any information that will enable them to rectify any reference or credit in subsequent printings.

The Geometer's Sketchpad® is a registered trademark of Key Curriculum Press.

CBL™ and CBR™ are trademarks of Texas Instruments Incorporated.

Canadian Cataloguing in Publication Data

Main entry under title:

Mathpower 10

Ontario ed.
Includes index.
ISBN 0-07-5529084

1. Mathematics. 2. Mathematics – Problems, exercises, etc.
I. Knill, George, date. II. Title: Mathpower ten.

QA107.M37648 2000   510   C00-930675-7

PUBLISHER: Diane Wyman
EDITORIAL CONSULTING: Michael J. Webb Consulting Inc.
ASSOCIATE EDITORS: Jean Ford, Mary Agnes Challoner, Janice Nixon
SENIOR SUPERVISING EDITOR: Carol Altilia
PERMISSIONS EDITOR: Ann Ludbrook
EDITORIAL ASSISTANTS: Joanne Murray, Erin Parton
PRODUCTION SUPERVISOR: Yolanda Pigden
ART DIRECTION: Wycliffe Smith Design, Inc.
COVER DESIGN: Dianna Little
INTERIOR DESIGN: Wycliffe Smith Design, Inc.
ELECTRONIC PAGE MAKE-UP: Tom Dart, Bruce Krever, Claire Milne, Alana Perez/
                                    First Folio Resource Group, Inc.
COVER ILLUSTRATIONS: Citrus Media
COVER IMAGE: Peter Pearson/Stone

MATHPOWER™ *10,*
Ontario Edition, **Reviewers**

The authors and editors of *MATHPOWER*™ *10, Ontario Edition*, wish to thank the reviewers listed below for their comments and suggestions. Their input has been invaluable in ensuring that *MATHPOWER*™ *10, Ontario Edition*, meets the needs of the students and the teachers of Ontario.

Patricia Angel,
Mathematics Education Consultant
Mississauga, Ontario

Anthony Azzopardi,
Mathematics Consultant
Toronto Catholic District School Board
Toronto, Ontario

Peter Clifford,
Mathematics Teacher
Earl Haig Collegiate
Toronto, Ontario

Chris Dearling,
Mathematics Education Consultant
Burlington, Ontario

Gerry Doerksen,
Head, Mathematics Department
Royal St. George's College
Toronto, Ontario

Fred Ferneyhough,
Head, Mathematics Department
Central Peel Secondary School
Brampton, Ontario

Jeff Irvine,
Head, Mathematics Department
Brampton Centennial Secondary School
Brampton, Ontario

Louis Lim,
Mathematics Teacher
Quinte Secondary School
Belleville, Ontario

Brian McCudden,
Mathematics Education Consultant
Etobicoke, Ontario

Susan Rozario,
Mathematics Teacher
Central Peel Secondary School
Brampton, Ontario

Peter Saarimaki,
Mathematics Coordinator
Toronto District School Board
Toronto, Ontario

Al Smith,
Mathematics Teacher
Lakefield District Secondary School
Lakefield, Ontario

Robert Smith,
Head, Mathematics Department
Lockerby Composite School
Sudbury, Ontario

Contents

CHAPTER 2

Analytic Geometry

CHAPTER 3

Polynomials

CHAPTER 4

Quadratic Functions

CHAPTER 5

Quadratic Equations

CHAPTER 6

Trigonometry

A Tour of Your Textbook

To understand the book's structure, begin by taking a brief tour of the following.

CHAPTER INTRODUCTION

Specific Expectations

• The specific expectations listed on the first page of each chapter describe the knowledge and skills that you are expected to develop and demonstrate. The list includes references to the sections in which the specific expectations are covered.

Modelling Math

• Each chapter opens with a real-life problem that can be solved using a mathematical model. Examples of mathematical models include graphs, diagrams, formulas, equations, tables of values, and computer models.

• The lessons in the chapter prepare you to solve the problem posed on the opening pages and related problems found at the end of some sections.

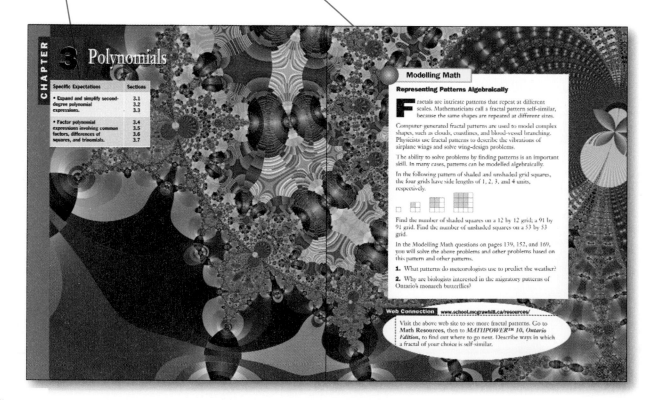

REVIEWING PREREQUISITE SKILLS

Getting Started

• Before the first numbered section in each chapter, a two-page Getting Started section reviews the mathematical skills you will need.

• The first page reviews skills in an interesting context.

• The second page is headed Review of Prerequisite Skills. Each skill area

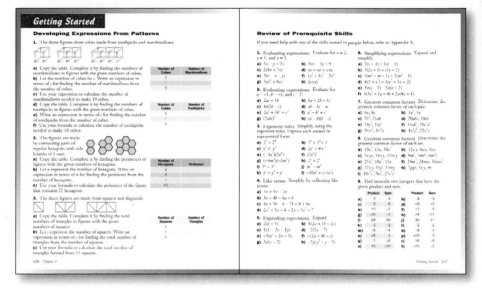

named in purple on a Review of Prerequisite Skills page is referenced to the alphabetical list of skills in **Appendix A: Review of Prerequisite Skills,** located at the back of the text.

Appendix A

• If you need help with any of the skills on the Review of Prerequisite Skills page at the beginning of each chapter, refer to this alphabetical list.

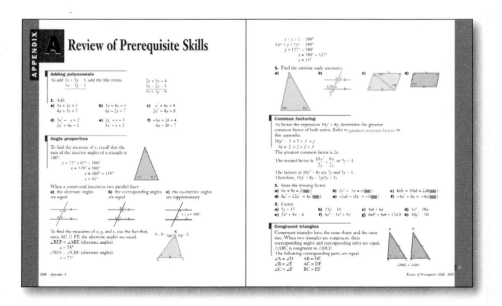

CONCEPT DEVELOPMENT

Investigations

• Most core sections introduce topics in an interesting context. You are then guided through an investigation.

• The investigation uses the process of inquiry, which allows you to discover the new concepts for yourself. This process is an important part of learning mathematics.

Examples

• The worked examples demonstrate how to use, and extend, what you have learned. They also provide model solutions to problems.

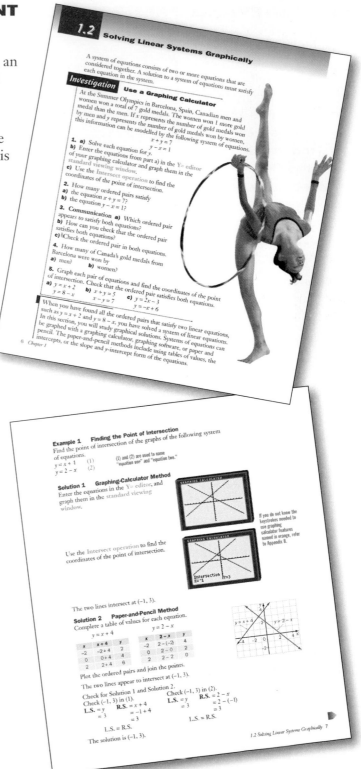

RICH PROBLEMS

- One rich problem is included at the end of each chapter before the Review of Key Concepts.

- These problems provide real-world contexts in which to explore concepts in a rich problem solving situation.

CAREER CONNECTIONS

- These activities give you the opportunity to investigate mathematics-related careers that make use of the chapter content.

REVIEW AND ASSESSMENT

Several features within the text provide opportunities for review and assessment:

Communicate Your Understanding

- Following each summary of Key Concepts are questions designed to help you communicate your understanding of what you have learned.

Achievement Check

- This feature provides questions designed to assess your knowledge and understanding, your problem solving skills, your communication skills, and your ability to apply what you have learned.

- Achievement Checks appear throughout the chapter, with one always at the end of the chapter test.

Key Concepts

- Following the worked examples, the concepts in the section are summarized.

- You can use this summary when you are doing homework or studying.

Practice

- Completing these questions allows you to master essential mathematical skills by practising what you have learned.

Applications and Problem Solving

- Mathematics is powerful when it is applied. The questions in this section allow you to use what you have learned to solve problems, and to apply and extend what you have learned.

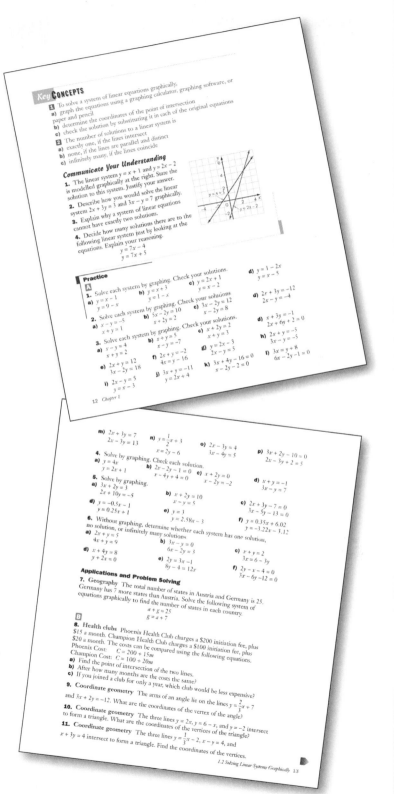

TECHNOLOGY

• Graphing calculators, geometry software, and scientific probes are technology tools that will make you a more powerful learner, by allowing you to explore mathematical concepts more easily and quickly.

• The use of these tools is integrated within the investigations, the worked examples, and the Practice and Applications and Problem Solving questions.

• Two appendixes at the back of the text provide specific instructions in the operation of graphing calculators and geometry software.

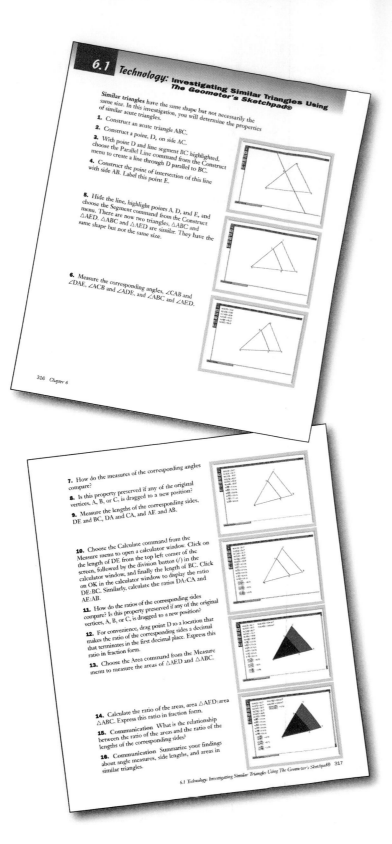

Appendix B: Graphing Calculator Keystrokes includes detailed instructions in an alphabetical listing of functions used in *MATHPOWER™ 10, Ontario Edition.*

Appendix C: Using *The Geometer's Sketchpad*® reviews the essential skills needed to operate this program.

• Technology Extension features provide additional instruction and opportunities to use technology tools in applications related to the chapter.

• Specific instructions in how to use scientific probes are included in the appropriate core section of the text.

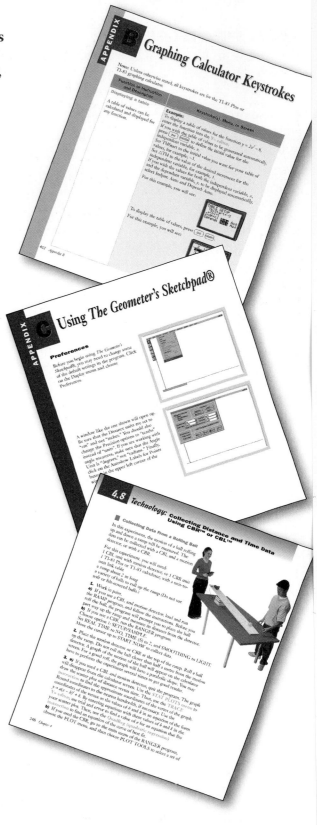

Review of Key Concepts

• At the end of each chapter are questions designed to review the concepts learned in the chapter.

• The review is organized section by section, and refers to each summary of Key Concepts in the chapter.

• A worked example is provided in each review section.

Chapter Test

• Each chapter includes a test to assess the skills addressed in the chapter.

• Each test includes an Achievement Check.

Cumulative Review

• The cumulative reviews that are found at the end of Chapters 2, 4, and 6, review concepts from the two preceding chapters.

• A fourth cumulative review, which is found after Chapter 6, reviews concepts from the whole text.

PROBLEM SOLVING

• In addition to developing your skill at solving problems as you work through the numerous problems throughout this text, *MATHPOWER 10*™, *Ontario Edition*, also teaches formal problem solving skills.

• In the first five chapters, there are ten sections that teach problem solving strategies. Each section focusses on one strategy. The section provides an example of how the strategy can be used and includes problems that can be solved using the strategy.

• At or near the end of each chapter, you will find a section headed **Problem Solving: Using the Strategies.** Each of these sections includes a variety of problems that can be solved using different strategies.

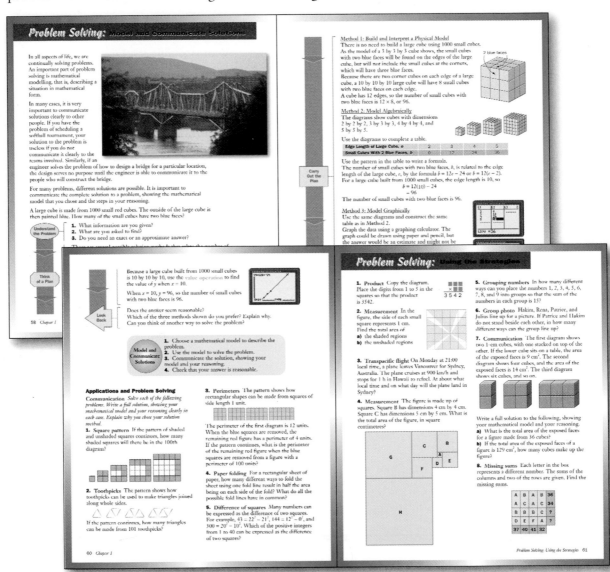

END-OF-TEXT FEATURES

Appendix A: Review of Prerequisite Skills

• This review is found on pages 398–411.

Appendix B: Graphing Calculator Keystrokes

• This review is found on pages 412–429.

Appendix C: Using *The Geometer's Sketchpad*®

• This review is found on pages 430–443.

Answers

• Answers are found on pages 444–469.

Glossary

• Mathematical terms used in the text are listed and defined on pages 470–483.

Indexes

• The book includes a technology index and a general index on pages 484–488.

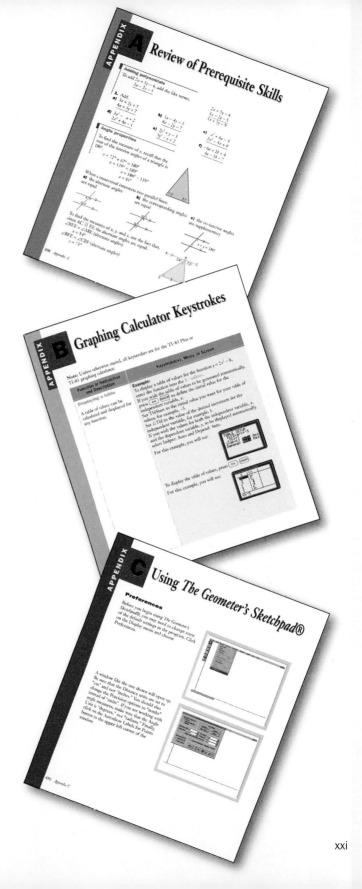

1 Linear Systems

Specific Expectations	Sections
• Determine the point of intersection of two linear equations graphically, with and without the use of graphing calculators or graphing software.	1.1 1.2
• Interpret the intersection point in the context of a realistic situation.	1.2
• Solve systems of two linear equations in two variables by the algebraic methods of substitution and elimination.	1.3 1.4 1.5
• Solve problems represented by linear systems of two equations in two variables arising from realistic situations, by using an algebraic method and by interpreting graphs.	1.2 1.3 1.5 1.6 1.7

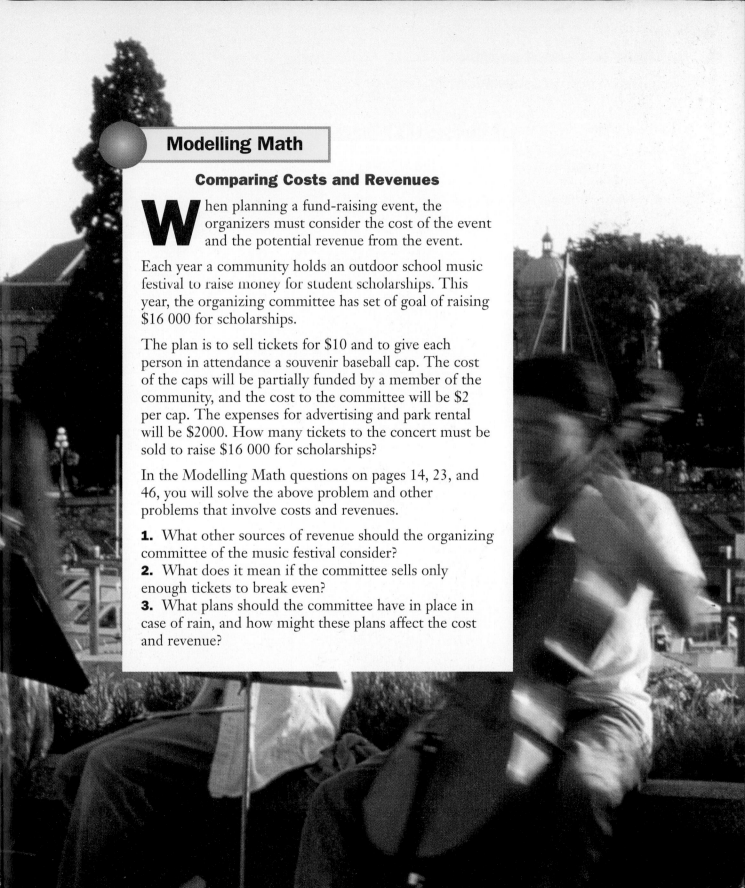

Modelling Math

Comparing Costs and Revenues

When planning a fund-raising event, the organizers must consider the cost of the event and the potential revenue from the event.

Each year a community holds an outdoor school music festival to raise money for student scholarships. This year, the organizing committee has set of goal of raising $16 000 for scholarships.

The plan is to sell tickets for $10 and to give each person in attendance a souvenir baseball cap. The cost of the caps will be partially funded by a member of the community, and the cost to the committee will be $2 per cap. The expenses for advertising and park rental will be $2000. How many tickets to the concert must be sold to raise $16 000 for scholarships?

In the Modelling Math questions on pages 14, 23, and 46, you will solve the above problem and other problems that involve costs and revenues.

1. What other sources of revenue should the organizing committee of the music festival consider?
2. What does it mean if the committee sells only enough tickets to break even?
3. What plans should the committee have in place in case of rain, and how might these plans affect the cost and revenue?

Getting Started

Social Insurance Numbers

In 1964, 9-digit Social Insurance Numbers (SINs) were introduced in Canada to identify people in their dealings with the federal government. The first digit in a SIN indicates the region in which the SIN was issued. A first digit of 1 shows that the SIN was issued in the Atlantic Provinces, 2 indicates Quebec, 4 and 5, Ontario, 6, the Prairies, and 7, the Pacific Region including the Territories.

The middle 7 digits in a SIN are assigned in numerical sequence. If the first 8 digits assigned to a SIN in the Atlantic Provinces are 123 456 77, then the first 8 digits in the next SIN to be issued will be 123 456 78. The final digit in a SIN is a check digit that is calculated from the other 8 digits. If the first 8 digits are represented as $pqr\ stu\ vw$, then the 9th digit can be found as shown in the example.

Step	Instruction	Example: SIN 123 456 78
1	Add $p + r + t + v$.	$p + r + t + v = 1 + 3 + 5 + 7$ $= 16$
2	Determine $2q$, $2s$, $2u$, and $2w$.	$2q = 2(2)$ $= 4$ $2s = 2(4)$ $= 8$ $2u = 2(6)$ $= 12$ $2w = 2(8)$ $= 16$
3	Add the digits in the results from step 2.	$4 + 8 + 1 + 2 + 1 + 6 = 22$
4	Add the results from steps 1 and 3.	$16 + 22 = 38$
5	Subtract the result of step 4 from the next highest multiple of 10.	$40 - 38 = 2$ The check digit is 2. The complete SIN is 123 456 782.

1. Communication When the result of step 4 is a multiple of 10, what do you think is the result of step 5? Explain.

2. Find the check digit needed to complete each SIN.
a) 765 432 10█   **b)** 234 567 89█   **c)** 444 444 44█   **d)** 111 111 11█

3. Communication Is each of the following SINs possible? Explain.
a) 285 461 783   **b)** 466 013 653   **c)** 354 821 902

4. Devise a SIN in which the check digit is 7; 0.

5. Communication If the number that results from step 4 of the example is represented by $10n + m$, the subtraction in step 5 can be represented by the expression $10(n + 1) - (10n + m)$.
a) Simplify $10(n + 1) - (10n + m)$.
b) When the check digit is 0, what is the value of m? Explain.
c) Use the results from parts a) and b) to suggest a second way of completing step 5.

Review of Prerequisite Skills

If you need help with any of the skills named in **purple** below, refer to Appendix A.

1. Simplifying expressions Simplify.
a) $3x + 2(1 - x)$ **b)** $4(x + 2) - 2x$
c) $2y - (5 - y)$ **d)** $-3(a - 1) - 2a$
e) $2(x + 3) + 4(x + 2)$ **f)** $2(z - 1) + 3(z - 2)$
g) $8(t + 4) - (t - 9)$ **h)** $5(x - 6) - 3(x - 7)$

2. Simplifying expressions Simplify.
a) $(2x + 3y) + (4x - 3y)$
b) $(3c - 4d) - (5c - 4d)$
c) $3(x + 2y) - 2(x + 3y)$
d) $5m - 2n + 5(n - m)$
e) $2x + y - z - (x - y - z)$
f) $p - 2q + 3r + 2(p + q - 2r)$

3. Solving equations Solve mentally.
a) $x + 3 = 11$ **b)** $c - 3 = -1$
c) $\dfrac{y}{3} = -2$ **d)** $2z = -10$

4. Solving equations Solve and check.
a) $3x + 1 = 22$ **b)** $4d - 3 = -15$
c) $6x - 1 = 11$ **d)** $\dfrac{m}{4} - 1 = 2$
e) $2(y + 3) = 5$ **f)** $4x - 2 = 2x + 1$
g) $\dfrac{t - 1}{3} = 5 - t$ **h)** $\dfrac{2y + 1}{3} = \dfrac{y - 1}{2}$
i) $\dfrac{x}{3} + \dfrac{1}{3} = -\dfrac{1}{2}$ **j)** $2.5x + 6.4 = -3.6$
k) $3(x + 3) = -2(2x - 1)$
l) $2(x - 7) + 3(x + 1) = -1$

5. Solving equations Solve for x.
a) $x + 3y = 11$ **b)** $5y - x = 8$
c) $x - 2y + 4 = 0$ **d)** $2x + 3y = 5$

6. Solving equations Solve for y.
a) $2x + y = 3$ **b)** $x - y = 2$
c) $2x + 4y = -1$ **d)** $3x - 2y = 4$

7. Graphing equations Graph using a table of values.
a) $x + y = 5$ **b)** $y = 3x - 2$
c) $y = -x + 3$ **d)** $2x - y = 4$

8. Graphing equations Graph using the intercepts.
a) $x + y = 7$ **b)** $x - y = 4$
c) $2x + y = 8$ **d)** $3x - 2y = 6$

9. Graphing equations Graph using the slope and y-intercept.
a) $y = x - 2$ **b)** $y = -x + 1$
c) $y = 2x$ **d)** $y = -2x + 3$

10. Graphing equations Graph each pair of lines and find the coordinates of the point of intersection.
a) $y = x - 2$ and $y = 4 - x$
b) $y = 3 - x$ and $y = x - 7$
c) $y = 5 - x$ and $y = x + 7$
d) $y = 2x$ and $y = x + 4$
e) $y = 2x + 3$ and $y = x - 1$
f) $y = 5 - 3x$ and $y = 2x - 5$

11. Adding polynomials Add.
a) $4x + 3y + 6$
    $5x - 7y - 5$
b) $6m^2 - m - 8$
    $7m^2 - 5m - 11$
c) $8a - 5b + 2$
    $-9a + 2b - 12$
d) $-8e - 2f + 7$
    $7e + 2f - 9$

12. Subtracting polynomials Subtract.
a) $3x - 5y + 3$
    $2x + 3y - 7$
b) $4t^2 - 2t - 8$
    $5t^2 + 3t + 3$
c) $-5a - 3b - 1$
    $4a - 6b - 2$
d) $6e + 5f - 3$
    $-6e + 5f - 2$

1 Ordered Pairs and One Equation

An equation in one variable, such as $2x + 1 = 7$, has one real value of x as a solution. In this case, the solution is 3.

An equation in two variables, such as $2x + y = 9$, has an infinite number of ordered pairs as solutions. Some of them are (0, 9), (1, 7), (3, 3) and (–1, 11). Any solution can be verified by substituting the values for x and y in the equation. The solution (–1, 11) is verified as follows.
For $2x + y = 9$,

L.S. $= 2x + y$ **R.S.** $= 9$
$= 2(-1) + 11$
$= -2 + 11$
$= 9$

Since L.S. = R.S., (–1, 11) satisfies the equation and is a solution.

1. Which of the ordered pairs satisfy the equation?
a) $x + y = 14$ (1, 13), (–3, 12), (24, –10)   **b)** $2x + 5y = -24$ (–2, –4), (–3, 6), (–12, 0)
c) $x - y = -1$ (2, 3), (–1, –2), (–5, 6)   **d)** $y = 3x - 4$ (1.5, –1.5), (0.5, –2.5), (2.5, 2.5)

2. Find the missing element of each ordered pair, so that the ordered pair satisfies the equation.
a) $x + y = 7$ (4, ■), (–2, ■), (■, –3), (■, 9)
b) $x - y = 5$ (7, ■), (–4, ■), (■, 6), (■, –7)
c) $2x + y = 9$ (5, ■), (■, –1), (–2, ■), (■, –11)
d) $y = 3x - 1$ (2, ■), (■, 8), (■, –13), (–2, ■)

2 Ordered Pairs and Two Equations

Two equations studied together are called a **system of equations**.
The following is a system of equations.
$$x + y = 7$$
$$x - 2y = 1$$
To verify that the ordered pair (5, 2) satisfies both equations, substitute the values for x and y in each equation.

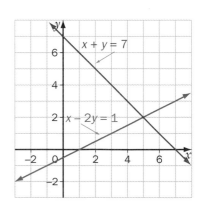

For $x + y = 7$,   For $x - 2y = 1$,
   L.S. $= x + y$ **R.S.** $= 7$ **L.S.** $= x - 2y$ **R.S.** $= 1$
     $= 5 + 2$ $= 5 - 2(2)$
     $= 7$ $= 1$
       L.S. = R.S.   L.S. = R.S.

Since (5, 2) satisfies both equations, the solution to the system is (5, 2).
The solution is modelled on the graph. Note that (5, 2) is the only point that lies on both lines.

1. Identify the ordered pair that satisfies both equations.

a) $x + y = 3$ $(0, 3), (1, 2), (2, 1)$
    $2x - y = 0$

b) $2x + y = -5$ $(-4, 3), (-8, 11), (-3, 1)$
    $x + 5y = 2$

c) $y = 2x - 1$ $(2, 3), (1, 1), (-1, 6)$
    $y = -x + 5$

d) $x + y = -2$ $(3, -4), (6, -8), (-7, 5)$
    $3x + 2y = 2$

e) $y = \dfrac{1}{2}x - 4$ $(4, -2), (2, -3), (-2, -5)$
    $y = 2x - 1$

f) $y = 2x + 15$ $(-4, 7), (7, -4), (-7, 1)$
    $y = -2x - 1$

2. Copy and complete each ordered pair so that it meets the stated condition.

a) $x + y = 1$ $(4, \blacksquare)$ satisfies the first equation but not the second.
    $3x - y = 3$

b) $2x - y = -1$ $(\blacksquare, 3)$ satisfies the second equation but not the first.
    $x + 2y = 12$

c) $y = 3x + 3$ $(\blacksquare, 0)$ satisfies both equations.
    $y = 2x + 2$

d) $y = 4x - 3$ $(\blacksquare, \blacksquare)$ satisfies neither equation.
    $y = -2x + 5$

3 Problem Solving

1. Newspaper ads The costs of placing a classified ad in two newspapers are as follows.

Daily Gleaner: fixed cost $25, plus $10/day
Daily Standard: fixed cost $10, plus $15/day

The costs can be modelled by the following system of equations.

Daily Gleaner: $C = 10n + 25$
Daily Standard: $C = 15n + 10$

where C is the total cost and n is the number of days for which the ad is run.

a) Find the missing element in the ordered pair $(3, \blacksquare)$ that satisfies both equations and is in the form (n, C).

b) What number of days gives equal costs for running the ad in each newspaper?

c) What is the total cost of running the ad for this number of days in either newspaper?

2. Communication a) An infinite number of ordered pairs, including $(0, 1), (1, 0)$, and $(2, -1)$, satisfy both equations. Explain why.

$$x + y = 1$$
$$2x + 2y = 2$$

b) Find two more ordered pairs that satisfy both equations.

3. Communication No ordered pair satisfies both equations. Explain why.

$$y = 2x + 1$$
$$y = 2x + 3$$

Solving Linear Systems Graphically

A system of equations consists of two or more equations that are considered together. A solution to a system of equations must satisfy each equation in the system.

Investigation   Use a Graphing Calculator

At the Summer Olympics in Barcelona, Spain, Canadian men and women won a total of 7 gold medals. The women won 1 more gold medal than the men. If x represents the number of gold medals won by men and y represents the number of gold medals won by women, this information can be modelled by the following system of equations.

$$x + y = 7$$
$$y - x = 1$$

1. a) Solve each equation for y.
b) Enter the equations from part a) in the Y= editor of your graphing calculator and graph them in the standard viewing window.
c) Use the Intersect operation to find the coordinates of the point of intersection.

2. How many ordered pairs satisfy
a) the equation $x + y = 7$?
b) the equation $y - x = 1$?

3. Communication a) Which ordered pair appears to satisfy both equations?
b) How can you check that the ordered pair satisfies both equations?
c) Check the ordered pair in both equations.

4. How many of Canada's gold medals from Barcelona were won by
a) men?   **b)** women?

5. Graph each pair of equations and find the coordinates of the point of intersection. Check that the ordered pair satisfies both equations.
a) $y = x + 2$ **b)** $x + y = 5$ **c)** $y = 2x - 3$
    $y = 8 - x$ $x - y = 7$ $y = -x + 6$

When you have found all the ordered pairs that satisfy two linear equations, such as $y = x + 2$ and $y = 8 - x$, you have solved a system of linear equations. In this section, you will study graphical solutions. Systems of equations can be graphed with a graphing calculator, graphing software, or paper and pencil. The paper-and-pencil methods include using tables of values, the intercepts, or the slope and y-intercept form of the equations.

Example 1 Finding the Point of Intersection

Find the point of intersection of the graphs of the following system of equations.

$y = x + 4$ (1)
$y = 2 - x$ (2)

(1) and (2) are used to name "equation one" and "equation two."

Solution 1 Graphing-Calculator Method

Enter the equations in the Y= editor, and graph them in the standard viewing window.

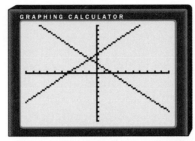

Use the Intersect operation to find the coordinates of the point of intersection.

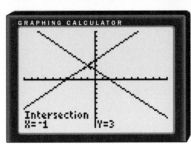

If you do not know the keystrokes needed to use graphing calculator features named in orange, refer to Appendix B.

The two lines intersect at (–1, 3).

Solution 2 Paper-and-Pencil Method

Complete a table of values for each equation.

$y = x + 4$

x	x + 4	y
–2	–2 + 4	2
0	0 + 4	4
2	2 + 4	6

$y = 2 - x$

x	2 – x	y
–2	2 – (–2)	4
0	2 – 0	2
2	2 – 2	0

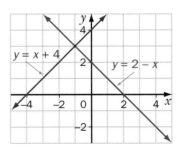

Plot the ordered pairs and join the points.

The two lines appear to intersect at (–1, 3).

Check for Solution 1 and Solution 2.

Check (–1, 3) in (1).

L.S. $= y$ **R.S.** $= x + 4$
   $= 3$ $= -1 + 4$
               $= 3$
     L.S. = R.S.

Check (–1, 3) in (2).

L.S. $= y$ **R.S.** $= 2 - x$
   $= 3$ $= 2 - (-1)$
               $= 3$
     L.S. = R.S.

The solution is (–1, 3).

Example 2   Solving a System Graphically

Solve the system of equations graphically.

$$2x + y = 5 \qquad (1)$$
$$x - 2y = 10 \qquad (2)$$

Solution 1   Graphing-Calculator Method

Write each equation in the slope and y-intercept form.

$$
\begin{aligned}
2x + y &= 5 & x - 2y &= 10 \\
y &= -2x + 5 & -2y &= -x + 10 \\
& & y &= \frac{1}{2}x - 5
\end{aligned}
$$

Enter the equations in the **Y= editor**, and graph them in the **standard viewing window**.

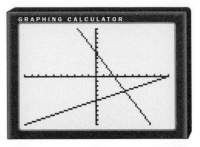

Use the **Intersect operation** to find the coordinates of the point of intersection.

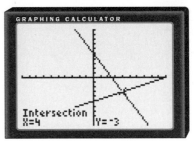

The coordinates of the point of intersection are $(4, -3)$.

Solution 2   Paper-and-Pencil Method

Write each equation in the slope and y-intercept form, as shown in Solution 1.

For the equation $y = -2x + 5$, the y-intercept is 5 and the slope is -2. Plot $(0, 5)$ and use the slope or the equation to find two other points, for example, $(-1, 7)$ and $(1, 3)$. Plot these two points and join the three points with a line.

For the equation $y = \frac{1}{2}x - 5$, the y-intercept is -5

and the slope is $\frac{1}{2}$. Plot $(0, -5)$.

Find and plot two other points, for example, $(2, -4)$ and $(-2, -6)$. Join the three points with a line.

The two lines appear to intersect at $(4, -3)$.

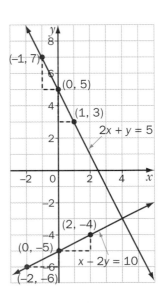

Check for Solution 1 and Solution 2.

Check (4, −3) in (1).   Check (4, −3) in (2).
L.S. $= 2x + y$ **R.S.** $= 5$ **L.S.** $= x − 2y$ **R.S.** $= 10$
$\quad = 2(4) + (−3)$ $\quad = 4 − 2(−3)$
$\quad = 8 − 3$ $\quad = 4 + 6$
$\quad = 5$ $\quad = 10$
$\qquad$ L.S. = R.S. $\qquad$ L.S. = R.S.
The solution is (4, −3).

Fractional solutions to linear systems can be estimated by graphing using paper and pencil, but the solutions may be approximate. Exact fractional solutions can be found by graphing using a graphing calculator.

Example 3   Finding Fractional Solutions
Solve the system of equations graphically.
$$2x + 5y = −20 \quad (1)$$
$$5x − 3y = −15 \quad (2)$$

Solution
To graph using a graphing calculator, write each equation in the slope and y-intercept form.

$2x + 5y = −20$ $\qquad$ $5x − 3y = −15$
$\quad 5y = −2x − 20$ $\qquad$ $−3y = −5x − 15$
$\quad y = −\dfrac{2}{5}x − 4$ $\qquad$ $y = \dfrac{5}{3}x + 5$

Enter the equations in the Y= editor, and graph them in the standard viewing window. Then, use the Intersect operation to determine the coordinates of the point of intersection.

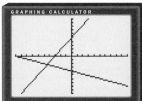
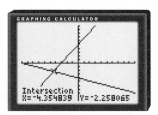

It is impossible to tell whether the decimal coordinates shown by the graphing calculator for the point of intersection are exact values. Therefore, use the Frac function to convert the decimals to fractions.

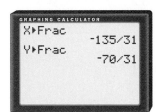

The solution is $\left(-\dfrac{135}{31}, -\dfrac{70}{31}\right)$.

Example 4   Numbers of Solutions

Graph each system of equations and determine the number of solutions.

a) $y = 2x + 3$ (1)   **b)** $x + y = 3$ (1)
    $y = 2x - 4$ (2) $2x + 2y = 6$ (2)

Solution

a) The lines have different y-intercepts but the same slope. For (1), the y-intercept is 3 and the slope is 2.

Plot $(0, 3)$. Find and plot two other points on the line, for example, $(1, 5)$ and $(-1, 1)$.

For (2), the y-intercept is -4 and the slope is 2.

Plot $(0, -4)$. Find and plot two other points on the line, for example, $(1, -2)$ and $(3, 2)$.

The lines are parallel and distinct, and do not intersect.

There is no solution to this system of equations.

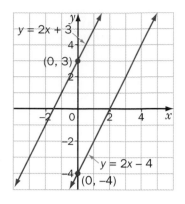

b) Use the intercepts to graph the lines.
For (1), two points are $(0, 3)$ and $(3, 0)$.
For (2), two points are $(0, 3)$ and $(3, 0)$.
The lines have the same slope and the same intercepts, so the lines coincide. Each equation has the same graph.

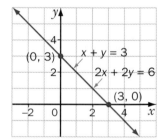

Two equations that have the same graph are called **equivalent equations**. Any ordered pair on the graph satisfies both equations.

This system of equations has an infinite number of solutions.

Note that the systems in Example 4 can be graphed using graphing software.

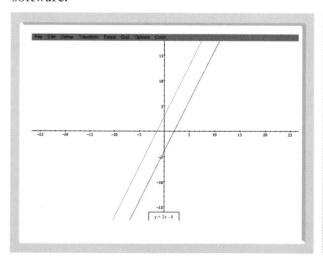

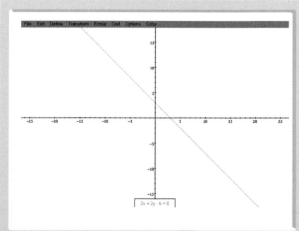

The graphs of two linear equations in two variables may intersect at one point, be parallel and distinct, or coincide.

Graphs of Lines	Slopes of Lines	Intercepts	Number of Solutions
Intersecting	Different	Different unless the lines intersect on one axis or at the origin	One
Parallel and distinct	Same	Different	None
Coincident	Same	Same	Infinitely many

Example 5   Analyzing Systems

Analyze each system to determine whether the system has one solution, no solution, or infinitely many solutions.

a) $2x + y = 6$ (1)
   $y - 8 = -2x$ (2)

b) $3x + y = 1$ (1)
   $6x + 2y = 2$ (2)

c) $2x + y - 4 = 0$ (1)
   $x + 2y - 6 = 0$ (2)

Solution

Before analyzing each system, express both equations in the form $y = mx + b$.

a) $y = -2x + 6$ (1)
   $y = -2x + 8$ (2)

b) $y = -3x + 1$ (1)
   $y = -3x + 1$ (2)

c) $y = -2x + 4$ (1)
   $y = -\dfrac{1}{2}x + 3$ (2)

Both lines have a slope of –2. Therefore, the lines are either parallel and distinct or they coincide. Since the y-intercepts are different, the lines must be parallel and distinct.

The system has no solution.

Both lines have the same slope, –3, and the same y-intercept, 1. The two lines coincide.

The system has infinitely many solutions.

The slopes of the lines are –2 and $-\dfrac{1}{2}$. The lines are not parallel and distinct, and they do not coincide. They intersect at a single point.

The system has one solution.

1 To solve a system of linear equations graphically,
a) graph the equations using a graphing calculator, graphing software, or paper and pencil
b) determine the coordinates of the point of intersection
c) check the solution by substituting it in each of the original equations

2 The number of solutions to a linear system is
a) exactly one, if the lines intersect
b) none, if the lines are parallel and distinct
c) infinitely many, if the lines coincide

Communicate Your Understanding

1. The linear system $y = x + 1$ and $y = 2x - 2$ is modelled graphically at the right. State the solution to this system. Justify your answer.

2. Describe how you would solve the linear system $2x + 3y = 3$ and $3x - y = 7$ graphically.

3. Explain why a system of linear equations cannot have exactly two solutions.

4. Decide how many solutions there are to the following linear system just by looking at the equations. Explain your reasoning.
$$y = 7x - 4$$
$$y = 7x + 5$$

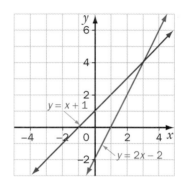

Practice

A

1. Solve each system by graphing. Check your solutions.
a) $y = x - 1$
$y = 9 - x$
b) $y = x + 3$
$y = 1 - x$
c) $y = 2x + 1$
$y = x - 2$
d) $y = 1 - 2x$
$y = x - 5$

2. Solve each system by graphing. Check your solutions.
a) $x - y = -5$
$x + y = 1$
b) $5x - 2y = 10$
$x + 2y = 2$
c) $3x - 2y = 12$
$x - 2y = 8$
d) $2x + 3y = -12$
$2x - y = -4$

3. Solve each system by graphing. Check your solutions.
a) $x - y = 4$
$x + y = 2$
b) $x + y = 5$
$x - y = -7$
c) $x + 2y = 2$
$x + y = 3$
d) $x + 3y = -1$
$2x + 6y + 2 = 0$

e) $2x + y = 12$
$3x - 2y = 18$
f) $2x + y = -2$
$4x = y - 16$
g) $y = 2x - 3$
$2x - y = 5$
h) $2x + y = -5$
$3x - y = -5$

i) $2x - y = 5$
$y = x - 3$
j) $3x + y = -11$
$y = 2x + 4$
k) $3x + 4y - 16 = 0$
$x - 2y - 2 = 0$
l) $3x = y + 8$
$6x - 2y - 1 = 0$

m) $2x + 3y = 7$
$2x - 3y = 13$

n) $y = \frac{1}{2}x + 3$
$x = 2y - 6$

o) $2x - 3y = 4$
$3x - 4y = 5$

p) $3x + 2y - 10 = 0$
$2x - 3y + 2 = 5$

4. Solve by graphing. Check each solution.

a) $y = 4x$
$y = 2x + 1$

b) $2x - 2y - 1 = 0$
$x - 4y + 4 = 0$

c) $x + 2y = 0$
$x - 2y = -2$

d) $x + y = -1$
$3x - y = 7$

5. Solve by graphing.

a) $3x + 2y = 3$
$2x + 10y = -5$

b) $x + 2y = 10$
$x - y = 5$

c) $2x + 3y - 7 = 0$
$3x - 5y - 13 = 0$

d) $y = -0.5x - 1$
$y = 0.25x + 1$

e) $y = 3$
$y = 2.58x - 3$

f) $y = 0.35x + 6.02$
$y = -3.22x - 3.12$

6. Without graphing, determine whether each system has one solution, no solution, or infinitely many solutions.

a) $2x + y = 5$
$4x + y = 9$

b) $3x - y = 0$
$6x - 2y = 3$

c) $x + y = 2$
$3x = 6 - 3y$

d) $x + 4y = 8$
$y + 2x = 0$

e) $2y = 3x - 1$
$8y - 4 = 12x$

f) $2y - x - 4 = 0$
$3x - 6y - 12 = 0$

Applications and Problem Solving

7. Geography The total number of states in Austria and Germany is 25. Germany has 7 more states than Austria. Solve the following system of equations graphically to find the number of states in each country.

$$a + g = 25$$
$$g = a + 7$$

8. Health clubs Phoenix Health Club charges a $200 initiation fee, plus $15 a month. Champion Health Club charges a $100 initiation fee, plus $20 a month. The costs can be compared using the following equations.

Phoenix Cost: $C = 200 + 15m$
Champion Cost: $C = 100 + 20m$

a) Find the point of intersection of the two lines.
b) After how many months are the costs the same?
c) If you joined a club for only a year, which club would be less expensive?

9. Coordinate geometry The arms of an angle lie on the lines $y = \frac{2}{3}x + 7$

and $3x + 2y = -12$. What are the coordinates of the vertex of the angle?

10. Coordinate geometry The three lines $y = 2x$, $y = 6 - x$, and $y = -2$ intersect to form a triangle. What are the coordinates of the vertices of the triangle?

11. Coordinate geometry The three lines $y = \frac{1}{3}x - 2$, $x - y = 4$, and

$x + 3y = 4$ intersect to form a triangle. Find the coordinates of the vertices.

12. Geometry Name the type of quadrilateral formed when the lines
$x - y = -3$, $y = x - 2$, $y = -\frac{1}{2}x + 5$, and $x + 2y + 12 = 0$ intersect.

C

13. Write an equation that forms a system of equations with $x + y = 4$, so that the system has
a) no solution   **b)** infinitely many solutions   **c)** one solution

14. Write a system of equations that has the point (3, 2) as
a) the only solution   **b)** one of infinitely many solutions

15. Communication If (0, 3) and (2, 4) are both solutions to a system of two linear equations, does the system have any other solutions? Explain.

16. Sketch a graph to represent a system of two equations with one solution, so that the two lines have
a) different x-intercepts and different y-intercepts
b) the same x-intercept but different y-intercepts
c) different x-intercepts but the same y-intercept
d) the same x-intercept and the same y-intercept

17. Graphing calculator For many systems solved graphically using a graphing calculator, the point of intersection does not fall within the standard viewing window.
a) Solve each of the following systems using a graphing calculator.

$y = -2x - 16$ $y = x - 24$ $y = x - 2$
$y = 4x + 59$ $y = -2x + 120$ $y = \dfrac{x}{2} - 10$

b) Communication Describe how you found suitable values for the window variables in each case.
c) Compare your answers to part b) with those of your classmates.

Modelling Math   Comparing Costs and Revenues

To raise money for a school reunion, students sell T-shirts. The cost of the T-shirts includes an $800 design and set-up charge, plus $4 per T-shirt. The T-shirts sell for $20 each. The cost and the revenue can be modelled by the following system of equations.
Dollar Cost: $d = 800 + 4t$
Dollar Revenue: $d = 20t$
a) Solve the system graphically.
b) The solution shows the break-even point, at which the cost and revenue are equal. How many T-shirts must the students sell to break even?
c) Suppose the students lose money. How many T-shirts are sold?
d) Suppose the students make a profit. How many T-shirts are sold?

The field of wildlife biology involves the study and management of wild animals and their natural habitats. Examples of the tasks undertaken by wildlife biologists are:

- estimating wildlife populations
- managing programs that control outbreaks of wildlife diseases
- predicting the effects on wildlife of environmental changes

1. Sea otters One animal studied by wildlife biologists is the sea otter, which is found along the shores of the North Pacific. Sea otters were almost extinct in 1910, because they had been over-hunted for their fine, silky brown fur. They are now protected by an international treaty. The two main populations of sea otters are along the coasts of California and Northern British Columbia and Alaska. Research indicates that the total number of sea otters is about 130 000 and that there are about 25 times as many sea otters in the north as in the south. The data can be modelled by the following system of equations.

$$n + s = 130\ 000$$
$$n = 25s$$

Solve the system of equations to find the approximate number of sea otters in each population.

2. Research Use your research skills to investigate
a) the qualifications needed to become a wildlife biologist
b) organizations that employ wildlife biologists
c) a species studied by wildlife biologists

Achievement Check

1   2   3   4

An Internet service provider offers three plans to its customers. The rates are as shown in the graph. Describe situations in which you would choose each of these plans. Then, describe situations in which your choice would change. Explain and justify your reasoning.

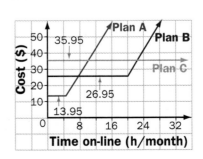

The Siberian tiger and the Amur leopard are in danger of becoming extinct. Both animals are found in the Russian Far East. The two main reasons for their plight are poaching and the destruction of their habitat. Scientists and environmental groups are working to save the animals.

Investigation   Use the Equations

Scientists have determined that the total number of tigers and leopards left is about 480, and that there are about 15 times as many tigers as leopards. The data can be modelled by the following system of equations.

$$t + l = 480 \quad (1)$$
$$t = 15l \quad (2)$$

1. a) What equation results when $15l$ is substituted for t in (1)?
b) Solve the resulting equation for l.

2. Communication a) How can the value of t be found?
b) Find its value.

3. What ordered pair satisfies the system of equations?

4. a) Solve (1) for either variable to write an expression for one variable in terms of the other.
b) Substitute the expression from part a) in (2). Solve the resulting equation.
c) Find the value of the second variable.
d) Is the resulting ordered pair the same as you found in question 3?

5. What are the approximate numbers of
a) Siberian tigers?
b) Amur leopards?

6. Solve each of the following systems of equations by substitution.

a) $x + y = 15$ **b)** $x + 2y = 10$ **c)** $2x + y = 2$
$\quad 2x - y = 0$ $\quad\quad x - 4y = 4$ $\quad\quad 3x + 2y = 1$

Web Connection www.school.mcgrawhill.ca/resources/

To investigate a plant or animal that is in danger of extinction, visit the above web site. Go to **Math Resources**, then to *MATHPOWER™ 10, Ontario Edition,* to find out where to go next. Write a short report on the plant or animal you chose, and explain why it is in danger of extinction. If possible, include mathematical models, such as tables and graphs, in your report.

Solving a system of two equations in two variables by substitution involves solving one equation for one variable in terms of the other variable, and then substituting to create a third equation in one variable.

Example 1   Solving by Substitution

Solve and check. $x + 4y = 6$ (1)
$2x - 3y = 1$ (2)

Solution

Since the coefficient of x in (1) is 1, solve (1) for x.

$$x + 4y = 6$$
$$x = 6 - 4y$$

At the point of intersection of the two lines, x must have the same value in both equations.

Substitute the expression $6 - 4y$ for x in (2).

Write (2): $2x - 3y = 1$
Substitute: $2(6 - 4y) - 3y = 1$
Expand: $12 - 8y - 3y = 1$
Simplify: $-11y = -11$
Solve for y: $y = 1$

The solution can be modelled graphically.

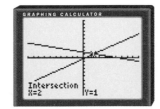

Substitute 1 for y in (2).
$$2x - 3y = 1$$
$$2x - 3(1) = 1$$
$$2x - 3 = 1$$
$$2x = 4$$
$$x = 2$$

Check in (1).   Check in (2).
L.S. $= x + 4y$ **R.S.** $= 6$ **L.S.** $= 2x - 3y$ **R.S.** $= 1$
    $= 2 + 4(1)$ $= 2(2) - 3(1)$
    $= 2 + 4$ $= 4 - 3$
    $= 6$ $= 1$
        L.S. = R.S.   L.S. = R.S.

The solution is (2, 1).

When the coordinates of the point of intersection of two lines are not integers, it can be difficult to find the exact solution from a paper-and-pencil graph. Exact solutions can be found algebraically or using a graphing calculator.

Example 2   Finding Exact Solutions

Solve and check. $5x - 3y - 2 = 0$ (1)
$$7x + y = 0 \qquad (2)$$

Solution

The coefficient of y in (2) is 1.
Solve for y in (2).
$$7x + y = 0$$
$$y = -7x$$

Substitute $-7x$ for y in (1).
Write (1): $5x - 3y - 2 = 0$
Substitute: $5x - 3(-7x) - 2 = 0$
Expand: $5x + 21x - 2 = 0$
Simplify: $26x - 2 = 0$

Solve for x. $x = \dfrac{2}{26}$ or $\dfrac{1}{13}$

Substitute $\dfrac{1}{13}$ for x in either of the original equations to find the value of y.

Substituting in (2) gives
$$7x + y = 0$$
$$7\left(\frac{1}{13}\right) + y = 0$$
$$\frac{7}{13} + y = 0$$
$$y = -\frac{7}{13}$$

Check in (1).
L.S. $= 5x - 3y - 2$ **R.S.** $= 0$
$$= 5\left(\frac{1}{13}\right) - 3\left(-\frac{7}{13}\right) - 2$$
$$= \frac{5}{13} + \frac{21}{13} - 2$$
$$= \frac{26}{13} - 2$$
$$= 0$$

Check in (2).
L.S. $= 7x + y$ **R.S.** $= 0$
$$= 7\left(\frac{1}{13}\right) + \left(-\frac{7}{13}\right)$$
$$= \frac{7}{13} - \frac{7}{13}$$
$$= 0$$

L.S. = R.S.

L.S. = R.S.

The solution is $\left(\dfrac{1}{13}, -\dfrac{7}{13}\right)$.

Example 4   Systems With Infinitely Many Solutions

Solve by substitution. $2x - y - 3 = 0$ (1)

$\qquad\qquad\qquad\quad 6x - 3y - 9 = 0$ (2)

Solution

The coefficient of y in (1) is -1.

Solve for y in (1).

$$2x - y - 3 = 0$$
$$2x - 3 = y$$

Substitute $2x - 3$ for y in (2).

Write (2):	$6x - 3y - 9 = 0$
Substitute:	$6x - 3(2x - 3) - 9 = 0$
Expand:	$6x - 6x + 9 - 9 = 0$
Simplify:	$6x - 6x = 9 - 9$
	$0x = 0$

Since the statement $0x = 0$ is true for all values of x, the system has infinitely many solutions.

The graph of the system shows that the lines coincide.

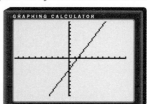

Key CONCEPTS

1 To solve a system of two linear equations in two variables by substitution,

a) solve one equation for one of its variables

b) substitute the expression from part a) in the other equation and solve for the variable

c) substitute the value of the variable found in part b) in one of the original equations to find the value of the other variable

d) check the solution in each of the original equations

2 If the statement that results from a solution is

a) not true for any value of a variable, the lines are parallel and distinct, and there is no solution

b) true for all values of a variable, the lines coincide and there are infinitely many solutions

Communicate Your Understanding

1. Explain why you can solve the system of linear equations $y = 3x - 8$ and $x + y = 4$ by substituting $3x - 8$ for y in the second equation.

2. Describe how you would solve the linear system $x + 4y = 3$ and $2x + 5y = 9$ by substitution.

3. What can you conclude if the solution to a linear system gives the equation

a) $0y = 0$?   **b)** $0x = 2$?

The exact solution to Example 2 can be modelled graphically using a graphing calculator.

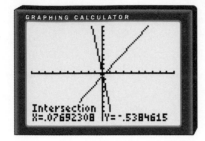
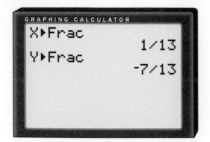

Example 3   Systems With No Solution

Solve by substitution.

$$2x + 2y = 7 \qquad (1)$$
$$x + y = 6 \qquad (2)$$

Solution

The coefficient of x in (2) is 1.
Solve for x in (2).

$$x + y = 6$$
$$x = 6 - y$$

Substitute $6 - y$ for x in (1).

Write (1): $2x + 2y = 7$
Substitute: $2(6 - y) + 2y = 7$
Expand: $12 - 2y + 2y = 7$
Simplify: $-2y + 2y = 7 - 12$
                      $0y = -5$

Since the statement $0y = -5$ is not true for any value of y, the system has no solution.

The graph of the system shows that the lines are parallel and distinct.

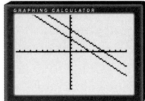

Practice

A

1. Solve each equation for x.

a) $x + 3y = 8$

b) $4y + x + 13 = 0$

c) $7y - x = -7$

d) $2y - x - 1 = 0$

2. Solve each equation for y.

a) $6x + y = 11$

b) $5x + y + 9 = 0$

c) $x - y = -2$

d) $3x - y + 4 = 0$

3. Solve each system of equations by substitution. If there is exactly one solution, check the solution.

a) $2x + y = 6$
$3x + 2y = 10$

b) $x + 3y = 2$
$2x + 5y = 3$

c) $x - 2y = 4$
$2x - 3y = 7$

d) $3x + y = -9$
$5x - 3y = -1$

e) $2x + 3y = 6$
$x + y = 3$

f) $x - y = 1$
$3x + y = 11$

g) $2x - y = 13$
$x + 2y = -6$

h) $3a + 4b = 15$
$a + b = 5$

i) $2x + 3y = 5$
$x - 4y = -14$

j) $2c - d + 2 = 0$
$3c + 2d + 10 = 0$

k) $a + 4b = 3$
$5b = -2a + 3$

l) $x - 2y = 5$
$2x - 3y = 6$

m) $2r - s = 2$
$3r - 2s = 3$

n) $5 = 2y - x$
$7 = 3y - 2x$

o) $x - 4y = 8$
$2x - 8y = 8$

p) $y = 5 - 2x$
$3x = 2y + 11$

q) $x + y - 4 = 0$
$2x = 8 - 2y$

r) $m + n + 6 = 0$
$2m - n - 3 = 0$

s) $6x = 3y + 2$
$y - 2x + 4 = 0$

t) $p = 3q - 2$
$9q - 3p - 6 = 0$

u) $3f = g - 4$
$2g = f + 3$

4. Find the exact solution to each linear system.

a) $4x - y = 3$
$6x - 2y = 5$

b) $3e - f - 2 = 0$
$5e + 2f = 3$

c) $2x - 5y = 12$
$x + 10y = -9$

d) $x + 3y = 0$
$3x - 6y = 5$

e) $x + 7y = 1$
$3x - 14y = -7$

f) $y = \frac{1}{2}x + 3$
$y = 5 - x$

g) $3a - 2b = -12$
$a - 4b = 8$

h) $2m - n = -2$
$6m + 7n = -1$

i) $4x + y = 0$
$x + 2y + 1 = 0$

Applications and Problem Solving

5. Communication Solve each system of equations by graphing and by substitution. Which method do you prefer? Why?

a) $x + y = 6$
$x - y = 42$

b) $2x + y = -4$
$4x + 3y = -6$

c) $2x + y = 5$
$2y = 2x + 1$

d) $6y + 3x = -4$
$x - 2y = -2$

B

6. Highest points The highest point in British Columbia is on Fairweather Mountain, f metres above sea level. The highest point in Ontario is on Ishpatina Ridge, i metres above sea level. The relationship between the heights can be modelled by the following system of equations.

$$f - i = 3970$$
$$f = 7i - 188$$

a) Communication Interpret each equation in words.
b) Solve the system of equations to find the height of Fairweather Mountain and the height of Ishpatina Ridge.

7. Measurement $\angle x$ and $\angle y$ are two acute angles in a right triangle. The measures of the angles are related by the following system of equations.

$$x + y = 90$$
$$y - 6 = 3x$$

a) Communication Interpret each equation in words.
b) Solve the system of equations to find the measure of each acute angle.

8. Theatre tickets The receipts from 550 people attending a play were $9184. The tickets cost $20 for adults and $12 for students. The relationship between the number of adult tickets sold, a, and the number of student tickets sold, s, can be modelled by the following system of equations.

$$a + s = 550$$
$$20a + 12s = 9184$$

a) Communication Interpret each equation in words.
b) Solve the system of equations to find the numbers of adult tickets and student tickets sold.

9. Coordinate geometry The three lines $x - y + 1 = 0$, $2x + y - 4 = 0$, and $x + y + 5 = 0$ intersect to form a triangle. Find the coordinates of the vertices of the triangle.

C

10. Simplify each system, and then solve it by substitution. Check each solution.

a) $2(x - 4) + y = 6$
$3x - 2(y - 3) = 13$

b) $2(x - 1) - 3(y - 3) = 0$
$3(x + 2) - (y - 7) = 20$

c) $2(3x - 1) - (y + 4) = -7$
$4(1 - 2x) - 3(3 - y) = -12$

d) $2(x - 1) - 4(2y + 1) = -1$
$x + 3(3y + 2) = 2$

11. Coordinate geometry The line $Ax + By = 8$ passes through the points (2, 1) and (4, –2). Find the values of A and B.

12. Three variables Use substitution to solve each system of equations. Write each solution as an ordered triple, (x, y, z).

a) $x + y + z = 3$
$y = 4x$
$z = -2x$

b) $2x - 3y + z = 10$
$x + 2z = 8$
$y + 4z = 11$

13. What value of m gives a system with no solution?
$$x(m - 1) - y + 6 = 0$$
$$2x + y - 3 = 0$$

14. What value of n gives a system with an infinite number of solutions?
$$2x - 4y - 4 = 0$$
$$y + 1 = nx$$

Modelling Math | **Comparing Costs and Revenues**

ABC Plumbing charges $70 for a service call, plus $50/h for the time worked. Quality Plumbers charges $50 for a service call, plus $55/h. The costs of the two plumbing companies can be compared using the following equations.

ABC Plumbing: $C = 70 + 50h$
Quality Plumbers: $C = 50 + 55h$

a) Solve the system of equations.

b) Communication Describe the situations in which each company costs a customer less. Explain your reasoning.

c) Communication Describe a situation in which the revenue for Quality Plumbers is $30 more than the revenue for ABC Plumbing. Explain your reasoning.

LOGIC POWER

Assume that no cubes are missing from the back or the base of the stack.
1. How many cubes are in the stack?
2. If the outside of the stack were painted green, how many cubes would have
a) 4 green faces?   **b)** 1 green face?

1.4 Investigation: Equivalent Equations

1 Equivalent Forms

An equation has an infinite number of equivalent forms. For example, multiplying each term in the equation $x - 3 = 1$ by 2 gives the equivalent form $2x - 6 = 2$. The solution to both equations is the same, $x = 4$. Equations with the same solution are called **equivalent equations.**

1. Write three ordered pairs that satisfy the equation $x + y = 6$.

2. a) Multiply both sides of the equation $x + y = 6$ by 2.
b) Do the ordered pairs you found in question 1 satisfy the new equation?

3. a) Multiply both sides of the equation $x + y = 6$ by -3.
b) Do the ordered pairs you found in question 1 satisfy the new equation?

4. Communication Are the three equations from questions 1, 2, and 3 equivalent? Explain.

5. Write three equations equivalent to each of the following equations.
a) $x + y = 2$ **b)** $x - y = 4$ **c)** $2x + y = 7$ **d)** $y = 4x - 3$

2 Equivalent Systems

Here are two systems of equations.

System A		**System B**	
$x - y = 3$	(1)	$x = 5$	(1)
$x + y = 7$	(2)	$y = 2$	(2)

1. Graph the two equations in system A on the same set of axes. Find the point of intersection.

2. Repeat question 1 for system B.

3. a) In system A, multiply (1) by 2 and multiply (2) by -1. Call the resulting system of equations system C.
b) Graph system C and find the point of intersection.

4. Communication Systems A, B, and C are called **equivalent systems**. Explain why.

5. Write a system of equations equivalent to the following system. Write each equation in your system in two variables.

$$x = 2$$
$$y = 1$$

3 Adding Equations

1. Graph the two equations on the same set of axes. Find the point of intersection.

$$x + 2y = 4 \quad (1)$$
$$x - y = 1 \quad (2)$$

2. Add (1) and (2) to form a new equation, (3), as follows.
a) Add the left side of (1) to the left side of (2). Simplify the expression.
b) Add the right side of (1) to the right side of (2).
c) Equate the results of parts a) and b).

3. Communication Graph (3) on the same set of axes as (1) and (2). What do the three lines have in common?

4. Communication Three systems of equations that can be formed from (1), (2), and (3) are: (1) and (2), (1) and (3), and (2) and (3).
How are the three systems related? Explain.

5. Communication How are systems P, Q, and R related? Explain.

System P	**System Q**	**System R**
$x + y = 1$	$x + y = 1$	$x - y = 5$
$x - y = 5$	$x = 3$	$x = 3$

The Beatles album *Anthology 1* was the first of three anthologies that traced their music from when the band formed in the late 1950s until it broke up in 1970.

Investigation Use the Equations

There are two discs in *Anthology 1*. The total number of tracks on both discs is 60. There are 8 more tracks on disc 1 than on disc 2. This information can be modelled by the following system of equations.

$$x + y = 60 \quad (1)$$
$$x - y = 8 \quad (2)$$

1. a) Add the left sides of (1) and (2), and then simplify.
b) Add the right sides of (1) and (2).
c) Equate the answers from parts b) and c) to form a new equation.
d) Solve the new equation from part c).

2. Communication a) How can the value of the second variable be found?
b) Find its value.

3. Which ordered pair satisfies the system of equations?

4. Check that the ordered pair satisfies both (1) and (2).

5. How many tracks are on each disc of *Anthology 1*?

6. Solve each system of equations using the above method.
a) $x + y = 17$
$x - y = 11$
b) $x - y = 7$
$2x + y = 20$
c) $4x - 3y = 19$
$x + 3y = 1$

The method used to solve each system of equations in the Investigation is known as elimination, because equations were combined to eliminate a variable. Each system could also have been solved by substitution. The substitution method works well when at least one variable in one or both equations has a coefficient of 1 or −1. With other coefficients, substitution may lead to complicated equations, and it may be better to use the elimination method.

The elimination method uses the following properties of equality.

Since	$4 = 4$		If	$a = b$
and	$3 = 3$		and	$c = d$
then	$4 + 3 = 4 + 3$		then	$a + c = b + d$
and	$4 - 3 = 4 - 3$		and	$a - c = b - d$

Example 1   Solving by Addition
Solve by elimination. Check the solution.

$$3x + 2y = 19 \quad (1)$$
$$5x - 2y = 5 \quad (2)$$

Solution
Adding the equations eliminates the y terms and creates an equation with one variable.

Write (1):	$3x + 2y = 19$	(1)
Write (2):	$5x - 2y = 5$	(2)
Add (1) and (2):	$8x = 24$	
Solve for x:	$x = 3$	

The solution can be modelled graphically.

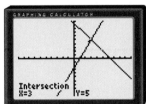

Substitute 3 for x in (1) or (2).
Substituting in (1) gives

$$3x + 2y = 19$$
$$3(3) + 2y = 19$$
$$9 + 2y = 19$$
$$2y = 10$$
$$y = 5$$

Check in (1).

L.S. $= 3x + 2y$ **R.S.** $= 19$
    $= 3(3) + 2(5)$
    $= 9 + 10$
    $= 19$
      L.S. = R.S.

Check in (2).

L.S. $= 5x - 2y$ **R.S.** $= 5$
    $= 5(3) - 2(5)$
    $= 15 - 10$
    $= 5$
      L.S. = R.S.

The solution is (3, 5).

Example 2   Solving Using Multiplication and Subtraction

Solve by elimination. Check the solution.

$$3x + 2y = 2 \quad (1)$$
$$4x + 5y = 12 \quad (2)$$

Solution

Neither addition nor subtraction will eliminate a variable.
Use multiplication to write a system of equivalent equations,
so that a variable can be eliminated by addition or subtraction.

Method 1: Eliminating y

Write (1):	$3x + 2y = 2$	(1)
Write (2):	$4x + 5y = 12$	(2)
Multiply (1) by 5:	$15x + 10y = 10$	(3)
Multiply (2) by 2:	$8x + 10y = 24$	(4)
Subtract (4) from (3):	$7x = -14$	
Solve for x:	$x = -2$	

Method 2: Eliminating x

Write (1):	$3x + 2y = 2$	(1)
Write (2):	$4x + 5y = 12$	(2)
Multiply (1) by 4:	$12x + 8y = 8$	(3)
Multiply (2) by 3:	$12x + 15y = 36$	(4)
Subtract (4) from (3):	$-7y = -28$	
Solve for y:	$y = 4$	

Substitute −2 for x in (1).

$$3x + 2y = 2$$
$$3(-2) + 2y = 2$$
$$-6 + 2y = 2$$
$$2y = 8$$
$$y = 4$$

Substitute 4 for y in (2).

$$4x + 5y = 12$$
$$4x + 5(4) = 12$$
$$4x + 20 = 12$$
$$4x = -8$$
$$x = -2$$

To substitute, use your mental math skills.

Check in (1).

L.S. = $3x + 2y$ **R.S.** = 2
     = $3(-2) + 2(4)$
     = $-6 + 8$
     = 2
        L.S. = R.S.

Check in (2).

L.S. = $4x + 5y$ **R.S.** = 12
     = $4(-2) + 5(4)$
     = $-8 + 20$
     = 12
        L.S. = R.S.

The solution is (−2, 4).

Example 3   Rewriting Equations

Solve and check. $0.6x - 0.3y = 2.4$ (1)
                $-0.4y + 0.7x - 2.9 = 0$ (2)

Solution

Rewrite the equations with like terms in the same column.

$$0.6x - 0.3y = 2.4 \quad (1)$$
$$0.7x - 0.4y = 2.9 \quad (2)$$

To clear the decimals, multiply each equation by 10.

Multiply (1) by 10: $10 \times 0.6x - 10 \times 0.3y = 10 \times 2.4$
Simplify: $6x - 3y = 24$ (3)
Multiply (2) by 10: $10 \times 0.7x - 10 \times 0.4y = 10 \times 2.9$
Simplify: $7x - 4y = 29$ (4)

Multiply (3) by 4:

Multiply (4) by 3:

Subtract:

Solve for x:

$$24x - 12y = 96$$
$$21x - 12y = 87$$
$$3x = 9$$
$$x = 3$$

Substitute 3 for x in (1):

$$0.6x - 0.3y = 2.4$$
$$0.6(3) - 0.3y = 2.4$$
$$1.8 - 0.3y = 2.4$$
$$-0.3y = 0.6$$
$$y = -2$$

Check in (1).

L.S. $= 0.6x - 0.3y$ **R.S.** $= 2.4$

$= 0.6(3) - 0.3(-2)$

$= 1.8 + 0.6$

$= 2.4$

        L.S. = R.S.

Check in (2).

L.S. $= -0.4y + 0.7x - 2.9$ **R.S.** $= 0$

$= -0.4(-2) + 0.7(3) - 2.9$

$= 0.8 + 2.1 - 2.9$

$= 0$

        L.S. = R.S.

The solution is $(3, -2)$.

Example 4   Solving Systems of Equations With Fractions

Solve and check. $\dfrac{x}{2} + \dfrac{y}{8} = 4$ (1)

$\dfrac{x}{3} - \dfrac{y}{2} = -2$ (2)

Solution

To clear fractions, multiply each equation by its lowest common denominator.

Multiply (1) by 8: $8 \times \dfrac{x}{2} + 8 \times \dfrac{y}{8} = 8 \times 4$

Simplify: $4x + y = 32$ (3)

Multiply (2) by 6: $6 \times \dfrac{x}{3} - 6 \times \dfrac{y}{2} = 6 \times (-2)$

Simplify: $2x - 3y = -12$ (4)

Multiply (3) by 3: $12x + 3y = 96$

Add: $14x = 84$

Solve for x: $x = 6$

Substituting 6 for x in (1) gives $y = 8$.

Check in (1).

L.S. $= \dfrac{x}{2} + \dfrac{y}{8}$ **R.S.** $= 4$

$= \dfrac{6}{2} + \dfrac{8}{8}$

$= 4$

     L.S. = R.S.

Check in (2).

L.S. $= \dfrac{x}{3} - \dfrac{y}{2}$ **R.S.** $= -2$

$= \dfrac{6}{3} - \dfrac{8}{2}$

$= -2$

     L.S. = R.S.

The solution is $(6, 8)$.

Key CONCEPTS

To solve a linear system in two variables by elimination,

a) clear decimals and fractions, if necessary

b) rewrite the equations with like terms in the same column, if necessary

c) multiply one or both equations by numbers to obtain two equations in which the coefficients of one variable are the same or opposites

d) add or subtract the equations to eliminate a variable, and solve the resulting equation for the remaining variable

e) substitute the value from d) into one of the original equations to find the value of the other variable

f) check the solution in each of the original equations

Communicate Your Understanding

1. Describe how you would solve the linear system $2x + y = 5$ and $3x - 2y = 4$ by elimination.

2. Explain why you might need to multiply each equation by a different number when solving a system of equations by elimination.

3. State the method you think is best to solve each system—graphing, substitution, or elimination. Explain why you chose each method.

a) $3x - 4y = 17$
$5x + 4y = 7$

b) $y = 5 - 2x$
$y = 2x + 3$

c) $5y = 11 - 2x$
$3x = -y - 3$

d) $2x + 3y = 5$
$5x + 4y = 16$

Practice

1. Solve each system of equations by elimination.

a) $x - y = 3$
$x + y = 7$

b) $x + y = 8$
$x - y = -2$

c) $x + y = 8$
$-x + y = 6$

d) $x + 3y = 7$
$x + y = 3$

2. Solve each system of equations by elimination. Check each solution.

a) $4a - 3b = -10$
$2a + 3b = 22$

b) $5x + 2y = -11$
$3x + 2y = -9$

c) $4x + 9y = -7$
$4x + 3y = -13$

d) $2m - 3n = 12$
$5m - 3n = 21$

e) $2p + 3q = -1$
$2p - 3q = -7$

f) $6y - 5x = -7$
$2y - 5x = -19$

3. Solve each linear system. Check each solution.

a) $4x + 3y = 7$
$2x + 3y - 5 = 0$

b) $2a = 3b + 7$
$5b = 2a - 9$

c) $-3 = 2m - 3n$
$2m + n = -15$

d) $4c = 3d - 8$
$8 = d - 4c$

4. Determine the values of the constant terms, so that the solution to each system is as shown.

a) $2x - 5y = ?$
$3x + 4y = ?$ Solution: $(3, 2)$

b) $x - 6y = ?$
$4x + 5y = ?$ Solution: $(-2, 3)$

5. Solve each system by elimination. Check each solution. If there is not exactly one solution, does the system have no solution or infinitely many solutions?

a) $x + 2y = -3$
$2x + 3y = -4$

b) $8c - 3d = -10$
$2c - 5d = 6$

c) $4x + 3y = 15$
$8x - 9y = 15$

d) $3r + 2s = 5$
$9r + 6s = 7$

e) $2x - 3y = 2$
$5x + 6y = 5$

f) $4x - 3y = 5$
$8x - 6y = 10$

g) $3a + 2b = 16$
$2a + 3b = 14$

h) $3m + 4n = -1$
$4m - 5n = -22$

i) $5p + 3q = -19$
$2p - 5q = 11$

6. Solve by elimination. Check each solution.

a) $38 = 2x - 5y$
$75 = 7x - 3y$

b) $6x + 5y = 22$
$3y = 4x + 36$

c) $3a - 7b - 13 = 0$
$4a - 5b - 13 = 0$

d) $6x - 5y = -3$
$2y - 9x = -1$

e) $3s + 4 = -4t$
$7s + 6t + 11 = 0$

f) $3c = 2 - 3d$
$5c = 3 - 2d$

g) $2d = 10 + 4e$
$3d = 6e + 15$

h) $10x = 17 - 15y$
$15x = 25y - 3$

i) $4x - 5 = 2y$
$1 = 5y - 10x$

7. Solve by elimination.

a) $0.3x - 0.5y = 1.2$
$0.7x - 0.2y = -0.1$

b) $1.7x + 3.5y = 0.01$
$0.6x + 1.2y = 0$

c) $0.2x - 0.3y = -0.1$
$0.5x - 0.4y = 0.8$

d) $0.2x - 0.3y = -0.6$
$0.5x + 0.2y = 2.3$

e) $4x + 5y = -0.5$
$3x + 7y = 0.6$

f) $0.5x - 1.3y = 1.23$
$4x - 2y = 0.6$

8. Solve by elimination.

a) $\dfrac{x}{3} - \dfrac{y}{2} = -3$
$\dfrac{x}{6} + \dfrac{y}{5} = 3$

b) $\dfrac{x}{3} + \dfrac{y}{4} = 2$
$\dfrac{2x}{3} - \dfrac{y}{2} = 0$

c) $\dfrac{4a}{3} - \dfrac{b}{4} = 9$
$\dfrac{5a}{6} + b = 1$

d) $x - y = 6$
$\dfrac{2x}{3} + \dfrac{y}{3} = 1$

e) $\dfrac{x}{3} - \dfrac{y}{6} = -\dfrac{2}{3}$
$\dfrac{x}{12} - \dfrac{y}{4} = 1\dfrac{1}{2}$

f) $\dfrac{1}{3}m - \dfrac{1}{6}n = \dfrac{1}{2}$
$\dfrac{m}{5} - \dfrac{3n}{10} = \dfrac{1}{2}$

Applications and Problem Solving

9. Communication State the method you would use to solve each system. Explain why you would choose each method.

a) $y = 6 - 3x$
$y = 2x + 1$

b) $2x - 5y = -1$
$3x + 5y = -14$

c) $4x + 3y = 15$
$x - 2y = 1$

d) $2x - 5y = 1$
$3x - 2y = -4$

e) $87x + 68y = 99$
$64x - 55y = 81$

f) $6x = 5y - 1$
$5x = 4y - 1$

10. Names of provinces Some provinces have names with First Nations origins. For example, "Ontario" comes from an Iroquois word meaning "beautiful water" or "beautiful lake." If the number of provincial names with First Nations origins is a, and the number with other origins is b, the numbers are related by the following equations.

$$a + b = 10$$
$$3a - 2b = 0$$

a) Communication Interpret each equation in words.

b) Find the number of provinces that have names with First Nations origins.

11. Sub prices At Lisa's Sub Shop, two ham subs and four roast-beef subs cost $34. Five ham subs and 6 roast-beef subs cost $61. If one ham sub costs $\$x$ and one roast-beef sub costs $\$y$, the information can be modelled by the following system of equations.

$$2x + 4y = 34$$
$$5x + 6y = 61$$

Solve the system of equations to find the cost of each type of sub.

12. Solve by elimination. Check each solution.

a) $3(x + 2) - (y + 7) = -1$
$5(x + 1) + 4(y - 3) = -24$

b) $5(m - 3) + 2(n + 4) = 10$
$3(m + 4) - 4(n + 3) = -21$

c) $2(a - 4) + 5(b + 1) = 8$
$3(a - 1) - 2(b - 2) = -11$

d) $4(x - 1) - 3(y + 4) = -11$
$3(x + 4) + 5(y - 6) = -7$

13. Literal coefficients Solve for x and y.

a) $x - y = a + b$
$x + y = a - b$

b) $bx + ay = 2ab$
$bx - ay = 4ab$

14. Coordinate geometry Find the coordinates of the vertices of a triangle whose sides lie on the following three lines.

$$2x + 5y - 16 = 0$$
$$4x - 3y - 6 = 0$$
$$3x + y + 2 = 0$$

15. For what values of the coefficients a and b is $(2, -1)$ the solution to the following linear system?

$$ax + by = -7$$
$$2ax - 3by = 1$$

16. Solve this system of equations for x and y by letting $a = \dfrac{1}{x}$ and $b = \dfrac{1}{y}$.

$$\frac{1}{x} + \frac{3}{y} = \frac{3}{4}$$
$$\frac{3}{x} - \frac{2}{y} = \frac{5}{12}$$

17. For what value of c will each system have infinitely many solutions?

a) $2x - 6y = c$
$6x - 18y = 30$

b) $cx - 4y = 14$
$-9x + 6y = -21$

18. For what value of c will each system have no solution?

a) $x + 2y = 6$
$cx - 4y = 8$

b) $cy + 1 = 5x$
$9y + 8 = 15x$

19. Communication The solution to a system of linear equations is (2, 5). If each equation is multiplied by 3 to produce a new system, is the solution to the new system (2, 5), (6, 15), or another ordered pair? Explain.

20. Write a system of equations in the following form.
$$Ax + By = C$$
$$Dx + Ey = F$$
A, B, C, D, E, and F must be different integers, and the solution must be (6, 5).

21. Write a system of linear equations that has:
• no coefficients equal to 0, 1, or −1
• integer coefficients and integer constants
• exactly one solution, as follows

a) (2, 5)   **b)** (−4, 7)   **c)** $\left(1, -\dfrac{2}{3}\right)$

Achievement Check
1   2   3   4

A triangle is formed by the intersection of the lines $2x + 3y = 14$, $4x - 5y = -16$, and the x-axis. Find the area of the triangle. Find the coordinates of the vertices of a triangle with half the area you found. Explain and justify your reasoning.

PATTERN POWER

Find the value represented by ■.

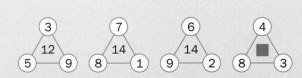

Technology Extension: Solving Linear Systems

A graphing calculator or a computer can be programmed to solve a system of linear equations in two variables. One type of program uses formulas for x and y found by solving the general case of a linear system.

$$ax + by = c \quad (1)$$
$$dx + ey = f \quad (2)$$

Solve for x by eliminating y.

	$ax + by = c$	(1)
	$dx + ey = f$	(2)
Multiply (1) by e:	$aex + bey = ce$	(3)
Multiply (2) by b:	$bdx + bey = bf$	(4)
Subtract (4) from (3):	$aex - bdx = ce - bf$	
Factor the left side:	$x(ae - bd) = ce - bf$	
Divide both sides by $ae - bd$:	$x = \dfrac{ce - bf}{ae - bd},\ ae - bd \neq 0$	

Solve for y by eliminating x.

	$ax + by = c$	(1)
	$dx + ey = f$	(2)
Multiply (2) by a:	$adx + aey = af$	(3)
Multiply (1) by d:	$adx + bdy = cd$	(4)
Subtract (4) from (3):	$aey - bdy = af - cd$	
Factor the left side:	$y(ae - bd) = af - cd$	
Divide both sides by $ae - bd$:	$y = \dfrac{af - cd}{ae - bd},\ ae - bd \neq 0$	

1 Solving Systems Using a Graphing Calculator Program

The graphing calculator program, which is suitable for a TI-83 or TI-83 Plus calculator, solves a linear system in which the coefficients and constant terms are labelled as shown.

$$Ax + By = C$$
$$Dx + Ey = F$$

```
PROGRAM:SOLVESYS
:Disp "ENTER COEFFICIENTS"
:Prompt A,B,C,D,E,F
:If AE–BD = 0
:Goto 1
:(CE–BF)/(AE–BD)→X
:(AF–CD)/(AE–BD)→Y
:Disp X,Y
:Stop
:Lbl 1
:If CE–BF = 0 or AF–CD = 0
:Then
:Disp "INFINITELY  MANY"
:Else
:Disp "NO SOLUTION"
```

1. Communication a) Describe what each line of the program does.
b) If $AE - BD = 0$, a system does not have exactly one ordered pair as its solution. Use examples to explain why the value of $CE - BF$ or $AF - CD$ determines whether there are infinitely many solutions or no solution.

2. Enter the program into your graphing calculator using the **PRGM key** and the **PRGM NEW menu**. Using the **PRGM EXEC menu**, execute the program to solve each of the following linear systems.

a) $4x - 7y = 10$
$3x + 2y = -7$

b) $1.7x - 0.3y = 8.9$
$x - 0.6y = 1$

c) $x - 4y = 8$
$2x = 8y + 16$

d) $2x = 3y + 7$
$4x - 6y = 5$

2 Solving Systems Using Preprogrammed Calculators

Some calculators, such as the TI-92 and TI-92 Plus, are preprogrammed with the capability to solve linear systems algebraically. The screen displays show how such a calculator can be used to solve the following system of equations by substitution.

$$4x - 3y = -20 \quad (1)$$
$$2x + 5y = 16 \quad (2)$$

- Use the solve function to solve (1) for x.

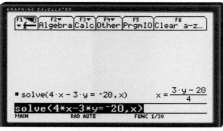

- Use the solve function to solve (2) for y, while using the with operator to substitute for x. The result is $y = 4$.

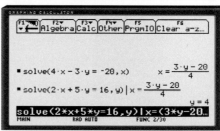

- Use the solve function to solve (1) or (2) for x, while using the with operator to substitute 4 for y. The result is $x = -2$, so the solution to the system is $(-2, 4)$.

1. Solve the following systems by substitution.

a) $3x + 4y = 22$
$5x - 2y = 2$

b) $2x - 3y = 13$
$8x + 3y = 7$

c) $2x - 5y = 6$
$4x + 3y = -1$

2. Communication Try to solve each of the following systems on the calculator by substitution. Explain your results.

a) $x + y = 1$
$2x + 2y = 2$

b) $x - y = 3$
$3x - 3y = 5$

Problem solving often involves the introduction of variables and the translation of information from words into equations.

1 Expressions in Two Variables

1. Numbers Let x represent the larger of two numbers, and y, the smaller. Write algebraic expressions for
a) the sum of the two numbers
b) the smaller subtracted from the larger
c) the larger subtracted from five times the smaller
d) the sum of six times the larger and two times the smaller

2. Flying speed A plane flies at x kilometres per hour in still air. The wind speed is y kilometres per hour. Write algebraic expressions for the speed of the plane when it is flying
a) into the wind   **b)** with the wind

3. Fitness centre A fitness centre charges an initiation fee of $\$x$, plus a monthly charge of $\$y$. Write algebraic expressions to show how much it costs to be a member for
a) 7 months   **b)** 15 months

4. Swim meet Tickets to a college swim meet cost $10 for general admission and $5 for students. There were x general admission tickets and y student tickets sold. Write algebraic expressions for
a) the total number of tickets sold
b) the revenue, in dollars, from the general admission tickets
c) the revenue, in dollars, from the student tickets
d) the total revenue from all the tickets

5. Investments Traci invested $\$x$ at 7% and $\$y$ at 6%. Write algebraic expressions for
a) the total amount of money Traci invested
b) the interest Traci earned at 7% in one year
c) the interest Traci earned at 6% in one year
d) the total interest Traci earned in one year

2 Equations in Two Variables

1. Write an equation to describe each relation.

a)

x	y
2	6
5	3
−1	9

b)

x	y
9	4
5	0
2	−3

c)

x	y
1	4
2	7
3	10

d)

x	y
2	3
0	−1
−2	−5

2. Introduce variables and translate each statement into an equation in two variables.

a) Basketball The sum of the length and the width of a basketball court is 40 m.

b) Department store In a department that sells bicycles and tricycles, the total number of wheels is 61.

3 Systems of Equations

1. Write a system of equations for each pair of relations.

a)

x	y
2	5
−1	8
−2	9

x	y
2	−1
8	5
9	6

b)

x	y
0	0
−1	−2
−3	−6

x	y
0	−4
3	−1
−3	−7

2. Puppet play For the puppet play at the library, x tickets for adults and y tickets for children were sold.

a) The total number of tickets sold was 256. Write an equation that relates x and y to the total number of tickets sold.

b) Tickets for adults cost $5 each and tickets for children cost $2 each. The total receipts were $767. Write an equation that relates x and y to the total receipts.

3. Introduce variables and write each of the following as a system of two equations in two variables.

a) Artists Pablo Picasso and Auguste Renoir produced a total of 295 paintings that have sold for more than $1 million each. Picasso accounted for 11 more of this total than Renoir.

b) Measurement The length of a rectangle is 6 cm greater than the width. The length and the width add to 46 cm.

c) Town areas The area of Collingwood is twice the area of Dryden. The difference in the areas of the two towns is 17 km^2.

d) Gymnastics meet Balcony seats for the gymnastics championships cost $10, and floor-level seats cost $15. The total number of tickets sold was 331. The total revenue from sales was $3915.

e) Measurement Two angles are supplementary. The measure of one angle is 4° less than three times the measure of the other angle.

The World Heritage Committee of the United Nations Educational, Scientific, and Cultural Organization (UNESCO) has compiled a list of natural and cultural wonders. These World Heritage Sites are so significant that responsibility for their protection belongs not just to their home countries, but to the world.

Some of these sites are the Pyramids, the Great Wall of China, the Galapagos Islands, and Mount Everest. The Pyramids and the Great Wall of China are examples of cultural sites, whereas the Galapagos Islands and Mount Everest are examples of natural sites.

Investigation   Use a Linear System

There are 13 World Heritage Sites in Canada, and there are 3 more natural sites than there are cultural sites. Let n represent the number of natural sites and c represent the number of cultural sites.

1. a) Write an equation that relates n and c to the total number of sites.
b) Write another equation to show how the number of natural sites is related to the number of cultural sites.
c) Write the equations from parts a) and b) as a linear system.

2. Communication Choose a method to solve the system. Explain and justify your choice.

3. Solve and check the system of equations.

4. How many of the World Heritage Sites in Canada are
a) natural sites?   **b)** cultural sites?

Web Connection   www.school.mcgrawhill.ca/resources/

To conduct research on the names and locations of the World Heritage Sites in Canada, visit the above web site. Go to **Math Resources**, then to *MATHPOWER™ 10, Ontario Edition,* to find out where to go next. List the names and locations of the World Heritage Sites in Canada. Indicate whether each site is natural or cultural.

Many problems that involve two unknown quantities can be solved using a system of linear equations.

Example 1   Investing Money

Tran had $10 000 to invest. She invested part of it in a term deposit paying 4% per annum and the remainder in bonds paying 5% per annum. If the total interest after one year was $440, how much did she invest at each rate?

Solution

Let x represent the money invested at 4%.
Let y represent the money invested at 5%.

Using a table is helpful.

	Tran's Investments		
	at 4%	at 5%	Total
Money Invested ($)	x	y	10 000
Interest Earned ($)	0.04x	0.05y	440

Write a system of equations.
Money invested: $\qquad\qquad x + y = 10\ 000 \qquad$ (1)
Interest earned: $\quad 0.04x + 0.05y = 440 \qquad$ (2)

Use substitution to solve the system.
From (1), $\qquad\qquad\qquad x + y = 10\ 000$
So, $\qquad\qquad\qquad\qquad x = 10\ 000 - y$
Substitute $10\ 000 - y$ for x in (2).
Write (2): $\qquad\qquad\qquad 0.04x + 0.05y = 440$
Substitute: $\qquad\quad 0.04(10\ 000 - y) + 0.05y = 440$
Expand: $\qquad\qquad 400 - 0.04y + 0.05y = 440$
Simplify: $\qquad\qquad\qquad 400 + 0.01y = 440$
Solve for y: $\qquad\qquad\qquad\quad 0.01y = 40$

$$y = \frac{40}{0.01}$$

$$y = 4000$$

Substitute 4000 for y in (1).
$$x + y = 10\ 000$$
$$x + 4000 = 10\ 000$$
$$x = 6000$$

Tran invested $6000 at 4% and $4000 at 5%.

Check, using the facts given in the problem.
Tran invested $10 000.
$6000 + $4000 = $10 000
The investments earned $440 in interest.
$6000 × 0.04 + $4000 × 0.05 = $240 + $200
$$= \$440$$

Example 2   Mixing Solutions

A chemistry teacher needs to make 10 L of 42% sulfuric acid solution. The acid solutions available are 30% sulfuric acid and 50% sulfuric acid, by volume. How many litres of each solution must be mixed to make the 42% solution?

Solution

Let x represent the number of litres of 30% sulfuric acid solution.
Let y represent the number of litres of 50% sulfuric acid solution.

Organize the information in a table.

	Acid Solutions		
	30% acid	50% acid	42% acid
Volume of Solution (L)	x	y	10
Volume of Pure Acid (L)	$0.3x$	$0.5y$	$0.42(10)$

Write a system of equations.

Solution:	$x + y = 10$	(1)
Pure acid:	$0.3x + 0.5y = 4.2$	(2)

Solve the system by substitution.
From (1), $x + y = 10$
So, $y = 10 - x$
Substitute $10 - x$ for y in (2).
Write (2): $0.3x + 0.5y = 4.2$
Substitute: $0.3x + 0.5(10 - x) = 4.2$
Expand: $0.3x + 5 - 0.5x = 4.2$
Simplify: $5 - 0.2x = 4.2$
Solve for x: $-0.2x = -0.8$
$$x = 4$$

Substitute 4 for x in (1).
$$x + y = 10$$
$$4 + y = 10$$
$$y = 6$$

So, 4 L of the 30% solution and 6 L of the 50% solution must be mixed to make the 42% solution.

Check against the given facts.
The total volume of 42% solution must be 10 L.
$$4 + 6 = 10$$
The 42% solution must contain $0.42(10)$ or 4.2 L of pure acid.
$$0.3(4) + 0.5(6) = 4.2$$

Example 3　Riverboat Cruise

A riverboat took 2 h to travel 24 km down a river with the current and 3 h to make the return trip against the current. Find the speed of the boat in still water and the speed of the current.

Solution

Let b represent the speed of the boat in still water.
Let c represent the speed of the current.
Then, $b + c$ represents the speed of the boat travelling down the river with the current, and $b - c$ represents the speed of the boat travelling up the river against the current.

Use the formula distance = speed × time, and use a table to organize the given facts.

Direction	Distance (km)	Speed (km/h)	Time (h)	Equation
Down the river	24	$b + c$	2	$2(b + c) = 24$
Up the river	24	$b - c$	3	$3(b - c) = 24$

Write a system of equations.
$$2(b + c) = 24 \qquad (1)$$
$$3(b - c) = 24 \qquad (2)$$

Solve the system by elimination to find the values of b and c.
Divide (1) by 2: $\quad b + c = 12 \qquad (3)$
Divide (2) by 3: $\quad \underline{b - c = 8} \qquad (4)$
Add (3) and (4): $\quad 2b = 20$
Solve for b: $\qquad b = 10$

Substituting 10 for b in (2) gives $c = 2$.

The speed of the boat in still water is 10 km/h, and the speed of the current is 2 km/h.

Check, using the facts given in the problem.
The speed of the boat travelling down the river is $10 + 2$ or 12 km/h.
The time to travel 24 km down the river is $24 \div 12$ or 2 h.
The speed of the boat travelling up the river is $10 - 2$ or 8 km/h.
The time to travel 24 km up the river is $24 \div 8$ or 3 h.

Example 4   Car Trip

Nikolas drove 500 km from Windsor to Peterborough in $5\frac{1}{2}$ h.

He drove part of the way at 100 km/h, and the rest of the way at 80 km/h. How far did he drive at each speed?

Solution

Let x represent the distance travelled at 100 km/h.
Let y represent the distance travelled at 80 km/h.

Organize the given information in a table.

Distance (km)	Speed (km/h)	Time (h)
x	100	$\dfrac{x}{100}$
y	80	$\dfrac{y}{80}$

Distance = speed × time,
so time = $\dfrac{\text{distance}}{\text{speed}}$.

Write a system of equations.

Total distance: $x + y = 500$ (1)

Total time: $\dfrac{x}{100} + \dfrac{y}{80} = \dfrac{11}{2}$ (2)

To clear the fractions in (2), multiply by the lowest common denominator.

Multiply (2) by 400: $400 \times \dfrac{x}{100} + 400 \times \dfrac{y}{80} = 400 \times \dfrac{11}{2}$

Simplify: $4x + 5y = 2200$ (3)

Multiply (1) by -4: $-4x - 4y = -2000$ (4)

Add (3) and (4): $y = 200$

Substituting 200 for y in (1) gives $x = 300$.

Nikolas drove 300 km at 100 km/h, and 200 km at 80 km/h.

Check.
The total distance was $300 + 200$ or 500 km.

The total time was $\dfrac{300}{100} + \dfrac{200}{80}$ or $5\frac{1}{2}$ h.

To solve a problem using a linear system,

a) read the problem carefully, identify the unknowns, and assign variables to the unknowns

b) determine how the unknowns are related

c) write a system of equations that shows relationships between the unknowns

d) solve the system of equations

e) check the solution, using the facts given in the problem

Communicate Your Understanding

1. Write a system of equations that could be used to solve each of the following problems. Explain your steps.

a) Sam invested $5000, part at 6% per annum and the remainder at 3% per annum. If the total interest after one year was $240, how much did he invest at each rate?

b) Shakira took a 440 km trip, travelling by bus and by train. The bus travelled at 80 km/h, and the train travelled at 100 km/h. The whole trip took 5 h. How far did she travel on the bus? on the train?

2. Describe how to check solutions to problems solved using a linear system.

Practice

A

1. Calculate.

a) the interest earned in 1 year on $2000 at 7%

b) the interest earned in 1 year on $300 at 5%

c) the interest earned in 1 year on $3500 at 6%

d) the interest earned in 1 year on x at 4%

2. Calculate.

a) the mass of salt in 100 kg of 30% salt solution, by mass

b) the volume of alcohol in 500 L of a 40% alcohol solution, by volume

c) the volume of antifreeze in x litres of a 30% antifreeze solution, by volume

d) the mass of silver in m kilograms of 9% silver alloy, by mass

3. Calculate.

a) the distance travelled in 4 h at 60 km/h

b) the distance travelled in x hours at 40 km/h

c) the time taken to travel 600 km at 50 km/h

d) the time taken to travel y kilometres at 90 km/h

Applications and Problem Solving

4. Numbers The sum of two numbers is 255. When the smaller is subtracted from the larger, the result is 39. Find the numbers.

5. Earning interest Isabel invested $8000, part at 9% per annum and the remainder at 4% per annum. After one year, the total interest from these investments was $420. How much did she invest at each rate?

6. Driving Kareem took 5 h to drive 470 km from Sudbury to Brantford. For part of the trip, he drove at 100 km/h. For the rest of the trip, he drove at 90 km/h. How far did he drive at each speed?

7. Patrol boat It took a patrol boat 5 h to travel 60 km up a river against the current, and 3 h for the return trip with the current. Find the speed of the boat in still water and the speed of the current.

8. Investments Hakim invested $15 000. He put part of it in a term deposit that paid 4% per annum, and the remainder in a treasury bill that paid 5% per annum. After one year, the total interest was $690. How much did Hakim invest at each rate?

B

9. Measurement Find the values of x and y.

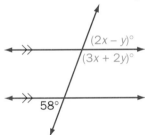

10. Vinegar solutions White vinegar is a solution of acetic acid in water. There are two strengths of white vinegar—a 5% solution and a 10% solution. How many millilitres of each solution must be mixed to make 50 mL of a 9% vinegar solution?

11. Acid solutions What volume, in millilitres, of a 60% hydrochloric acid solution must be added to 100 mL of a 30% hydrochloric acid solution to make a 36% hydrochloric acid solution?

12. Measurement Use the diagram to find the values of x and y.

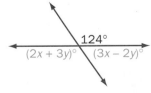

13. Flying speed A plane took 4 h to fly 2200 km from Saskatoon to Toronto with a tail wind. The return trip, with a head wind, took 5 h. Find the speed of the plane in still air and the wind speed.

14. Pool table The perimeter of a pool table is about 7.8 m. Four times the length equals nine times the width. What are the dimensions of the table, in metres?

15. Fitness Playing tennis burns energy at a rate of about 25 kJ/min. Cycling burns energy at about 35 kJ/min. Hans exercised by playing tennis and then cycling. He exercised for 50 min altogether and used a total of 1450 kJ of energy. For how long did he play tennis?

16. Measurement The rectangle has an area of m square units and a perimeter of $2m$ units. What is the value of x?

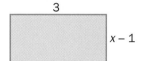

17. Driving distance Erica drove from Sarnia at 80 km/h. Aisha left Sarnia one hour later and drove along the same road at 100 km/h. How far from Sarnia did Aisha overtake Erica?

C

18. For two numbers whose sum is q and whose difference is r, write an expression for each number in terms of q and r.

19. Road trips From his home in Point Alexander, Dan drove to Belleville at an average speed of 75 km/h. From her home in Chalk River, Ashley drove through Point Alexander to Belleville at an average speed of 85 km/h. The distance from Chalk River to Point Alexander is 18 km. If Dan and Ashley left home at the same time,
a) after what length of time did Ashley overtake Dan?
b) how far were they from Point Alexander when Ashley overtook Dan?

20. Three variables When three numbers are added in pairs, the sums of the pairs are 22, 39, and 45. What are the three numbers?

21. Communication Can the following equations describe the relationship between the side lengths in a triangle? Explain.
$$a + b + c = 13$$
$$b = 2a$$
$$a = c - 5$$

22. Communication Write a word problem that can be solved using a system of linear equations and that has the solution (7, 5). Have a classmate check that your problem gives the correct solution.

23. Fencing The sport of fencing has three main forms: sabre, foil, and épée. Sabre bouts take place within a rectangle of perimeter 52 m. Decide whether the perimeter and each of the following pieces of information are sufficient to allow you to find the dimensions of the rectangle. Explain and justify your reasoning. Find the dimensions of the rectangle, where possible.

a) The width is 22 m less than the length.
b) The sum of the length and the width is 26 m.
c) The length is twelve times the width.
d) The perimeter is 28 m less than the perimeter of a basketball court.

Career Connection   Metallurgy

In your daily life, you make extensive use of metals, either in their pure state, or more often, in combinations called alloys. For example, when you take a drink of water, you may make use of a stainless steel tap attached to a copper pipe. The many uses that you make of electricity depend on the metal wires that carry the current.

The science and technology of metals is known as metallurgy. This field involves the extraction of metals from ores, purifying metals, and preparing metals for use.

1. Gold jewellery Pure, or 24-karat, gold is very soft, so it is rarely used for jewellery. Most gold jewellery contains a certain percent of gold, mixed with cheaper metals that make it harder. Suppose a jewellery maker has some 18-karat gold, which contains 75% gold, and some 9-karat gold, which contains 37.5% gold. What mass of each should the jewellery maker melt and mix to make 150 g of 15-karat gold, which contains 62.5% gold?

2. Research Choose a use of metal that interests you. Use your research skills to investigate how the metal is made.

3. Research Use your research skills to investigate how metallurgists are trained and where they work.

Refer to the music festival problem on the second page of this chapter.
a) Write an equation to model the dollar cost and an equation to model the dollar revenue for the festival.
b) Solve the system of equations to determine the number of tickets that must be sold for the community to break even.
c) Determine the number of tickets that must be sold to raise $16 000 for scholarships.

NUMBER POWER

In a magic square, the sum of the numbers in each row, column, and diagonal is the same. The following are two special magic squares, which have been partially completed.

	twenty-two	
twenty-eight	fifteen	
twelve		twenty-five

4		8
	7	3
	5	

a) Copy and complete each square.
b) Lee Sallow, who discovered the two squares, called them alphamagic partners. How are the squares related?

Rich Problem

Ape/Monkey Populations

The Primates are classified as an order of mammals. There are two main suborders of the Primates — the Prosimians and the Anthropoidea. The Prosimians, such as lemurs, have small brains. The Anthropoidea, including monkeys and apes, have larger brains.

Scientists have studied fossils to track changes in the population of Primates over millions of years.

1 Graphing and Interpreting Data

The table gives the percent of apes and the percent of monkeys in the ape/monkey population from 20 million years ago to the present.

Time (millions of years ago)	Percent of Ape/Monkey Population	
	Apes	Monkeys
20	80	20
10	30	70
7	15	85
4	10	90
0	6	94

1. On a grid like the one shown, draw two graphs on the same set of axes, representing the percent of apes in the ape/monkey population versus time, and the percent of monkeys in the ape/monkey population versus time.

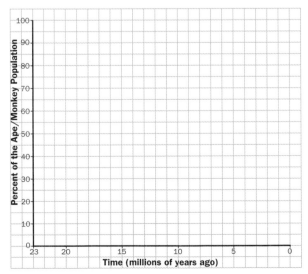

For apes, the points (20, 80), (10, 30), and (7, 15) are linear, so draw a line segment with endpoints (20, 80) and (7, 15). The points (7, 15), (4, 10), and (0, 6) are not linear, so draw a smooth curve through (4, 10) with endpoints (7, 15) and (0, 6). For monkeys, the points (20, 20), (10, 70), and (7, 85) are linear, so draw a line segment with endpoints (20, 20) and (7, 85). The points (7, 85), (4, 90), and (0, 94) are not linear, so draw a smooth curve through (4, 90) with endpoints (7, 85) and (0, 94).

2. From the graphs, estimate the percent of the ape/monkey population 23 million years ago that was made up of

a) apes   **b)** monkeys

3. If the graphs had remained linear, estimate when apes would have become extinct.

1. Give possible reasons why the percent of monkeys in the ape/monkey population has increased and the percent of apes has decreased.

2. Give possible reasons why apes have not become extinct.

3. a) Estimate the coordinates of the point of intersection of the two graphs.
b) What do the coordinates of the point of intersection represent?

4. Do the graphs show that there are more monkeys alive now than there were 20 million years ago? Explain.

5. a) Determine the slope of the linear portion of each graph.
b) The line for apes falls from left to right, yet the slope is positive. The line for monkeys rises from left to right, yet the slope is negative. Explain why.

6. A slope is a rate of change. Interpret the slope of the linear portion of each graph.

7. Scientists have no data for the ape/monkey population before 23 million years ago. Explain why.

Technology Extension

1. Use the **STAT EDIT** menu and the linear regression instruction of a graphing calculator to determine the equation of the linear portion of each graph.

2. Find the exact coordinates of the point of intersection of the graphs.

3. Explain any differences in the coordinates you found in question 2 and the coordinates you found by estimation.

REVIEW OF Key CONCEPTS

1.1–1.2 Solving Linear Systems Graphically

Refer to the Key Concepts on page 12.

To solve the following system by graphing, write the
equations in the slope and y-intercept form.

$$3x + y = 8 \quad (1)$$
$$2x - y = 2 \quad (2)$$

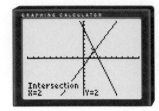

$3x + y = 8$	$2x - y = 2$
$y = 8 - 3x$	$-y = -2x + 2$
	$y = 2x - 2$

Graph the equations. Find the point of intersection.
The solution is (2, 2).
Check by substituting 2 for x and 2 for y in both of the original equations.

1. Solve each system by graphing. Check your solutions.

a) $y = x - 5$
  $y = 3 - x$

b) $m + 2n = 2$
  $3m + 2n = -6$

c) $p - q = 1$
  $p + 2q = 7$

d) $2x + y = 2$
  $2x + y + 4 = 0$

e) $x - y - 4 = 0$
  $5x - y - 8 = 0$

f) $a + b = 4$
  $3a = 12 - 3b$

g) $3x - 2y = -8$
  $x - 2y = -4$

h) $2x - y = -4$
  $2x + y = 6$

2. Solve each system graphically.

a) $4x + 3y = 1$
  $4x - 3y = 14$

b) $3x + y = 1$
  $x + 4y = 3$

3. Without graphing, determine whether each system has one solution,
no solution, or infinitely many solutions.

a) $3c + d = 4$
  $6c + 2d = 8$

b) $4x - 2y = 0$
  $2x - y = 3$

c) $x + 5y = 9$
  $x - y = 3$

d) $x + 2y - 7 = 0$
  $3x + 6y - 14 = 0$

4. Deserts The two largest deserts in the world are the Sahara Desert and
the Australian Desert. The sum of their areas is 13 million square kilometres.
The area of the Sahara Desert is 5 million square kilometres more than the
area of the Australian Desert. Solve the following system graphically to find
the area of each desert, in millions of square kilometres.

$$s + a = 13$$
$$s = a + 5$$

5. Profit A company manufactures and sells paddles. Its manufacturing
costs are $500, plus $10 per paddle. The company sells the paddles for $18.
The cost and revenue can be represented by the following system of equations.

Dollar Cost: $\quad d = 500 + 10p$

Dollar Revenue: $\quad d = 18p$

a) Communication What does each variable represent?

b) Solve the system graphically.

c) How many paddles must be sold for the company to make a profit?

Refer to the Key Concepts on page 20.

To solve the following system by substitution, solve one equation for a variable that has a coefficient of 1 or –1, and then substitute in the second equation.

$$2x + y = 2 \qquad (1)$$
$$3x + 2y = 5 \qquad (2)$$

Solve (1) for y: $\qquad\qquad\qquad\qquad y = 2 - 2x$
Substitute $2 - 2x$ for y in (2): $\;3x + 2(2 - 2x) = 5$
$$3x + 4 - 4x = 5$$
$$-x = 1$$
$$x = -1$$

Substitute –1 for x in one of the original equations and solve for y.
Substitute –1 for x in (1): $\qquad\quad 2x + y = 2$
$$2(-1) + y = 2$$
$$-2 + y = 2$$
$$y = 4$$

The solution is (–1, 4).
Check by substituting –1 for x and 4 for y in both of the original equations.

6. Solve each system by substitution. Check each solution.

a) $y = 6 - 2x$
$\quad\;\; 3x + 2y = 10$

b) $3x + y - 2 = 0$
$\quad\;\; 5x + 2y - 3 = 0$

c) $3s + 5t = 2$
$\quad\;\; s + 4t = -4$

d) $x + 4y = -3$
$\quad\;\; 2x + 8y = -6$

e) $3x + 2y = 9$
$\quad\;\; -x + 3y = 8$

f) $2f + g = 4$
$\quad\;\; 4f + 2g = 9$

g) $7 = b - 2a$
$\quad\;\; 4 = a + b$

h) $3m - 6n = 1$
$\quad\;\; m + 3n = 2$

7. Simplify each system, and then solve it by substitution. Check each solution.

a) $2(x - 1) + y = 2$
$\quad\;\; 3x - 4(y + 3) = 5$

b) $3(x + 1) - (y + 7) = -2$
$\quad\;\; 4x + 5(y - 3) = -6$

8. **Canadian place names** The two most common place names in Canada are Mount Pleasant and Centreville. The total number of places with these names is 31. The number of places called Centreville is one less than the number of places called Mount Pleasant. This information can be modelled by the following linear system.

$$m + c = 31$$
$$c = m - 1$$

Solve the system by substitution to find the number of places in Canada with each name.

Refer to the Key Concepts on page 30.

To solve by elimination, multiply one or both equations by numbers to obtain two equations in which the coefficients of one variable are the same or opposites.

$$2x - 3y = 10 \qquad (1)$$
$$5x + 2y = 6 \qquad (2)$$

Multiply (1) by 2: $4x - 6y = 20$
Multiply (2) by 3: $\underline{15x + 6y = 18}$
Add: $19x = 38$
                       $x = 2$

Substitute 2 for x in (1): $2(2) - 3y = 10$
                              $4 - 3y = 10$
                                $-3y = 6$
                                  $y = -2$

The solution is $(2, -2)$.
Check by substituting 2 for x and -2 for y in both of the original equations.

9. Solve each system of equations by elimination. Check each solution.

a) $2x + 3y = 4$
$4x - 3y = -10$

b) $4a + 5b = -3$
$4a + 9b = 1$

c) $3x + 4y = 17$
$7x - 2y = 17$

d) $5m + 4n = 5$
$3m - 2n = 3$

e) $2x - 3y = 8$
$4x - 6y = 10$

f) $2x + 5y = 3$
$4x + 10y - 6 = 0$

g) $3c + 2d = -12$
$2c + 3d = -13$

h) $2x - 5y = 3$
$3x + 2y = 14$

10. **Communication** Which method would you use to solve each system of equations? Explain. Then, solve and check each system.

a) $y = x - 1$
$y = 2x + 3$

b) $5x - y = 4$
$3x + y = 4$

c) $3m - 4n = 4$
$m + 6n = 5$

d) $4x + 7y = 10$
$3x - 5y = -13$

11. Simplify and solve the system. Check the solution.
$$3(x + 1) - 4(y - 1) = 13$$
$$5(x + 2) + 2(y + 3) = 0$$

12. Solve. Check each solution.

a) $\dfrac{x}{3} + \dfrac{y}{2} = 3$

$\dfrac{2x}{3} - \dfrac{3y}{4} = -1$

b) $0.5x - 0.4y = 0.5$
$3x + 0.8y = 1.4$

13. Resort costs A weekend at Bayview Lodge costs $360 and includes two nights' accommodation and four meals. A week costs $1200 and includes seven nights' accommodation and ten meals. If n represents the cost of one night, and m represents the cost of one meal, the relationship between the costs can be modelled by the following system of equations.
$$2n + 4m = 360$$
$$7n + 10m = 1200$$
Determine the cost of one night and the cost of one meal.

1.6–1.7 Solving Problems Using Linear Systems

Refer to the Key Concepts on page 43.

14. Car wash The Outdoors Club held a car wash to raise money. They washed cars for $5 each and vans for $7 each. They washed 45 vehicles and earned $243. How many of each type of vehicle did they wash?

15. Buying bonds Li bought a Canada Savings Bond paying 5.5% interest and a provincial government bond paying 6.5% interest. She invested a total of $15 000 and earned $925 in interest in the first year. How much did she pay for each bond?

16. Lawn fertilizer One lawn fertilizer is 24% nitrogen, and another is 12% nitrogen. How much of each fertilizer should be mixed to obtain 100 kg of fertilizer that is 21% nitrogen?

17. Tail wind A small plane took 3 h to fly 960 km from Ottawa to Halifax with a tail wind. On the return trip, flying into the wind, the plane took 4 h. Find the wind speed and the speed of the plane in still air.

18. Car trip Maria drove from Owen Sound to Ottawa, a distance of 550 km. The trip took 7 h. Maria drove at 70 km/h for part of the trip, and at 85 km/h for the remainder of the trip. How far did she drive at 70 km/h?

Chapter Test

1. Solve each system by graphing. Check your solutions.

a) $y = x - 1$
$y = 2x - 5$

b) $x - y = 1$
$3x + 2y = -12$

c) $y = 4x + 4$
$x + 5y = -1$

d) $m + 5n + 9 = 0$
$3m - n - 5 = 0$

2. Solve each system graphically.

a) $y = 2x + 5$
$y = -4x + 1$

b) $2x + 3y = 8$
$3x - 5y = 2$

3. Communication Describe the graph of a system of equations with each number of solutions.

a) one

b) none

c) infinitely many

4. Solve each system by substitution. Check each solution.

a) $2x + y = 6$
$3x - 2y = 2$

b) $x + 2y + 2 = 0$
$2x - 6y + 9 = 0$

5. Solve each system by elimination. Check each solution.

a) $-2x + 5y = -3$
$2x - 3y = 1$

b) $3x + 2y = 8$
$2x + 3y = 7$

6. Solve each system by any method. Check each solution. If there is not exactly one solution, does the system have no solution or infinitely many solutions?

a) $5x - 3y = 9$
$2x - 5y = -4$

b) $3a + b - 4 = 0$
$2a - 10 = 3b$

c) $10x + 2 = 6y$
$5x = 3y - 1$

d) $x = 2 - 2y$
$y + \dfrac{1}{2}x = -1$

e) $\dfrac{x}{3} + \dfrac{y}{4} = -1$
$2x + y = -8$

f) $3p - 6q = 0$
$4p + q = 3$

g) $2x + 3y = -2$
$8x + 5y = -6$

h) $0.2x + 0.7y = 1.5$
$0.3x - 0.2y = 1$

i) $\dfrac{x}{5} + \dfrac{y}{3} = 3$
$\dfrac{x}{2} - \dfrac{y}{12} = 2$

j) $2(m + 1) - (n - 4) = 15$
$3(m - 1) + 4(n + 2) = 2$

7. Longest rivers The Mackenzie, the longest river in Canada, is 1056 km longer than the Yukon, the second longest river. The total length of the two rivers is 7426 km. Find the length of each river.

8. Granola One type of granola is 30% fruit, and another type is 15% fruit. What mass of each type of granola should be mixed to make 600 g of granola that is 21% fruit?

9. Investments Zach invested in a term deposit that paid 4% interest per annum and in a municipal bond that paid 6% interest per annum. If he invested a total of $13 000 and earned $700 interest in a year, how much did he invest at each rate?

10. Flying speeds A plane flew 3000 km from Calgary to Montréal with the wind in 5 h. The return flight into the wind took 6 h. Find the wind speed and the speed of the plane in still air.

Achievement Check

1   2   3   4

A street has a row of 15 new houses for sale. The middle house is on the most desirable piece of property and is the most expensive. The second house from one end costs $3000 more than the first house, the third house costs $3000 more than the second house, and so on, up to and including the middle house. The second house from the other end costs $5000 more than the first house, the third house costs $5000 more than the second house, and so on, up to and including the middle house. All the houses on the street cost a total of $3 091 000. What is the selling price of the house at each end of the street? Explain and justify your reasoning.

Problem Solving: Use a Data Bank

A data bank is a collection of information organized so that the information is easy to retrieve. A data bank can give you the information you need to solve a problem.

Amelia Earhart (1898–1937) was one of the world's leading aviators. Her solo flights in small planes broke a number of speed, altitude, and distance records. Her flight from Harbour Grace, Newfoundland, to Culmore, Ireland, was the second solo flight across the Atlantic. She was the first person to fly solo across the Pacific from Hawaii to California.

On her flight across the Pacific, Amelia Earhart took off from Honolulu, Hawaii, on January 11, 1935, at 17:16 local time. She landed in Oakland, California, at 13:31 local time on January 12. She flew a distance of 3875 km. Find her average speed, to the nearest kilometre per hour.

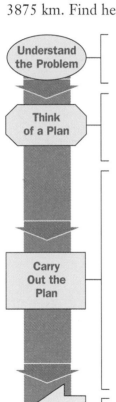

Understand the Problem

1. What information are you given?
2. What are you asked to find?
3. Do you need an exact or an approximate answer?

Think of a Plan

The average speed can be found by dividing the distance flown by the time taken. The time taken must first be calculated. Honolulu, Hawaii, and Oakland, California, are in different time zones, which can be found on a time zone map in a print or electronic data bank.

Carry Out the Plan

Honolulu is in time zone −10, so Honolulu is 10 h behind Greenwich Mean Time (GMT). When Amelia Earhart left Honolulu on January 11, the time in Greenwich was 17:16 + 10, or 03:16 GMT on January 12. California is in time zone −8, so it is 8 h behind GMT. The time when she landed was 13:31 + 8 or 21:31 GMT on January 12. From 03:16 GMT on January 12 to 21:31 GMT on January 12 is 18 h 15 min or 18.25 h.

$$\text{Average speed} = \frac{\text{distance flown}}{\text{time taken}}$$

$$= \frac{3875}{18.25}$$

$$\doteq 212 \text{ km/h}$$

Estimate

$$4000 \div 20 = 200$$

Her average speed was 212 km/h, to the nearest kilometre per hour.

Look Back

Does the answer seem reasonable?

Could you calculate the flying time without working in GMT?

Use a Data Bank

1. Locate the information you need.
2. Solve the problem.
3. Check that your answer is reasonable.

Applications and Problem Solving

Research *Use a print or electronic source, such as a data bank or the Internet, to find the data you need to solve the following problems.*

1. Transatlantic flight Charles Lindbergh was the first person to fly solo across the Atlantic. He left New York City at 07:52 local time on May 20, 1927, and landed in Paris at 23:21 local time on May 21. He flew 5830 km.
a) Calculate the time he took to fly from New York City to Paris.
b) Find his average speed, to the nearest kilometre per hour.

2. Moons Most planets in our solar system have moons. Which planets have a moon that is larger than the planet Mercury?

3. Land area Suppose the land area of each province were divided equally among all the people living in that province. In which province would a person receive
a) the most land?　　**b)** the least land?

4. Communication Species at risk are grouped into five categories: extinct, extirpated, endangered, threatened, or vulnerable.
a) What does each category mean?
b) What things are included when the word *species* is used?
c) What is the total number of species now at risk in Canada?
d) What is the average annual rate of increase in the species at risk in Canada?
f) What is the current estimate of the rate of extinction of species worldwide?

5. National debt If Canada's current national debt were divided equally among all Canadians, what would be each person's share?

6. Coastal communities What percent of Canadians live in coastal communities?

7. Renewable energy a) What percent of Canadian energy comes from renewable sources, such as solar and wind power?
b) What is the projected percent increase in renewable-energy use over the next 25 years?
c) What country produces the most wind energy? What percent of this country's wind-energy production is Canada's wind-energy production?

8. Canada a) What percent of the world's population lives in Canada?
b) What percent of the world's energy consumption is used by Canadians?

9. Education a) What is the projected increase in the number of children aged 5 to 14 in Canada from the year 2021 to the year 2041?
b) Estimate the number of new schools needed to accommodate the increase.
c) Estimate the number of additional teachers needed.

10. Communication Which is the sunniest province in Canada? Explain.

11. Itinerary Route 66 was a popular two-lane highway that started in Chicago and ended in Los Angeles. Much of Route 66 still exists, but most travellers now prefer to use the superhighways that run parallel to it. The cities on Route 66 include Chicago, Springfield (Illinois), St. Louis, Springfield (Missouri), Tulsa, Oklahoma City, Amarillo, Tucumcari, Albuquerque, Gallup, Flagstaff, Needles, Barstow, and Los Angeles. A newspaper reporter, writing a story about Route 66, leaves Chicago on May 10 at 08:00. Assume that the reporter drives at 80 km/h for a maximum of 6 h/day and sleeps each night at one of the places on the list. Write an itinerary for the reporter.

12. Communication Write a problem that requires the use of a data bank. Have a classmate solve your problem.

Problem Solving: Model and Communicate Solutions

In all aspects of life, we are continually solving problems. An important part of problem solving is mathematical modelling, that is, describing a situation in mathematical form.

In many cases, it is very important to communicate solutions clearly to other people. If you have the problem of scheduling a softball tournament, your solution to the problem is useless if you do not communicate it clearly to the teams involved. Similarly, if an engineer solves the problem of how to design a bridge for a particular location, the design serves no purpose until the engineer is able to communicate it to the people who will construct the bridge.

For many problems, different solutions are possible. It is important to communicate the complete solution to a problem, showing the mathematical model that you chose and the steps in your reasoning.

A large cube is made from 1000 small red cubes. The outside of the large cube is then painted blue. How many of the small cubes have two blue faces?

Understand the Problem

1. What information are you given?
2. What are you asked to find?
3. Do you need an exact or an approximate answer?

Think of a Plan

There are several possible solution methods that relate the number of small cubes with two blue faces to the size of the large cube.
• Method 1: Build and Interpret a Physical Model
Build a model of a cube and use it to describe how many small cubes have two blue faces.
• Method 2: Model Algebraically
Look for a pattern using large cubes of different sizes, write a formula, and use the formula to calculate the answer.
• Method 3: Model Graphically
Look for a pattern for large cubes of different sizes, graph the results, and extrapolate to find the answer.

Method 1: Build and Interpret a Physical Model

There is no need to build a large cube using 1000 small cubes. As the model of a 3 by 3 by 3 cube shows, the small cubes with two blue faces will be found on the edges of the large cube, but will not include the small cubes at the corners, which will have three blue faces.

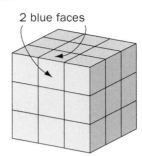

2 blue faces

Because there are two corner cubes on each edge of a large cube, a 10 by 10 by 10 large cube will have 8 small cubes with two blue faces on each edge.

A cube has 12 edges, so the number of small cubes with two blue faces is 12×8, or 96.

Method 2: Model Algebraically

The diagrams show cubes with dimensions 2 by 2 by 2, 3 by 3 by 3, 4 by 4 by 4, and 5 by 5 by 5.

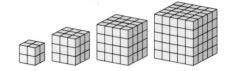

Use the diagrams to complete a table.

Edge Length of Large Cube, e	2	3	4	5
Small Cubes With 2 Blue Faces, b	0	12	24	36

Use the pattern in the table to write a formula.

The number of small cubes with two blue faces, b, is related to the edge length of the large cube, e, by the formula $b = 12e - 24$ or $b = 12(e - 2)$.

For a large cube built from 1000 small cubes, the edge length is 10, so

$$b = 12(10) - 24$$
$$= 96$$

The number of small cubes with two blue faces is 96.

Carry
Out the
Plan

Method 3: Model Graphically

Use the same diagrams and construct the same table as in Method 2.

Graph the data using a graphing calculator. The graph could be drawn using paper and pencil, but the answer would be an estimate and might not be exact. The problem requires an exact answer.

Let $b = y$ and $e = x$. Enter the data as two lists using the STAT EDIT menu.

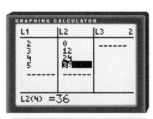

Choose suitable window variables using the window editor. Graph y versus x on a scatter plot using the STAT PLOTS menu.

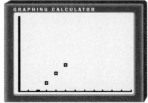

Draw the line of best fit using the linear regression instruction.

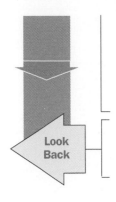

Because a large cube built from 1000 small cubes is 10 by 10 by 10, use the value operation to find the value of y when $x = 10$.

When $x = 10$, $y = 96$, so the number of small cubes with two blue faces is 96.

Look Back

Does the answer seem reasonable?
Which of the three methods shown do you prefer? Explain why.
Can you think of another way to solve the problem?

Model and Communicate Solutions

1. Choose a mathematical model to describe the problem.
2. Use the model to solve the problem.
3. Communicate the solution, showing your model and your reasoning.
4. Check that your answer is reasonable.

Applications and Problem Solving

Communication *Solve each of the following problems. Write a full solution, showing your mathematical model and your reasoning clearly in each case. Explain why you chose your solution method.*

1. Square pattern If the pattern of shaded and unshaded squares continues, how many shaded squares will there be in the 100th diagram?

2. Toothpicks The pattern shows how toothpicks can be used to make triangles joined along whole sides.

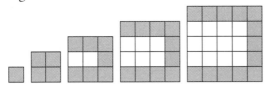

If the pattern continues, how many triangles can be made from 101 toothpicks?

3. Perimeters The pattern shows how rectangular shapes can be made from squares of side length 1 unit.

The perimeter of the first diagram is 12 units. When the blue squares are removed, the remaining red figure has a perimeter of 4 units. If the pattern continues, what is the perimeter of the remaining red figure when the blue squares are removed from a figure with a perimeter of 100 units?

4. Paper folding For a rectangular sheet of paper, how many different ways to fold the sheet using one fold line result in half the area being on each side of the fold? What do all the possible fold lines have in common?

5. Difference of squares Many numbers can be expressed as the difference of two squares. For example, $43 = 22^2 - 21^2$, $144 = 12^2 - 0^2$, and $300 = 20^2 - 10^2$. Which of the positive integers from 1 to 40 can be expressed as the difference of two squares?

Problem Solving: Using the Strategies

1. Product Copy the diagram. Place the digits from 1 to 5 in the squares so that the product is 3542.

3 5 4 2

2. Measurement In the figure, the side of each small square represents 1 cm. Find the total area of
a) the shaded regions
b) the unshaded regions

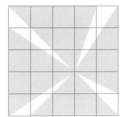

3. Transpacific flight On Monday at 21:00 local time, a plane leaves Vancouver for Sydney, Australia. The plane cruises at 900 km/h and stops for 1 h in Hawaii to refuel. At about what local time and on what day will the plane land in Sydney?

4. Measurement The figure is made up of squares. Square B has dimensions 4 cm by 4 cm. Square C has dimensions 5 cm by 5 cm. What is the total area of the figure, in square centimetres?

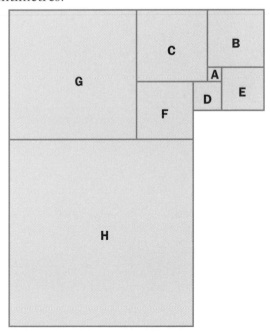

5. Grouping numbers In how many different ways can you place the numbers 1, 2, 3, 4, 5, 6, 7, 8, and 9 into groups so that the sum of the numbers in each group is 15?

6. Group photo Hakim, Rena, Patrice, and Julius line up for a picture. If Patrice and Hakim do not stand beside each other, in how many different ways can the group line up?

7. Communication The first diagram shows two 1-cm cubes, with one stacked on top of the other. If the lower cube sits on a table, the area of the exposed faces is 9 cm^2. The second diagram shows four cubes, and the area of the exposed faces is 14 cm^2. The third diagram shows six cubes, and so on.

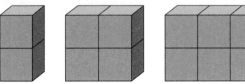

Write a full solution to the following, showing your mathematical model and your reasoning.
a) What is the total area of the exposed faces for a figure made from 36 cubes?
b) If the total area of the exposed faces of a figure is 129 cm^2, how many cubes make up the figure?

8. Missing sums Each letter in the box represents a different number. The sums of the columns and two of the rows are given. Find the missing sums.

A	B	A	B	36
A	C	A	C	34
B	B	B	C	?
D	E	F	A	?
37	40	41	32	

Specific Expectations	Sections
• Determine the formulas for the midpoint and length of a line segment and use these formulas to solve problems.	2.1 2.2 2.3 2.4 2.5
• Determine the equation for a circle having centre (0, 0) and radius r, by applying the formula for the length of a line segment; identify the radius of a circle of centre (0, 0), given its equation; and write the equation, given the radius.	2.1
• Solve multi-step problems, using the concepts of the slope, the length, and the midpoint of line segments.	2.4 2.5
• Communicate the solutions to multi-step problems in good mathematical form, giving clear reasons for the steps taken to reach the solutions.	2.4 2.5
• Determine the characteristics of a triangle whose vertex coordinates are given.	2.1 2.4
• Determine the characteristics of a quadrilateral whose vertex coordinates are given.	2.1 2.3 2.4
• Verify the geometric properties of a triangle or quadrilateral whose vertex coordinates are given.	2.1 2.3 2.4

Modelling Math

Analyzing a Design

Quilts with traditional designs are made by sewing together many matching square blocks. Each block has a design made from small pieces of fabric sewn together. Many traditional designs use triangular- and quadrilateral-shaped pieces on the square blocks.

To help determine the exact sizes and shapes of the pieces, quilters may draw the pattern of the block on grid paper. The diagram shows one block of a maple leaf design on a grid that measures 40 cm by 40 cm.

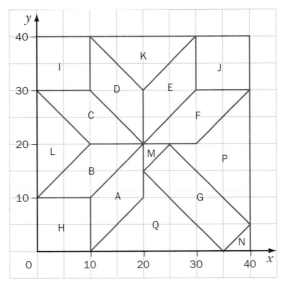

Verify that the diagonals of quadrilateral G bisect each other.

In the Modelling Math questions on pages 73, 80, 98, and 105, you will solve the above problem and other problems that involve the quilt design.

1. Make up your own quilt design using triangles and quadrilaterals on a 40 cm by 40 cm grid.

2. Give possible reasons why traditional quilts were made by sewing together square blocks.

Street Geometry

In Euclidean geometry, the Pythagorean Theorem is used to calculate the distance between two points. The Euclidean distance, d_E, between the theatre and the arena in the diagram, is $\sqrt{41}$ blocks, or about 6.4 blocks.

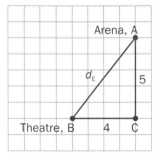

$$AB^2 = BC^2 + AC^2$$
$$d_E^2 = 4^2 + 5^2$$
$$= 16 + 25$$
$$= 41$$
$$d_E = \sqrt{41}$$
$$\doteq 6.4$$

The taxicab distance, d_T, between the theatre and the arena, is 9 blocks. This is the smallest number of blocks a taxi could drive or a person could walk from A to B.

1. Find d_T and d_E for each of the following pairs of points. Round to the nearest tenth, if necessary.
a) A and B
b) C and D
c) E and F
d) G and H
e) A and C
f) B and D

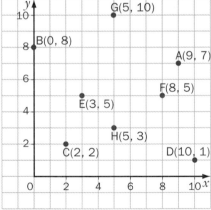

2. Communication When is the taxicab distance between two points equal to the Euclidean distance?

3. a) Mark a point, A, on a sheet of grid paper. Then, mark a set of points so that the taxicab distance of each point from point A is 7 units. If you marked all the points in the set, what figure would you form?
b) If you repeated part a), but you marked a set of points so that the Euclidean distance of each point from point A is 7 units, what figure would you form?

Review of Prerequisite Skills

If you need help with any of the skills named in **purple** below, refer to Appendix A.

1. Evaluating radicals Evaluate.

a) $\sqrt{81}$

b) $\sqrt{169}$

c) $\sqrt{1.44}$

d) $\sqrt{0.49}$

2. Evaluating radicals Evaluate, to the nearest tenth.

a) $\sqrt{23}$

b) $\sqrt{7.5}$

c) $\sqrt{405}$

d) $\sqrt{1253}$

3. Pythagorean Theorem In each right triangle, find the unknown side length, to the nearest tenth of a unit.

a)

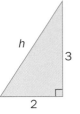

b)

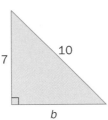

c)

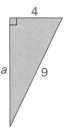

d)

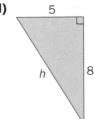

4. Lengths of line segments Find the length of the line segment joining each of the following pairs of points.

a) (4, 2) and (9, 2)

b) (−6, 4) and (1, 4)

c) (−7, −3) and (−1, −3)

d) (5, −1) and (−6, −1)

5. Lengths of line segments Find the length of the line segment joining each of the following pairs of points.

a) (5, 9) and (5, 2)

b) (−3, 6) and (−3, −5)

c) (2, −3) and (2, −8)

d) (−5, 0) and (−5, −8)

6. Slope Evaluate mentally.

a) $\dfrac{6-2}{3-1}$

b) $\dfrac{10-1}{5-2}$

c) $\dfrac{5-(-1)}{8-2}$

d) $\dfrac{1-9}{2-4}$

e) $\dfrac{5-(-1)}{-3-(-1)}$

f) $\dfrac{-3-(-2)}{-2-(-1)}$

7. Slope Find the slope of the line passing through each of the following pairs of points.

a) (0, 0) and (3, 4)

b) (0, 0) and (−1, −3)

c) (1, 6) and (2, 8)

d) (−1, 4) and (1, 7)

e) (−5, 4) and (−2, −1)

f) (0, 4) and (2, 0)

g) (3, 5) and (6, 5)

h) (2, 1) and (2, 6)

i) (−6, −1) and (−4, −6)

j) (8, −1) and (4, −4)

8. Slope What is the slope of

a) the line $y = 3x - 2$?

b) a line parallel to $y = 3x - 2$?

c) a line perpendicular to $y = 3x - 2$?

Length of a Line Segment

Urban planners work with the public, the business community, and politicians to plan the development of communities. Planners are involved in such decisions as approving new streets, designing parks, and evaluating proposals for new buildings, including houses, office towers, schools, and hospitals.

For centuries, many cities and towns have been planned using rectangular street grids, which are convenient to use and can be extended in any direction.

Investigation Develop a Method

1. Copy the graph of line segment AB onto grid paper.

a) Locate point C, below point B, so that △ABC is a right triangle, with AB the hypotenuse. Write the coordinates of point C on the grid.

b) Find the lengths of legs AC and BC.

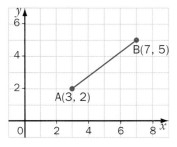

2. Use the lengths of AC and BC and the Pythagorean Theorem to calculate the length of AB.

3. Communication Would the length of AB change if the right triangle was formed by locating point C above point A? Explain.

4. Communication If you are given the coordinates of the endpoints of any line segment, describe a method for finding the length of the segment without plotting the points.

5. Use the method from question 4 to find the length of the line segment joining each of the following pairs of points. Round each answer to the nearest tenth, if necessary.

a) C(2, 3) and D(10, 9)   **b)** E(2, 4) and F(7, 1)
c) G(–3, 1) and H(4, 5)

6. The diagram models the street grid for a neighbourhood. The dimensions are in metres.

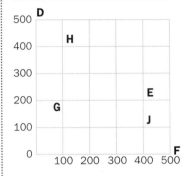

When considering pedestrian traffic in a modern city or town, planners often assume that the walking speed is about 1.2 m/s. Assuming this speed and ignoring the time it takes to cross streets, what is the shortest time it would take to walk from

a) F to G?
b) D to E, to the nearest second?

7. Suppose that urban planners proposed a diagonal street from H to J. How long would it take to walk from H to J along this street, to the nearest second?

8. Using all or part of the diagonal street, what is the shortest time each of the walks in question 6 would take, to the nearest second?

Numbers such as $\sqrt{7}$ and $\sqrt{10}$ cannot be written as a fraction or a terminating decimal. These square roots are non-terminating, non-repeating decimals, or **irrational numbers**.

Approximate values of irrational numbers can be found by estimation or using a calculator. If the solution to a problem is left in radical form as $\sqrt{7}$, it is called an exact solution. If $\sqrt{7}$ is estimated or found on a calculator, the result is called an approximate solution.

Example 1   Length of a Line Segment

Determine the length of the line segment joining A(3, 1) and B(6, 9).
Express the length as
a) an exact solution
b) an approximate solution, to the nearest tenth

Solution

a) Draw the line segment AB.
Construct right triangle ABC.
The coordinates of C are (6, 1).

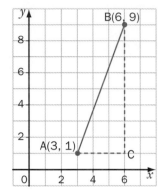

Length of AC = 3
Length of BC = 8

Use the Pythagorean Theorem.

$$(AB)^2 = (AC)^2 + (BC)^2$$
$$AB = \sqrt{(AC)^2 + (BC)^2}$$
$$= \sqrt{3^2 + 8^2}$$
$$= \sqrt{9 + 64}$$
$$= \sqrt{73}$$

The exact length of the line segment joining A and B is $\sqrt{73}$.

b) The length of the line
segment joining A and B is
8.5, to the nearest tenth.

Estimate

$\sqrt{64} = 8$ $\sqrt{81} = 9$
$\sqrt{73} \doteq 8.5$

The formula for the length of a line segment may be generalized as follows.
The points $A(x_1, y_1)$ and $B(x_2, y_2)$ represent any two points on a grid.

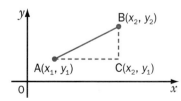

$$(AB)^2 = (\text{change in } x)^2 + (\text{change in } y)^2$$
$$AB = \sqrt{(\text{change in } x)^2 + (\text{change in } y)^2}$$
$$AB = \sqrt{(x_2 - x_1)^2 + (y_2 - y_1)^2}$$
$$\text{or } l = \sqrt{(x_2 - x_1)^2 + (y_2 - y_1)^2}$$

Example 2   Using the Length Formula

Find the length of the line segment joining C(2, −4) and D(−3, 5), to the nearest tenth.

Solution

Let $(x_1, y_1) = (2, -4)$ and $(x_2, y_2) = (-3, 5)$.

$$\text{Then } CD = \sqrt{(x_2 - x_1)^2 + (y_2 - y_1)^2}$$
$$= \sqrt{(-3-2)^2 + (5-(-4))^2}$$
$$= \sqrt{(-5)^2 + 9^2}$$
$$= \sqrt{25+81}$$
$$= \sqrt{106}$$
$$\doteq 10.3$$

Estimate

$$\sqrt{100} = 10$$

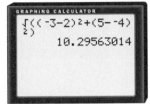

The length of the line segment joining C and D is 10.3, to the nearest tenth.

Example 3   Classifying a Triangle by Side Length

$\triangle DEF$ has vertices D(1, 3), E(−3, 2), and F(−2, −2).

a) Classify the triangle by side length.

b) Determine the perimeter of the triangle, to the nearest tenth.

Solution

a) Find the exact length of each side of $\triangle DEF$.

$$DE = \sqrt{(x_2 - x_1)^2 + (y_2 - y_1)^2}$$
$$= \sqrt{(-3-1)^2 + (2-3)^2}$$
$$= \sqrt{(-4)^2 + (-1)^2}$$
$$= \sqrt{16+1}$$
$$= \sqrt{17}$$

$$EF = \sqrt{(x_2 - x_1)^2 + (y_2 - y_1)^2}$$
$$= \sqrt{(-2-(-3))^2 + (-2-2)^2}$$
$$= \sqrt{(1)^2 + (-4)^2}$$
$$= \sqrt{1+16}$$
$$= \sqrt{17}$$

$$FD = \sqrt{(x_2 - x_1)^2 + (y_2 - y_1)^2}$$
$$= \sqrt{(1-(-2))^2 + (3-(-2))^2}$$
$$= \sqrt{3^2 + 5^2}$$
$$= \sqrt{9+25}$$
$$= \sqrt{34}$$

Technology Extension

Geometry software can be used to show that side lengths are equal.

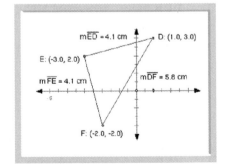

In $\triangle DEF$, DE = EF.
The triangle is isosceles.

b) The perimeter, P, is the sum of the side lengths.

$$P = \sqrt{17} + \sqrt{17} + \sqrt{34}$$
$$\doteq 14.1$$

Estimate

$$\sqrt{16} + \sqrt{16} + \sqrt{36} = 4 + 4 + 6$$
$$= 14$$

The following shows the result when a radical is squared.

Since $2 \times 2 = 4$
then $\sqrt{4} \times \sqrt{4} = 4$
and $\left(\sqrt{4}\right)^2 = 4$

In general, $\left(\sqrt{x}\right)^2 = x$, when $x \geq 0$.

This result and the distance formula can be used to write the equation of a circle having centre O(0, 0) and radius r.
Let P(x, y) be any point on the circle.
Then, OP = r.
The formula for the length, l, of a line segment is

$$l = \sqrt{(x_2 - x_1)^2 + (y_2 - y_1)^2}$$

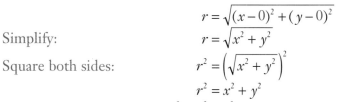

Substitute r for l, (x, y) for (x_2, y_2), and (0, 0) for (x_1, y_1).

$$r = \sqrt{(x-0)^2 + (y-0)^2}$$

Simplify:
$$r = \sqrt{x^2 + y^2}$$

Square both sides:
$$r^2 = \left(\sqrt{x^2 + y^2}\right)^2$$
$$r^2 = x^2 + y^2$$
or $x^2 + y^2 = r^2$

So, the equation of a circle having centre O(0, 0) and radius r is
$$x^2 + y^2 = r^2$$

Example 4   Finding the Radius of a Circle Given its Equation

Determine the radius of a circle with centre (0, 0) and equation $x^2 + y^2 = 49$.

Solution

An equation of the circle with centre (0, 0) and radius r is
$$x^2 + y^2 = r^2$$
In the equation $x^2 + y^2 = 49$, $r^2 = 49$ The square roots of 49 are 7 and –7,
so $r = 7$ but the radius cannot be negative.

The radius of a circle with centre (0, 0) and equation $x^2 + y^2 = 49$ is 7.

Example 5   Writing an Equation of a Circle Given its Radius

Write an equation for the circle with centre (0, 0) and radius 4.

Solution

An equation of the circle with centre (0, 0) and radius r is
$$x^2 + y^2 = r^2$$
Substitute 4 for r: $x^2 + y^2 = 4^2$
$$x^2 + y^2 = 16$$
An equation for the circle with centre (0, 0) and radius 4 is $x^2 + y^2 = 16$.

Key CONCEPTS

1 To find the length of a line segment joining (x_1, y_1) and (x_2, y_2), use the formula $l = \sqrt{(x_2 - x_1)^2 + (y_2 - y_1)^2}$.

2 An equation of the circle with centre O(0, 0) and radius r is $x^2 + y^2 = r^2$.

Communicate Your Understanding

1. Describe how you would find the length of the line segment joining the points P(1, 2) and Q(4, 7). Explain and justify your steps.

2. Explain why the value under the radical sign in the length formula is never negative.

3. When you use the length formula to find the length of a line segment joining two points, does it matter which point is represented by (x_1, y_1) and which point is represented by (x_2, y_2)? Explain your reasoning using an example. Compare your example with a classmate's.

4. Describe how you would find the radius of the circle whose equation is $x^2 + y^2 = 81$.

5. Describe how you would write an equation for the circle with centre (0, 0) and radius 2.

Practice

A

1. Determine the length of the line segment joining each pair of points. Express each length as an exact solution and as an approximate solution, to the nearest tenth.
a) (2, 1) and (3, 5)
b) (3, −5) and (−6, 7)
c) (3, 0) and (4, −1)
d) (−1, 2) and (−6, −3)
e) (2, 1) and (2, 9)
f) (4, −7) and (11, −7)
g) (8.1, 3.7) and (3.2, −5.4)
h) (0.1, 0.2) and (−0.1, −0.2)

2. Write an equation for the circle with centre (0, 0) and the given radius.
a) radius 3
b) radius 6
c) radius 10
d) radius 11

3. The following are equations of circles with centre (0, 0). Determine the radius of each circle. Round to the nearest tenth, if necessary.
a) $x^2 + y^2 = 64$
b) $x^2 + y^2 = 4$
c) $x^2 + y^2 = 144$
d) $x^2 + y^2 = 1$
e) $x^2 + y^2 = 30$
f) $x^2 + y^2 = 1.21$

4. Determine the radius of each circle, given its centre and a point on its circumference. Round each radius to the nearest tenth, if necessary.
a) centre (0, 0), point (3, 4)
b) centre (0, 0), point (2, 7)
c) centre (0, 0), point (−4, −6)
d) centre (0, 0), point (−11, 3)

5. Measurement Given the coordinates of the vertices, classify each triangle as equilateral, isosceles, or scalene. Then, find each perimeter, to the nearest tenth.
a) A(2, 5), B(−2, −1), C(6, −1)   **b)** D(−2, −5), E(−3, 2), F(1, 3)
c) P(2, 1), Q(5, 3), R(0, 4)   **d)** G(3, 0), H(0, $3\sqrt{3}$), I(−3, 0)

Applications and Problem Solving

6. Street grid The grid models the streets in a neighbourhood. The distances are in metres. Assume that the walking speed is 1.2 m/s, and ignore the time it takes to cross streets. If a diagonal street were constructed as shown, determine the shortest time needed for each of the following walks, to the nearest second.
a) P to Q   **b)** P to R   **c)** R to S   **d)** T to P

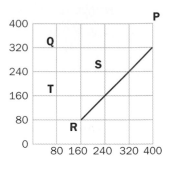

7. Measurement A quadrilateral has vertices P(3, 5), Q(−4, 3), R(−3, −2), and S(5, −4). Find the lengths of the diagonals, to the nearest tenth.

8. Measurement The vertices of a right triangle are S(−2, −2), T(10, −2), and R(4, 4). Find the area of the triangle.

9. Coast guard A coast guard patrol boat is located 5 km east and 8 km north of the entrance to St. John's harbour. A tanker is 9 km east and 6 km south of the entrance. Find the distance between the two ships, to the nearest tenth of a kilometre.

10. Measurement Verify that A(4, 2), B(−2, −2), and C(2, −8) are the vertices of an isosceles triangle.

11. Measurement Verify that C(−5, −1) is the midpoint of the line segment joining A(−2, 5) and B(−8, −7).

12. Measurement Determine the perimeter of the quadrilateral with vertices A(3, 2), B(−2, 4), C(−4, −2), and D(4, −1)
a) as an exact solution   **b)** as an approximate solution, to the nearest tenth

13. Measurement The coordinates of the endpoints of the diameter of a circle are (6, 4) and (−2, 0). Find the exact length of the radius of the circle.

14. Measurement Show that the quadrilateral with vertices K(3, 4), L(2, 0), M(−3, −2), and N(−1, 3) is a kite. Then, determine the perimeter, to the nearest tenth.

15. Measurement Show that the parallelogram with vertices W(1, 3), X(4, 1), Y(1, −1), and Z(−2, 1) is a rhombus. Then, determine the perimeter, to the nearest tenth.

16. Write an equation for the circle with centre (0, 0), if the given point lies on its circumference.

a) A(4, 3)   **b)** B(5, −12)   **c)** C(−6, −2)

17. Telephone grid At one time, telephone companies determined the cost of a long-distance telephone call using the distance between the two stations and the length of the call. To determine the distance, a coordinate grid was superimposed over North America. The origin, (0, 0), was located off the northeast coast of Canada. Every North American city and town had a set of coordinates in the form (horizontal, vertical). The coordinates gave the distance, in kilometres, of the location from the origin. The coordinates for five cities are shown in the table.

City	Coordinates
Edmonton	(3978, 2520)
Montréal	(1015, 2104)
Ottawa	(1142, 2232)
Toronto	(1268, 2540)
Washington, D.C.	(807, 2867)

a) Calculate the distance, to the nearest 10 kilometres, between Toronto and Ottawa; Montréal and Edmonton; Ottawa and Washington, D.C.

b) Use your research skills to find the flying distance between each pair of cities in part a). How accurate was the telephone grid system?

18. Algebra Write an expression for the length of the line segment joining each pair of points.

a) (a, b) and (2a, 2b)   **b)** (x, 2y) and (2x, −y)
c) (m + 1, n − 1) and (m − 1, 2n − 1)   **d)** (2p, −p) and (4p, 3p)

19. Algebra The point (x, −1) is 13 units from the point (3, 11). What are the possible values of x?

20. List all the points that have whole-number coordinates and are
a) 5 units from the origin   **b)** 10 units from the point (2, 1)

Modelling Math | **Analyzing a Design**

Refer to the maple leaf design on the grid on page 63.
1. Determine the perimeter of each of the following, to the nearest tenth of a centimetre.
a) triangle M   **b)** quadrilateral C   **c)** quadrilateral P

2. Communication How do the perimeters of quadrilateral A and triangle K compare? Explain.

2.2 *Investigation:* Midpoints of Horizontal and Vertical Line Segments

1 Midpoints of Horizontal Line Segments

1. Graph each line segment. Count units to find the coordinates of M, the midpoint of each line segment.
a) The endpoints of AB are A(1, 4) and B(9, 4).
b) The endpoints of CD are C(–3, 2) and D(7, 2).
c) The endpoints of EF are E(0, –3) and F(6, –3).
d) The endpoints of GH are G(–7, –2) and H(–1, –2).
e) The endpoints of IJ are I(–2, 0) and J(10, 0).

2. Communication Describe the relationship between the coordinates of the midpoint of a horizontal line segment and the coordinates of the endpoints.

3. Given the endpoints of each line segment, find the coordinates of the midpoint without plotting the points.
a) K(2, 3) and L(6, 3)   **b)** P(–1, 1) and Q(5, 1)
c) R(–7, 5) and S(–3, 5)   **d)** V(0, –5) and W(8, –5)

4. AB is a line segment joining the points A(2, 3) and B(10, 3). Find the coordinates of the three points that divide AB into four equal parts.

2 Midpoints of Vertical Line Segments

1. Graph each line segment. Count units to find the coordinates of M, the midpoint of each line segment.
a) The endpoints of AB are A(2, 8) and B(2, 2).
b) The endpoints of CD are C(5, 6) and D(5, –2).
c) The endpoints of EF are E(–3, –1) and F(–3, –5).
d) The endpoints of GH are G(–2, –4) and H(–2, 0).
e) The endpoints of IJ are I(0, 8) and J(0, –2).

2. Communication Describe the relationship between the coordinates of the midpoint of a vertical line segment and the coordinates of the endpoints.

3. Given the endpoints of each line segment, find the coordinates of the midpoint without plotting the points.
a) S(4, 7) and T(4, 1)   **b)** P(1, 4) and Q(1, –6)
c) V(–2, –4) and W(–2, 4)
d) L(0, 9) and N(0, 1)

4. CD is a line segment joining the points C(3, 8) and D(3, –4). Find the coordinates of the three points that divide CD into four equal parts.

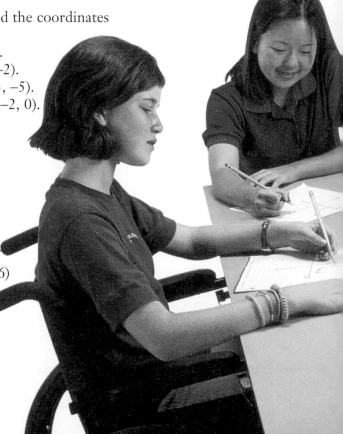

Midpoint of a Line Segment

When you look in a mirror, your reflection image is the same distance behind the mirror as you are in front of it. The line segment that connects your eyes and the image of your eyes is perpendicular to the mirror. The midpoint of this line segment lies on the mirror.

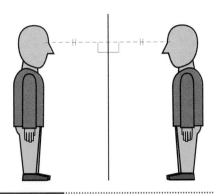

Investigation **Use the Diagrams**

Each diagram shows a green mirror line, a line segment joining a point and its reflection image, and the midpoint of the segment. If the original point is labelled A, then the image point is labelled A′, which is read "A prime."

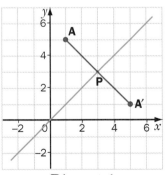

Diagram 1

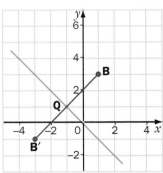

Diagram 2

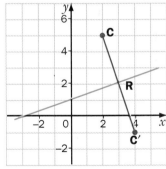

Diagram 3

1. a) In diagram 1, what are the coordinates of A? the image point A′? the midpoint P?

b) In diagram 2, what are the coordinates of B? the image point B′? the midpoint Q?

c) In diagram 3, what are the coordinates of C? the image point C′? the midpoint R?

2. a) How is the x-coordinate of P related to the x-coordinates of A and A'?

b) How is the y-coordinate of P related to the y-coordinates of A and A'?

3. a) How is the x-coordinate of Q related to the x-coordinates of B and B'?

b) How is the y-coordinate of Q related to the y-coordinates of B and B'?

4. a) How is the x-coordinate of R related to the x-coordinates of C and C'?

b) How is the y-coordinate of R related to the y-coordinates of C and C'?

5. Communication Write a rule for finding the coordinates of the midpoint of a line segment using the coordinates of the endpoints. Have a classmate use your rule to find the midpoint of a line segment.

6. Find the coordinates of the midpoint of each of the following line segments, given the coordinates of the endpoints.
a) A(4, 9), B(2, 1)   **b)** C(0, –2), D(–2, 4)   **c)** E(–3, –4), F(–1, 6)

If A has coordinates (x_1, y_1) and B has coordinates (x_2, y_2), then the coordinates of the midpoint, M, of the segment AB are

$$\left(\frac{x_1 + x_2}{2}, \frac{y_1 + y_2}{2} \right)$$

Example 1   Midpoint of a Line Segment
Determine the coordinates of the midpoint, M, of the line segment with endpoints A(–2, –3) and B(4, 7).

Solution
Substitute into the formula for midpoint.

$$\left(\frac{x_1 + x_2}{2}, \frac{y_1 + y_2}{2} \right)$$

The midpoint of A(–2, –3) and B(4, 7) is

$$\left(\frac{-2 + 4}{2}, \frac{-3 + 7}{2} \right) = (1, 2)$$

The coordinates of the midpoint, M, are (1, 2).

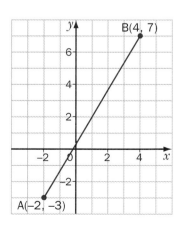

Example 2   Diagonals of a Parallelogram

Verify that the diagonals of the parallelogram with vertices P(−2, 1), Q(3, 3), R(4, −1), and S(−1, −3) bisect each other.

Solution

If the diagonals have the same midpoint, then they bisect each other. Use the formula for midpoint to find the midpoint of each diagonal.

$$\left(\frac{x_1 + x_2}{2}, \frac{y_1 + y_2}{2} \right)$$

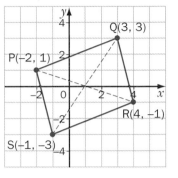

The midpoint of PR is $\left(\frac{-2+4}{2}, \frac{1+(-1)}{2} \right) = (1,\ 0)$.

The midpoint of QS is $\left(\frac{3+(-1)}{2}, \frac{3+(-3)}{2} \right) = (1,\ 0)$.

The diagonals have the same midpoint.
The diagonals of the parallelogram bisect each other.

Key CONCEPTS

To find the midpoint, M, of a line segment joining (x_1, y_1) and (x_2, y_2), use the midpoint formula, $\left(\frac{x_1 + x_2}{2}, \frac{y_1 + y_2}{2} \right)$.

Communicate Your Understanding

1. Describe how you would find the coordinates of the midpoint of the line segment with endpoints P(8, 1) and Q(2, 7).

2. Describe how the midpoint formula makes use of arithmetic averages.

3. Draw a diagram to illustrate the following conjecture.
If DE = FE, then E is the midpoint of DF.
Then, draw a counterexample diagram to show the conjecture is not true.

4. Consider a line segment with two endpoints whose coordinates are integers. Describe any relationships between the coordinates of the endpoints such that the coordinates of the midpoints are integers.

Practice

A

1. Determine the midpoint of each line segment from the given endpoints.
a) (5, 7) and (3, 9)
b) (4, 2) and (6, 8)
c) (−1, 0) and (1, −6)
d) (−2, −4) and (−2, 8)
e) (−3, −3) and (−1, −7)
f) (5, 4) and (−3, 4)

g) (0.2, 1.5) and (3.6, 0.3)
h) $\left(\frac{1}{2}, \frac{5}{2} \right)$ and $\left(\frac{3}{2}, -\frac{7}{2} \right)$

i) (200, 125) and (403, 174)
j) (a, b) and (c, d)

Applications and Problem Solving

2. A diameter of a circle joins the points C(–7, –4) and D(–1, 10). What are the coordinates of the centre of the circle?

3. A parallelogram has vertices A(–2, –2), B(3, 3), C(7, 4), and D(2, –1). Verify that the diagonals bisect each other.

B

4. The endpoints of AB are A(10, 16) and B(–6, –12). Find the coordinates of the points that divide the segment into four equal parts.

5. For a line segment DE, one endpoint is D(6, 5) and the midpoint is M(4, 2). Find the coordinates of endpoint E.

6. For a line segment AB, one endpoint is A(0, 6) and the midpoint is M(4, 7). Find the coordinates of endpoint B.

7. For a line segment PQ, one endpoint is P(–2, –6) and the midpoint is M(–4, 1). Find the coordinates of endpoint Q.

8. The centre of a circle has coordinates (0, 0). One endpoint of a diameter of the circle has coordinates (–3, 2). What are the coordinates of the other endpoint of the diameter?

9. Measurement A quadrilateral has vertices P(0, 8), Q(–4, 4), R(2, –2), and S(6, 4). Find the perimeter of the figure whose vertices are the midpoints of the sides of the quadrilateral.

10. Verify that the diagonals of the rectangle with vertices P(–1, 4), Q(–2, 1), R(4, –1), and S(5, 2) bisect each other.

11. Verify that the diagonals of the square with vertices A(–2, 1), B(2, –1), C(0, –5), and D(–4, –3) bisect each other.

12. Measurement A quadrilateral ABCD has vertices A(4, –2), B(6, 6), C(0, 8), and D(–2, 4).
a) Find the coordinates of the following points.
        E, the midpoint of AB
        F, the midpoint of BC
        G, the midpoint of CD
        H, the midpoint of AD
b) Verify that the length of EF equals the length of GH.
c) Verify that the length of FG equals the length of EH.

13. For the line segment ST, S has coordinates (6, 2) and T is on the *y*-axis. The midpoint, M, of ST is on the *x*-axis. Find the coordinates of T and M.

14. Measurement Triangle RST has vertices R(4, 4), S(–6, 2), and T(2, 0). Find the lengths of the three medians.

15. Verify that M is the midpoint of line segment AB by using the length formula.

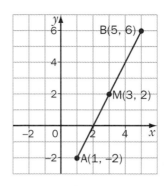

16. Measurement A right triangle has vertices P(2, 3), Q(6, −5), and R(−6, −1). Verify that the midpoint of the hypotenuse is equidistant from each vertex of the triangle.

17. Building a road Historic Fort Bragg is to be rebuilt for visitors. A map of the area around the fort is drawn on a coordinate grid. The coordinates of the fort are (5.2, 16.6). A straight road is to be constructed to the fort from a point on a highway with coordinates (12.8, 7.8). The federal government has agreed to pay half the cost of the road. Construction costs are $790/m.
a) Find the coordinates of the midpoint of the road.
b) If one unit of length on the grid represents 1 km, use the midpoint to find half the length of the road.
c) Calculate the federal government's cost.
d) Communication Describe a different method of solving the problem.

18. Communication A jeep is travelling in a straight line across a flat, empty desert. On a navigational map with 1 unit representing 1 km, the starting point of the jeep is at (−140, −70) and its destination is at (280, 50). There is a refueling depot with an emergency transmitter half way along the route. During the journey, the jeep shows signs that engine trouble will soon develop. The driver must decide whether to turn back to the start, try for the refuelling depot, or continue to the end of the trip. If the jeep travels at 30 km/h, what should the driver do in each of the following situations? Explain.
a) The signs of engine trouble develop after 4 h.
b) The signs of engine trouble develop after 11 h.

C

19. Algebra Write the coordinates of the midpoint between each of the following pairs of points.
a) (x, y) and $(2x, 2y)$ **b)** $(4a, 3b)$ and $(8a, −b)$
c) $(m + 1, n + 3)$ and $(m − 1, n − 2)$ **d)** $(2t, 3t + 1)$ and $(−4t, 1 − t)$

20. Algebra The endpoints of PQ are P(3, −4) and Q(11, c). The midpoint of PQ is M(d, 3). Find the values of c and d.

21. Algebra For a line segment GH, one endpoint is G(p, q) and the midpoint is M(c, d). Find the coordinates of endpoint H.

22. Algebra A line segment has endpoints A(x_1, y_1) and B(x_2, y_2). Find expressions in terms of x_1, x_2, y_1, and y_2 for the coordinates of the points that divide AB into four equal parts.

23. The base of an isosceles triangle lies on the x-axis. The coordinates of the midpoints of the equal sides of the triangle are (2, 3) and (−2, 3). What are the coordinates of the vertices of the triangle?

24. The midpoints of the equal sides of an isosceles triangle have coordinates (4, 3) and (4, −1). What are the coordinates of the vertices of the triangle if
a) two vertices lie on the y-axis?   **b)** only one vertex lies on the y-axis?

25. Communication Decide whether each statement is always true, sometimes true, or never true. Explain.
a) Two line segments with the same midpoint have the same length.
b) Two parallel line segments have the same midpoint.
c) The midpoint of a line segment is equidistant from the endpoints of the segment.
d) A point equidistant from the endpoints of a line segment is the midpoint of the segment.

26. Communication Without using the word *midpoint*, describe to a classmate the meaning of the midpoint of a line segment in two different ways.

Modelling Math   Analyzing a Design

Refer to the maple leaf design on the grid on page 63.
1. Verify that the diagonals of quadrilateral F bisect each other.

2. Communication Is the result of question 1 true for all the other quadrilaterals in the design? Explain.

Achievement Check
1   2   3   4

Point C(2, 1) is the midpoint of line segment AB.
a) Find the coordinates of points A and B if they are both on axes. Explain and justify your reasoning.
b) If point A is located on an axis, but point B is not on an axis, in which quadrant(s) can B be located? Explain and justify your reasoning.

Technology Extension: Programming a Graphing Calculator

1 Length of a Line Segment

The graphing calculator program shows how to calculate the length of a line segment connecting two points with coordinates (x_1, y_1) and (x_2, y_2).

PROGRAM:LENGTH
:ClrHome
:Input "X1=",P
:Input "Y1=",Q
:Input "X2=",R
:Input "Y2=",S
:R−P→X
:S−Q→Y
:$\sqrt{(X^2+Y^2)}$ →L
:Disp "LENGTH IS",L

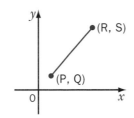

1. Communication Describe what each line of the program does.

2. Using the **PRGM NEW menu**, enter the program into your graphing calculator. Using the **PRGM EXEC menu**, execute the program to find the distance between each of the following pairs of points.
a) (6, 7) and (1, 3), to the nearest tenth
b) (−4, −9) and (−2, 8), to the nearest tenth
c) (3.7, 16.2) and (11.8, −9.9), to the nearest hundredth

2 Midpoint of a Line Segment

1. Modify the length program to find the coordinates of the midpoint of a line segment, given the coordinates of its endpoints.

2. Have a classmate check your program by using it to find the midpoint of a line segment with the following endpoints.
a) (4, 10) and (−6, 2)   **b)** (3, −6) and (2, −1)   **c)** (2.4, −1.6) and (−1.8, −5.3)

3 Collinear Points

1. Program a calculator to determine whether three points are collinear, given the coordinates of the points.

Recall that points that lie on the same line are collinear.

2. Use the program to determine whether the following points are collinear.
a) (8, 5), (4, −1), and (−6, −16)   **b)** (−1, −1), (4, −11), and (−6, 8)

3. Two points on a line are given. Find one other point on the line. Use the program to check your answer.
a) (3, 4) and (5, 5)   **b)** (0, 3) and (3, −2)

4. Geometry software Explore how you could use geometry software to establish whether three points are collinear.

Review: Equations of Lines

1 Using the Point-Slope Form

Recall that the **point-slope form** of an equation of a line is $y - y_1 = m(x - x_1)$, where (x_1, y_1) is any point on the line and m is the slope.

The **standard form** of an equation of a line is $Ax + By + C = 0$, where A, B, and C are integers, A and B are not both zero, and variables x and y represent real numbers.

Example 1 Writing Equations Given a Point and the Slope

Write an equation in standard form for the line through A(3, −4) with slope $-\dfrac{1}{2}$.

Solution

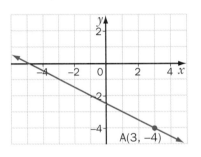

Use the point-slope form:

$$y - y_1 = m(x - x_1)$$

$(x_1, y_1) = (3, -4)$ and $m = -\dfrac{1}{2}$

Substitute known values:

$$y - (-4) = -\frac{1}{2}(x - 3)$$

$$y + 4 = -\frac{1}{2}(x - 3)$$

Expand:

$$y + 4 = -\frac{1}{2}x + \frac{3}{2}$$

Multiply both sides by 2:

$$2y + 8 = -x + 3$$

Write in standard form:

$$x + 2y + 5 = 0$$

An equation in standard form for the line through A(3, −4) with slope $-\dfrac{1}{2}$ is $x + 2y + 5 = 0$.

Example 2 Writing Equations Given Two Points

Write an equation in standard form for a line through A(−3, −2) and B(1, 6).

Solution

To use the point-slope form, you need a point on the line and the slope. Use the two points to find the slope.

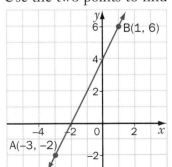

$$m_{AB} = \frac{y_2 - y_1}{x_2 - x_1}$$

$$= \frac{6 - (-2)}{1 - (-3)}$$

$$= \frac{8}{4}$$

$$= 2$$

Use either of the known points for (x_1, y_1).
Using A$(-3, -2)$ for (x_1, y_1),
$$y - y_1 = m(x - x_1)$$
$$y - (-2) = 2(x - (-3))$$
$$y + 2 = 2(x + 3)$$
$$y + 2 = 2x + 6$$
$$0 = 2x - y + 4$$

An equation in standard form for the line through A$(-3, -2)$ and B$(1, 6)$ is $2x - y + 4 = 0$.

Example 3   Equations of Horizontal and Vertical Lines
Write an equation in standard form for
a) the horizontal line through C$($ $)$
b) the vertical line through D$(-$

Solution
a) For the horizontal line through C$(2, 3)$, the y-coordinate of every point on the line is 3. So, an equation of the line is $y = 3$.
An equation in standard form for the horizontal line through C$(2, 3)$ is $y - 3 = 0$.

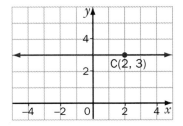

b) The slope of a vertical line is not defined, so the point-slope form cannot be used to write an equation of the line.
For the vertical line through D$(-4, 1)$, the x-coordinate of every point on the line is -4. So, an equation of the line is $x = -4$.
An equation in standard form for the vertical line through D$(-4, 1)$ is $x + 4 = 0$.

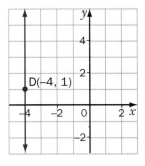

Practice

1. Write an equation in standard form for the line that passes through the given point and has the given slope.

a) $(3, 5)$; $m = 2$ **b)** $(4, 2)$; $m = 5$ **c)** $(-6, 6)$; $m = -3$

d) $(-2, -1)$; $m = -4$ **e)** $(2, -8)$; $m = \dfrac{1}{2}$ **f)** $(1, -3)$; $m = -\dfrac{1}{2}$

g) $(4, -\dfrac{1}{2})$; $m = 1$ **h)** $(-\dfrac{1}{3}, 3)$; $m = \dfrac{3}{2}$ **i)** $(-1, -1)$; $m = -1.5$

2. Write an equation in standard form for the line through the given points.
a) $A(4, 5)$ and $B(3, 7)$ **b)** $C(-2, 9)$ and $D(1, 0)$
c) $E(-3, -6)$ and $F(-5, -7)$ **d)** $G(-2, -3)$ and $H(3, -1)$
e) $J(-2, 3)$ and $K(2, 8)$ **f)** $L(0, 4)$ and $M(-3, 0)$

3. Write an equation in standard form for the horizontal line and the vertical line through each point.

a) $(4, 5)$ **b)** $(-3, 2)$ **c)** $(-5, -6)$ **d)** $\left(\dfrac{1}{2}, 8\right)$

e) $\left(9, -\dfrac{1}{3}\right)$ **f)** $(0, -9)$ **g)** $(-1, 0)$ **h)** $(0, 0)$

---

2   Using the Slope and *y*-Intercept Form

The equation $y = mx + b$ is the **slope and *y*-intercept form** of a line. The slope is m, and the *y*-intercept is b.

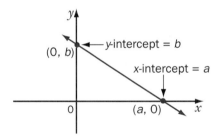

Example 1   Finding the Slope and *y*-Intercept Given an Equation
Find the slope and *y*-intercept of the line $2x + 3y - 6 = 0$.

Solution
Rewrite the equation in the form $y = mx + b$.

$$2x + 3y - 6 = 0$$
$$3y = -2x + 6$$
$$\frac{3y}{3} = \frac{-2x}{3} + \frac{6}{3}$$
$$y = -\frac{2}{3}x + 2$$

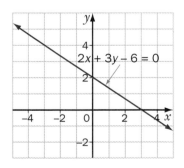

The slope is $-\dfrac{2}{3}$ and the *y*-intercept is 2.

Example 2 Finding the Slope and y-Intercept Given Two Points

Find the slope and y-intercept of the line through the points F(3, −1) and G(5, 7).

Solution

To write an equation in the form $y = mx + b$, first find the slope using the given points.

$$m_{FG} = \frac{y_2 - y_1}{x_2 - x_1}$$

$$= \frac{7 - (-1)}{5 - 3}$$

$$= \frac{8}{2}$$

$$= 4$$

Use the point-slope form and either of the known points for (x_1, y_1).
Using F(3, −1) for (x_1, y_1),

$$y - y_1 = m(x - x_1)$$
$$y - (-1) = 4(x - 3)$$
$$y + 1 = 4(x - 3)$$
$$y + 1 = 4x - 12$$
$$y = 4x - 13$$

For $y = mx + b$, m is the slope and b is the y-intercept.
For $y = 4x - 13$, the slope is 4 and the y-intercept is −13.

So, the line that passes through the points F(3, −1) and G(5, 7) has a slope of 4 and a y-intercept of −13.

Technology Extension

To find an equation using a graphing calculator, input the coordinates of the two given points in two lists using the **STAT EDIT** menu. Then, use the **LinReg (linear regression) instruction** to find an equation for the line.

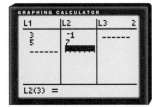

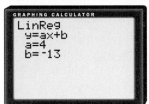

Practice

1. Find the slope and y-intercept of each line.

a) $y = 3x + 4$ **b)** $4x + y - 6 = 0$ **c)** $x - y + 5 = 0$
d) $x - 2y = 8$ **e)** $3x + 6y - 8 = 0$ **f)** $0 = x - 4y - 4$
g) $5x - 2y - 6 = 0$ **h)** $2x + 3y = 0$ **i)** $10x + 0.5y - 3 = 0$

2. Find the slope and y-intercept of the line that passes through the following pairs of points.

a) (2, 4) and (4, 6)   **b)** (1, 2) and (−2, 5)   **c)** (−3, −1) and (1, 7)
d) (4, −2) and (5, −5)   **e)** (−2, −2) and (0, −1)   **f)** (2, 0) and (4, −1)
g) (−2, −1) and (−3, −5)   **h)** (3, 2) and (−2, 3)   **i)** (7, 4) and (1, 2)

3 Parallel and Perpendicular Lines

Parallel Lines
• Two non-vertical lines are parallel if they have the same slope.
• All vertical lines, which have undefined slopes, are parallel.

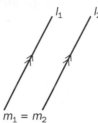

$m_1 = m_2$

Perpendicular Lines
• Two lines are perpendicular if the product of their slopes is -1. We say that the slopes are negative reciprocals.
• A vertical line is perpendicular to a horizontal line.

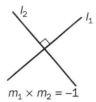

$m_1 \times m_2 = -1$

Example 1   Parallel Lines

Write an equation of the line parallel to $2x + y - 5 = 0$ and passing through the point A(-1, 5).

Solution

To use the point-slope form, you need a point on the line and the slope of the line. The slope of the new line equals the slope of $2x + y - 5 = 0$, because the lines are parallel.
To find the slope of $2x + y - 5 = 0$, write the equation in the form $y = mx + b$.

$$2x + y - 5 = 0$$
$$y = -2x + 5$$

The slope of $2x + y - 5 = 0$ is -2.
The slope of a line parallel to $2x + y - 5 = 0$ is also -2.
A point on the line is A(-1, 5).

Use the point-slope form: $y - y_1 = m(x - x_1)$
Substitute known values: $y - 5 = -2(x - (-1))$
Simplify: $y - 5 = -2(x + 1)$
Expand: $y - 5 = -2x - 2$
Write in standard form: $2x + y - 3 = 0$

An equation of the line parallel to $2x + y - 5 = 0$ and passing through the point A(-1, 5) is $2x + y - 3 = 0$.

Example 2   Perpendicular Lines

Write an equation of the line perpendicular to $3x + y - 6 = 0$ and passing through the point P(5, 2).

Solution

To use the point-slope form, you need a point on the line and the slope of the line. The slope of the new line is the negative reciprocal of the slope of $3x + y - 6 = 0$, because the lines are perpendicular.

To find the slope of $3x + y - 6 = 0$, write the equation in the form $y = mx + b$.

$$3x + y - 6 = 0$$
$$y = -3x + 6$$

The slope of $3x + y - 6 = 0$ is -3.

The slope, m, of a line perpendicular to $3x + y - 6 = 0$

is the negative reciprocal of -3, which is $\dfrac{1}{3}$.

A point on the line is P(5, 2).

Use the point-slope form: $y - y_1 = m(x - x_1)$

Substitute known values: $y - 2 = \dfrac{1}{3}(x - 5)$

Expand: $y - 2 = \dfrac{1}{3}x - \dfrac{5}{3}$

Multiply both sides by 3: $3y - 6 = x - 5$

Write in standard form: $0 = x - 3y + 1$

An equation of the line perpendicular to $3x + y - 6 = 0$ and passing through the point P(5, 2) is $x - 3y + 1 = 0$.

I don't get it!!!!!

Practice

1. Determine an equation for each of the following lines.
a) the line parallel to $y = 3x + 4$ and passing through the point (2, 1)
b) the line parallel to $2x - y = 7$ and passing through the point (−3, 2)
c) the line parallel to $x + 2y - 5 = 0$ and passing through the point (5, −3)
d) the line parallel to $3x - 9y - 1 = 0$ and having the same y-intercept as $2x + y - 8 = 0$

2. Determine an equation for each of the following lines.
a) the line perpendicular to $y = -2x + 4$ and passing through the point (4, 6)
b) the line perpendicular to $x - 3y - 1 = 0$ and passing through the point (1, −1)
c) the line perpendicular to $x + 2y - 8 = 0$ and passing through the point (−3, −4)
d) the line perpendicular to $4x - 2y + 3 = 0$ and having the same x-intercept as $2x + 3y - 10 = 0$

Investigation   Use the Diagram

A baseball diamond can be modelled on a coordinate grid by placing the origin at home plate, with first base on the *x*-axis. The distance between the bases is 27.4 m. The pitcher's mound is on the diagonal from home plate to second base and is 18.4 m from home plate.

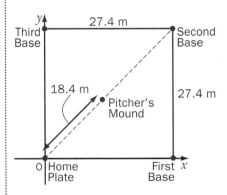

1. What are the coordinates of home plate and the three bases?

2. What are the slopes of
a) the sides of the diamond?
a) the diagonals of the diamond?

3. Communication a) How are the slopes of perpendicular lines related?
b) Are the diagonals of the diamond perpendicular?
c) Are the two sides that meet at first base perpendicular? Explain.

4. Communication a) What are the coordinates of the midpoint of each diagonal of the diamond?
b) Do the diagonals bisect each other? Explain.

5. What is the distance from home plate to the point of intersection of the diagonals, to the nearest tenth of a metre?

6. Is the pitcher's mound at the point of intersection of the diagonals?

Example 1   Midpoints of Two Sides of a Triangle

The vertices of a triangle are A(−3, 6), B(1, −6), and C(5, 2). If M is
the midpoint of AB and N is the midpoint of AC, verify that
a) MN is parallel to BC   **b)** MN is half the length of BC

Solution

a) Use the midpoint formula, $\left(\dfrac{x_1+x_2}{2},\ \dfrac{y_1+y_2}{2}\right)$, to find the

coordinates of M and N.

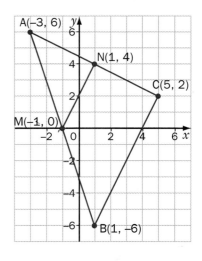

The midpoint of AB is $\left(\dfrac{-3+1}{2},\ \dfrac{6+(-6)}{2}\right)=(-1,\ 0)$.

The midpoint of AC is $\left(\dfrac{-3+5}{2},\ \dfrac{6+2}{2}\right)=(1,\ 4)$.

So, the midpoints are M(−1, 0) and N(1, 4).

If MN is parallel to BC, then these two segments have the
same slope. Find the slopes of MN and BC.

For MN, $m=\dfrac{y_2-y_1}{x_2-x_1}$ For BC, $m=\dfrac{y_2-y_1}{x_2-x_1}$

$m_{MN}=\dfrac{4-0}{1-(-1)}$ $m_{BC}=\dfrac{2-(-6)}{5-1}$

$\phantom{m_{MN}}=\dfrac{4}{2}$ $\phantom{m_{BC}}=\dfrac{8}{4}$

$\phantom{m_{MN}}=2$ $\phantom{m_{BC}}=2$

Since the slopes are equal, MN is parallel to BC.

b) Use the length formula to find the lengths of MN and BC.

$MN=\sqrt{(x_2-x_1)^2+(y_2-y_1)^2}$ $BC=\sqrt{(x_2-x_1)^2+(y_2-y_1)^2}$

$=\sqrt{(1-(-1))^2+(4-0)^2}$ $=\sqrt{(5-1)^2+(2-(-6))^2}$

$=\sqrt{4+16}$ $=\sqrt{16+64}$

$=\sqrt{20}$ $=\sqrt{80}$

GRAPHING CALCULATOR
√(20)/√(80)
.5

$\sqrt{20}\div\sqrt{80}=0.5$

So, MN is half the length of BC.

Example 2   Right Bisector of a Chord

The equation of a circle with centre O(0, 0) is $x^2 + y^2 = 25$.
The points A(−3, 4) and B(5, 0) are the endpoints of chord AB.
DE right bisects the chord AB at F. Verify that the centre of the
circle lies on the right bisector of chord AB.

Solution

a) DE right bisects AB at F.
Use the coordinates of A and B and the midpoint formula to find the
coordinates of F.

$$\left(\frac{x_1 + x_2}{2}, \frac{y_1 + y_2}{2}\right) = \left(\frac{-3+5}{2}, \frac{4+0}{2}\right)$$
$$= (1, 2)$$

The coordinates of F are (1, 2).

Since DE is perpendicular to AB, the slope of DE
is the negative reciprocal of the slope of AB.
Find the slope of AB, whose endpoints are
A(−3, 4) and B(5, 0).

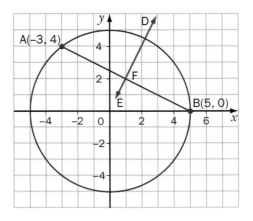

$$m = \frac{y_2 - y_1}{x_2 - x_1}$$
$$m_{AB} = \frac{0-4}{5-(-3)}$$
$$= \frac{-4}{8}$$
$$= -\frac{1}{2}$$

The slope of AB $= -\frac{1}{2}$, so the slope of DE is 2.

Use the slope of DE and the coordinates of F to write an equation for DE.
Use the point-slope form: $y - y_1 = m(x - x_1)$
$(x_1, y_1) = (1, 2)$ and $m = 2$.
Substitute known values: $y - 2 = 2(x - 1)$
Expand: $y - 2 = 2x - 2$
Write in standard form: $0 = 2x - y$
An equation for DE, the right bisector of AB, is $2x - y = 0$.

The centre of the circle, O(0, 0), lies on the right bisector of AB if the
coordinates of O satisfy the equation $2x - y = 0$.
Substitute (0, 0) in $2x - y = 0$.
L.S. $= 2x - y$ **R.S.** $= 0$
        $= 2(0) - (0)$
        $= 0$
            L.S. = R.S.
The centre of the circle lies on the right bisector of chord AB.

Example 3　Equations of Medians, Right Bisectors, and Altitudes

$\triangle ABC$ has vertices A(3, 4), B(–5, 2), and C(1, –4).
Determine

a) an equation for CD, the median from C to AB
b) an equation for GH, the right bisector of AB
c) an equation for CE, the altitude from C to AB

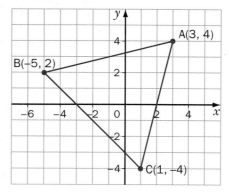

Solution

a) Find the coordinates of D, the midpoint of AB.

$$\left(\frac{x_1 + x_2}{2}, \frac{y_1 + y_2}{2}\right) = \left(\frac{3 + (-5)}{2}, \frac{4 + 2}{2}\right)$$
$$= (-1, 3)$$

The coordinates of D are (–1, 3).

Find the slope of CD, whose endpoints are C(1, –4) and
D(–1, 3).

$$m = \frac{y_2 - y_1}{x_2 - x_1}$$

$$m_{CD} = \frac{3 - (-4)}{-1 - 1}$$

$$= \frac{7}{-2}$$

$$= -\frac{7}{2}$$

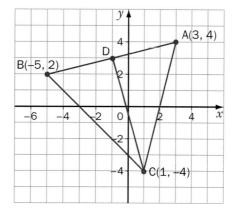

Use the slope of CD, and the coordinates of C or D, to write an equation for CD.

Use the point-slope form: $\qquad y - y_1 = m(x - x_1)$
$(x_1, y_1) = (1, -4)$ and $m = -\dfrac{7}{2}$

Substitute known values: $\qquad y - (-4) = -\dfrac{7}{2}(x - 1)$

$$y + 4 = -\frac{7}{2}(x - 1)$$

Expand: $\qquad\qquad\qquad\quad y + 4 = -\dfrac{7}{2}x + \dfrac{7}{2}$

Multiply both sides by 2: $\qquad 2y + 8 = -7x + 7$
Write in standard form: $\qquad 7x + 2y + 1 = 0$

An equation for CD, the median from C to AB, is $7x + 2y + 1 = 0$.

b) GH right bisects AB at D.

From part a), the coordinates of D are (–1, 3).
Since GH is perpendicular to AB, the slope of GH is
the negative reciprocal of the slope of AB.
Find the slope of AB, whose endpoints are A(3, 4) and
B(–5, 2).

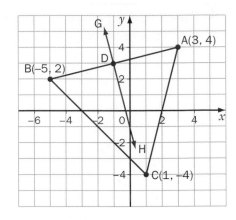

$$m = \frac{y_2 - y_1}{x_2 - x_1}$$

$$m_{AB} = \frac{2 - 4}{-5 - 3}$$

$$= \frac{-2}{-8}$$

$$= \frac{1}{4}$$

The slope of AB $= \frac{1}{4}$, so the slope of GH is –4.

Use the slope of GH, and the coordinates of D, to write an
equation for GH.

Use the point-slope form: $y - y_1 = m(x - x_1)$
$(x_1, y_1) = (-1, 3)$ and $m = -4$.
Substitute known values: $y - 3 = -4(x - (-1))$
Simplify: $y - 3 = -4(x + 1)$
Expand: $y - 3 = -4x - 4$
Write in standard form: $4x + y + 1 = 0$

An equation of GH, the right bisector of AB, is $4x + y + 1 = 0$.

c) Since CE is perpendicular to AB, the slope of CE
is the negative reciprocal of the slope of AB.

From part b), the slope of AB $= \frac{1}{4}$. So, the slope of
CE is –4.

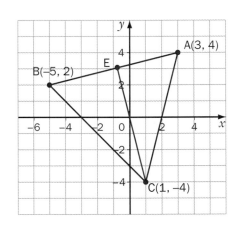

Use the slope of CE, and the coordinates of C, to write
an equation for CE.

Use the point-slope form: $y - y_1 = m(x - x_1)$
$(x_1, y_1) = (1, -4)$ and $m = -4$.
Substitute known values: $y - (-4) = -4(x - 1)$
Simplify: $y + 4 = -4x + 4$
Write in standard form: $4x + y = 0$

An equation for CE, the altitude from C to AB,
is $4x + y = 0$.

Recall that the **circumcentre** of a triangle is the point of intersection of the perpendicular bisectors of the sides of the triangle. This point is called the circumcentre because it is the centre of a circle that passes through all the vertices of the triangle.

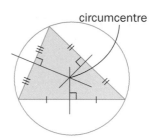
circumcentre

Example 4   Locating a Circumcentre
$\triangle DEF$ has vertices D(4, 2), E(−6, 4), and F(−2, −4). AB right bisects EF at S. GH right bisects DF at T. Determine the coordinates of the circumcentre of $\triangle DEF$.

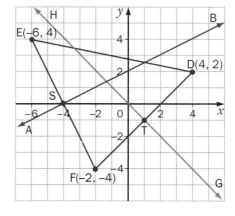

Solution
The circumcentre is the point at which AB and GH intersect.
Write equations to represent AB and GH.
Solve the resulting linear system to find the point at which they intersect.

First, write an equation for AB.
AB right bisects EF at S. Find the coordinates of S, the midpoint of EF.
$$\left(\frac{x_1 + x_2}{2}, \frac{y_1 + y_2}{2} \right) = \left(\frac{-6 + (-2)}{2}, \frac{4 + (-4)}{2} \right)$$
$$= (-4, \ 0)$$
The coordinates of S are (−4, 0).

Since AB is perpendicular to EF, the slope of AB is the negative reciprocal of the slope of EF.
Find the slope of EF, whose endpoints are E(−6, 4) and F(−2, −4).

$$m = \frac{y_2 - y_1}{x_2 - x_1}$$
$$m_{EF} = \frac{-4 - 4}{-2 - (-6)}$$
$$= \frac{-8}{4}$$
$$= -2$$

The slope of EF is −2, so the slope of AB is $\frac{1}{2}$.

Use the slope of AB and the coordinates of S to write an equation for AB.

Use the point-slope form: $\quad y - y_1 = m(x - x_1)$

$(x_1, y_1) = (-4, 0)$ and $m = \dfrac{1}{2}$.

Substitute known values: $\quad y - 0 = \dfrac{1}{2}(x - (-4))$

Simplify: $\quad\quad\quad\quad\quad\quad\quad y = \dfrac{1}{2}(x + 4)$

Multiply both sides by 2: $\quad 2y = x + 4$

Write in standard form: $\quad x - 2y + 4 = 0$

An equation for AB, the right bisector of EF, is $x - 2y + 4 = 0$.

Similarly, an equation for GH, the right bisector of DF, is found to be $x + y = 0$.

To find the coordinates of the circumcentre of $\triangle$DEF, solve the system of equations.

$$x - 2y + 4 = 0 \quad (1)$$
$$x + y = 0 \quad (2)$$

Solve (2) for x: $\quad\quad\quad\quad\quad\quad\quad x = -y$

Substitute $-y$ for x in (1): $\quad -y - 2y + 4 = 0$

Simplify: $\quad\quad\quad\quad\quad\quad\quad -3y + 4 = 0$

Solve for y: $\quad\quad\quad\quad\quad\quad\quad y = \dfrac{4}{3}$

Substituting $\dfrac{4}{3}$ for y in (2) gives $x = -\dfrac{4}{3}$.

The coordinates of the circumcentre of $\triangle$DEF are $\left(-\dfrac{4}{3}, \dfrac{4}{3}\right)$.

The system can also be solved graphically.

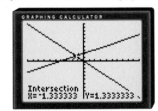

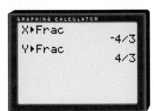

Key CONCEPTS

The following formulas can be used to determine characteristics of geometric figures and to verify geometric properties.

Slope of a line segment: $m = \dfrac{y_2 - y_1}{x_2 - x_1}$

Length of a line segment: $l = \sqrt{(x_2 - x_1)^2 + (y_2 - y_1)^2}$

Midpoint of a line segment: $\left(\dfrac{x_1 + x_2}{2}, \dfrac{y_1 + y_2}{2} \right)$

Point-slope form of the equation of a line: $y - y_1 = m(x - x_1)$
Slope and y-intercept form of the equation of a line: $y = mx + b$

Communicate Your Understanding

1. $\triangle DEF$ has vertices D(5, 2), E(0, 3), and F(4, –3). Describe how you would verify that $\triangle DEF$ is an isosceles right triangle.

2. $\triangle KLM$ has vertices K(2, 2), L(0, –2), and M(4, 0). Describe how you would find an equation for each of the following. Explain and justify your reasoning.
a) the median from M to KL
b) the altitude from K to LM
c) the right bisector of KM

3. The equation of a circle with centre O(0, 0) is $x^2 + y^2 = 20$. The points A(4, 2) and B(–2, 4) are the endpoints of chord AB. Describe how you would verify that the centre of the circle lies on the right bisector of chord AB.

Practice

A

1. A quadrilateral has vertices O(0, 0), P(3, 5), Q(8, 6), and R(5, 1). Verify that OPQR is a parallelogram.

2. Given the points X(1, 4), Y(–2, 2), and Z(3, 1), verify that $\triangle XYZ$ is a right triangle.

3. The vertices of a triangle are K(2, 6), L(4, 10), and M(8, –2). Let P be the midpoint of KL and Q be the midpoint of LM. Verify that
a) PQ is parallel to KM   **b)** PQ is half the length of KM

4. Verify that the quadrilateral with vertices P(2, 3), Q(5, –1), R(10, –1), and S(7, 3) is a rhombus.

5. The vertices of a quadrilateral are K(–1, 0), L(1, –2), M(4, 1), and N(2, 3). Verify that
a) KLMN is a rectangle   **b)** the lengths of the diagonals of KLMN are equal

6. Determine an equation for the right bisector of the line segment joining A(3, 6) and B(−1, 2).

7. Verify that the given point lies on the perpendicular bisector of the given line segment.
a) point A(3, 4); line segment BC, with endpoints B(2, 1) and C(6, 5)
b) point P(1, 3); line segment QR, with endpoints Q(−3, 1) and R(3, −1)
c) point K(−2, −4); line segment LM, with endpoints L(0, 2) and M(4, −6)

8. The equation of a circle with centre O(0, 0) is $x^2 + y^2 = 10$. The points C(3, 1) and D(1, −3) are the endpoints of chord CD. EF right bisects chord CD at G. Verify that the centre of the circle lies on the right bisector of chord CD.

9. The vertices of a quadrilateral are A(0, 0), B(2, 3), C(5, 1), and D(3, −2). Verify that the diagonals of ABCD are perpendicular to each other.

10. Verify that the quadrilateral with vertices O(0, 0), P(3, 5), Q(13, 7), and R(5, 1) is a trapezoid.

11. Verify that the quadrilateral with vertices P(−2, 2), Q(−2, −3), R(−5, −5), and S(−5, 0) is a parallelogram.

12. A triangle has vertices K(−2, 2), L(1, 5), and M(3, −3). Verify that
a) the triangle has a right angle
b) the midpoint of the hypotenuse is the same distance from each vertex

13. Quadrilateral PQRS has vertices P(0, 6), Q(−6, −2), R(2, −4), and S(4, 2). Verify that the quadrilateral formed by joining the midpoints of the sides of PQRS is a parallelogram.

14. △ABC has vertices A(3, 4), B(−5, 2), and C(1, −4). Determine an equation for
a) CD, the median from C to AB
b) AE, the altitude from A to BC
c) GH, the right bisector of AC

15. A triangle has vertices X(0, 0), Y(4, 4), and Z(8, −4).
a) Write an equation for each of the three medians.
b) Recall that the **centroid** of a triangle is the point of intersection of the medians of the triangle. Use the equations from part a) to verify that (4, 0) is the centroid of △XYZ.

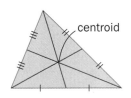
centroid

16. △AOB has vertices A(4, 4), O(0, 0), and B(8, 0). EF right bisects AB at P. GH right bisects OA at Q. Determine the coordinates of the circumcentre of △DEF.

17. △POR has vertices P(0, 6), O(0, 0), and R(6, 0). Determine the coordinates of the centroid of △POR.

Applications and Problem Solving

B

18. The sides of a triangle have the equations $y = -\frac{1}{2}x + 1$, $y = 2x - 4$, and $y = -3x - 9$. Verify that the triangle is an isosceles right triangle.

19. The sides of a parallelogram have the equations $x = 0$, $y = \frac{1}{6}x + 3$, $x = 6$, and $y = \frac{1}{6}x - 2$. Verify that the diagonals intersect at the point $(3, 1)$.

20. A triangle has vertices U(5, 5), V(1, –3), and W(–3, –1). Verify that
a) $\triangle$UVW is a right triangle
b) the median from the right angle to the hypotenuse is half as long as the hypotenuse

21. A quadrilateral has vertices K(–1, 4), L(2, 2), M(0, –1), and N(–3, 1). Verify that
a) the quadrilateral is a square
b) each diagonal of the quadrilateral is the perpendicular bisector of the other diagonal
c) the diagonals of the quadrilateral are equal in length

22. Given $\triangle$ABC with vertices A(–7, 3), B(–2, –3), and C(4, 2),
a) classify the triangle by side length
b) verify that one median of the triangle is perpendicular to one of the sides

23. Communication Determine whether the point T(2, –1) lies on the perpendicular bisector of line segment UV, with endpoints U(3, 5) and V(–3, –1). Explain and justify your reasoning.

24. A quadrilateral has vertices D(–4, –1), E(0, –4), F(6, 0), and G(0, 4). Verify for each pair of adjacent sides that the line segment joining their midpoints is parallel to a diagonal of the quadrilateral.

25. a) Use the side lengths to classify the quadrilateral with vertices E(2, 3), F(4, –1), G(–2, –9), and H(–2, 1).
b) Verify that the midpoints of the sides of quadrilateral EFGH are the vertices of a rectangle.

26. Pocket billiards The game of pocket billiards is played on a rectangular table with dimensions 240 cm by 120 cm.
a) A coordinate grid is superimposed on the table, as shown. If one unit on each axis represents 1 cm, state the coordinates of the four corner pockets and the centre spot, which is exactly in the middle of the table.
b) If a ball is on the centre spot, there are two directions in which the ball can be hit into a pocket at the right-hand end. Verify that these directions are not perpendicular.

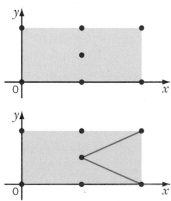

C

27. A quadrilateral has vertices P(–3, 1), Q(–1, –5), R(11, 1), and S(1, 3). Verify that

a) quadrilateral PQRS is a trapezoid

b) the line segment joining the midpoints of the two non-parallel sides is parallel to the bases

c) the line segment from part b) is half as long as the sum of the lengths of the bases

28. Verify that the triangle with vertices A(0, 0), B($\sqrt{3}$, –1), and C($\sqrt{3}$, 1) is equilateral.

29. A triangle has vertices A(0, 0), B(6, 4), and C(12, –4).

a) Verify that the centroid of $\triangle$ABC is at (6, 0).

b) The **orthocentre** of a triangle is the point at which the three altitudes intersect. Verify that $\left(\dfrac{56}{9}, \dfrac{14}{3}\right)$ is the orthocentre of $\triangle$ABC.

c) Verify that $\left(\dfrac{53}{9}, -\dfrac{7}{3}\right)$ is the circumcentre of $\triangle$ABC.

d) Verify that the centroid, the orthocentre, and the circumcentre of $\triangle$ABC are all collinear.

30. Communication Write a verification problem similar to one of the problems in this exercise. Have a classmate solve your problem.

Modelling Math | Analyzing a Design

Refer to the maple leaf design on the grid on page 63.
1. Verify that triangle L is a right triangle.
2. Verify that quadrilateral G is a rectangle.
3. Verify that quadrilateral B is a parallelogram.
4. Verify that the line segment joining the midpoints of any two sides of triangle K is parallel to the third side and half the length of the third side.

Web Connection www.school.mcgrawhill.ca/resources/

To investigate other traditional Canadian quilt designs, visit the above web site. Go to **Math Resources,** then to *MATHPOWER™ 10, Ontario Edition,* to find out where to go next. Find three traditional designs and describe the geometric shapes on each design.

Many structures that we see from day to day, including houses, office buildings, bridges, and so on, have resulted from the skills of construction workers. Even the simpler aspects of construction work, such as ensuring that the walls of a room are at right angles to the floor, require a knowledge of mathematics.

1. Rectangular frame A wooden frame is to be a 5 m by 3 m rectangle. To ensure that the angles in a frame are as close as possible to right angles, builders often check the lengths of the diagonals.

a) Draw a diagram of a 5 m by 3 m rectangle and superimpose a coordinate grid, so that one vertex of the rectangle is at the origin, and the length of the rectangle lies along the *x*-axis. If one unit on each axis represents 1 m, what are the coordinates of the vertices?

b) What should be the exact length of each diagonal to verify that a 5 m by 3 m frame is rectangular?

c) Communication Is it possible to measure the exact length from part b)? What would a builder do in this situation? Explain.

2. Research Use your research skills to find information about a major construction project that interests you.

3. Research Choose a construction career, and use your research skills to investigate the education and training required.

LOGIC POWER

XY and YZ are the diagonals of two faces of a cube.
a) What is the measure of ∠XYZ?
b) Explain your reasoning.

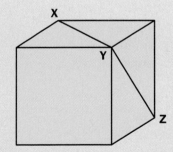

Alberta is Canada's main oil-producing province, but there are significant oil fields elsewhere in Canada. One of the latest to be exploited is Hibernia, which is under the Atlantic Ocean on the Grand Banks. The Hibernia drilling platform is located 315 km east-southeast of St. John's, Newfoundland.

Oil is transported to shore from an offshore oil platform by oil tankers. The platform must also receive regular visits from supply ships.

Investigation   Use the Diagram

1. A radar operator on an oil platform is monitoring the positions and courses of ships on a radar screen. In the diagram, the innermost ring represents a distance of 5 km from the platform, P. Each successive ring represents an additional 5-km distance from the platform.

a) What is the scale of the diagram?

b) Draw the diagram and trace the positions of the labelled points.

2. Use the diagram to estimate the closest distance, in kilometres, that each of the following ships will come to the platform.

a) ship A, on a course of 180°

b) ship B, on a course of 270°

c) ship C, on a course of 120°

3. In question 2, if the closest distance from a ship to the platform is drawn as a line segment, at about what angle does this segment meet the line that represents the course of the ship?

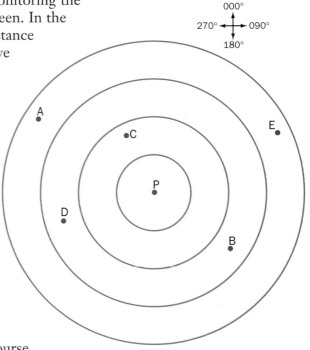

Example 1　Distance From the Origin to a Line

Determine the shortest distance from the origin to the line $y = 2x - 10$

a) as an exact solution

b) as an approximate solution, to the nearest tenth

Solution

a) The shortest distance is the perpendicular distance OA
from the point O(0, 0) to the line $y = 2x - 10$.
To find the length of OA, first find the
coordinates of A.

The slope of $y = 2x - 10$ is 2.
Since $y = 2x - 10$ and OA are perpendicular,
the product of their slopes is −1.

So, the slope of OA is $-\dfrac{1}{2}$.

> Recall that, in the slope and
> y-intercept form, $y = mx + b$, m is
> the slope, and b is the y-intercept.

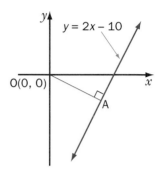

To find an equation for OA, use the point-slope form
and substitute known values.

$$y - y_1 = m(x - x_1)$$
$$y - 0 = -\frac{1}{2}(x - 0)$$
$$y = -\frac{1}{2}x$$

To find the coordinates of A, solve the following system of equations.

$$y = 2x - 10 \quad (1)$$
$$y = -\frac{1}{2}x \quad\quad (2)$$

Substitute $-\dfrac{1}{2}x$ for y in (1):　　$-\dfrac{1}{2}x = 2x - 10$

Multiply both sides by 2:　　　$-x = 4x - 20$
Subtract $4x$ from both sides:　　$-5x = -20$
Solve for x:　　　　　　　　　$x = 4$

Substitute 4 for x in (2):　$y = -\dfrac{1}{2}(4)$
$$= -2$$

> The coordinates of A can
> also be found graphically.

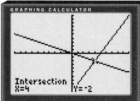

The solution to the system can be checked by substitution in (1) and (2).

The coordinates of A are (4, −2).

Use the distance formula to find the distance from O(0, 0) to A(4, −2).
$$l = \sqrt{(x_2 - x_1)^2 + (y_2 - y_1)^2}$$
$$OA = \sqrt{(4 - 0)^2 + (-2 - 0)^2}$$
$$= \sqrt{20}$$

The shortest distance from the origin to the line $y = 2x - 10$ is exactly $\sqrt{20}$.

b) The shortest distance from the origin to the line $y = 2x - 10$ is 4.5, to the nearest tenth.

Estimate
$\sqrt{16} = 4$ $\sqrt{25} = 5$
$\sqrt{20} \doteq 4.5$

Example 2   Distance From Any Point to a Line

Find the distance from the point $P(-1, 3)$ to the line $x + y - 5 = 0$, to the nearest tenth.

Solution

Find the coordinates of Q, the point of intersection of the line $x + y - 5 = 0$ and the perpendicular from P.

The line $x + y - 5 = 0$, or $y = -x + 5$, has slope -1.

So, the perpendicular PQ has slope 1.

An equation of the line passing through $P(-1, 3)$ with slope 1 can be determined using the point-slope form, as follows.

$$y - y_1 = m(x - x_1)$$
$$y - 3 = 1(x - (-1))$$
$$y - 3 = x + 1$$
$$-4 = x - y$$

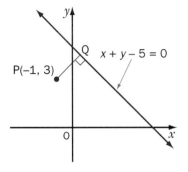

To find the coordinates of Q, solve the following system of equations.

$$x + y - 5 = 0 \quad (1)$$
$$x - y = -4 \quad (2)$$

Rearrange (1): $x + y = 5$
Write (2): $x - y = -4$
Add: $2x = 1$
Solve for x: $x = 0.5$

Substitute 0.5 for x in (2): $0.5 - y = -4$
$$-y = -4.5$$
$$y = 4.5$$

The coordinates of Q are $(0.5, 4.5)$.   Remember to check the coordinates of Q in (1) and (2).

Use the distance formula to find the distance from $P(-1, 3)$ to $Q(0.5, 4.5)$.

$$l = \sqrt{(x_2 - x_1)^2 + (y_2 - y_1)^2}$$
$$PQ = \sqrt{(0.5 - (-1))^2 + (4.5 - 3)^2}$$
$$= \sqrt{1.5^2 + 1.5^2}$$
$$\doteq 2.1$$

Estimate
$\sqrt{2 + 2} = \sqrt{4}$
$= 2$

The distance from $P(-1, 3)$ to the line $x + y - 5 = 0$ is 2.1, to the nearest tenth.

Key CONCEPTS

To determine the distance from a given point to a line whose equation is given,
a) write an equation for the perpendicular from the given point to the given line
b) find the coordinates of the point of intersection of the perpendicular and the given line
c) use the distance formula

Communicate Your Understanding

1. Describe how you would find the distance from the point P(4, 2) to the line $x - y = 0$.

2. The equation of a horizontal line is $y = 5$. Explain how to find the distance from the point P(3, 1) to the line $y = 5$.

Practice

A

1. Find the exact value of the shortest distance from the origin to each line.
a) $y = x - 4$ **b)** $y = x + 6$ **c)** $y = 3x - 10$ **d)** $y = -2x - 5$

e) $y = -2$ **f)** $x - 3 = 0$ **g)** $y = \frac{2}{3}x - 13$ **h)** $y = -\frac{1}{2}x - 5$

2. Find the shortest distance from the origin to each line, to the nearest tenth.
a) $x - y = 3$ **b)** $x + y + 2 = 0$ **c)** $x + 2y = 4$ **d)** $3x - 4y = -6$
e) $6x + 8y - 5 = 0$ **f)** $4x = 6y + 13$ **g)** $2x + 3y = 9$ **h)** $x - 5y + 11 = 0$

3. Find the shortest distance from the given point to the given line. Round to the nearest tenth, if necessary.
a) (2, 2) and $y = x + 1$ **b)** (5, 0) and $y = 0.5x + 5$
c) (3, 1) and $x + y = -2$ **d)** (−3, 0) and $x - y = -10$
e) (3, −1) and $2x - y + 3 = 0$ **f)** (−1, 2) and $x - 4y + 1 = 0$
g) (0, −1) and $5x + 2y + 3 = 0$ **h)** (−2, −1) and $2x + y + 3 = 0$

4. Find the distance from A(−2, −2) to the line joining B(5, 2) and C(−1, 4), to the nearest hundredth.

5. Communication Calculate the distance from the point K(−10, −13) to the line $8x - 5y + 15 = 0$. Explain the answer in terms of the relationship between the point and the line.

6. Find the exact distance from the point D(4, −2) to the line segment joining the points E(1, 3) and F(−4, −2).

7. Find the distance from the point P(4, 1) to the line segment joining the points Q(1, −8) and R(−4, 2) as
a) an exact value
b) an approximate value, to the nearest tenth

Applications and Problem Solving

8. Find the distance from the point P(3, 5) to the line $x = -2$.

9. Find the distance from the point Q(−2, −2) to the line $y = 3$.

B

10. A line has y-intercept of 8 and x-intercept of −12. What is the shortest distance from the origin to this line, to the nearest tenth?

11. Measurement A triangle has vertices A(−4, −2), B(2, 4), and C(3, −3).
a) Classify the triangle by side length.
b) Verify that exactly one vertex of the triangle lies on the perpendicular bisector of the opposite side.
c) Determine the area of the triangle.

12. Measurement a) For the triangle whose vertices are A(1, −1), B(0, 5), and C(−3, 0), determine the length of each altitude.
b) Calculate the area of △ABC.

13. The equation of a circle with centre O(0, 0) is $x^2 + y^2 = 10$. The points P(1, 3) and Q(−3, −1) are endpoints of chord PQ. Find the exact distance from the centre of the circle to the chord.

14. The equation of a circle with centre O(0, 0) is $x^2 + y^2 = 17$. The points M(1, 4) and N(4, −1) are endpoints of chord MN. Find the distance from the centre of the circle to the chord, to the nearest tenth.

C

15. Measurement a) Find the distance from the point of intersection of the lines $2x + 3y = 10$ and $3x - y = 4$ to the line $5x - 6y = 1$, to the nearest hundredth.
b) Find the area of the triangle formed by the three lines, to the nearest hundredth.

16. Measurement Find the area of the trapezoid with vertices K(−4, 3), L(−1, 4), M(10, 1), and N(−5, −4).

17. Write equations for two lines that meet each of the following sets of conditions. Compare your equations with your classmates'.
a) slope is $\frac{1}{2}$; shortest distance from origin is $\sqrt{13}$
b) slope is −3; shortest distance from origin is $\sqrt{5}$

Modelling Math | **Analyzing a Design**

Refer to the maple leaf design on the grid on page 63.

1. The entire block is a 40 by 40 square. Find an equation for the block diagonal with a negative slope.

2. Determine the exact distance to the block diagonal with the negative slope
a) from the point (10, 0)   **b)** from the point (40, 30)

3. Communication Explain how you know that the block diagonal with the negative slope is a mirror line for the points (10, 0) and (40, 30).

4. Communication For quadrilaterals B and E, identify the pairs of vertices for which the block diagonal with the negative slope is a mirror line. Explain and justify your reasoning.

Achievement Check

1   2   3   4

Two parallel lines have the equations $y = x + 4$ and $y = x - 2$. Two additional lines are drawn to form a square. What is the side length of the square? Write possible equations for the additional lines. Explain and justify your reasoning.

PATTERN POWER

a) Describe how the numbers in the second row of the chart are related to the numbers in the first row.
b) Find the missing number.

48	25	39	82
32	10	27	16
15	35	63	
53	75	97	46

Technology Extension: Analytic Geometry Using The Geometer's Sketchpad®

If you need an introduction to the use of *The Geometer's Sketchpad®*, refer to Appendix C.

For each of the following investigations, choose the Show Grid command in the Graph menu to display a grid. Also choose the Snap to Grid command in the Graph menu. The grid will display a point A at the origin and a point B at (1, 0). Dragging point B will change the scale of the graph.

1 Equations of Lines

An equation cannot be entered and graphed using *The Geometer's Sketchpad®*. However, if a line is drawn, the program will display the equation of the line.

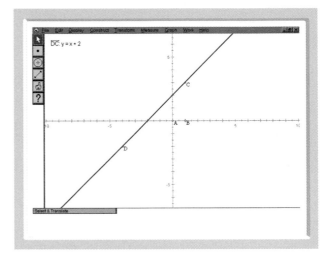

1. Click and hold the Line Tool on the left side of the screen. A horizontal window will open, which allows you to choose a line segment, a ray, or a line. To choose a line, move over to the line option and release the mouse.

2. To plot the points C(1, 3) and D(–4, –2), first click on the Point Tool. Move the cursor to coordinates (1, 3) on the grid and click. Then, move the cursor to coordinates (–4, –2) and click. Select the points.

3. Construct a line through the points.

4. Select the line and choose the Equation command from the Measure menu. The equation will be shown in the upper left corner of the screen. Record the equation in your notebook.

5. Determine the equation of the line passing through each of the following pairs of points. Record the equations in your notebook.
a) (3, 4) and (–1, 8)　　**b)** (2, –3) and (–2, 0)
c) (–6, –4) and (4, 4)　　**d)** (0, –5) and (5, 0)

2 Equations of Medians

Medians of triangles are line segments. *The Geometer's Sketchpad®* calculates the equations of lines but not the equations of line segments. Therefore, to determine the equation of a median of a triangle, construct a line through a vertex of the triangle and the midpoint of the opposite side.

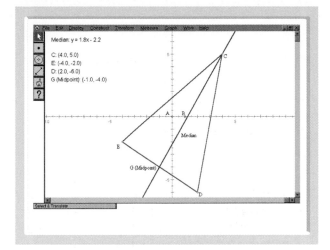

1. Construct △CDE on the grid with vertices C(4, 5), D(2, –6), and E(–4, –2).

2. Construct the midpoint of DE.

3. Construct a line through vertex C and the midpoint of DE.

4. Select the line and choose the Equation command from the Measure menu. Find the equation of the median, which will be shown in the upper left corner of the screen.

5. Communication Make a conjecture about the areas of the two triangles on either side of the median.

6. Measure the areas of the two triangles on either side of the median. How do the areas compare?

7. Communication Drag any of the vertices of △CDE to test your conjecture for various types of triangles. Record your results in your notebook.

3 The Centroid of a Triangle

The centroid of a triangle is the point at which the medians intersect.

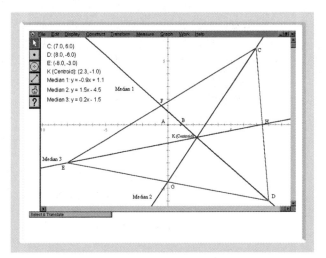

1. Construct △CDE on the grid with vertices C(7, 6), D(8, –6), and E(–8, –3).

2. To construct the three midpoints, select all three sides, click on the Construct menu, and choose the Point At Midpoint command.

3. Construct the three lines through the vertices and the midpoints of the opposite sides.

4. Find the equations of the medians and the coordinates of their point of intersection. Record your results in your notebook. The point of intersection is called the centroid. Label it K.

5. Communication Make a conjecture about the areas of the six smallest triangles formed by the three medians of a triangle.

6. Measure the areas of the six smallest triangles. How do the areas compare?

7. Communication Drag any of the vertices of △CDE to test your conjecture for various types of triangles. Record your results in your notebook.

8. Communication Explain why you can balance a cardboard triangle on your finger by using the centroid as the balance point.

9. The centroid divides each median into two line segments. For each median of △CDE, find the ratio of the length of the longer segment to the length of the shorter segment. It you want to use the software to calculate the ratio, refer to the method in question 10 on page 317.

10. How do the three ratios you found in question 9 compare? Is this true for the medians of any triangle?

11. Communication Describe how the coordinates of the centroid of a triangle can be determined from the coordinates of the vertices.

4 Equations of Altitudes

An altitude of a triangle is a line segment. To determine the equation of an altitude, construct a line that passes through a vertex of the triangle and is perpendicular to the opposite side.

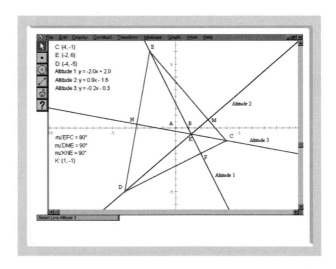

1. Construct △CDE on the grid with vertices C(4, –1), D(–4, –5), and E(–2, 6).

2. Construct the three lines that pass through the vertices and are perpendicular to the opposite sides.

3. Find the equations of the altitudes and the coordinates of their point of intersection. Record your results in your notebook. The point of intersection is called the orthocentre. Label it K.

4. Communication Investigate whether the altitudes of any triangle intersect inside the triangle. Describe your findings.

5 Equations of Right Bisectors

1. Construct △CDE on the grid with vertices C(4, –1), D(–6, –3), and E(2, 5).

2. Construct the right bisectors of CD, DE, and CE.

3. Find the equations of the right bisectors and the coordinates of their point of intersection. This point is the circumcentre of the triangle.

4. Communication Investigate whether the right bisectors of the sides of any triangle intersect inside the triangle. Record your findings in your notebook.

5. Construct a circle with the circumcentre as the centre and one of the vertices of the triangle as a point on the circle.

6. Communication Drag any of the vertices of the triangle to new positions to form different types of triangles. Describe the results.

6 Right Bisectors of Chords

1. Set up a grid. Select the point at the origin (0, 0) and create a new point at C(5, 0). From the Construct menu, choose the Circle By Center And Point command. You will have a circle with centre (0, 0) and radius 5 cm.

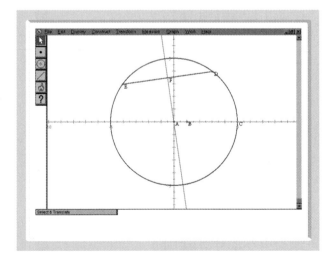

2. Remove the highlighting and choose a different colour. Create points at D(3, 4) and E(–4, 3), and construct the line segment that joins them.

3. Remove the highlighting and choose a third colour. Construct the right bisector of chord DE. Does the right bisector pass through the centre of the circle?

4. Select point D and the circle. From the Display menu, choose the Animate command. A window entitled Path Match will open. Make the choices indicated in the graphic to the right. Click on the Animate button, and point D travels around the circle. Does the property you observed in question 3 change?

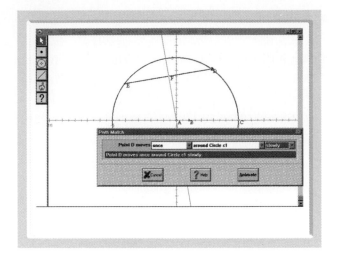

7 Midpoints of Sides of Triangles

1. Construct a triangle with vertices C(2, 6), D(6, –4), and E(–6, –2).

2. To construct the midpoints of CD and CE, highlight these sides, click on the Construct menu, and choose the Point At Midpoint command. Construct the line segment FG by joining these midpoints.

3. Measure the lengths and slopes of FG and ED.

4. How do the slopes and lengths of FG and ED compare?

5. Drag point C to new locations. Does the relationship between the slopes and lengths of FG and ED change for different locations of point C?

6. Communication Describe how the line segment joining the midpoints of two sides of a triangle is related to the third side.

8 Midpoints of Sides of Quadrilaterals

1. Construct a quadrilateral with vertices C(4, 6), D(4, –4), E(–6, –1), and F(–2, 5).

2. To construct the four midpoints, select all four sides, click on the Construct menu, and choose the Point At Midpoint command.

3. Remove the highlighting and select a new colour. Construct line segments connecting adjacent pairs of midpoints to make a new quadrilateral.

4. Communication Classify the new quadrilateral. Justify your decision.

5. Drag point C to new locations. Does each new quadrilateral formed have the same classification as the one in question 4?

6. Communication Summarize your findings about the quadrilateral formed by joining the midpoints of the sides of a quadrilateral.

Rich Problem

School Boundaries

When a mathematical model is used to represent a real situation, assumptions may be made to simplify the model. In spite of the assumptions, information learned from the model can often be applied to the real situation.

In the following problems, all streets are assumed to be perpendicular and straight, and to have no width. All blocks are assumed to be the same length.

A community is built on a 10 by 10 coordinate grid, as shown. There are three schools, A at $(9, 8)$, B at $(2, 7)$, and C at $(6, 1)$. Copy the grid and plot the schools on it.

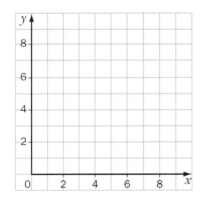

1. A student lives at every street corner represented on the grid. Draw school boundaries to separate the areas served by each school, so that each student's walking distance to school is as short as possible. If a student lives the same distance from two schools, decide which one the student should attend.

2. There are plans to build a swimming pool so that
• students from school A have the shortest distance to walk from school to the pool;
• students from school C have the longest distance to walk from school to the pool;
• students from school C do not walk more than 8 blocks.
How many locations for the pool are possible?

REVIEW OF Key CONCEPTS

2.1 Length of a Line Segment

Refer to the Key Concepts on page 71.

To find the exact length of the line segment joining (4, 6) and (2, −3), and the approximate length, to the nearest tenth, use the length formula.

$$l = \sqrt{(x_2 - x_1)^2 + (y_2 - y_1)^2}$$
$$= \sqrt{(2 - 4)^2 + (-3 - 6)^2}$$
$$= \sqrt{(-2)^2 + (-9)^2}$$
$$= \sqrt{85}$$
$$\doteq 9.2$$

The exact length is $\sqrt{85}$, and the approximate length is 9.2, to the nearest tenth.

To determine the radius of a circle with centre (0, 0) and equation $x^2 + y^2 = 81$, compare it to the general equation $x^2 + y^2 = r^2$. In the equation $x^2 + y^2 = 81$, $r^2 = 81$, so $r = 9$.
The radius of a circle with centre (0, 0) and equation $x^2 + y^2 = 81$ is 9.

1. Find the exact length of the line segment joining each pair of points.
a) A(7, 9) and B(1, 1)   **b)** W(4, 5) and X(−2, 3)
c) E(−2, 8) and F(−5, 5)   **d)** R(−10, 5) and T(4, −1)
e) U(1.2, −0.4) and V(−0.8, 3.6)

2. Write an equation for the circle with centre (0, 0) and the given radius.
a) radius 12   **b)** radius 20

3. The following equations model circles with centre (0, 0). Determine the radius of each circle. Round to the nearest tenth, if necessary.
a) $x^2 + y^2 = 121$ **b)** $x^2 + y^2 = 20$
c) $x^2 + y^2 = 400$ **d)** $x^2 + y^2 = 0.49$

4. Measurement △ABC has vertices A(4, 5), B(−1, 2), and C(5, 1).
a) Classify the triangle by side length.
b) Determine the perimeter of the triangle, to the nearest tenth.

5. Measurement Determine the perimeter of the quadrilateral with vertices E(2, 4), F(−2, 3), G(−3, −2), and H(3, −4), to the nearest tenth.

6. Measurement Verify that D(0, 3), E(−1, −6), and F(4, −2) are the vertices of an isosceles triangle.

7. Measurement a) Verify that the quadrilateral with vertices P(3, 3), Q(0, 1), R(3, −1), and S(6, 1) is a rhombus.
b) Determine the exact perimeter of the rhombus.

2.2–2.3 Midpoint of a Line Segment

Refer to the Key Concepts on page 77.

To determine the coordinates of the midpoint of the line segment with endpoints A(–4, 9) and B(6, 1), use the formula for midpoint.

$$\left(\frac{x_1 + x_2}{2}, \frac{y_1 + y_2}{2}\right) = \left(\frac{-4+6}{2}, \frac{9+1}{2}\right)$$
$$= (1, 5)$$

The coordinates of the midpoint are (1, 5).

8. Find the coordinates of the midpoint of each line segment.

a) P(2, –7) and Q(–3, 5) **b)** S(6, –2) and T(2, 2)

c) M(2, –5) and N(5, –1) **d)** G(–2, 0) and H(–4, 3)

e) V(2.9, 3.2) and W(3.1, –4.2) **f)** A$\left(3\frac{1}{2}, \frac{1}{2}\right)$ and B$\left(-2\frac{1}{2}, 1\frac{1}{2}\right)$

9. For a line segment KL, one endpoint is K(5,1) and the midpoint is M(1, 4). Find the coordinates of endpoint L.

10. Measurement △ABC has vertices A(1, 4), B(–3, –2), and C(3, 0). Find the lengths of the three medians. Express each length as

a) an exact value **b)** an approximate value, to the nearest tenth

11. Measurement Quadrilateral PQRS has vertices P(0, 7), Q(–2, 1), R(4, –1), and S(6, 3). A second quadrilateral is formed by joining the midpoints of the sides of quadrilateral PQRS. Show that the opposite sides of the second quadrilateral are equal.

12. Verify that the diagonals of the rectangle with vertices A(–4, 1), B(–1, 3), C(3, –3), and D(0, –5) bisect each other.

2.4 Verifying Properties of Geometric Figures

Refer to the Key Concepts on page 95.

To verify that the quadrilateral with vertices A(3, 4), B(1, 1), C(4, –4), and D(6, –1) is a parallelogram, calculate the slopes of the sides.

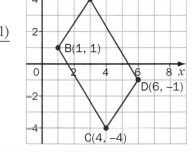

$$m = \frac{y_2 - y_1}{x_2 - x_1}$$

$m_{AB} = \dfrac{4-1}{3-1}$ $m_{DC} = \dfrac{-1-(-4)}{6-4}$ $m_{BC} = \dfrac{-4-1}{4-1}$ $m_{AD} = \dfrac{4-(-1)}{3-6}$

$= \dfrac{3}{2}$ $= \dfrac{3}{2}$ $= -\dfrac{5}{3}$ $= -\dfrac{5}{3}$

Since the slopes of opposite sides are equal, opposite sides are parallel. The quadrilateral is a parallelogram.

13. Verify that a quadrilateral with vertices K(2, –5), L(7, –3), M(1, 4), and N(–4, 2) is a parallelogram.

14. A square has vertices at U(–2, 1), V(2, 3), W(4, –1), and X(0, –3). Verify that the diagonals perpendicularly bisect each other.

15. Given $\triangle DEF$ with vertices D(–4, –1), E(4, 3), and F(0, –5), verify that
a) $\triangle DEF$ is isosceles
b) the line segment joining the midpoints of the equal sides is parallel to the third side and half the length of the third side

16. Quadrilateral RSTU has vertices R(2, 4), S(–2, 2), T(–1, 0), and U(3, 2). Verify that
a) quadrilateral RSTU is a rectangle
b) the diagonals of the rectangle bisect each other and are equal in length

17. Quadrilateral ABCD has vertices A(3, 4), B(–1, 2), C(–3, –4), and D(5, –6). Verify that
a) the quadrilateral formed by joining the midpoints of the sides of quadrilateral ABCD is a rhombus
b) the diagonals of the rhombus bisect each other at right angles

18. $\triangle DEF$ has vertices D(4, 5), E(–4, 3), and F(0, –5). Determine
a) an equation of EB, the median from E to DF
b) an equation of FA, the altitude from F to DE
c) an equation of PQ, the right bisector of EF

19. $\triangle ABC$ has vertices A(4, 2), B(0, 4), and C(–2, –2). Determine the coordinates of the circumcentre of $\triangle ABC$.

20. $\triangle PQR$ has vertices P(1, 3), Q(–1, –1), and R(5, 1). Determine the coordinates of the centroid of $\triangle ABC$.

21. Determine the equation of the right bisector of the line segment joining C(–3, 5) and D(3, 2).

22. The equation of a circle with centre O(0, 0) is $x^2 + y^2 = 20$. The points P(2, –4) and Q(4, 2) are the endpoints of chord PQ. AB right bisects the chord PQ at C. Verify that the centre of the circle lies on the right bisector of chord PQ.

2.5 Distance From a Line

Refer to the Key Concepts on page 103.

To find the distance from the point P(1, 0) to the line $x - 2y + 4 = 0$, to the nearest tenth, first write the equation $x - 2y + 4 = 0$ in the slope and y-intercept form to find the slope of the line.

$$y = \frac{1}{2}x + 2$$

The slope of the line is $\frac{1}{2}$.

So, the slope of the perpendicular from P(1, 0) to $x - 2y + 4 = 0$ is -2.
To find the equation of the perpendicular, use the point-slope form, where $(x_1, y_1) = (1, 0)$ and $m = -2$.

$$y - y_1 = m(x - x_1)$$
$$y - 0 = -2(x - 1)$$
$$y = -2x + 2$$
$$2x + y = 2$$

Then, solve the following system of equations to find the point of intersection.

$$x - 2y + 4 = 0 \qquad (1)$$
$$2x + y = 2 \qquad (2)$$

The point of intersection is (0, 2).
Finally, use the distance formula to find the distance from (0, 2) to (1, 0).
The distance from the point P(1, 0) to the line $x - 2y + 4 = 0$ is 2.2, to the nearest tenth.

---

23. Find the shortest distance from the origin to each line. Round to the nearest tenth, if necessary.

a) $y = x + 5$ **b)** $y = -2x + 1$ **c)** $y = \frac{1}{3}x - 4$

d) $x + y = 8$ **e)** $x + 2y = 10$ **f)** $x + 2y + 2 = 0$

24. Find the shortest distance from the given point to the given line. Round to the nearest tenth, if necessary.
a) (1, 4) and $y = x - 5$
b) (−2, 2) and $2x + y = 8$
c) (−1, −3) and $x + 3y - 9 = 0$

25. Find the distance from the point P(−3, 6) to the line $x = 4$.

26. Find the distance from the point Q(4, −3) to the line $y = 2$.

27. Measurement △RST has vertices R(−3, 4), S(−1, 0), and T(3, 2).
a) Find the length of the altitude from S to RT.
b) Find the area of the triangle.

Chapter Test

1. Find the exact distance between each pair of points.
a) (4, −1) and (1, 3)
b) (2, 0) and (4, −5)

2. Write an equation for the circle with centre (0, 0) and the given radius.
a) radius 3
b) radius 7

3 The following are equations of circles with centre (0, 0). Determine the exact radius of each circle.
a) $x^2 + y^2 = 100$
b) $x^2 + y^2 = 15$

4. Measurement The endpoints of a diameter of a circle are (−1, −3) and (3, 6). Calculate the radius of the circle, to the nearest tenth.

5. Measurement The vertices of a right triangle are A(3, 3), B(−1, 4), and C(1, −5). Find the area of the triangle.

6. Measurement The vertices of a triangle are R(3, 0), S(−1, 3), and T(0, −2).
a) Classify the triangle by side length.
b) Find the perimeter of the triangle, to the nearest tenth.

7. Determine the coordinates of the midpoint of the line segment with endpoints (−2, −5) and (−8, 3).

8. For the line segment DE, one endpoint is D(3, 1) and the midpoint is M(0, −4). Find the coordinates of endpoint E.

9. Measurement △DEF is a right triangle with vertices D(−2, 5), E(−4, 1), and F(2, 3). Verify that the midpoint of the hypotenuse is equidistant from the three vertices of the triangle.

10. Verify that the vertices A(−6, 1), B(2, −5), C(6, 1), and D(2, 4) are the vertices of a trapezoid.

11. Quadrilateral RSTU has vertices R(3, 2), S(0, 4), T(−2, 1), and U(1, −1). Verify that
a) quadrilateral RSTU is a square
b) the diagonals of quadrilateral RSTU perpendicularly bisect each other and are equal in length

12. The midpoints of the sides of quadrilateral RSTU, with vertices R(–4, 1), S(–2, 5), T(2, 1), and U(2, –7), are joined to form a quadrilateral. Verify that the quadrilateral formed is a parallelogram.

13. Determine the equation of the right bisector of the line segment joining E(2, 6) and F(4, –2).

14. △ABC has vertices A(6, 3), B(2, 5), and C(0, 1). Determine the coordinates of the circumcentre of △ABC.

15. Find the shortest distance from the origin to each line. Round to the nearest tenth, if necessary.
a) $y = x + 3$
b) $2x - y + 7 = 0$

16. Find the shortest distance from the point (3, 1) to the line $3x + y = -2$, to the nearest tenth.

17. The equation of a circle with centre O(0, 0) is $x^2 + y^2 = 40$. The points A(–2, 6) and B(–6, –2) are endpoints of chord AB. DE right bisects chord AB at F.
a) Verify that the centre of the circle lies on the right bisector of chord AB.
b) Find the distance from the centre of the circle to chord AB, to the nearest tenth.

Achievement Check

1   2   3   4

The longest crude-oil pipeline in the world is the one from Edmonton, Alberta, to Buffalo, New York, a distance of 2858 km. In one region, the pipeline follows the path given by $y = 2x + 20$, where each unit on the grid represents 1 km. A town in that region is centred at (50, 5) and has radius 5 km. New by-laws require that the pipeline not be within 50 km of an urban area. How close does the pipeline come to the town? Does the pipeline need to be rerouted? If so, what is the minimum length of the existing pipeline that must be rerouted? Explain and justify your reasoning.

Mathematics is a search for patterns. Many people look for patterns in their work. Detectives look for patterns at crime scenes. Wildlife biologists look for patterns in animal populations. Patterns can be used to make predictions.

Tutankhamun became king of ancient Egypt around 1334 B.C., when he was only 9 years old. The location of his tomb was unknown for over three thousand years, until a team of archaeologists discovered it in 1922. Among the 5000 items found in the tomb were boards used for the ancient game of Senet. A Senet board consists of a 3 by 10 grid of squares. Find the total number of squares of all sizes on a Senet game board.

Understand the Problem

1. What information are you given?
2. What are you asked to find?
3. Do you need an exact or an approximate answer?

Think of a Plan

Start with smaller grids and look for a pattern. Use the pattern to write a rule that relates the dimensions of the grid to the total number of squares.

Carry Out the Plan

Use diagrams to show the smaller grids. Then, set up a table.

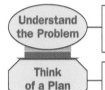

3 by 1   3 by 2   3 by 3   3 by 4   3 by 5

Dimensions of Grid	Number of Squares			
	1 by 1	2 by 2	3 by 3	Total
3 by 1	3	0	0	3
3 by 2	6	2	0	8
3 by 3	9	4	1	14
3 by 4	12	6	2	20
3 by 5	15	8	3	26

Starting with the 3 by 2 grid, the total number of squares increases by 6 for the addition of each extra column of squares to the grid. For a 3 by n grid, where n is the number of columns and $n > 1$, the total number of squares is related to n, as shown in the following table.

Dimensions of Grid	Number of Squares
3 by 2	$6 \times 2 - 4 = 8$
3 by 3	$6 \times 3 - 4 = 14$
3 by 4	$6 \times 4 - 4 = 20$
3 by n	$6 \times n - 4$

For the 3 by 10 game board, the total number of squares is $6(10) - 4 = 56$. So, there are 56 squares of all sizes on a Senet game board.

Look Back

Are there other ways to use the patterns in the table to predict the answer?

Look for a Pattern

1. Use the given information to find a pattern.
2. Use the pattern to solve the problem.
3. Check that your answer is reasonable.

Applications and Problem Solving

1. Grid squares Find the total number of squares on each grid.
a) 4 squares by 10 squares
b) 5 squares by 12 squares
c) chessboard (8 by 8)
d) Snakes and Ladders board (10 by 10)

2. Communication If it is possible to climb stairs one step at a time or two steps at a time, the following are three different ways to climb three steps.
• one step, then one step, then one step
• two steps, then one step
• one step, then two steps
How many different ways are there to climb 15 steps? Describe your problem solving method.

3. Tables of values Find a rule that relates x and y. Then, copy and complete each table.

a)

x	y
0	4
1	5
2	6
3	7
9	
	20
21	

b)

x	y
0	1
1	3
2	5
3	7
8	
	25
50	

c)

x	y
1	8
2	7
5	4
6	
	1
9	

d)

x	y
19	12
16	9
14	7
12	
9	
	0

e)

x	y
1	2
2	5
3	10
4	17
	37
20	
100	

f)

x	y
1	3
2	7
3	11
4	15
10	
	63
30	

4. Standard form Predict the last digit if each number is expressed in standard form.
a) 4^{98} **b)** 7^{99}

5. Asterisk pattern How many asterisks are there in
a) the 12th figure?   **b)** the 35th figure?

6. Sequences Write the next 3 terms in each sequence.
a) 6, 12, 11, 22, 21, 42, ▨, ▨, ▨
b) 2, 4, 6, 10, 16, 26, ▨, ▨, ▨
c) 1, 2, 5, 10, 17, 26, ▨, ▨, ▨

7. Table patterns The numbers in each of the columns A, B, C, D, and E are found by applying different rules to the numbers in columns p and q. Determine each rule. Then, copy and complete the table.

p	q	A	B	C	D	E
−4	2	−6	6	−6	12	−7
2	−8	10	−10	−4	−60	−15
−5	6					
1	−4					
−3	−6					

8. Communication a) How many odd numbers are in this series?
$1 + 3 + 5 + 7 + \ldots + 287 + 289 + 291$
b) Explain how you could use the number of odd numbers in the series to find the sum of these odd numbers.

9. Sequences Find the next term in each sequence.
a) 873, 168, 48, 32, ▨
b) 47, 29, 18, 11, 7, ▨

10. Communication Write a problem that can be solved by finding a pattern. Have a classmate solve your problem.

About how many recordings are played by the radio stations in Ontario in a day?

Rich estimation problems like this one are also known as **Fermi problems**. They are named after Enrico Fermi (1901–1954). He was a leading research scientist, who won the Nobel Prize for physics in 1938 and spent the last part of his career as a professor at the University of Chicago. He liked to show his students that they had the knowledge to answer seemingly impossible questions that he posed.

The importance of Fermi problems is to illustrate the difference between *guessing* and *estimation*. Although guessing may produce a reasonable answer to a problem, you do not know how much confidence to place in the answer. When estimating the answers to Fermi problems, you will need to make some assumptions. If the estimated answer seems to be unreasonable, go back and check your assumptions.

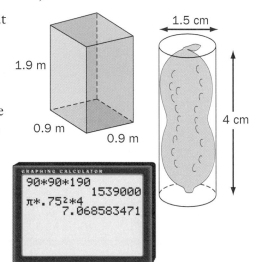

About how many peanuts in the shell would be needed to fill a telephone booth?

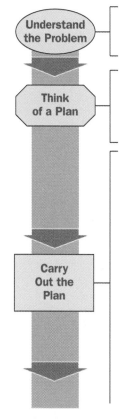

Understand the Problem

1. What information are you given?
2. What are you asked to find?
3. Do you need an exact or an approximate answer?

Think of a Plan

The problem is a volume problem, in which you need to estimate how many small objects are needed to fill a large object. The number of small objects, n, can be found using
$$n = \text{(large volume)} \div \text{(small volume)}$$

Carry Out the Plan

You can use your research skills to find that the inside of a telephone booth approximates a square-based prism. The side length of the base is about 0.9 m, and the height is about 1.9 m.

Assume that peanuts in a shell approximate a cylinder with a diameter of about 1.5 cm and a height of about 4 cm.

The volume of a telephone booth, in cubic centimetres, is about $90 \times 90 \times 190$, or about $1\ 540\ 000$ cm^3.

The volume of peanuts in the shell, in cubic centimetres, is about $\pi \times 0.75^2 \times 4$, or about 7 cm^3.

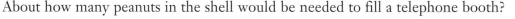

1.5 cm

1.9 m

0.9 m
0.9 m

4 cm

GRAPHING CALCULATOR
```
90*90*190
          1539000
π*.75²*4
    7.068583471
```

$$\text{So, } n \doteq \frac{1\,540\,000}{7}$$
$$= 220\,000$$

About 220 000 peanuts in the shell would be needed to fill a telephone booth.

Look Back

Does the answer seem reasonable?
Is there a way to improve the estimate?

Solve Rich Estimation Problems

1. Locate the information you need.
2. Decide what assumption(s) to make.
3. Estimate the solution to the problem.
4. Check that your estimate is reasonable.

Applications and Problem Solving

Communication *Use your research skills to locate any missing information. You could use such sources as the Internet, a reference book, or an expert on the topic. For some problems, you may need to use a survey or measurement. Then, solve each problem and describe how you found the necessary information.*

1. Ten-dollar bills About how many ten-dollar bills would it take to paper the walls of your classroom?

2. Toothpicks About how many flat toothpicks would be needed to cover the floor of your school gym?

3. Bananas Estimate the number of bananas it would take to fill all the lockers in your school.

4. Pianos Estimate the number of pianos in Ontario.

5. Pizza deliveries Estimate the number of pizzas that will be delivered in Ontario this year.

6. Phone calls About how many minutes do all the students in your school spend on the phone in a school month?

7. Radio About how many recordings are played by all the radio stations in Ontario in a day?

8. Lake Ontario Estimate the number of drops of water in Lake Ontario.

9. Laughter About how many times does a grade 10 student laugh in a day?

10. Calculators Estimate the total number of times the students in your school press a calculator key in a school week.

11. Doughnut shops Estimate the number of doughnut shops in Canada.

12. Buildings About what percent of the land area in your city or town is covered by buildings?

13. Communication Write a problem similar to question 1, 2, or 3. Have a classmate solve your problem.

Problem Solving: Using the Strategies

1. Circles on a grid
Copy the diagram. Place six circles in six different small squares, so that there is no more than one circle in each row, column, or diagonal.

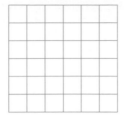

2. Basketball tournament St. Mary's High School entered a basketball tournament. In the first round, each team played one game, and the losers dropped out. Each winner from the first round played one game in the second round, and the losers dropped out. This process continued until a winner was declared. St. Mary's won the tournament by winning 5 games. How many teams were in the tournament?

3. Cube net
Three views of a cube are shown. Copy the net and label it with the correct letters.

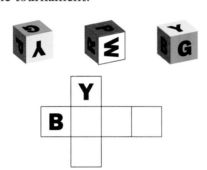

4. Astronomy research a) The moon has a diameter of 3476 km. How does the surface area of the moon compare with the surface area of the smallest planet in the solar system? What assumption have you made?
b) How many times as great is the volume of the sun as the combined volumes of all the planets in the solar system?

5. Cheese sticks A restaurant menu includes orders of 6, 9, and 20 cheese sticks. To get 15 sticks, you can order 6 sticks and 9 sticks. You cannot order 16 sticks, because no combination of 6, 9, or 20 adds to 16. What is the largest number of sticks that you *cannot* order?

6. Standard form If each of the following numbers is written in standard form, what is the final digit?
a) 9^{32} **b)** 12^{33}

7. Breakfast cereal About how many boxes of breakfast cereal are sold each year in Canada?

8. Congruent shapes
The shape is to be divided into six congruent parts by cutting along the grid lines. What shapes can the congruent parts have?

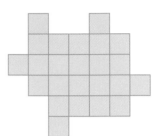

9. Sequence a) Draw the next three squares in the sequence.

| 1 | 2 | 3 | 4 | 5 | 6 |

b) Communication Describe the pattern in words.
c) Draw the 75th square.
d) Draw the 153rd square.

10. Fractions Find the product.
$$\left(1-\frac{1}{2}\right)\left(1-\frac{1}{3}\right)\left(1-\frac{1}{4}\right)\cdots\left(1-\frac{1}{57}\right)$$

11. Communication A rectangular solid is to be made using 60 blocks, each of which is a 1-cm cube. Write a full solution to the following, showing your mathematical model and your reasoning.
a) How many rectangular solids are possible?
b) How many different surface areas are possible?

Cumulative Review: Chapters 1 and 2

Chapter 1 Linear Systems

1. Solve by graphing.

a) $y = 3x + 1$
$y = 4x + 15$

b) $4x + y = -1$
$6x - y = 6$

2. Solve each system by substitution. Check each solution.

a) $x + 4y = 3$
$2x + 5y = 3$

b) $2a + b = 2$
$3a - 2b = 3$

3. Solve each system by elimination. Check each solution. If there is not exactly one solution, does the system have no solution or infinitely many solutions?

a) $8a - 3b = 10$
$7a + 3b = 20$

b) $5x - 8y = 12$
$10x - 16y = 24$

c) $2x - 3y = 6$
$5x - 4y = 1$

d) $5p + 8q = 4$
$3p + 10q = 5$

4. Selling produce Portobello mushrooms sell for $6.60/kg and oyster mushrooms sell for $11.00/kg. Find the mass of each type of mushroom in 1-kg bags selling for $8.36.

5. River patrol It took a patrol boat 3 h to travel 48 km up a river against the current and 2 h for the return trip with the current. Find the speed of the boat in still water and the speed of the current.

6. Investing Carlos invested $12 000, part in a term deposit that paid 4% per annum and the remainder in bonds that paid 5% per annum. The total interest after one year was $560. How much did he invest at each rate?

7. Acid solutions A chemistry teacher needs to make 20 L of 36% sulfuric acid solution. The acid solutions available are 30% sulfuric acid solution and 40% sulfuric acid solution. How many litres of each solution should be mixed to make the 36% solution?

Chapter 2 Analytic Geometry

1. Find the length of the line segment joining each pair of points. Express each length as an exact solution and as an approximate solution, to the nearest tenth.

a) M(3, 7) and A(1, 3)

b) B(5, −1) and C(−3, 4)

2. Find the coordinates of the midpoint of each line segment, given the endpoints.

a) M(1, 13) and N(9, −3)

b) W(7, −2) and Z(−2, −3)

3. Write an equation for the circle with centre (0, 0) and radius 12.

4. Determine the radius of a circle with centre (0, 0) and equation $x^2 + y^2 = 36$.

5. Measurement $\triangle RST$ has vertices R(−1, −1), S(−2, 4), and T(−6, 0).

a) Classify the triangle by side length.

b) Find the perimeter, to the nearest tenth.

6. The vertices of a kite are G(2, 5), H(5, 1), I(8, 2), and J(7, 5). Verify that

a) the diagonals are perpendicular

b) one, and only one, of the diagonals bisects the other diagonal

7. Quadrilateral DEFG has vertices D(−4, 1), E(−2, −3), F(6, −1), and G(2, 3). Verify that the quadrilateral formed by joining the midpoints of the sides of DEFG is a parallelogram.

8. $\triangle ABC$ has vertices A(2, 1), B(8, 3), and C(4, 7). Determine

a) an equation for BD, the median from B to AC

b) an equation for CE, the altitude from C to AB

c) an equation for FG, the right bisector of BC

9. Measurement Find the shortest distance from the point (5, 4) to the line $x + y = 5$. Express the distance as

a) an exact value

b) an approximate value, to the nearest tenth

CHAPTER 3

Polynomials

Specific Expectations	Sections
• Expand and simplify second-degree polynomial expressions.	3.1 3.2 3.3
• Factor polynomial expressions involving common factors, differences of squares, and trinomials.	3.4 3.5 3.6 3.7

Modelling Math

Representing Patterns Algebraically

Fractals are intricate patterns that repeat at different scales. Mathematicians call a fractal pattern self-similar, because the same shapes are repeated at different sizes.

Computer-generated fractal patterns are used to model complex shapes, such as clouds, coastlines, and blood-vessel branching. Physicists use fractal patterns to describe the vibrations of airplane wings and solve wing-design problems.

The ability to solve problems by finding patterns is an important skill. In many cases, patterns can be modelled algebraically.

In the following pattern of shaded and unshaded grid squares, the four grids have side lengths of 1, 2, 3, and 4 units, respectively.

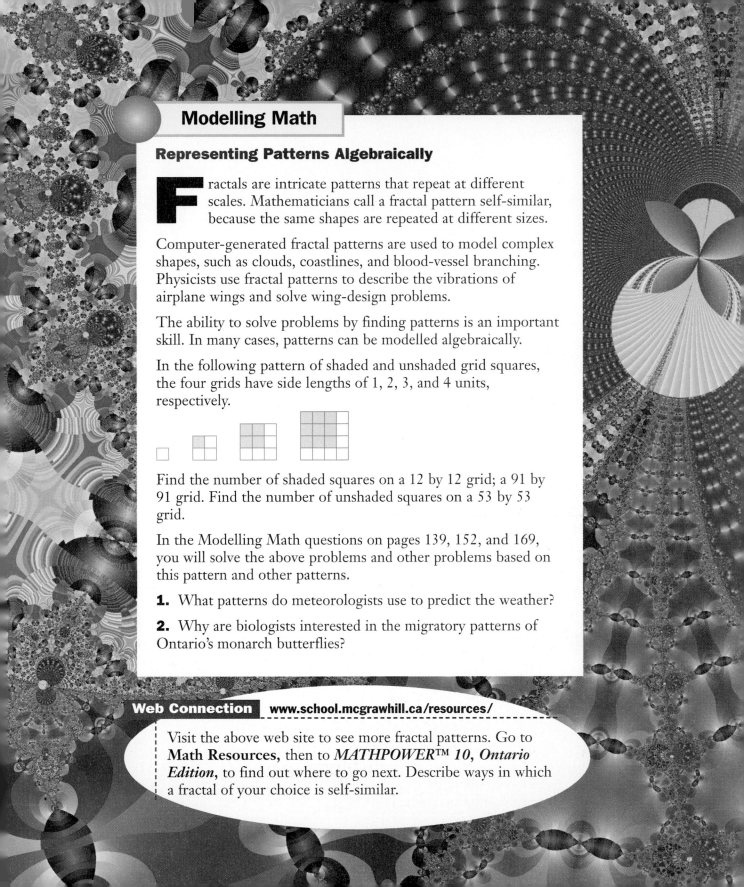

Find the number of shaded squares on a 12 by 12 grid; a 91 by 91 grid. Find the number of unshaded squares on a 53 by 53 grid.

In the Modelling Math questions on pages 139, 152, and 169, you will solve the above problems and other problems based on this pattern and other patterns.

1. What patterns do meteorologists use to predict the weather?

2. Why are biologists interested in the migratory patterns of Ontario's monarch butterflies?

Web Connection www.school.mcgrawhill.ca/resources/

Visit the above web site to see more fractal patterns. Go to **Math Resources,** then to *MATHPOWER*™ *10, Ontario Edition,* to find out where to go next. Describe ways in which a fractal of your choice is self-similar.

Getting Started

Developing Expressions From Patterns

1. The three figures show cubes made from toothpicks and marshmallows.

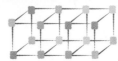

a) Copy the table. Complete it by finding the numbers of marshmallows in figures with the given numbers of cubes.
b) Let the number of cubes be *c*. Write an expression in terms of *c* for finding the number of marshmallows from the number of cubes.
c) Use your expression to calculate the number of marshmallows needed to make 10 cubes.
d) Copy the table. Complete it by finding the numbers of toothpicks in figures with the given numbers of cubes.
e) Write an expression in terms of *c* for finding the number of toothpicks from the number of cubes.
f) Use your formula to calculate the number of toothpicks needed to make 10 cubes.

Number of Cubes	Number of Marshmallows
1	
⋮	
5	

Number of Cubes	Number of Toothpicks
1	
⋮	
5	

2. The figures are made by connecting pairs of regular hexagons with side lengths of 1 unit.

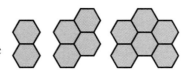

a) Copy the table. Complete it by finding the perimeters of figures with the given numbers of hexagons.
b) Let *n* represent the number of hexagons. Write an expression in terms of *n* for finding the perimeter from the number of hexagons.
c) Use your formula to calculate the perimeter of the figure that contains 22 hexagons.

Number of Hexagons	Perimeter
2	
4	
⋮	
10	

3. The three figures are made from squares and diagonals.

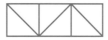

a) Copy the table. Complete it by finding the total numbers of triangles in figures with the given numbers of squares.
b) Let *s* represent the number of squares. Write an expression in terms of *s* for finding the total number of triangles from the number of squares.
c) Use your formula to calculate the total number of triangles formed from 15 squares.

Number of Squares	Number of Triangles
1	
⋮	
5	

Review of Prerequisite Skills

If you need help with any of the skills named in **purple** below, refer to Appendix A.

1. Evaluating expressions Evaluate for $x = 2$, $y = 1$, and $z = 3$.

a) $5x - y + 2z$ **b)** $4xz - 3y + 9$

c) $2(4x + 7y)$ **d)** $yz - xz + xyz$

e) $5(z - x - y)$ **f)** $3y^2 + 4z^2 - 2x^2$

g) $3y(7 + 8z)$ **h)** $(xyz)^2$

2. Evaluating expressions Evaluate for $a = -3$, $b = -1$, and $c = 2$.

a) $2ac - 5b$ **b)** $6a - 2b - 3c$

c) $4a(2b - c)$ **d)** $ab - bc - ac$

e) $2a^2 + 3b^2 - c^2$ **f)** $a^3 - b^3 + c^3$

g) $(2abc)^2$ **h)** $(a - b)(b - c)$

3. Exponent rules Simplify, using the exponent rules. Express each answer in exponential form.

a) $2^3 \times 2^4$ **b)** $3^2 \times 3^4 \times 3$

c) $y^4 \times y^5$ **d)** $2y^2 \times 4y^3$

e) $(-4a^3)(2a^4)$ **f)** $(2x^2)^3$

g) $(-6m^3)(-2m^4)$ **h)** $2^5 \div 2^3$

i) $3^2 \div 3^2$ **j)** $m^7 \div m^4$

k) $y^5 \times y^3 \div y^2$ **l)** $-20a^4 \div (-5a^2)$

4. Like terms Simplify, by collecting like terms.

a) $3x + 5x - 2x$

b) $3a + 4b - 6a + b$

c) $4a + 5b - 6 - 7b + 8 + 4a$

d) $2x^2 + 3x - 4 - 2x + 5x^2 - 7$

5. Expanding expressions Expand.

a) $2(x - 5)$ **b)** $4(2a + 3b - 2c)$

c) $4(1 - 2x + 5y)$ **d)** $-2(3x - 7)$

e) $-3(x^2 - 2x - 1)$ **f)** $-(2a - 4b - c)$

g) $3x(x + 2)$ **h)** $-2y(y^2 + y - 3)$

6. Simplifying expressions Expand and simplify.

a) $2(x + 1) + 3(x - 1)$

b) $5(2y + 1) - (5y - 2)$

c) $3(m^2 + m + 1) + 2(m^2 - 1)$

d) $4(1 + x^2) - 3(x^2 - 3x - 2)$

e) $5x(x - 3) - 2x(x + 2)$

f) $3(3z^2 - 5z - 4) + 2z(4z - 1)$

7. Greatest common factors Determine the greatest common factor of each pair.

a) $6y$, $8y$ **b)** $3x^2$, $5x$

c) $7b^2$, $21ab$ **d)** $20abc$, $30ab$

e) $18y^3$, $12y^2$ **f)** $15cd^2$, $10c^2d$

g) $9rst^2$, $4r^2st$ **h)** $4x^2y^2$, $22x^2y$

8. Greatest common factors Determine the greatest common factor of each set.

a) $10x^2$, $15x$, $30x^3$ **b)** $12xy$, $4wz$, $8xz$

c) $7xyz$, $14xy$, $21txy$ **d)** $9m^3$, $3mt^2$, $6m^2t$

e) $25x^3$, $10x^2$, $15x$ **f)** $24m^2$, $28mn$, $36mn^2$

g) $22xy$, $11y^2$, $33wy$ **h)** $7pqr$, $5xy$, $8t$

i) $18r^2s^3$, $9rs^2$, $27r^3s^2$

9. Find mentally two integers that have the given product and sum.

	Product	Sum		Product	Sum
a)	4	4	**b)**	6	5
c)	5	6	**d)**	−8	−2
e)	12	−7	**f)**	12	8
g)	−20	−1	**h)**	24	−11
i)	24	10	**j)**	30	17
k)	1	−2	**l)**	−2	−1
m)	−5	−4	**n)**	−9	0
o)	−6	1	**p)**	−10	3
q)	7	−8	**r)**	16	−8
s)	16	−10	**t)**	−15	−2

Investigation Evaluate the Expression

When a dolphin leaps vertically out of the water, the dolphin's speed just before it breaks the surface is about 7 m/s. The dolphin's approximate height, in metres, above the water t seconds after breaking the surface can be found using the expression $7t - 5t^2$.

1. How high is the dolphin after
a) 0.5 s?   **b)** 1 s?

2. **Communication** After 1 s, is the dolphin still climbing or is it diving back toward the water? How do you know?

3. To the nearest tenth of a second, find the time at which the dolphin reaches its maximum height.

4. What is the dolphin's maximum height?

5. If a dolphin were swimming on the moon and left the water at 7 m/s, the dolphin's approximate height after t seconds could be found using the expression $7t - 0.8t^2$. To the nearest second, find the time the dolphin would take to reach its maximum height.

A **monomial** is a number, a product of one or more variables, or the product of a number and one or more variables. A **numerical coefficient** is the number part of a monomial.

numerical coefficient → $7t$ ← variable, monomial

A **polynomial** is an algebraic expression formed by adding or subtracting monomials. Each monomial is called a **term** of the polynomial. Polynomials are classified in two ways. One way uses the number of terms they have.

Monomials have 1 term.	Binomials have 2 terms.	Trinomials have 3 terms.
7	$x + 17$	$x^2 + 4x - 3$
$5x$	$x - y$	$2a + 3b - 4c$
$-4m^2n$	$2m^2 - 4mn$	$2x^2 - 2xy + 3y^2$

Polynomials with more than three terms are simply called *polynomials*.

Polynomials are also classified using the exponents of their variables. The **degree** of a term is the sum of the exponents of its variables.

$3x^2$ is a term of degree 2, because the only exponent is 2.

$4m^2n^3$ is a term of degree 5, because the sum of the exponents 2 and 3 is 5.

The degree of a polynomial is the highest degree of any of its terms.

Polynomial	Number of Terms	Classified by Number of Terms	Degree	Classified by Degree
5	1	monomial	0	constant
$3x$	1	monomial	1	linear
$4x + 2$	2	binomial	1	linear
$x^2 + 4x + 1$	3	trinomial	2	quadratic
$3x^3 + x^2 - x - 7$	4	polynomial	3	cubic

The terms of a polynomial are usually written so that the exponents of the variable are in descending order or ascending order.

Descending order: $2x^3 + 3x^2 - 4x + 9$
Ascending order: $9 - 4x + 3x^2 + 2x^3$

Terms that have the same variable factors, such as $7x$ and $5x$, are called **like terms**. Simplify an expression containing like terms by adding their coefficients. This process is known as **collecting like terms**.

$$7x + 3y + 5x - 2y = 12x + y \qquad 3x^2 + 4xy - 6xy + 8x^2 = 11x^2 - 2xy$$

Example 1   Adding Polynomials
Simplify $(x^2 + 4x - 2) + (2x^2 - 6x + 9)$.

Solution
To add polynomials, collect like terms.
$$\begin{aligned}
(x^2 + 4x - 2) + (2x^2 - 6x + 9) &= x^2 + 4x - 2 + 2x^2 - 6x + 9 \\
&= x^2 + 2x^2 + 4x - 6x - 2 + 9 \\
&= 3x^2 - 2x + 7
\end{aligned}$$

Example 2   Subtracting Polynomials
Simplify $(6m^2 - mn + 4) - (7m^2 + 4mn - 2)$.

Solution
To subtract, add the opposite.

One way is to multiply each term to be subtracted by -1.

$$\begin{aligned}
(6m^2 - mn + 4) - (7m^2 + 4mn - 2) &= (6m^2 - mn + 4) - 1(7m^2 + 4mn - 2) \\
&= 6m^2 - mn + 4 - 7m^2 - 4mn + 2 \\
&= -m^2 - 5mn + 6
\end{aligned}$$

Recall the distributive property.
$a(b + c) = ab + ac$

Example 3   Multiplying Monomials

Multiply.

a) $(2x^2)(7x)$ **b)** $(-4a^2b)(3ab^3)$

Solution

Multiply the numerical coefficients. Then, multiply the variables using the exponent rules for multiplication.

a) $(2x^2)(7x) = (2)(7)(x^2)(x)$

$$= 14x^3$$

b) $(-4a^2b)(3ab^3) = (-4)(3)(a^2)(a)(b)(b^3)$

$$= -12a^3b^4$$

Example 4   Dividing Monomials

Simplify $\dfrac{20x^3y^4}{-5x^2y^2}$. Assume that the denominator does not equal zero.

Solution

Divide the numerical coefficients. Then, divide the variables using the exponent rules for division.

$$\frac{20x^3y^4}{-5x^2y^2} = \left(\frac{20}{-5}\right)\left(\frac{x^3}{x^2}\right)\left(\frac{y^4}{y^2}\right)$$

$$= -4xy^2$$

Example 5   Expanding and Simplifying Expressions

Expand and simplify $3x(x - 2) - 2x(2x + 5)$.

Solution

Use the distributive property to multiply each term inside the brackets by the term outside the brackets. Then, simplify by collecting like terms.

$$3x(x - 2) - 2x(2x + 5) = 3x(x - 2) - 2x(2x + 5)$$

$$= 3x^2 - 6x - 4x^2 - 10x$$

$$= -x^2 - 16x$$

Key CONCEPTS

1 To add polynomials, collect like terms.

2 To subtract a polynomial, add its opposite.

3 To multiply monomials, multiply the numerical coefficients. Then, multiply the variables using the exponent rules for multiplication.

4 To divide monomials, divide the numerical coefficients. Then, divide the variables using the exponent rules for division.

5 To multiply a polynomial by a monomial, use the distributive property to multiply each term in the polynomial by the monomial.

Communicate Your Understanding

1. Describe how you would simplify each of the following.

a) $(2x^2 - 3x + 2) + (x^2 + 2x - 5)$ **b)** $(5x^2 + 4x - 7) - (6x^2 - 3x + 3)$

c) $(4xy^3)(-2x^2y)$ **d)** $\dfrac{-15x^3y^2}{3x^2y}$

2. Describe how you would expand and simplify $2x(x - 3) - 4(x^2 + x)$.

3. Explain why $x^0 = 1$.

Practice

A

1. Classify each polynomial by degree and by number of terms.

a) $4y + 7$ **b)** $2x^2 - 8x$ **c)** $3a^3 - 3a - 1$
d) $5w^3 - 3w^2 + w - 6$ **e)** $8x$ **f)** 78

2. Evaluate each expression for the given value(s) of the variable(s).

a) $x^2 - 7x + 12$ for $x = 3$ **b)** $4a^2 - 5a + 8$ for $a = 2$
c) $2x^2 - 3xy + 4y^2$ for $x = 2, y = -1$

3. Write each polynomial in descending order of x.

a) $6x^2 - 5x + 4x^3 - 7$ **b)** $1 - 8x^2 - 3x^3$

4. Write each polynomial in ascending order of x.

a) $2x - 5x^3 - 6x^2 + 11$ **b)** $-4 + 3x^3 - 2x^2 - 5x^4$

5. Simplify.

a) $(3x + 4) + (5x + 2)$ **b)** $(7a - 6) + (2a + 9)$ **c)** $(2 - 3yz) + (7 + 6yz)$
d) $(m + n) + (5m - 2n)$ **e)** $(5x + 7) - (2x + 1)$ **f)** $(6a - 2b) - (4a + b)$
g) $(c + d) - (c - d)$ **h)** $(2m - n) - (3m + 4n)$

6. Simplify.

a) $(3x^2 - 6x + 9) + (4x^2 + 7x + 8)$ **b)** $(7x^2 + 3xy - 2y^2) + (8x^2 - xy - y^2)$
c) $(2a^2 - 2a - 7) - (a^2 - 6a - 11)$ **d)** $(3t^2 - 12) - (4t^2 + 5t + 7)$
e) $(2x + 4) + (3x - 2) - (5x + 8)$ **f)** $(5x^2 - y^2) - (3x^2 + 2y^2) - (x^2 + 3y^2)$

7. Multiply.

a) $(4x)(7x^2)$ **b)** $(3ab)(-4ab^2)$ **c)** $(-6m^2n^3)(-7mn^2)$
d) $(-2xyz^3)(-4x^3y^2)$ **e)** $(8r^3s^2t)(4s^3t)$ **f)** $(2xy)(-3x^2y^3)(-3x^2)$

8. Simplify. Assume that no denominator equals zero.

a) $\dfrac{24x^4}{6x}$ **b)** $\dfrac{18a^2b}{9ab}$ **c)** $\dfrac{-36xy^2}{4y^2}$

d) $\dfrac{-27a^2bc^4}{-3abc^2}$ **e)** $\dfrac{-40x^3y^4z^2}{8x^3y^3}$ **f)** $\dfrac{-75s^2t^5}{-25s^2t^2}$

9. Expand.

a) $2x(3x - 4)$ **b)** $3a(4a - 3b)$ **c)** $-4t(5s - t)$
d) $-x(2x - 7)$ **e)** $-3m(m - 6)$ **f)** $(3x - 1)2$
g) $(4a + 3)(5a)$ **h)** $(1 - 6y)(-3)$ **i)** $(x - 3)(-4x)$

10. Expand and simplify.

a) $2(x - 4) + 5(x + 3)$ **b)** $3(m - 3) - 6(m - 7)$ **c)** $4(2x - 7) - 5(4x + 9)$
d) $5(3t - 7) - (4t + 1)$ **e)** $4x + 3(2x - 5) + 6(1 - 5x)$ **f)** $8(1 - 3y) - 4 + 2(8y - 7)$

11. Expand.

a) $6(3a - 4b - 9)$ **b)** $-4(3t^2 - t - 1)$ **c)** $-(4m^2 - m - 7)$
d) $7(9y^2 - 3y - 7)$ **e)** $-5(2x^2 + 3xy - y^2)$ **f)** $4(2y^2 + 3y - 1)$
g) $-6x(3x - 6y - 9)$ **h)** $2a(3 - 4b + 5a)$ **i)** $-a(3a + 4b - 2c)$

12. Expand and simplify.

a) $3x(x - 4) - x(x + 5) - 2x(x - 1)$ **b)** $4a(a + 3b) + 2b(2a - b) - 6(a - b)$
c) $2(x^2 - 3x - 4) - 3(4x^2 - x + 5)$ **d)** $3(y^2 - y - 1) - 2y(3y - 6)$
e) $3s(2s - t - 1) + 2(st + 4s + 5)$

Applications and Problem Solving

13. Write a polynomial with the given number of terms and degree.

a) 1 term, degree 3   **b)** 2 terms, degree 1   **c)** 3 terms, degree 2

14. Free fall The approximate distance, in metres, an object falls during free fall is given by the expression $4.9t^2$, where t seconds is the time during which the object falls. An object falling from the same height as the top of First Canadian Place in Toronto would hit the ground after 7.7 s. Calculate the height of the building, to the nearest metre.

B

15. Communication a) Subtract $2x^2 - 3x + 4$ from $3x^2 + 4x - 5$.
b) Subtract $3x^2 + 4x - 5$ from $2x^2 - 3x + 4$.
c) Compare your answers from parts a) and b). What can you conclude about reversing the order of subtraction?

16. Measurement Given the perimeter, P, and the lengths of two sides of the triangle, find the length of the third side.

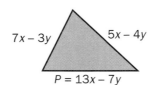

$7x - 3y$ $5x - 4y$

$P = 13x - 7y$

17. Ancient pyramid The Pyramid of the Moon at Teotihuacán in Mexico has a rectangular base. The length is 10 m more than the width. Therefore, if the width is represented by x, the length is $x + 10$.

a) Write and expand an expression that represents the area of the base.
b) If x represents 140 m, what is the area of the base, in square metres?

18. Measurement For the rectangular prism, write and simplify an expression that represents
a) the volume
b) the surface area

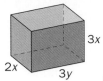

3x
2x
3y

19. Packaging A pizza of diameter d just fits inside a square box.
a) Write an expression for the area of the pizza in terms of d.
b) Write an expression for the area of the bottom of the box in terms of d.
c) Divide your expression from part a) by your expression from part b).
d) Use your result from part c) to find the percent of the area of the bottom of the box that the pizza covers. Round your answer to the nearest percent.

20. Shakespeare's theatre Most of Shakespeare's plays were first produced at the Globe Theatre, which was built in 1599 in London, England. The width and length of the rectangular stage of the Globe Theatre can be represented by the expressions $3x$ and $4x + 1$.
a) Write and expand an expression that represents the area of the stage.
b) If x represents 3 m, calculate the area of the stage, in square metres.

C

21. State two values of y for which the value of $3y^2 + 4y - 14$ is a perfect square.

22. Measurement The area of the shaded region is 400 cm². Find the dimensions of the large rectangle.

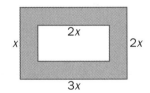

x   2x   2x
3x

Achievement Check

1 2 3 4

If you follow these instructions, you will end up with your birthdate (month/day/year). Analyze this birthday trick algebraically to explain why it works.

Start with the number of the month in which you were born.
Multiply by four.
Add thirteen.
Multiply by twenty-five.
Subtract two hundred.
Add your birthdate (day of the month).
Double the number you now have.
Subtract forty.
Multiply by fifty.
Add the last two digits of your birth year.
Subtract 10 500.
You should now have your birthdate (month/day/year).

Canadian architect Arthur Erickson has designed many buildings. He designed Simon Fraser University around a walkway and meeting place known as the Central Mall. The mall is covered by a rectangular glazed roof supported on girders. The area of a rectangle can be used to model the product of two binomials.

Investigation Use a Model

1. The large rectangle is made up of a square, A, and three rectangles, B, C, and D.

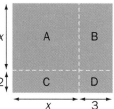

a) Determine the areas of A, B, C, and D.

b) Add the areas of A, B, C, and D to write an expression for the area of the large rectangle. Collect like terms and write the expression in descending powers of x.

2. Write an expression for
a) the length of the rectangle
b) the width of the rectangle

3. Use the expressions for the length and width to write an expression for the area of the rectangle. Do not expand.

4. How do the quantities represented by your two expressions for the area compare?

5. Communication Write a rule for multiplying two binomials.

6. Use your rule to multiply the following. Check your results by modelling with diagrams.
a) $(x + 1)(x + 3)$ **b)** $(x + 2)(x + 4)$ **c)** $(2x + 1)(x + 2)$

7. Check your results in question 6 by substituting 1 for x.

Example 1   Using the Distributive Property

Find the product $(x + 1)(x + 2)$.

Solution

To multiply two binomials, use the distributive property.

$$(x + 1)(x + 2) = x(x + 2) + 1(x + 2)$$
$$= x^2 + 2x + x + 2$$
$$= x^2 + 3x + 2$$

Note that, in Example 1, the same result can be obtained by multiplying each term in the first binomial by each term in the second binomial. You can remember this method with the acronym FOIL, which stands for adding the products of the First terms, Outside terms, Inside terms, and Last terms.

$$(x + 1)(x + 2) = (x + 1)(x + 2)$$
$$= x^2 + 2x + x + 2$$
$$= x^2 + 3x + 2$$

The diagram models the product.

Example 2   Using FOIL and Verifying the Solution

Find the product $(3y - 2)(4y + 1)$. Verify the solution by substituting 1 for y.

Solution

Use FOIL.

$$(3y - 2)(4y + 1) = (3y - 2)(4y + 1)$$
$$= 12y^2 + 3y - 8y - 2$$
$$= 12y^2 - 5y - 2$$

Verify by substituting 1 for y in the original product and in the simplified expression.

$$(3y - 2)(4y + 1) = (3 - 2)(4 + 1) \qquad 12y^2 - 5y - 2 = 12 - 5 - 2$$
$$= (1)(5) \qquad\qquad\qquad\qquad = 5$$
$$= 5$$

Therefore, $(3y - 2)(4y + 1) = 12y^2 - 5y - 2$.

Example 3   Expanding and Simplifying

Expand and simplify $3(2x - 1)(x + 4)$.

Solution

First, find the product of the binomials. Then, multiply by 3.

$$3(2x - 1)(x + 4) = 3(2x - 1)(x + 4)$$
$$= 3(2x^2 + 8x - x - 4)$$
$$= 3(2x^2 + 7x - 4)$$
$$= 6x^2 + 21x - 12$$

Example 4   Expanding and Simplifying

Expand and simplify $2(3y + 2)(y - 1) - (y - 2)(2y + 1)$.

Solution

$$2(3y + 2)(y - 1) - (y - 2)(2y + 1) = 2(3y + 2)(y - 1) - (y - 2)(2y + 1)$$
$$= 2(3y^2 - 3y + 2y - 2) - (2y^2 + y - 4y - 2)$$
$$= 2(3y^2 - y - 2) - 1(2y^2 - 3y - 2)$$
$$= 6y^2 - 2y - 4 - 2y^2 + 3y + 2$$
$$= 4y^2 + y - 2$$

Key CONCEPTS

1 To find the product of two binomials, use either of the following.
a) the distributive property
b) FOIL, which stands for the sum of the products of the First terms, Outside terms, Inside terms, and Last terms
2 Verify the product of two binomials by substituting a convenient value for the variable in the original product and in the simplified expression.

Communicate Your Understanding

1. Describe how you would expand and simplify each of the following.
a) $(x - 3)(x + 5)$ **b)** $4(x - 5)(x - 1)$

2. Describe how you would check that
$(x - 3)(x + 4) = x^2 + x - 12$.

3. Explain how the diagram models the product
$(x + 4)(x + 5)$.

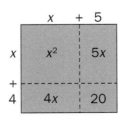

Practice

A

1. Find the product.
a) $(x + 1)(x + 5)$ **b)** $(x + 4)(x + 3)$ **c)** $(a + 4)(a + 4)$
d) $(y + 5)(y + 6)$ **e)** $(x - 4)(x - 3)$ **f)** $(a - 4)(a - 2)$
g) $(b - 1)(b - 5)$ **h)** $(y - 9)(y - 9)$ **i)** $(x - 6)(x + 3)$
j) $(c + 2)(c - 8)$ **k)** $(t + 10)(t - 10)$ **l)** $(q - 2)(q + 5)$

2. Expand. Verify the solution by substituting 1 for the variable.
a) $(c + 3)(c - 4)$ **b)** $(x + 2)(x - 5)$ **c)** $(y + 6)(y - 2)$
d) $(a + 9)(a - 5)$ **e)** $(x - 3)(x + 3)$ **f)** $(b - 7)(b + 10)$
g) $(y - 12)(y + 3)$ **h)** $(x - 7)(x + 1)$ **i)** $(4 + x)(7 - x)$
j) $(2 - y)(3 - y)$ **k)** $(x + 7)(x + 7)$ **l)** $(b - 8)(b + 8)$

3. Expand and simplify.
a) $(x + 5)(2x + 1)$ **b)** $(3y + 1)(y + 2)$ **c)** $(x - 1)(2x - 1)$
d) $(a - 3)(2a - 5)$ **e)** $(5y - 7)(y + 3)$ **f)** $(x - 5)(4x + 3)$
g) $(3x - 4)(3x - 4)$ **h)** $(1 - 6t)(4 + 5t)$ **i)** $(3a - 5)(3a + 5)$

4. Expand the following.
a) $2(x + 3)(x + 5)$ **b)** $4(x - 9)(x + 5)$
c) $-(a + 3)(a - 2)$ **d)** $10(x + 7)(x - 5)$
e) $3(2x - 1)(3x - 2)$ **f)** $-2(4y + 1)(y - 3)$
g) $0.5(x - 1)(x + 3)$ **h)** $1.8(x + 1)(x + 1)$

5. Expand and simplify.
a) $(x + 6)(x + 4) + (x + 2)(x + 3)$ **b)** $(y - 3)(y - 1) - (y + 2)(y - 6)$
c) $(2x - 3)(x + 5) + (3x + 4)(4x + 1)$ **d)** $2(m + 3)(m + 5) + 4(2m + 3)$
e) $3(x - 4)(x + 3) - 2(4x - 1)$ **f)** $5(3t - 4)(2t - 1) - (6t - 5)$
g) $2(3x + 2)(3x + 2) - 3(2x - 1)(2x - 1)$ **h)** $12 - 2(3y - 2)(3y + 2) - (2y + 5)(2y + 5)$

Applications and Problem Solving

6. a) Verify that $(x + 6)(x + 2) \neq x^2 + 12$ by substituting 1 for x.
b) Expand $(x + 6)(x + 2)$ correctly.

B

7. a) Communication Explain how the diagram
models the product $(2x + y)(3x + 2y)$.
b) State the product in simplified form.

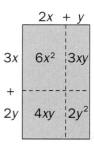

8. Expand and simplify.
a) $(3x + y)(x + 4y)$ **b)** $(4a - b)(2a - 5b)$ **c)** $(5m + 2n)(4m - 3n)$
d) $(4s - 3t)(5s - 6t)$ **e)** $(7a + 8b)(a - b)$ **f)** $(-3a + 4b)(2a + 3b)$

9. Construction A square building of side x metres is extended by 10 m on one side and 5 m on the other side to form a rectangle.
a) Express the new area as the product of 2 binomials.
b) Evaluate the new area for $x = 20$.

10. Diving Annie Pelletier won a bronze medal for Canada in women's springboard diving at the Summer Olympics in Atlanta. She dove from a springboard with dimensions that can be represented by the binomials $7x - 2$ and $x - 10$.
a) Multiply the binomials.
b) If x represents 70 cm, what was the area of the board, in square centimetres? in square metres?

11. Measurement Write and simplify an expression to represent the area of each figure.

a)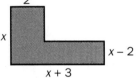

b)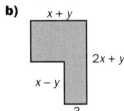

12. Measurement Write and simplify an expression to represent the area of the shaded region.

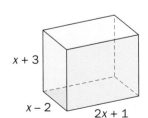

$5x - 1$

$3x + 4$ $x + 1$
             $x - 1$

C

13. Pattern The diagrams show the first three rectangles in a pattern.
a) State the area of the 4th rectangle.
b) Write a product of two binomials to represent the area of the nth rectangle in terms of n.
c) Multiply the binomials from part b).
d) State the area of the 28th rectangle, in square centimetres.

3 cm ▢ 4 cm   4 cm ▢ 5 cm   5 cm ▢ 6 cm
$n = 1$ $n = 2$ $n = 3$

14. Measurement The dimensions of a rectangular prism are represented by binomials, as shown.
a) Write, expand, and simplify an expression that represents the surface area of this prism.
b) If x represents 5 cm, what is the surface area, in square centimetres?

$x + 3$

$x - 2$ $2x + 1$

15. Communication Is the product of two binomials always a trinomial? Explain using examples.

16. Communication a) Describe the pattern in words.
b) Copy and evaluate the numerical expressions.
c) Generalize the pattern by letting the first number in the second bracket be x. Write expressions for the other numbers in terms of x. Then, write an algebraic expression that matches the pattern in the numerical expressions. Expand and simplify the algebraic expression.
d) How does the simplified expression explain the answer to part b)?

$$(2 \times 3) - (1 \times 4)$$
$$(3 \times 4) - (2 \times 5)$$
$$(4 \times 5) - (3 \times 6)$$
$$(5 \times 6) - (4 \times 7)$$

Modelling Math | **Representing Patterns Algebraically**

a) Communication Describe the pattern in words.
b) Copy and evaluate the numerical expressions.
c) How is each answer related to the middle number of the three that are multiplied together?
d) Generalize the pattern by letting the middle number in the three that are multiplied together be x. Write expressions for the other numbers in terms of x. Then, write an algebraic expression that matches the pattern in the numerical expressions. Expand and simplify the algebraic expression.
e) Communication How does the simplified expression explain the answer to part c)?

$$1 \times 2 \times 3 + 2$$
$$2 \times 3 \times 4 + 3$$
$$3 \times 4 \times 5 + 4$$
$$4 \times 5 \times 6 + 5$$

NUMBER POWER

Copy the diagram. Place the digits from 1 to 9 in the boxes to make the statements true. Use the order of operations.

$$\square \div \square + \square = 5$$

$$\square \times \square - \square = 5$$

$$\square + \square - \square = 5$$

The Haida have lived on the coast of the Queen Charlotte Islands for at least 6000 years. Haida houses, known as plank houses, were built using large posts, beams, and planks cut from local cedars. The largest of the Haida houses was built around 1850 at Masset. The base of the house at Masset was a square.

Investigation   Look for Patterns

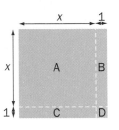

The side lengths and areas of squares can be modelled using diagrams. In the diagram shown, the side length of the large square is $x + 1$, so the area is $(x + 1)^2$. Expanding $(x + 1)^2$, or adding the areas of A, B, C, and D in the diagram, results in the simplified trinomial that models the area of the large square, $x^2 + 2x + 1$.

1. Copy and complete the table by expanding and simplifying.

Binomial Squared	Simplified Trinomial
$(x + 3)^2$	
$(x - 4)^2$	$(x-4)(x-4)\ \ x^2 -4x -4x +16$
$(2x + 3)^2$	
$(3x - 2)^2$	
$(5x + 3y)^2$	
$(2x - 5y)^2$	
$(a + b)^2$	
$(a - b)^2$	

2. Communication a) Compare the first term in each trinomial to the first term in each binomial. What is the pattern?
b) Compare the last term in each trinomial to the second term in each binomial. What is the pattern?
c) Compare the middle term in each trinomial to the two terms in each binomial. What is the pattern?

3. Communication Write a rule for squaring a binomial.

1. Copy and complete the table.

Multiplication	Simplified Product
$(x + 4)(x - 4)$	
$(y - 5)(y + 5)$	
$(2x - 1)(2x + 1)$	
$(3x + 2y)(3x - 2y)$	
$(a + b)(a - b)$	

2. Communication How are the two binomials in each multiplication
a) alike?   **b)** different?

3. Communication a) How do the terms in the product compare with
the two binomials in each multiplication?
b) Explain why there are only two terms in the product.

4. Communication Write a rule for finding this type of product of
two binomials.

Example 1   Squaring Binomials
Expand.
a) $(3x + 1)^2$ **b)** $(3x - y)^2$

Solution
Use the patterns for squaring binomials.

a) $(a + b)^2 = a^2 + 2ab + b^2$
$(3x + 1)^2 = (3x)^2 + 2(3x)(1) + (1)^2$
$= 9x^2 + 6x + 1$

b) $(a - b)^2 = a^2 - 2ab + b^2$
$(3x - y)^2 = (3x)^2 - 2(3x)(y) + (y)^2$
$= 9x^2 - 6xy + y^2$

A product of the type $(a + b)(a - b)$ is known as the product of the sum
and difference of two terms.
$$(a + b)(a - b) = a^2 - b^2$$

Example 2   Product of the Sum and Difference
Expand.
a) $(2x + 5)(2x - 5)$ **b)** $(4x + 3y)(4x - 3y)$

Solution
Use the pattern for the product of the sum and difference.

a) $(a + b)(a - b) = a^2 - b^2$
$(2x + 5)(2x - 5) = (2x)^2 - (5)^2$
$= 4x^2 - 25$

b) $(a + b)(a - b) = a^2 - b^2$
$(4x + 3y)(4x - 3y) = (4x)^2 - (3y)^2$
$= 16x^2 - 9y^2$

Example 3   Simplifying Expressions

Expand and simplify $2(3x + 4)^2 - (4x + 5)(4x - 5)$.

Solution

$$\begin{aligned} 2(3x + 4)^2 - (4x + 5)(4x - 5) &= 2(9x^2 + 24x + 16) - (16x^2 - 25) \\ &= 18x^2 + 48x + 32 - 16x^2 + 25 \\ &= 2x^2 + 48x + 57 \end{aligned}$$

Key CONCEPTS

1 To square a binomial, use one of the following patterns.

$(a + b)^2 = a^2 + 2ab + b^2$

$(a - b)^2 = a^2 - 2ab + b^2$

2 To find the product of the sum and difference of two terms, use the following pattern.

$(a + b)(a - b) = a^2 - b^2$

Communicate Your Understanding

1. Describe how you would expand and simplify each of the following.

a) $(2x + 1)^2$ **b)** $(3x - 4)^2$ **c)** $(4x - 5)(4x + 5)$

2. Using examples, explain why the product of the sum and difference of two terms has only two terms in the expansion.

Practice

A

1. What is the first term in each product?

a) $(x + 7)^2$ **b)** $(a - 9)^2$ **c)** $(2x - 1)^2$ **d)** $(9t + 5)^2$

e) $(3y + 6)^2$ **f)** $(7p - 2)^2$ **g)** $(4j + 1)^2$ **h)** $(6q - 8)^2$

2. What is the middle term, including its sign, in each product?

a) $(x - 3)^2$ **b)** $(y + 8)^2$ **c)** $(x + y)^2$ **d)** $(a - b)^2$

e) $(2x + 3)^2$ **f)** $(4a - 5)^2$ **g)** $(3x + 2y)^2$ **h)** $(6p - 7)^2$

3. Write the missing factor.

a) $(a - 7)(\blacksquare) = a^2 - 49$ **b)** $(x + 2)(\blacksquare) = x^2 - 4$

c) $(\blacksquare)(3m - 7) = 9m^2 - 49$ **d)** $(9x + 8)(\blacksquare) = 81x^2 - 64$

e) $(x - y)(\blacksquare) = x^2 - y^2$ **f)** $(\blacksquare)(2x + 3b) = (4a^2 - 9b^2)$

4. Expand.

a) $(x + 5)^2$ **b)** $(y + 1)^2$

c) $(x - 6)^2$ **d)** $(m - 3)^2$

e) $(x + 3)(x - 3)$ **f)** $(y + 6)(y - 6)$

g) $(m - 7)(m + 7)$ **h)** $(t - 8)(t + 8)$

5. Expand.

a) $(3x + 2)^2$ **b)** $(5x - 1)^2$ **c)** $(2x + 3)(2x - 3)$ **d)** $(2m + 7)^2$

e) $(3y - 2)(3y + 2)$ **f)** $(4y - 3)^2$ **g)** $(1 + 5m)(1 - 5m)$ **h)** $(2 - 3t)^2$

6. Expand.

a) $(2x + 3y)(2x - 3y)$ **b)** $(2x + 3y)^2$

c) $(3a - b)(3a + b)$ **d)** $(4t - 5s)^2$

e) $(4m - 5n)(4m + 5n)$ **f)** $(3c + 7d)^2$

g) $(y + 6x)(y - 6x)$ **h)** $(a - 8b)^2$

7. Expand and simplify.

a) $(x + 4)^2 + (x - 2)^2$ **b)** $(y + 6)(y - 6) + (y + 7)^2$

c) $(m - 8)^2 - (m - 1)(m + 1)$ **d)** $2(a + 3)(a - 3) + 3(a + 2)^2$

e) $4(2x + 1)^2 - 2(3x - 7)^2$ **f)** $5(3t - 1)^2 - 4(4t - 5)(4t + 5)$

8. Expand and simplify.

a) $(x - 7)(x + 5) - 2(x + 6)^2$ **b)** $(2x - 3)^2 - (3x - 1)(4x + 5)$

c) $3(3m + 1)(m - 4) - 4(2m + 3)(2m - 3)$ **d)** $3t^2 - (3 - 2t)^2 + 5(2t - 1)(2t + 1)$

e) $12 - 2(3y + 1)^2 - (y - 9)(3y + 2)$ **f)** $2(1 - 3t)^2 - 4(1 - 3t)(1 + 3t)$

g) $4(5s + t)(5s - t) - 6(3t^2 - t)$ **h)** $2(3m - n)^2 - 3(2m - 5)(m + 3)$

i) $(x + 2y)(x - 2y) + (2x + y)^2$ **j)** $3(a - 2b)^2 - 4(2a + b)^2$

Applications and Problem Solving

9. a) Verify that $(x + 3)^2 \neq x^2 + 9$ by substituting 1 for x.

b) Expand $(x + 3)^2$ correctly.

10. Flag areas The International Red Cross, which is staffed mainly by volunteers, has twice won the Nobel Peace Prize for its medical and welfare work around the world. The flag of the International Red Cross is a square. For two International Red Cross flags of different sizes, the difference between the side lengths is 10 cm.

a) Let the shorter side length be x. Write an expression for the longer side length.

b) Write an expression that represents the area of each flag. Expand and simplify, if possible.

c) If x represents 25 cm, what is the area of each flag, in square centimetres?

B

11. Rewrite each multiplication as a product of the sum and difference of two numbers, as shown. Copy and complete the table.

Numbers	$(a + b)(a - b)$	Product
33×27	$(30 + 3)(30 - 3)$	891
24×16		
47×53		
62×58		

12. Multiply each of the following, using the method in question 11.

a) $(10 + 2)(10 - 2)$ **b)** $(15 + 3)(15 - 3)$ **c)** $(20 - 2)(20 + 2)$

d) 14×6 **e)** 17×23 **f)** 32×28

13. Use $x = y - 2$ to write each of the following in terms of y. Then, expand and simplify.

a) $x^2 - 2x + 3$ **b)** $3x^2 + 5x - 9$

14. Measurement Write, expand, and simplify an expression that represents the surface area of the rectangular prism.

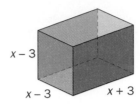

$x - 3$

$x - 3$ $x + 3$

15. Measurement The length of an edge of a cube is represented by the expression $2x - y$. Write, expand, and simplify an expression that represents the surface area of the cube.

16. Rewrite in the form $(a + b)^2$ or $(a - b)^2$.

a) $x^2 + 14x + 49$ **b)** $x^2 - 16x + 64$ **c)** $4a^2 + 12a + 9$

d) $9b^2 - 24b + 16$ **e)** $64m^2 - 32m + 4$ **f)** $81n^2 + 90n + 25$

17. Change one term in each trinomial, so that it can be written as the square of a binomial.

a) $x^2 + 12x + 18$ **b)** $a^2 + 7a + 16$ **c)** $y^2 - 9y + 9$

d) $m^2 - 4m + 16$ **e)** $4x^2 - 4x + 2$ **f)** $9y^2 + 10y + 4$

18. Expand and simplify.

a) $(x^2 + 1)^2$ **b)** $(y^2 - 1)^2$ **c)** $(x^2 + y^2)^2$ **d)** $(x^2 - y^2)^2$

e) $(2x^2 + 3)^2$ **f)** $(3y^2 - 4)^2$ **g)** $(x^2 - 2y^2)^2$ **h)** $(4x^2 + 3y^2)^2$

19. Expand and simplify.

a) $(x^2 + 1)(x^2 - 1)$ **b)** $(y^2 - 2)(y^2 + 2)$ **c)** $(x^2 + y^2)(x^2 - y^2)$

d) $(8a^2 + 3)(8a^2 - 3)$ **e)** $(3x^2 + 2y^2)(3x^2 - 2y^2)$ **f)** $(4 - 3c^2)(4 + 3c^2)$

20. Measurement The side length of a square is represented by x centimetres. The length of a rectangle is 3 cm greater than the side length of the square. The width of the rectangle is 3 cm less than the side length of the square. Which figure has the greater area and by how much?

21. Communication If a square garden is made into a rectangle by shortening two opposite sides by 5 m each and lengthening the other two sides by 5 m each, how do the areas of the original garden and the new garden compare? Explain.

C

22. Measurement The side length of the square is $a + b + c$.
a) Write, expand, and simplify an expression that represents the area of the square.
b) Use your result from part a) to expand $(2x + 3y + 1)^2$.

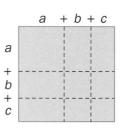

23. Which of the following numbers of terms are not possible as the product of two binomials?

> 1 term
> 2 terms
> 3 terms
> 4 terms
> 5 terms

Give reasons for your answers, and provide examples where necessary.

24. Measurement If a right triangle has one side of length 8 units, possible whole-number lengths of the other side and the hypotenuse can be found as follows. List pairs of whole numbers whose product is 8^2 or 64.

$$64 = 64 \times 1 \qquad\qquad 64 = 16 \times 4$$
$$64 = 32 \times 2 \qquad\qquad 64 = 8 \times 8$$

Then, find whether each pair of whole numbers represents the product of the sum and difference of two whole numbers.

$$64 = 32 \times 2 \qquad\qquad 64 = 16 \times 4$$
$$= (17 + 15)(17 - 15) \qquad = (10 + 6)(10 - 6)$$
$$= 17^2 - 15^2 \qquad\qquad = 10^2 - 6^2$$

For the products 64×1 and 8×8, there are no pairs of whole numbers with either a sum of 64 and a difference of 1, or a sum of 8 and a difference of 8. Thus, if a right triangle has one side of length 8 units, the other side and the hypotenuse could measure 6 units and 10 units, or 15 units and 17 units.
a) Find the possible whole-number lengths of the second side and the hypotenuse for each of the following right triangles.

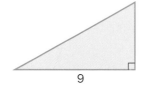
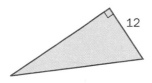

b) Communication Explain why the method works.

Technology Extension: Multiplying Binomials With a Graphing Calculator

Complete each of the following using the expand function of a graphing calculator that has the capability to expand and simplify the products of binomials.

1 Multiplying Binomials

1. Expand.

a) $(4x + 3)(2x + 9)$

b) $(2x - 5)(3x + 5)$

c) $(2y - 3)(10y - 11)$

d) $(4x + 3y)(8x - 7y)$

e) $(5x - 2y)(3y + 4x)$

f) $(x + 2)(x - 1) - (x - 6)(x - 2)$

g) $(2x - 3)(2x + 1) + (3x - 2)(x + 5)$

h) $2(y - 2)(3y - 1) - 3(2y - 3)(2y + 5)$

i) $5(2x + y)(x - y) + (3x + 2y)(4x + 3y)$

2 Special Products

1. Expand.

a) $(x + 15)^2$

b) $(t - 5)^2$

c) $(9 - y)^2$

d) $(4m^2 + 7)^2$

e) $(6 - 5r)^2$

f) $(8x + 3y)^2$

2. Expand.

a) $(2x + 11)(2x - 11)$

b) $(4 + 5x)(4 - 5x)$

c) $(3y + 5x)(3y - 5x)$

3. Expand and simplify.

a) $(x + 1)^2 - (x - 1)^2$

b) $(x + 3)(x - 3) - (x + 2)^2$

c) $3(4y + 3)^2 - (2y + 1)^2$

d) $2(3 + 2m)^2 - 3(4m - 1)^2$

3.4 Common Factors

The terms in the expression $2x + 2y$ have the common factor 2, because $2x = 2 \times x$ and $2y = 2 \times y$. Removing the common factor from the expression $2x + 2y$ gives the expression $2(x + y)$, which is written in factored form.

The minimum stopping distance of a car, in metres, on dry, level concrete, is modelled by the polynomial $0.2s + 0.007s^2$, where s is the car's speed in kilometres per hour. The terms in the polynomial $0.2s + 0.007s^2$ have the common factor s.

Investigation Use a Model

To factor $2x^2 + 4x$, use diagrams of the two rectangles whose areas model the expression $2x^2 + 4x$. Use each diagram to write the area as a product of the length and width.

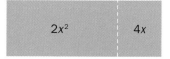 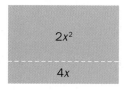

To give the areas shown, the dimensions must be as follows.

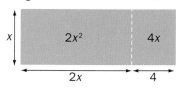 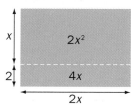

$2x^2 + 4x = x(2x + 4)$
So, x is a common factor of $2x^2 + 4x$.

$2x^2 + 4x = 2x(x + 2)$
So, $2x$ is a common factor of $2x^2 + 4x$.

The greatest common factor of $2x^2 + 4x$ is $2x$, so $2x^2 + 4x = 2x(x + 2)$.

Copy the following diagrams, which model the areas of rectangles A, B, C, and D. Find the dimensions of these rectangles, and then copy and complete the table shown on the next page. The first row has been completed for you.

A

B

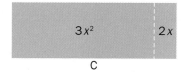

C

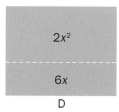

D

Rectangle	Area	Width	Length	Width x Length
A	$x^2 + x$	x	$x + 1$	$x(x + 1)$
B				
C				
D				

1. Communication For each rectangle in the preceding table, removing a common factor from the expression in the "Area" column gives the expression in the "Width × Length" column. Write a rule for removing a common factor from an expression.

2. Use your rule to factor each of the following polynomials.
a) $5x^2 + 20x$ **b)** $6x^2 - 3x$ **c)** $12ab + 8ac - 4ad$

3. a) Factor the expression $0.2s + 0.007s^2$ for finding the minimum stopping distance of a car on dry, level concrete.
b) Calculate the minimum stopping distance, in metres, for a speed of 50 km/h; of 90 km/h.

A polynomial is factored when it is written as the product of polynomials. We will consider that a polynomial is completely factored when no more variable factors can be removed and no more integer factors, other than 1 or −1, can be removed.

In factoring polynomials with integer coefficients, we will find factors with integer coefficients. This process is called **factoring over the integers**. Factoring $2x + 4$ over the integers gives $2(x + 2)$ as the factored form, not $4\left(\dfrac{x}{2} + 1\right)$.

The polynomial $2x + 5$ cannot be factored over the integers.

Example 1   Monomial Common Factor
Factor $8x^3 - 6x^2y^2 + 4x^2y$.

Solution
The greatest common factor of the coefficients, 8, 6, and 4, is 2.
The greatest common factor of the variable parts, x^3, x^2y^2, and x^2y, is x^2.
Therefore, the greatest common factor of the polynomial is $2x^2$.
$$8x^3 - 6x^2y^2 + 4x^2y = 2x^2(4x) - 2x^2(3y^2) + 2x^2(2y)$$
$$= 2x^2(4x - 3y^2 + 2y)$$

Example 2   Binomial Common Factor

Factor $4x(w + 1) + 5y(w + 1)$.

Solution

Think of $(w + 1)$ as one factor.

$4x(w + 1) + 5y(w + 1) = (w + 1)(4x) + (w + 1)(5y)$
$= (w + 1)(4x + 5y)$

Think $4xz + 5yz$, which factors as $z(4x + 5y)$.

Some polynomials do not have a common factor in all of their terms. These polynomials can sometimes be factored by grouping terms that do have a common factor.

Example 3   Factoring by Grouping

Factor $ac + bc + ad + bd$.

Solution

Group terms that have a common factor.

$ac + bc + ad + bd = (ac + bc) + (ad + bd)$ or $ac + bc + ad + bd = (ac + ad) + (bc + bd)$
$= c(a + b) + d(a + b)$ $= a(c + d) + b(c + d)$
$= (c + d)(a + b)$ $= (a + b)(c + d)$

Key CONCEPTS

1 To factor a polynomial with a common monomial factor, remove the greatest common factor of the coefficients and the greatest common factor of the variable parts.

2 To factor a polynomial with a common binomial factor, think of the binomial as one factor.

3 To factor a polynomial by grouping, group pairs of terms with a common factor.

Communicate Your Understanding

1. Describe how you would factor each of the following.

a) $4x^3 + 2x^2 - 8x$ **b)** $2x(a - b) - 3(a - b)$

2. Describe how you would factor $2x + 2y + x^2 + xy$ by grouping.

3. Using examples, explain how you would determine the common factor of a polynomial.

Practice

A

1. Factor, if possible.

a) $5x + 25$ **b)** $4x + 13$ **c)** $9y - 9$

d) $3x - 15y$ **e)** $25x^2 + 10x$ **f)** $4ax + 8ay - 6az$

g) $5pqr - pqs - 10pqt$ **h)** $2x^2 - 2x - 6$ **i)** $3y^2 - 9y - 20$

2. Factor, if possible.

a) $9a^3 + 27b^2$ **b)** $3x^5 - 6x^3 + 9x$

c) $12y - 8y^2 + 24y^3$ **d)** $24w^5 + 6w^3$

e) $6rst + 3rs - 7t$ **f)** $33ab + 22bc - 11b^2$

g) $24xy^2 + 16x^2y$ **h)** $35xy - 10y^2$

i) $5rst - 15ab + 7cd$ **j)** $24xy^2 - 12xy + 36x^2y$

k) $27a^2b^3 + 9a^2b^2 - 18a^3b^2$ **l)** $6m^3n^2 + 18m^2n^3 - 12mn^2$

3. Factor, if possible.

a) $5x(a + b) + 3(a + b)$ **b)** $3m(x - 1) + 5(x - 1)$

c) $7x(m + 4) - 3(m - 4)$ **d)** $4y(p + q) - x(p + q)$

e) $4t(m + 7) + (m + 7)$ **f)** $3t(x - y) - (x + y)$

4. Factor by grouping.

a) $wx + wy + xz + yz$ **b)** $xy + 12 + 4x + 3y$

c) $x^2 + x - xy - y$ **d)** $m^2 - 4n + 4m - mn$

e) $2x^2 + 6y + 4x + 3xy$ **f)** $5m^2t - 10m^2 + t^2 - 2t$

Applications and Problem Solving

5. Vertical motion If an object is thrown vertically upward at a speed of v metres per second, the approximate height of the object, in metres, after t seconds is given by the expression $vt - 5t^2$.

a) A ball is thrown vertically upward at a speed of 20 m/s. Write the expression that gives the height of the ball, in metres, after t seconds.

b) Make a table to find the height of the ball after 0 s, 1 s, 2 s, 3 s, 4 s, and 5 s.

c) What is the maximum height of the ball?

d) Communication Why does the height of the ball after 5 s have no meaning?

e) At what times is the height 0 m?

f) Factor the expression you wrote in part a).

g) Communication How does the factored expression let you determine the times when the height of the ball is 0 m?

6. Measurement Write an expression for the area of each shaded region as a polynomial and then in factored form

a)

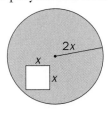

b)

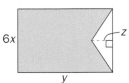

c)

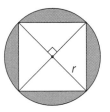

d)

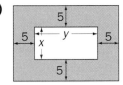

e)

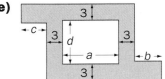

f)

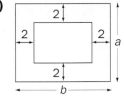

7. Communication If it is possible to remove a common factor from the expression $2x^2 + ky + 4$, where k is an integer, what can you state about the possible values of k? Explain.

C

8. a) Write a polynomial in which there are three terms, each numerical coefficient is 1, and the greatest common factor is st^2.
b) Write your polynomial in factored form.

9. a) Write a polynomial that has four terms with different numerical coefficients and a greatest common factor of $3xy$.
b) Write your polynomial in factored form.

10. Communication Write a problem similar to questions 8 and 9. Have a classmate solve your problem.

Modelling Math | Representing Patterns Algebraically

Each figure is made from squares with a side length of 1 unit.

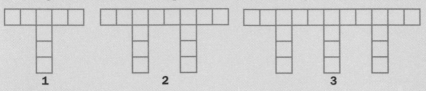

1   2   3

a) Copy and complete the table for the pattern.

Figure	1	2	3	4	5
Number of Squares					
Perimeter					

b) Write an expression to model the number of squares in each figure in terms of the figure number, n.

c) Factor the expression you found in part b).

d) Use the factored expression from part c) to find the number of squares in the 75th figure; the 103rd figure.

e) What figure has 170 squares?

f) Write an expression to model the perimeter of each figure in terms of the figure number, n.

g) Factor the expression you found in part f).

h) Use the factored expression from part g) to find the perimeter of the 68th figure; the 104th figure.

i) What figure has a perimeter of 270 units?

j) Write an expression to model the perimeter of each figure in terms of the number of squares, s.

k) Factor the expression you found in part j).

l) Use the factored expression from part k) to find the perimeter of a figure with 92 squares; 314 squares.

m) How many squares are in the figure with a perimeter of 306 units? 858 units?

LOGIC POWER

Communication Describe a way to time the boiling of an egg for 15 min using a 7-min hourglass timer and an 11-min hourglass timer.

The JumboTron in the Skydome is one of the largest video display boards in the world. The area of this rectangular board can be represented by the trinomial $x^2 + 26x + 25$. To find the length and the width of the rectangle, the trinomial can be written as the product of two binomials. This process is known as factoring the trinomial.

Investigation **Use a Model**

Rectangles can be used as a model for factoring trinomials. If a rectangle can be drawn so that its area represents a trinomial, then the length and width of the rectangle represent the factors of the trinomial.

1. The large rectangle models the trinomial $x^2 + 4x + 3$.
a) What is the length of the large rectangle?
b) What is the width of the large rectangle?

2. Copy and complete the statement $x^2 + 4x + 3 = ($▬$)($▬$)$.

3. Use the diagrams to find the factors of each of the following trinomials. Write each answer in the form $x^2 + $■$x + $■$ = (x + $■$)(x + $■$)$.
a) $x^2 + 3x + 2$ **b)** $x^2 + 5x + 6$ **c)** $x^2 + 6x + 8$

   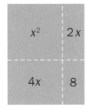

4. Communication From each of your answers to question 3, how are the following related?
a) the first term in the trinomial and the first terms in the binomials
b) the coefficient of the middle term in the trinomial and the second terms in the binomials
c) the last term in the trinomial and the second terms in the binomials

5. a) Factor the expression $x^2 + 26x + 25$ to find binomials that represent the length and width of the JumboTron.
b) If x represents 9 m, what are the length and the width of the JumboTron, in metres?

Another way to factor trinomials of the form $x^2 + bx + c$ is to study a general expansion.

$$\begin{aligned}(x + m)(x + n) &= x^2 + nx + mx + mn \\ &= x^2 + mx + nx + mn \\ &= x^2 + (m + n)x + mn\end{aligned}$$

Compare the above result to the general trinomial $x^2 + bx + c$.

$$\begin{array}{ccccc} x^2 & + & bx & + & c \\ \updownarrow & & \updownarrow & & \updownarrow \\ x^2 & + & (m + n)x & + & mn \end{array}$$

This comparison shows that $b = m + n$ and $c = mn$.

So, you can factor a trinomial of the form $x^2 + bx + c$ by finding two terms whose sum is b and whose product is c.

Example 1 Factoring Trinomials

Factor $x^2 - 8x + 12$. Check by substitution.

Solution

For $x^2 - 8x + 12$, $b = -8$ and $c = 12$. Use a table to find two integers whose product is 12 and whose sum is -8. The only two integers with a product of 12 and a sum of -8 are -6 and -2.

	Product of 12		Sum
	12	1	13
	−12	−1	−13
	6	2	8
*	−6	−2	−8
	4	3	7
	−4	−3	−7

So, $x^2 - 8x + 12 = (x - 6)(x - 2)$.

Check.

Let $x = 1$.

$$\begin{aligned}\textbf{L.S.} &= x^2 - 8x + 12 \\ &= (1)^2 - 8(1) + 12 \\ &= 1 - 8 + 12 \\ &= 5\end{aligned} \qquad \begin{aligned}\textbf{R.S.} &= (x - 6)(x - 2) \\ &= (1 - 6)(1 - 2) \\ &= (-5)(-1) \\ &= 5\end{aligned}$$

L.S. = R.S.

From Example 1, note that factoring is the inverse operation of expanding.

Factoring →

$x^2 - 8x + 12 = (x - 6)(x - 2)$

← Expanding

Example 2   Removing a Common Factor

Factor $3x^2 + 3x - 18$ completely.

Solution

First, remove the common factor.
$3x^2 + 3x - 18 = 3(x^2 + x - 6)$
For $x^2 + x - 6$, $b = 1$ and $c = -6$.
The two integers whose product is -6 and whose
sum is 1 are 3 and -2.
So, $x^2 + x - 6 = (x + 3)(x - 2)$
and $3x^2 + 3x - 18 = 3(x + 3)(x - 2)$.

Product of –6		Sum
6	–1	5
–6	1	–5
★ 3	–2	1
–3	2	–1

It may be quicker
and easier to use
mental math than
to make a table.

Example 3   Trinomials With Two Variables

Factor $x^2 - 2xy - 15y^2$.

Solution

To factor $x^2 - 2xy - 15y^2$, find two integers with a
product of -15 and a sum of -2.
The two integers are -5 and 3.
So, $x^2 - 2xy - 15y^2 = (x - 5y)(x + 3y)$.

Product of –15		Sum
15	–1	14
–15	1	–14
5	–3	2
★ –5	3	–2

Many trinomials, such as $x^2 + 3x + 5$, cannot be
factored over the integers. No two integers have a
product of 5 and a sum of 3.

Key CONCEPTS

1 To factor a trinomial in the form $x^2 + bx + c$,
a) write x as the first term in each binomial factor
b) write the second terms, which are two numbers whose sum is b and
whose product is c
2 When factoring a trinomial, first remove any common factors.

Communicate Your Understanding

1. Describe how you would factor each of the following.
a) $x^2 + 8x + 15$ **b)** $4x^2 - 24x + 32$

2. Explain why substituting 1 for the variable in a trinomial and in its
factored form is a way to check if the factors are correct.

Practice

1. If possible, find two integers with the given product and sum.

	Product	Sum		Product	Sum
a)	15	8	**b)**	18	11
c)	–30	7	**d)**	–20	–8
e)	10	7	**f)**	10	–7
g)	36	–13	**h)**	36	–15

2. Factor, if possible. Check by substituting $x = 1$ into the expanded form and the factored form.

a) $x^2 + 5x + 4$ **b)** $x^2 + 8x + 15$ **c)** $t^2 + 9t + 12$

d) $r^2 - 13r + 42$ **e)** $n^2 + 11n + 30$ **f)** $r^2 - 7r + 10$

g) $w^2 - 10w + 16$ **h)** $x^2 - 9x + 24$ **i)** $m^2 - 10m + 24$

3. Factor, if possible.

a) $y^2 - y - 20$ **b)** $x^2 + 7x - 18$ **c)** $t^2 + t - 18$

d) $n^2 - 10n - 24$ **e)** $r^2 + 7r - 20$ **f)** $x^2 - 8x - 20$

4. Factor, if possible.

a) $m^2 + 18m + 80$ **b)** $m^2 + m - 12$ **c)** $x^2 + 2x + 5$

d) $r^2 - 17r + 42$ **e)** $y^2 - 17y + 72$ **f)** $x^2 - 6x - 16$

g) $y^2 - 2y - 4$ **h)** $m^2 + 7m - 6$ **i)** $x^2 - 10x + 21$

j) $w^2 + 12w + 20$ **k)** $r^2 - r - 30$ **l)** $y^2 - 20y + 36$

m) $n^2 - 4n + 5$ **n)** $8 + 7y - y^2$ **o)** $16 - 6x - x^2$

5. Factor, if possible.

a) $x^2 + 12xy + 35y^2$ **b)** $a^2 - 4ab - 77b^2$ **c)** $c^2 - cd - 2d^2$

d) $x^2 + 5xy - 36y^2$ **e)** $x^2 - 4xy + 6y^2$ **f)** $p^2 + 14pq - 32q^2$

6. Factor completely.

a) $3x^2 + 12x + 9$ **b)** $5y^2 + 40y + 60$ **c)** $4t^2 - 8t - 60$

d) $6x^2 + 18x - 24$ **e)** $ax^2 + 10ax - 24a$ **f)** $x^3 + 18x^2 + 72x$

g) $2x^2 - 22x + 56$ **h)** $5w^2 + 20w - 60$ **i)** $3x - 2x^2 - x^3$

Applications and Problem Solving

7. Signboard On the outside of the Skydome, there is a large, rectangular, electronic signboard. The approximate area of the signboard can be represented by the trinomial $x^2 - 3x - 4$.
a) Factor $x^2 - 3x - 4$ to find binomials that represent the length and width of the signboard.
b) If x represents 17 m, find the length and width of the signboard, in metres.

B

8. The area of a rectangle is represented by the expression $x^2 + 9x + 20$.
a) Factor the expression.
b) A smaller rectangle is 1 unit shorter on each side than the first rectangle. Write a factored expression for the area of the smaller rectangle.
c) Expand the expression for the area of the smaller rectangle.
d) What is the difference in the areas of the rectangles?

9. a) Movies Each letter shown in the table represents a different integer. The letter Y represents 5.

Letter	A	C	E	K	M	N	O	P	S	T	Y
Integer											5

Factor the following five trinomials. In each case, write the factored form with the larger binomial first. For example, the factored form of $x^2 + 2x - 8$ would be written as $(x + 4)(x - 2)$, because $x + 4 > x - 2$. Use the factored forms to find the integer represented by each capital letter. Then, copy and complete the table.

$x^2 + 20x - 96 = (x + M)(x + A)$
$x^2 - 27x + 72 = (x + N)(x + C)$
$x^2 - 16x - 80 = (x + E)(x + T)$
$x^2 - 25x - 84 = (x + S)(x + K)$
$x^2 + 9x - 90 = (x + P)(x + O)$

b) Replace each of the following integers with its corresponding letter from part a) to name a Canadian movie producer who was a silent-comedy pioneer, and find the films for which he was famous.

Name: 24   −4 −24 −28
          3   4   −3   −3   4 −20 −20
Films: −28   4   5   3 −20   −6   −3   4
          −28 −6   15   3

10. Communication a) Complete the factoring by supplying the missing terms.

$x^2 + 6x + \blacksquare = (x + \blacksquare)(x + \blacksquare)$

$x^2 - 5x + \blacksquare = (x - \blacksquare)(x - \blacksquare)$

$x^2 + \blacksquare x + 12 = (x + \blacksquare)(x + \blacksquare)$

$x^2 - \blacksquare x + 5 = (x - \blacksquare)(x - \blacksquare)$

$x^2 - \blacksquare x - 12 = (x - \blacksquare)(x + \blacksquare)$

b) Compare your answers with a classmate's. Which cases have more than one solution? Explain.

C

11. Communication Find three values of k such that each trinomial can be factored over the integers. Explain and justify your reasoning.

a) $x^2 + 2x + k$ **b)** $x^2 - 7x + k$

12. Factor.

a) $x^4 + 2x^2 + 1$ **b)** $x^4 + x^2 - 6$

c) $x^4 - 3x^2 - 10$ **d)** $x^4 + 10x^2y + 9y^2$

13. Factor.

a) $(x + a)^2 + 3(x + a) + 2$ **b)** $(x - b)^2 + 4(x - b) - 5$

14. Communication a) Copy and complete each statement.

$x^2 - 2x - 35 = (\rule{2cm}{0.4pt})(\rule{2cm}{0.4pt})$

$t^2 + 3t - 40 = (\rule{2cm}{0.4pt})(\rule{2cm}{0.4pt})$

b) How do the factors help you determine the values of the variable that give the trinomial a value of zero?

15. Make up five trinomials in the form $x^2 + bx + c$. Make three factorable and two impossible to factor. Exchange trinomials with a classmate. Try to factor each other's trinomials.

NUMBER POWER

In the diagram, each letter represents a number. The numbers outside the square show the sums of each row, three of the columns, and one diagonal. What is the sum of the second column?

A	B	B	C	20
B	A	C	C	21
B	C	C	A	21
D	D	A	D	25
21	■	21	23	25

3.6 Factoring $ax^2 + bx + c$, $a \neq 1$

Canadian swimmer Marianne Limpert won a silver medal in the 200-m individual medley at the Summer Olympics in Atlanta. She swam in a pool whose area can be represented by the trinomial $3x^2 + 17x + 10$.

In some trinomials, such as $3x^2 + 17x + 10$, the numerical coefficient of the x^2 term is not 1. Rectangles can be used as models to factor trinomials of this type.

Investigation Use a Model

1. The large rectangle models the trinomial $2x^2 + 5x + 2$.

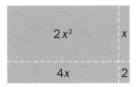

a) What is the length of the rectangle?
b) What is the width of the rectangle?

2. Copy and complete the statement $2x^2 + 5x + 2 = ($ ▬▬▬ $)($ ▬▬▬ $)$.

3. Use the diagrams to find the factors of each of the following trinomials.
a) $2x^2 + 3x + 1$ **b)** $2x^2 + 5x + 3$ **c)** $3x^2 + 7x + 2$

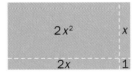
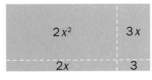
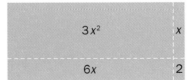

4. a) Factor the expression $3x^2 + 17x + 10$ to find binomials that represent the length and the width of the Olympic swimming pool in Atlanta.

b) If x represents 16 m, what are the dimensions of the pool, in metres?

Another way to factor trinomials of the form $ax^2 + bx + c$, $a \neq 1$, is to use the guess and check strategy.

Example 1   Factoring by Guess and Check
Factor $3x^2 - 5x - 2$.

Solution
For the trinomial $3x^2 - 5x - 2$, the possible first terms of the binomial factors are $3x$ and x.

$$3x^2 - 5x - 2 = (3x \qquad)(x \qquad)$$

The product of the second terms of the binomials must be -2.
The terms could be 2 and -1, or -2 and 1.

List all the possible pairs of factors and expand to see which pair gives the correct middle term of the trinomial.

	GUESS		CHECK
Possible Factors	Expansion	Trinomial	Is the middle term correct?
$(3x + 2)(x - 1)$	$3x^2 - 3x + 2x - 2$	$3x^2 - x - 2$	No
$(3x - 1)(x + 2)$	$3x^2 + 6x - x - 2$	$3x^2 + 5x - 2$	No
$(3x - 2)(x + 1)$	$3x^2 + 3x - 2x - 2$	$3x^2 + x - 2$	No
$(3x + 1)(x - 2)$	$3x^2 - 6x + x - 2$	$3x^2 - 5x - 2$	Yes

Therefore, $3x^2 - 5x - 2 = (3x + 1)(x - 2)$.

Another way to factor trinomials of the form $ax^2 + bx + c$, $a \neq 1$, is to break up the middle term into two parts, and then factor by grouping.

$$2x^2 + 11x + 12$$

Break up the middle term: $= 2x^2 + 8x + 3x + 12$ $11x = 8x + 3x$
Group terms: $= (2x^2 + 8x) + (3x + 12)$
Remove common factors: $= 2x(x + 4) + 3(x + 4)$
Remove a common binomial factor: $= (x + 4)(2x + 3)$
So, $2x^2 + 11x + 12 = (x + 4)(2x + 3)$.

Note that, when the middle term is broken up, the resulting two terms can be written in either order before terms are grouped. Reversing the above order gives
$$2x^2 + 11x + 12 = 2x^2 + 3x + 8x + 12$$
$$= (2x^2 + 3x) + (8x + 12)$$
$$= x(2x + 3) + 4(2x + 3)$$
$$= (2x + 3)(x + 4)$$
So, $2x^2 + 11x + 12 = (2x + 3)(x + 4)$, which is the same result as before.

The two terms to substitute for the middle term of the trinomial are not obvious. There are many pairs of terms that add to give $11x$, yet only one pair allows you to factor by grouping.

To find the correct pair of terms, look at the expansion of $(2x + 3)(x + 4)$. Compare the result to the trinomial $2x^2 + 11x + 12$. Note that this trinomial is of the form $ax^2 + bx + c$, where $a = 2$, $b = 11$, and $c = 12$.

$$(2x + 3)(x + 4) = (2x + 3)(x + 4)$$

$$= 2x^2 + 8x + 3x + 12 \qquad 8 + 3 = 11, \text{ or } b$$
$$= 2x^2 + 11x + 12 \qquad 8 \times 3 = 2 \times 12, \text{ or } a \times c$$

$$8 + 3 = 11$$
$$2x^2 + 11x + 12 = 2x^2 + 8x + 3x + 12$$
$$8 \times 3 = 24$$
$$2 \times 12 = 24$$

So, to factor $2x^2 + 11x + 12$, the middle term was replaced by two terms whose coefficients have a sum of 11, or b, and a product of 24, or $a \times c$.

Example 2   Breaking up the Middle Term

Factor $6m^2 + 13m - 5$.

Solution

For $6m^2 + 13m - 5$, $a = 6$, $b = 13$, and $c = -5$.
Find two integers whose product is $a \times c$, or -30, and whose sum is b, or 13.
The only two integers that have a product of -30 and a sum of 13 are 15 and -2.

Product of –30		Sum
30	–1	29
–30	1	–29
15	–2	13
–15	2	–13
10	–3	7
–10	3	–7
6	–5	1
–6	5	–1

$$6m^2 + 13m - 5$$

Break up the middle term: $\quad = 6m^2 - 2m + 15m - 5$
Group terms: $\quad = (6m^2 - 2m) + (15m - 5)$
Remove common factors: $\quad = 2m(3m - 1) + 5(3m - 1)$
Remove a common binomial factor: $\quad = (3m - 1)(2m + 5)$
So, $6m^2 + 13m - 5 = (3m - 1)(2m + 5)$.

Example 3   Removing a Common Factor

Factor $10x^2 - 22x + 4$.

Solution

Remove the common factor, and then proceed as before.
$10x^2 - 22x + 4 = 2[5x^2 - 11x + 2]$
To factor $5x^2 - 11x + 2$, find two integers whose product is 10 and whose sum is -11. The integers are -10 and -1.

Product of 10		Sum
10	1	11
–10	–1	–11
5	2	7
–5	–2	–7

$2[5x^2 - 11x + 2] = 2[5x^2 - 10x - x + 2]$
$\qquad = 2[(5x^2 - 10x) + (-x + 2)]$
$\qquad = 2[5x(x - 2) - 1(x - 2)]$
$\qquad = 2[(x - 2)(5x - 1)]$
$\qquad = 2(x - 2)(5x - 1)$

So, $10x^2 - 22x + 4 = 2(x - 2)(5x - 1)$.

Example 4   Trinomials With Two Variables

Factor $4x^2 - 5xy - 6y^2$.

Solution

To factor $4x^2 - 5xy - 6y^2$, find two integers with a product of -24 and a sum of -5. The integers are -8 and 3.

$$4x^2 - 5xy - 6y^2 = 4x^2 - 8xy + 3xy - 6y^2$$
$$= (4x^2 - 8xy) + (3xy - 6y^2)$$
$$= 4x(x - 2y) + 3y(x - 2y)$$
$$= (x - 2y)(4x + 3y)$$

So, $4x^2 - 5xy - 6y^2 = (x - 2y)(4x + 3y)$.

Product of –24		Sum
24	–1	23
–24	1	–23
12	–2	10
–12	2	–10
8	–3	5
★ –8	3	–5
6	–4	2
–6	4	–2

Many trinomials of the form $ax^2 + bx + c$, $a \neq 1$, such as $2x^2 + 3x + 6$, cannot be factored over the integers. No two integers have a product of 12 and a sum of 3.

· ·

Key CONCEPTS

1 To factor a trinomial in the form $ax^2 + bx + c$, either use guess and check or break up the middle term.

2 To factor by guess and check, list all the possible pairs of factors and expand to see which pair gives the correct middle term of the trinomial.

3 To factor by breaking up the middle term,

a) replace the middle term, bx, by two terms whose coefficients have a sum of b and a product of $a \times c$

b) group pairs of terms and remove a common factor from each pair

c) remove the common binomial factor

Communicate Your Understanding

1. Describe how you would factor $2x^2 + 7x + 3$.

2. Which method of factoring do you prefer—guess and check or breaking up the middle term? Use examples to explain and justify your choice.

Practice

1. Factor, if possible. Check each factored form by substituting $x = 1$ into the expanded form and the factored form.

a) $2y^2 + 9y + 9$ **b)** $3m^2 + 10m + 3$ **c)** $5t^2 + 7t + 2$

d) $4r^2 + 12r + 3$ **e)** $2x^2 + 11x + 14$ **f)** $6x^2 + 11x + 3$

2. Factor, if possible.

a) $2x^2 - 5x + 3$ **b)** $3x^2 - 5x + 2$ **c)** $3t^2 - 10t + 8$

d) $5m^2 - 11m + 2$ **e)** $6m^2 - 13m + 6$ **f)** $4y^2 - 11y + 9$

3. Factor, if possible.

a) $2x^2 - x - 6$ **b)** $6x^2 - 5x - 4$ **c)** $2t^2 + 9t - 5$

d) $15n^2 - n - 2$ **e)** $3x^2 + x - 4$ **f)** $5y^2 - 14y - 3$

g) $8x^2 - 10x - 3$ **h)** $9x^2 - 15x - 4$ **i)** $10t^2 + 11t - 6$

4. Factor, if possible.

a) $4t^2 + 8t + 3$ **b)** $10x^2 - 17x + 3$ **c)** $5t^2 + 2t - 2$

d) $2y^2 + 11y + 15$ **e)** $8y^2 - 22y + 12$ **f)** $6x^2 + x - 4$

g) $6r^2 + 15r + 9$ **h)** $12y^2 - 11y + 2$ **i)** $4x^2 - 18x - 10$

j) $2m^3 + 7m^2 - 30m$ **k)** $2t^3 + 9t^2 + 4t$ **l)** $18s^2 - 7s - 1$

m) $12r^2 + 27r + 15$ **n)** $5r^2s - 7rs + 2s$ **o)** $6 + 5y - 4y^2$

p) $2 - 7m + 3m^2$ **q)** $12 + 18t + 8t^2$ **r)** $6 + 5y - 6y^2$

5. Factor.

a) $6m^2 + mn - 2n^2$ **b)** $3x^2 + 7xy + 2y^2$ **c)** $10a^2 - 3ab - b^2$

d) $2x^2 - 11xy + 5y^2$ **e)** $6c^2 + 13cd + 2d^2$ **f)** $6x^2 - 9xy + 3y^2$

g) $2m^2 - 4mn - 6n^2$ **h)** $4y^2 + 4xy - 8x^2$ **i)** $6a^2 + 14ab - 12b^2$

Applications and Problem Solving

6. Transportation Sydney Harbour Bridge in Australia is unusually wide for a long-span bridge. It carries two rail lines, eight road lanes, a cycle lane, and a walkway.

a) Factor the expression $10x^2 - 7x - 3$ to find binomials that represent the length and the width of the bridge.

b) If x represents 50 m, what are the length and the width of the bridge, in metres?

7. Famous Canadians The letters shown in the table each represent a different integer. The letter Y represents -7, as shown.

Letter	A	C	D	E	H	I	J	L	M
Integer									
Letter	N	O	R	S	T	U	W	Y	
Integer								-7	

a) Factor the following 5 trinomials. In each case, write the factored form with the smaller coefficient of x first. For example, the factored form of $6x^2 + 11x + 4$ would be written as $(2x + 1)(3x + 4)$, because $2 < 3$. Use the factored forms to find the integer represented by each capital letter. Then, copy and complete the table.

$10x^2 - 29x + 10 = (Ax + U)(Cx + D)$
$4x^2 - 27x + 18 = (Wx + L)(Ex + H)$
$18x^2 - 27x + 4 = (Jx + I)(Mx + N)$
$56x^2 + 15x + 1 = (Ox + W)(Rx + W)$
$10x^2 - 91x + 9 = (Wx + S)(Tx + N)$

b) Replace each of the following integers with its corresponding letter from part a) to find the names of four famous Canadians. Find out what each of them is famous for.

Name 1: 3 7 -1 -4
           6 -4 10 5 -3 4 -6 -6

Name 2: -1 4 -2
           -3 2 -1 -6 2 -1

Name 3: 6 2 8 -9 -3 2 -6 -6
           6 5 -6 -5 -3 2 -1

Name 4: 4 6 -4 -6 -7
           -9 10 7 1 4

8. List all values of k such that each trinomial can be factored over the integers.

a) $3x^2 + kx + 5$ **b)** $5x^2 + kx + 8$
c) $3x^2 + kx - 2$ **d)** $4x^2 + kx - 9$

9. Factor.

a) $2x^4 + 3x^2 + 1$ **b)** $2x^4 + 5x^2 - 3$
c) $3x^4 - x^2 - 4$ **d)** $6x^4 - 13x^2 + 6$
e) $2x^4 + 5x^2y + 2y^2$ **f)** $3x^4 + 11x^2y - 4y^2$

A space shuttle returning to Earth must withstand very high temperatures when it enters the atmosphere. About 70% of the shuttle is covered with two sizes of square insulating tiles. There are about 20 000 of the smaller tiles on its lower surface and about 7000 of the larger tiles on the tops of the wings and the sides of the fuselage.

If the area of one of the larger square tiles is represented by a^2, and the area of one of the smaller square tiles is represented by b^2, the difference in their areas is $a^2 - b^2$. A polynomial written in the form $a^2 - b^2$ is called a **difference of squares**.

Investigation   Study the Diagrams

Figure 1

Figure 2

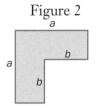

Divide Figure 2 into areas I and II.

Rotate area II and attach it to area I to make a rectangle.

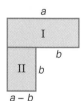

1. Write an expression for each of the following.
a) the area of Figure 1
b) the area of Figure 2
c) the length of the rectangle formed from areas I and II
d) the width of the rectangle formed from areas I and II

2. Write an expression for the area of the rectangle in terms of the length and the width. Do not expand the expression.

3. How is your expression from question 2 related to your expression for the area of Figure 2 in question 1b)?

4. Communication Write a rule for factoring the difference of squares.

5. The two sizes of square tiles on the space shuttle have side lengths of 20 cm and 15 cm. Use your rule from question 4 to calculate the difference in their areas without squaring any numbers.

Web Connection www.school.mcgrawhill.ca/resources/

To learn more about the design of the space shuttle, visit the above web site. Go to **Math Resources,** then to *MATHPOWER™ 10, Ontario Edition,* to find out where to go next. Describe an aspect of the shuttle design, using diagrams and other mathematical models as necessary.

Example 1   Factoring a Difference of Squares
Factor $9x^2 - 16$.

Solution
Use the pattern for the difference of squares.
$$a^2 - b^2 = (a + b)(a - b)$$
$$9x^2 - 16 = (3x)^2 - 4^2$$
$$= (3x + 4)(3x - 4)$$

Example 2   Removing a Common Factor
Factor $8x^2 - 18y^2$.

Solution
Remove the common factor. Then, factor the difference of squares.
$$8x^2 - 18y^2 = 2(4x^2 - 9y^2)$$
$$= 2(2x + 3y)(2x - 3y)$$

The trinomial that results from squaring a binomial is called a **perfect square trinomial**. Perfect square trinomials can be factored using the patterns from squaring binomials.
$$a^2 + 2ab + b^2 = (a + b)^2$$
$$a^2 - 2ab + b^2 = (a - b)^2$$

In a perfect square trinomial, the following conditions are met:
• The first and last terms are perfect squares.
• The middle term is twice the product of the square roots of the first and last terms.

Example 3   Perfect Square Trinomials

a) Verify that $4x^2 + 20x + 25$ is a perfect square trinomial.
b) Factor it.

Solution

a) $4x^2 = (2x)^2$ and $25 = 5^2$, so the first and last terms are perfect squares.
$20x = 2(2x)(5)$, so the middle term is twice the product of the square roots of the first and last terms.
So, $4x^2 + 20x + 25$ is a perfect square trinomial.

b) Use the appropriate perfect square trinomial pattern.

$$a^2 + 2ab + b^2 = (a + b)^2$$
$$4x^2 + 20x + 25 = (2x)^2 + 2(2x)(5) + 5^2$$
$$= (2x + 5)^2$$

Key CONCEPTS

1 To factor a polynomial in the form $a^2 - b^2$, use the pattern for the difference of squares.
$$a^2 - b^2 = (a + b)(a - b)$$
2 To factor a perfect square trinomial, use the patterns for squaring binomials.
$$a^2 + 2ab + b^2 = (a + b)^2$$
$$a^2 - 2ab + b^2 = (a - b)^2$$

Communicate Your Understanding

1. Describe how you would factor each of the following.

a) $x^2 - 36$ **b)** $2x^2 - 18$ **c)** $x^2 - 6x + 9$

2. Can $4x^2 + 9$ be factored using the pattern for the difference of squares or the patterns for squaring binomials? Explain and justify your reasoning.

3. If the first and last terms of a trinomial are perfect squares, how can you determine the middle term that will make a perfect square trinomial?

Practice

A

1. Factor, if possible. Check each factored form by substituting 1 for the variable(s) in the expanded form and the factored form.

a) $x^2 - 9$

b) $y^2 - 16$

c) $z^2 + 81$

d) $25a^2 - 36$

e) $1 - 64t^2$

f) $36 - 49a^2$

g) $49 + x^2$

h) $25x^2 - 64y^2$

i) $4t^2 - 9s^2$

j) $100p^2 - 121q^2$

k) $16^2 - 81y^2$

l) $225b^2 - a^2$

2. State whether each trinomial is a perfect square trinomial. If it is, factor it.

a) $x^2 + 6x + 9$
b) $y^2 - 10y + 25$
c) $x^2 - 8x + 4$
d) $4t^2 + 4t + 1$
e) $16t^2 + 24t + 9$
f) $49 + 14x + x^2$
g) $1 - 16t + 64t^2$
h) $9x^2 - 24x + 16$
i) $4 + 28r + 49r^2$
j) $81x^2 - 72xy + 64y^2$
k) $121m^2 - 22m + 1$
l) $9a^2 + 12ab + 4b^2$

3. Factor fully, if possible.

a) $y^2 - 144$
b) $25x^2 + 5y + 1$
c) $9a^2 - 24a + 16$
d) $2x^2 - 32$
e) $y^2 + 36$
f) $3x^2 + 6x + 3$
g) $m^2 - 14m + 49$
h) $4p^2 + 20pq + 25q^2$
i) $49x^2 - 121y^2$
j) $80a^2 - 45b^2$
k) $100x^2 + 10x + 1$
l) $y^3 - 36y$
m) $y^3 - 18y^2 + 81y$
n) $36x^2 + 100y^2$
o) $3x^3 - 48x$
p) $5m^3 - 40m^2 + 80m$
q) $81x^2 - 144$
r) $3b^2 - 300$

Applications and Problem Solving

4. Numbers Evaluate by factoring the difference of squares.

a) $53^2 - 47^2$
b) $45^2 - 35^2$
c) $820^2 - 180^2$

5. Volleyball The area of a volleyball court, excluding the service areas, can be represented by the trinomial $2x^2 - 4x + 2$.
a) Factor the trinomial completely.
b) If the length of the court is twice the width, use the factors from part a) to write expressions that represent the length and the width.
c) If x represents 10 m, what are the length and the width of the court, in metres?

B

6. Factor.

a) $(x + 2)^2 - 9$
b) $16 - (y - 3)^2$
c) $(m + 1)^2 - (m + 2)^2$
d) $x^4 + 22x^2 + 121$
e) $t^6 - 18t^3 + 81$
f) $\dfrac{x^2}{4} - \dfrac{1}{9}$
g) $25x^4 - 81$
h) $(2x + y)^2 - (2x - y)^2$

7. Determine the value(s) of k such that each trinomial is a perfect square.

a) $x^2 + kx + 16$
b) $9x^2 + kx + 49$
c) $x^2 + 4x + k$
d) $4x^2 - 12x + k$
e) $kx^2 + 40x + 16$
f) $kx^2 - 24xy + 9y^2$

8. Measurement The volume of a rectangular prism is represented by the polynomial $2x^3 - 24x^2 + 72x$.
a) Factor the polynomial completely.
b) If the expression for each dimension of the prism includes x, what are the expressions that represent the possible sets of dimensions?
c) If x represents 8 cm, what are the possible dimensions of the prism?
d) Communication Could x represent 5 cm? Explain.

9. Integers If a and b are integers, find values of a and b such that $a^2 - b^2$ is 21.

10. Measurement The area of a square is represented by the expression $49 - 28x + 4x^2$, where x represents a positive integer. What are the possible values for the perimeter of the square?

11. Factor.

a) $(x + 3)^2 - y^2$

b) $x^2 - 4x + 4 - 9y^2$

c) $4x^2 + 12xy + 9y^2 - 4z^2$

d) $x^4 - 2x^2y + y^2 - z^2$

12. Measurement A circle has an area of $(9x^2 + 30x + 25)\pi$ square centimetres, where x is a positive integer. Determine the smallest diameter that the circle can have.

Modelling Math   Representing Patterns Algebraically

The four grids, which were shown on page 125, have side lengths of 1, 2, 3, and 4 units, respectively.

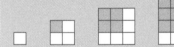

a) Communication Describe the pattern in the number of shaded grid squares.

b) If s represents the side length of the grid, write an expression in terms of s for finding the number of shaded grid squares. Write your expression in factored form.

c) Use your expression to find the number of shaded grid squares on a 12 by 12 grid; a 91 by 91 grid.

d) If the number of shaded grid squares is 529, what is the side length of the grid?

e) The total number of grid squares on a grid of side length s is s^2. Subtract the expression you found in part b) from s^2 to find an expression that represents the number of unshaded squares in terms of s.

f) Use your expression from part e) to find the number of unshaded squares on a 53 by 53 grid.

Career Connection Manufacturing

In manufacturing industries, useful products are made from raw materials. The clothes you wear, the computers you use, and the vehicles you ride in have all been manufactured.

In Ontario, manufacturing accounts for about one quarter of the economic output and employs about a million people. The top three manufacturing industries in the province produce transportation equipment, electrical and electronic products, and processed food.

1. **Concrete pipe** A large concrete pipe is manufactured in 10-m sections. The inner radius of the pipe is 1 m, and the outer radius is 1.2 m.

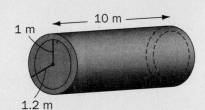

a) The volume of a cylinder is given by the expression $\pi r^2 h$, where r is the radius and h is the height. Without squaring any numbers, write an expression that represents the difference between the volume of a cylinder of height 10 m with radius 1.2 m and the volume of a cylinder of height 10 m with radius 1 m. Express your answer in the form of a monomial multiplied by a difference of squares.

b) Factor the expression from part a) using the pattern for the difference of squares. Then, express the difference in the volumes in the form ■π, where ■ represents a number.

c) **Communication** Explain why the difference from part b) represents the volume of concrete used to manufacture the section of pipe.

d) Calculate the volume of concrete used, to the nearest tenth of a cubic metre.

2. **Communication** Describe a way to answer question 1 without using the difference of squares.

3. **Research** Choose a manufacturing industry that is important in your part of the province. Use your research skills to describe how the industry contributes to the economy in your area.

LOGIC POWER

Put a number in each blank so that the statement is true.

"In this sentence, the number of occurrences of 1 is ▮, of 2 is ▮, of 3 is ▮, of 4 is ▮, and of 5 is ▮."

Technology Extension: Factoring Polynomials With a Graphing Calculator

Complete each of the following using the **factor function** of a graphing calculator that has the capability to factor polynomials.

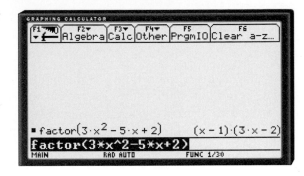

1 Factoring Polynomials

1. Remove the common factor.

a) $6x^2 + 15x - 12$

b) $14y^2 - 42y + 21$

c) $20x + 15x^2 + 10$

d) $4x^2y + 6xy - 8xy^2$

e) $3p^3q + 18p^2q^2 + 6pq^3$

f) $12a^3b^2 + 4a^2b^3 + 8ab^4 - 6b^5$

2. Factor, if possible.

a) $x^2 + 19x + 34$

b) $x^2 - 6x - 72$

c) $x^2 - 24x + 40$

d) $15 - 8t + t^2$

e) $4n^2 + 13n + 9$

f) $2m^2 - 5m + 6$

g) $5x^2 - 17x - 12$

h) $15y^2 + 11y - 14$

i) $x^2 + 7xy + 10y^2$

j) $3x^2 - 14xy + 8y^2$

k) $15a^2 - ab - 6b^2$

l) $14x^2 + 55xy - 36y^2$

m) $(x + a)^2 + 6(x + a) + 8$

n) $(x - y)^2 - 5(x - y) + 6$

o) $x^4 + 2x^2 - 15$

3. Factor completely.

a) $3x^2 - 30x + 27$

b) $4x^2 + 10x - 24$

c) $75y^2 + 215y + 40$

d) $2u^2 - 6uv + 4v^2$

e) $36x^2 + 42xy - 18y^2$

f) $x^3 + 3x^2 + 2x$

g) $4t^3 - 26t^2 - 14t$

h) $30x^4 + 87x^2 + 30$

i) $24x^4 - 16x^2 - 8$

2 Factoring Special Products

1. Factor.

a) $25x^2 + 60x + 36$

b) $9y^2 - 30y + 25$

c) $9n^2 - 64$

d) $25 - 169x^2$

e) $4x^2 - 9y^2$

f) $49a^2 - 56ab + 16b^2$

2. Factor completely.

a) $16m^2 - 64$

b) $36 - 16x^2$

c) $125x^4 - 80$

d) $72x^2 - 98y^4$

e) $2x^2 - 28x + 98$

f) $12x^2 + 60x + 75$

g) $32w^3 - 160w^2 + 200w$

h) $300 - 48x^4$

i) $36y^4 + 120x^2y^2 + 100x^4$

3. Write two special products that can be factored. Have a classmate factor them.

Rich Problem

Gwennap Pit

The parish of Gwennap is located in Cornwall in south-western England. In past centuries, Gwennap was an important tin-mining centre.

In the sixteenth century, part of one of the mines collapsed, forming a large hole in the ground. In 1806, terraces were cut to create an outdoor amphitheatre, with a circular stage surrounded by rings of seats. Each ring of seats is about 1 m wide. The amphitheatre is known as Gwennap Pit.

1 Writing Expressions for Areas

Each ring of seats has an inner radius and an outer radius. The area of each ring is the difference between the area of a circle with the outer radius and the area of a circle with the inner radius.

1. If the circular stage has a radius of r metres, write an expression for its area in terms of r.

Key Concepts

• Following the worked examples, the concepts in the section are summarized.

• You can use this summary when you are doing homework or studying.

Practice

• Completing these questions allows you to master essential mathematical skills by practising what you have learned.

Applications and Problem Solving

• Mathematics is powerful when it is applied. The questions in this section allow you to use what you have learned to solve problems, and to apply and extend what you have learned.

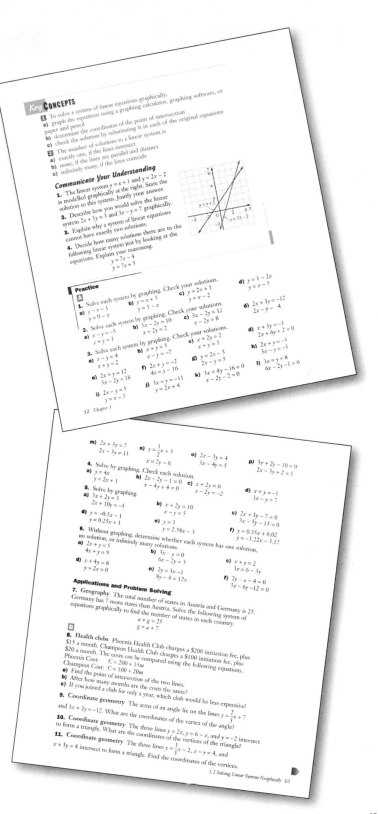

TECHNOLOGY

• Graphing calculators, geometry software, and scientific probes are technology tools that will make you a more powerful learner, by allowing you to explore mathematical concepts more easily and quickly.

• The use of these tools is integrated within the investigations, the worked examples, and the Practice and Applications and Problem Solving questions.

• Two appendixes at the back of the text provide specific instructions in the operation of graphing calculators and geometry software.

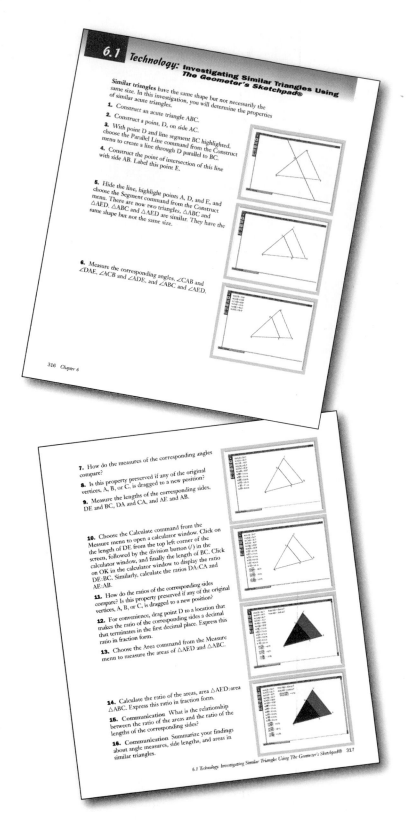

Appendix B: Graphing Calculator Keystrokes includes detailed instructions in an alphabetical listing of functions used in *MATHPOWER*™ *10, Ontario Edition*.

Appendix C: Using *The Geometer's Sketchpad*® reviews the essential skills needed to operate this program.

• Technology Extension features provide additional instruction and opportunities to use technology tools in applications related to the chapter.

• Specific instructions in how to use scientific probes are included in the appropriate core section of the text.

RICH PROBLEMS

• One rich problem is included at the end of each chapter before the Review of Key Concepts.

• These problems provide real-world contexts in which to explore concepts in a rich problem solving situation.

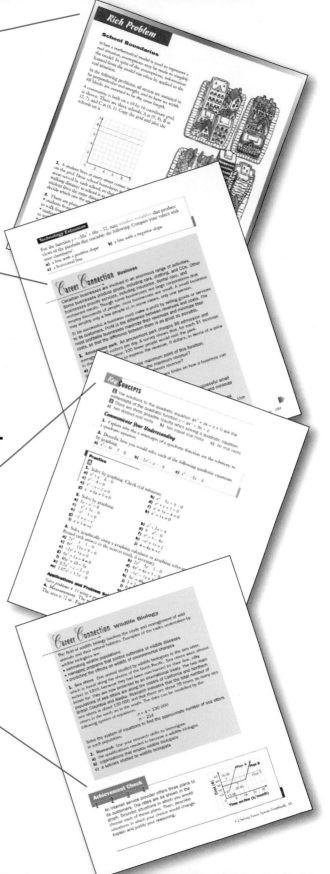

CAREER CONNECTIONS

• These activities give you the opportunity to investigate mathematics-related careers that make use of the chapter content.

REVIEW AND ASSESSMENT

Several features within the text provide opportunities for review and assessment:

Communicate Your Understanding

• Following each summary of Key Concepts are questions designed to help you communicate your understanding of what you have learned.

Achievement Check

• This feature provides questions designed to assess your knowledge and understanding, your problem solving skills, your communication skills, and your ability to apply what you have learned.

• Achievement Checks appear throughout the chapter, with one always at the end of the chapter test.

2. For the first ring of seats around the stage, what is the inner radius in terms of r? the outer radius in terms of r?

3. a) Write an expression in terms of r for the area of the first ring of seats.
b) Simplify the expression from part a). Write the result in factored form.

4. Repeat question 3 for
a) the second ring   **b)** the third ring
c) the fourth ring   **d)** the fifth ring

5. Communication a) Describe the pattern in the factored expressions for the areas of the first five rings.
b) Use the pattern to write an expression for the area of the nth ring in terms of n and r.
c) Use the expression from part b) to write an expression for the area of the eighth ring in terms of r.

6. If the radius of the stage is about 2.5 m, find the area of each of the following, to the nearest square metre.
a) the fifth ring   **b)** the seventh ring
c) the tenth ring   **d)** the twelfth ring

7. a) Write and simplify an expression in terms of r for the total area of all 13 rings of seats. Express the answer in factored form.
b) Find the total area of all 13 rings of seats, to the nearest 10 m^2.

2 Writing Expressions for Circumferences

Each ring of seats has an inner circumference and an outer circumference.

1. If the circular stage has a radius of r metres, write an expression in terms of r for the inner circumference of the first ring of seats.

2. Write an expression in terms of r for the inner circumference of each of the following rings of seats. Leave each expression in factored form.
a) the second ring   **b)** the third ring
c) the sixth ring   **d)** the thirteenth ring

3. a) Write and simplify an expression in terms of r to represent the total of the inner circumferences of all 13 rings of seats. Express the answer in factored form.
b) Find the total of the inner circumferences of all 13 rings of seats, to the nearest 10 m.

3 Estimating Seating Capacities

1. Communication Estimate the number of people who can comfortably sit in each of the following. Explain your reasoning.
a) the first ring   **b)** the fifth ring
c) the eighth ring   **d)** the whole amphitheatre

2. The world's largest known crater is near Sudbury and has a radius of 125 km. About how many people could comfortably sit on a 1-m wide ring around the top of the crater?

REVIEW OF *Key* CONCEPTS

Refer to the Key Concepts on page 130.

a) To add $(3x^2 - x - 2) + (x^2 + 4x + 5)$, collect like terms.

$$(3x^2 - x - 2) + (x^2 + 4x + 5) = 3x^2 - x - 2 + x^2 + 4x + 5$$
$$= 3x^2 + x^2 - x + 4x - 2 + 5$$
$$= 4x^2 + 3x + 3$$

b) To subtract $(6x^2 + x - 1) - (4x^2 + 2x - 3)$, add the opposite of the second polynomial.

$$(6x^2 + x - 1) - (4x^2 + 2x - 3) = (6x^2 + x - 1) + (-4x^2 - 2x + 3)$$
$$= 6x^2 + x - 1 - 4x^2 - 2x + 3$$
$$= 2x^2 - x + 2$$

c) To multiply $(-3x^2y^2)(-2xy^2)$, multiply the numerical coefficients, then the variables.

$$(-3x^2y^2)(-2xy^2) = (-3)(-2)(x^2)(x)(y^2)(y^2)$$
$$= 6x^3y^4$$

d) To divide $\dfrac{20x^2y^3}{-2xy^2}$, divide the numerical coefficients, then the variables.

$$\frac{20x^2y^3}{-2xy^2} = \left(\frac{20}{-2}\right)\left(\frac{x^2}{x}\right)\left(\frac{y^3}{y^2}\right)$$
$$= -10xy$$

e) To simplify $3x(x - 2) - 2x(3x + 1)$, use the distributive property. Then, collect like terms.

$$3x(x - 2) - 2x(3x + 1) = 3x(x - 2) - 2x(3x + 1)$$
$$= 3x^2 - 6x - 6x^2 - 2x$$
$$= -3x^2 - 8x$$

1. Simplify.
a) $(2x + y) + (3x - 4y)$
b) $(5x^2 - 3x + 4) + (3x^2 - x - 1)$
c) $(3a^2 - a - 2) - (4a^2 + 5a + 6)$
d) $(2m^2 + 2mn - n^2) - (m^2 - mn - 2n^2)$

2. Multiply.
a) $(3xy^2)(-4x^3y^2)$
b) $(-4rs^3t^2)(-6rst^4)$

3. Simplify.
a) $\dfrac{20a^2b^3c}{-5ab^3c}$
b) $\dfrac{-36m^3n^4p^2}{-9m^3np}$

4. Expand and simplify.
a) $3(x - 4) + 5(x + 6)$
b) $6(a + 3) - 2(a - 5)$
c) $2t(3t - 4) + t(2t + 5)$
d) $3(y^2 - y - 1) - (2y^2 - 3y + 4)$

3.2 Multiplying Binomials

Refer to the Key Concepts on page 136.

a) To find and verify the product $(2x + 5)(x - 4)$, use FOIL.

$$(2x + 5)(x - 4) = (2x + 5)(x - 4)$$
$$= 2x^2 - 8x + 5x - 20$$
$$= 2x^2 - 3x - 20$$

b) To expand and simplify $4(3x + 1)(x - 2) - 2(x + 1)(4x + 1)$, first use FOIL to multiply the binomials. Then, remove brackets and collect like terms.

Solution

$$4(3x + 1)(x - 2) - 2(x + 1)(4x + 1) = 4(3x^2 - 6x + x - 2) - 2(4x^2 + x + 4x + 1)$$
$$= 4(3x^2 - 5x - 2) - 2(4x^2 + 5x + 1)$$
$$= 12x^2 - 20x - 8 - 8x^2 - 10x - 2$$
$$= 4x^2 - 30x - 10$$

5. Find the product.
a) $(x - 2)(x + 4)$ **b)** $(a + 5)(a - 6)$
c) $(2y - 3)(3y + 4)$ **d)** $(3x + y)(x - 4y)$

6. Expand and simplify.
a) $2(x + 1)(x - 3)$ **b)** $-2(y - 1)(y + 4)$
c) $4(m - 2)(3m - 1)$ **d)** $3(2x + 1)(2x - 3)$

7. Expand and simplify.
a) $(y + 4)(y - 3) + (y - 2)(y - 3)$ **b)** $(2x - 1)(x - 4) - (3x + 2)(3x - 1)$
c) $3(2a + 3)(2a - 1) - 4(a^2 - 7)$ **d)** $4(2x - 1)(x + 3) + 3(x - 2)(3x - 4)$

3.3 Special Products

Refer to the Key Concepts on page 142.

a) To expand $(4x + 5)^2$ and $(2x - 3)^2$, use the patterns for squaring binomials.

$$(a + b)^2 = a^2 + 2ab + b^2$$
$$(4x + 5)^2 = (4x)^2 + 2(4x)(5) + (5)^2$$
$$= 16x^2 + 40x + 25$$

$$(a - b)^2 = a^2 - 2ab + b^2$$
$$(2x - 3)^2 = (2x)^2 - 2(2x)(3) + (3)^2$$
$$= 4x^2 - 12x + 9$$

b) To expand $(5x + 2)(5x - 2)$, use the pattern for the product of the sum and difference.

$$(a + b)(a - b) = a^2 - b^2$$
$$(5x + 2)(5x - 2) = (5x)^2 - (2)^2$$
$$= 25x^2 - 4$$

8. Expand.

a) $(x + 4)^2$　　　　　　**b)** $(y - 4)(y + 4)$　　　　　**c)** $(a - 5)^2$

d) $(3t + 1)(3t - 1)$　　　**e)** $(2x - 3y)^2$　　　　　　**f)** $(5a + 3b)(5a - 3b)$

g) $2(3m + 1)^2$　　　　　**h)** $(1 - 2x)^2$　　　　　　　**i)** $3(4x + 3)(4x - 3)$

9. Expand and simplify.

a) $(m - 3)(m + 3) + (m - 4)^2$　　　　　**b)** $(x - 6)^2 - (x + 5)(x - 5)$

c) $3(2t + 1)^2 + 2(3t - 1)(3t + 1)$　　　**d)** $2(3x + 2y)(3x - 2y) - 3(3x - y)^2$

10. Communication a) Two numbers that differ by two can be multiplied by squaring their average, and then subtracting 1. For example, $14 \times 16 = 15^2 - 1$, which is $225 - 1$, or 224. How does the product of the sum and difference $(x + 1)(x - 1)$ explain the method?

b) Develop a similar method for multiplying two numbers that differ by 4.

c) Show how the product of the sum and difference explains your method from part b).

3.4　Common Factors

Refer to the Key Concepts on page 149.

a) To factor $2xy - 8xz + 4x$, remove the greatest common factor, which is $2x$.
$2xy - 8xz + 4x = 2x(y - 4z + 2)$

b) To factor $5y^4 - 10y^3 + 15y^2$, remove the greatest common factor, which is $5y^2$.
$5y^4 - 10y^3 + 15y^2 = 5y^2(y^2 - 2y + 3)$

c) To factor $3y(x - 2) - 5(x - 2)$, remove the common binomial factor, $(x - 2)$.
$3y(x - 2) - 5(x - 2) = (x - 2)(3y - 5)$

d) To factor $x^2 + xy + y + x$ by grouping, group pairs of terms with a common factor.
$$\begin{aligned} x^2 + xy + y + x &= (x^2 + x) + (xy + y) \\ &= x(x + 1) + y(x + 1) \\ &= (x + 1)(x + y) \end{aligned}$$

11. Factor, if possible.

a) $5t - 35$　　　　　**b)** $5y^2 + 20y$

c) $7st - 22mn$　　　**d)** $2xy - 8xy^2 - 4x^2y^3$

12. Factor, if possible.

a) $m(x + 4) - 3(x + 4)$　　　**b)** $5a(y - 2) + 7(y + 2)$　　　**c)** $2x(m + n) - (m + n)$

13. Factor by grouping.

a) $mx + my + 2x + 2y$　　　**b)** $x^2 - xy - x + y$　　　**c)** $2m^2 - 3t - 6m + mt$

14. Measurement The diagram shows two concentric circles of radii r and $r + 3$.

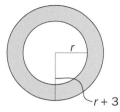

a) Write an expression in terms of r for the area of the smaller circle.
b) Write an expression in terms of r for the area of the larger circle. Expand and simplify the expression.
c) Subtract the expression you wrote in part a) from the simplified expression in part b). Factor the result.
d) If r represents 5 cm, calculate the area of the shaded part of the diagram, to the nearest tenth of a square centimetre.

3.5 Factoring $x^2 + bx + c$

Refer to the Key Concepts on page 155.

To factor $x^2 - 7x + 10$, where $a = 1$, $b = -7$, and $c = 10$, use a table to find two integers whose product is 10 and whose sum is -7. The only two integers with a product of 10 and a sum of -7 are -5 and -2. So, $x^2 - 7x + 10 = (x - 5)(x - 2)$.

Product of 10		Sum
10	1	11
−10	−1	−11
5	2	7
* −5	−2	−7

15. Factor, if possible.
a) $x^2 - x - 12$
b) $y^2 + 3y - 18$
c) $m^2 + 11m + 24$
d) $t^2 - 8t + 15$
e) $x^2 + 3x + 4$
f) $n^2 - 13n + 40$
g) $w^2 - w - 30$
h) $14 + 5m - m^2$
i) $x^2 + 9xy + 8y^2$
j) $c^2 - 10cd + 16d^2$

16. Factor fully.
a) $2x^2 - 2x - 40$
b) $ay^2 + 12ay - 28a$
c) $3x^2 + 12x - 36$
d) $5x^2 - 15x + 10$

17. Write two different trinomials that have $x + 3$ as a factor.

18. Write two different trinomials that have $x - 2$ as a factor.

Refer to the Key Concepts on page 162.

a) To factor $2x^2 - 5x - 3$ by guess and check, list all the possible pairs of factors and expand to see which pair gives the correct middle term.

GUESS			CHECK
Possible Factors	Expansion	Trinomial	Is the middle term correct?
$(2x + 3)(x - 1)$	$2x^2 - 2x + 3x - 3$	$2x^2 + x - 3$	No
$(2x - 3)(x + 1)$	$2x^2 + 2x - 3x - 3$	$2x^2 - x - 3$	No
$(2x - 1)(x + 3)$	$2x^2 + 6x - x - 3$	$2x^2 + 5x - 3$	No
$(2x + 1)(x - 3)$	$2x^2 - 6x + x - 3$	$2x^2 - 5x - 3$	Yes

Therefore, $2x^2 - 5x - 3 = (2x + 1)(x - 3)$.

b) To factor $5x^2 + 12x + 4$, where $a = 5$, $b = 12$, and $c = 4$, break up the middle term.

Find two integers whose product is $a \times c$, or 20, and whose sum is b, or 12. The only two integers with a product of 20 and a sum of 12 are 10 and 2.

Product of 20		Sum
20	1	21
–20	–1	–21
10	2	12
–10	–2	–12
5	4	9
–5	–4	–9

$*$ marks the row: 10, 2, 12

$$5x^2 + 12x + 4 = 5x^2 + 10x + 2x + 4$$
$$= (5x^2 + 10x) + (2x + 4)$$
$$= 5x(x + 2) + 2(x + 2)$$
$$= (x + 2)(5x + 2)$$

So, $5x^2 + 12x + 4 = (x + 2)(5x + 2)$.

19. Factor, if possible.

a) $5m^2 + 17m + 6$
b) $6x^2 + 7x + 2$
c) $2x^2 - 7x + 5$
d) $3t^2 + 4t - 20$
e) $2m^2 + 2m - 3$
f) $6y^2 + y - 1$
g) $6x^2 - x - 1$
h) $9z^2 - 9z + 2$
i) $2x^2 + 11xy + 5y^2$
j) $4p^2 - 3pq - 7q^2$

20. Factor fully.

a) $4x^2 + 6x + 2$
b) $9t^2 + 3t - 6$
c) $20m^2 - 8m - 12$
d) $3y^3 - 7y^2 + 2y$

21. **Basketball** The backboard behind a basketball net is a rectangle whose area can be represented by the trinomial $77x^2 - 38x - 7$.

a) Factor $77x^2 - 38x - 7$ to find binomials that represent the length and the width of the backboard.

b) If x represents 17 cm, find the dimensions of the backboard, in centimetres.

3.7 Factoring Special Quadratics

Refer to the Key Concepts on page 167.

a) To factor $25x^2 - 9$, use the pattern for the difference of squares.
$$a^2 - b^2 = (a + b)(a - b)$$
$$25x^2 - 9 = (5x)^2 - 3^2$$
$$= (5x + 3)(5x - 3)$$

b) To factor $4x^2 - 28x + 49$, use the appropriate perfect square trinomial pattern.
$$a^2 - 2ab + b^2 = (a - b)^2$$
$$4x^2 - 28x + 49 = (2x)^2 - 2(2x)(7) + 7^2$$
$$= (2x - 7)^2$$

22. Factor, if possible.

a) $x^2 - 25$

b) $1 - 49m^2$

c) $m^2 + 16$

d) $49t^2 - 81s^2$

e) $4a^2 - 16b^2$

f) $144p^2 - q^2$

23. Determine whether the trinomial is a perfect square trinomial. If it is, factor it.

a) $x^2 + 10x + 25$

b) $y^2 - 12y + 36$

c) $9t^2 - 6t + 1$

d) $m^2 + 6m + 16$

e) $4x^2 + 12x + 9$

f) $25r^2 - 20rs + 4s^2$

24. Factor fully.

a) $5x^2 - 5$

b) $16m^2 - 36n^2$

c) $18y^2 + 60y + 50$

d) $5x^2 - 20xy + 20y^2$

25. Egyptian pyramid The North Stone Pyramid at Dahshur in Egypt has a square base with an area that can be represented by the trinomial $9x^2 - 12x + 4$.

a) Factor the trinomial to find a binomial that represents the side length of the base.

b) If x represents 74 m, what is the side length of the base, in metres?

Chapter Test

1. Simplify.

a) $(3y^2 - 2y + 1) + (5y^2 - y - 4)$ **b)** $(2x^2 - 3x - 5) - (2x^2 + 4x - 7)$

2. Simplify.

a) $(-2ab^2)(-5a^3b^3)$ **b)** $\dfrac{-45x^3yz^2}{-9x^2y}$

3. Expand and simplify.

a) $2(m - 5) - 4(2m + 1)$ **b)** $4x(2x - 3) - x(3x - 1)$

c) $2a(a^2 - 2a - 1) - 3a(2a^2 + a - 2)$

4. Find the product.

a) $(y - 3)(y + 5)$ **b)** $(3x - 2)(2x - 1)$

c) $(2a + b)(a - 3b)$

5. Expand and simplify.

a) $(3m + 2)(m - 3) - (2m - 1)(m + 3)$ **b)** $2(3x + 1)(x + 2) - 3(4x - 5)$

6. Expand and simplify.

a) $(x - 1)^2$ **b)** $(2y - 3)(2y + 3)$

c) $(x + 2y)^2$ **d)** $2(3x + 1)^2 + 3(2x - 1)(2x + 1)$

7. Factor.

a) $4m^2 - 28m$ **b)** $3ab - 9ab^2 + 6a^2b$

c) $x(m - 2) - 4(m - 2)$ **d)** $y^2 + 2x + 2y + xy$

8. Factor.

a) $x^2 - 7x + 12$ **b)** $a^2 + 4a - 21$

c) $y^2 + 9y + 20$ **d)** $t^2 - 6t - 27$

e) $x^2 + 6xy + 5y^2$ **f)** $m^2 - 9mn + 14n^2$

9. Factor fully.

a) $3x^2 - 3x - 6$ **b)** $4t^2 - 28t + 40$

c) $ay^2 + ay - 12a$

10. Factor.

a) $3t^2 + 8t + 5$ **b)** $2m^2 - 9m + 4$

c) $6x^2 - x - 2$ **d)** $4y^2 + 4y - 3$

e) $5r^2 - 11rs + 2s^2$ **f)** $4x^2 - 8xy - 5y^2$

11. Factor.

a) $x^2 - 4$

b) $1 - 36m^2$

c) $36t^2 - 49s^2$

d) $121a^2 - b^2$

e) $x^2 + 8x + 16$

f) $y^2 - 6y + 9$

g) $4t^2 - 4t + 1$

h) $4m^2 + 20m + 25$

12. Factor fully.

a) $3y^2 - 27$

b) $9t - 4t^3$

c) $8x^2 + 24x + 18$

d) $x^3 - 4x^2 + 4x$

13. Baseball In baseball, the first base bag is a square. Its side length can be represented by the expression $5x + 3$.

a) Write and expand an expression to represent the area of the top of the bag.

b) If x represents 7 cm, what is the area of the top of the bag, in square centimetres?

14. Bank note The face of a Canadian $20 bill has an area that can be represented by the expression $10x^2 + 9x - 40$.

a) Factor $10x^2 + 9x - 40$ to find expressions that represent the dimensions of the bill.

b) If x represents 32 mm, what are the dimensions of the bill, in millimetres?

Achievement Check

1. List all values of b for which each trinomial can be factored over the integers. Explain and justify your reasoning.

a) $x^2 + bx + 24$

b) $x^2 + bx - 18$

2. Find three values of c such that each trinomial can be factored over the integers. Explain and justify your reasoning.

a) $2x^2 + 3x + c$

b) $3x^2 - 8x + c$

3. Develop a problem in which the value of a must be found in a trinomial that can be factored over the integers. Include a solution to your problem.

Logical thinking is a skill that can be improved with practice and applied in school, at work, and in everyday life.

Justine is a nature photographer. One day she drove from her cottage on the lake into town to get supplies. She left her cottage at 08:00, stopped several times to take pictures, and arrived in town at 15:00. She left for her cottage at 08:00 the next morning. She followed the same road back, stopped several times to take more pictures, and arrived at her cottage at 15:00. Show that there is one point on the road where Justine was exactly the same distance from her cottage at exactly the same time on both days.

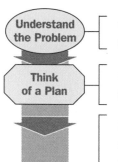

Understand the Problem
1. What information are you given?
2. What are you asked to find?

Think of a Plan
On the same set of axes, draw graphs of Justine's two trips, showing the distance from her cottage versus the time of day.

Carry Out the Plan
Since she made several stops during each trip, the graphs are not linear. The two graphs must intersect at some point.

At the point of intersection, Justine is exactly the same distance from her cottage at exactly the same time on both days.

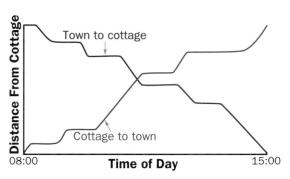

Look Back
Check that the solution agrees with the given information.

Could you solve the problem if, on the return trip, Justine left town at 10:00 and arrived at her cottage at 16:00? if she left town at 16:00 and arrived at her cottage at 21:00?

Use Logic
1. Organize the information.
2. Draw conclusions from the information.
3. Check that your answer is reasonable.

Applications and Problem Solving

1. Summer courses There are five courses in the School for the Arts summer program—painting, sculpting, music, drama, and film. Terri can choose three of the courses. In how many different combinations can she choose the three courses?

2. Whole numbers Find the two whole numbers less than 100 that satisfy the following conditions.
- Dividing by 2 gives a remainder of 1.
- Dividing by 3 gives a remainder of 1.
- Dividing by 4 gives a remainder of 1.
- Dividing by 5 gives a remainder of 0.

3. Hockey Three sportscasters, Aaron, Sandra, and Francois, predicted the winners of the same four hockey games on a Saturday night. Aaron said that Vancouver, Toronto, Edmonton, and Chicago would win. Sandra chose Montréal, Edmonton, Boston, and Toronto. Francois said that Calgary, Vancouver, Edmonton, and Montréal would win. No one chose Detroit to win. Which teams played each other?

4. System of equations In the system of equations, find the values of h and g.

$$a + b = c$$
$$c + d = e$$
$$a + e = f$$
$$f + g = h$$
$$h - e = 7$$
$$b + d + f = 30$$
$$a = 4$$

5. Number pattern The numbers 1 to 6 are arranged so that the difference between a pair of numbers appears between and below the pair of numbers. Use the same pattern to make a triangle with the numbers from 1 to 10. The 5 and the 7 have been placed for you.

6. Numbers in words Suppose you start to write the whole numbers in words, starting at one. Remember that 101 is written "one hundred one." In what number will
a) the letter "a" appear for the first time?
b) the letter "b" appear for the first time?

7. Toothpicks There are 3 piles of toothpicks, one with 11 toothpicks, one with 7, and the third with 6. You are to get 8 toothpicks in each pile in 3 moves. In one move, you must add to any pile exactly as many toothpicks as it already has, and all the toothpicks added must come from one other pile.

8. Cycle races The first time Rohana and Emma raced 20 km on bicycles, Emma was 2 km from the finish line when Rohana finished. The next day, Rohana agreed to start 2 km behind Emma, so that Rohana would ride 22 km and Emma, 20 km. If each of them rode at the same speed as she did during the first race, who won the second race?

9. Travelling times Chen and Sharif travelled from Acton to Beamsville on foot. Chen walked half the distance and ran half the distance. Sharif walked half the time and ran half the time. If they walked at the same speed and ran at the same speed, who arrived in less time, or was it a tie?

10. Lunch meeting Dylan is meeting his sister and four of her women friends for lunch. The five women are called Alicia, Rachel, Lani, Donna, and Casey. Three of the women are under 30 years old, and two are over 30. Two of the women are lawyers, and three are doctors. Alicia and Lani are in the same age group. Donna and Casey are in different age groups. Rachel and Casey have the same profession. Lani and Donna have different professions. Dylan's sister is a lawyer and is over 30. Who is Dylan's sister?

11. Communication Write a problem similar to question 7 or 10. Have a classmate solve your problem.

A valid way to solve many problems is to guess at the answer and then check to see if it is correct. You may find it necessary to improve your guess until you get the correct answer.

An architect is designing the parking lot for the club house at a golf course. The club house has dimensions 23 m by 20 m.

One possible design for the parking lot is an L-shape of uniform width, as shown in the diagram. The architect knows that an area of 14 m^2 is needed for each parking space, and that another 10 m^2 per space must be allowed for access routes. What is the width of the L-shaped parking lot, if there must be 100 parking spaces?

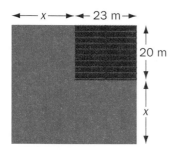

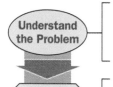

Understand the Problem

1. What information are you given?
2. What are you asked to find?
3. Do you need an exact or an approximate answer?

Think of a Plan

Determine the total area needed for the parking lot. Write an equation that relates this area to the width of the lot. Solve the equation to find the width.

Each parking space requires an area of 14 + 10 or 24 m².
For 100 parking spaces, the total area is 100 × 24 or 2400 m².

The parking lot can be divided into two rectangles, as shown.

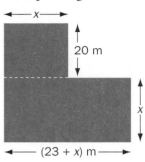

The total area is given by
$$20x + x(23 + x) = x(20 + 23 + x)$$
$$= x(43 + x)$$
So, $x(43 + x) = 2400$

Solve the equation by guess and check.

Guess   **Check**

Value of x	Value of $x(43 + x)$	Does $x(43 + x) = 2400$?
30	30(73) = 2190	Too low
35	35(78) = 2730	Too high
33	33(76) = 2508	Too high
32	32(75) = 2400	2400 checks!

Estimate

$30 \times 80 = 2400$

The width of the parking lot is 32 m.

How could you set up a spreadsheet to solve the problem by guess and check?

Carry Out the Plan

Look Back

Guess and Check

1. Guess an answer that fits some of the facts.
2. Check the answer against the other facts.
3. If necessary, adjust the guess and check again.

Applications and Problem Solving

1. Research Write your guess for each question. Compare each answer with a classmate's. Then, use your research skills to find the correct value.
a) How many kilometres long is the Trans-Canada Highway?
b) How many students are enrolled in your school?
c) How long would it take to drive from Halifax to Ottawa at a speed of 80 km/h?
d) How much does it cost to heat your school for a year?
e) Mount Logan is Canada's tallest mountain. How many metres tall is it?

2. Basketball In one game, the starting five players on the Westview basketball team scored a total of 93 points. Mary scored the fewest points. Sasha scored 5 more points than Mary. Paula scored 2 more points than Sasha. Amandi scored 2 more points than Paula. Heather scored 3 more points than Amandi. How many points did each player score?

3. Textbook Petra opened her math book to a place where the product of the page numbers was 14 042. What were the page numbers?

4. System of equations The letters x, y, and z represent integers.
$$x - y - z = 2$$
$$x \div y \div z = 2$$
Find the values of x, y, and z that satisfy both equations. There are two solutions.

5. Difference of squares The whole number 5 can be written as the difference of squares of two whole numbers as follows:
$$3^2 - 2^2 = 5$$
The whole number 4 can be written as the difference of squares of two whole numbers as follows:
$$2^2 - 0^2 = 4$$
There are five whole numbers less than 20 that cannot be written as the difference of squares of two whole numbers. What are they?

6. Number puzzle Copy the diagram. The number 9 has been placed in a circle. Place each of the other numbers from 1 to 10 in the other circles, so that each of the five lines adds to the same multiple of 6.

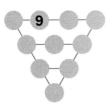

7. Vehicles Kurt washed the wheels of the cars and motorcycles parked on the dealership lot. If there were 32 vehicles, and he washed 110 wheels, how many motorcycles were there?

8. Shopping plaza The property occupied by a small, one-storey shopping plaza includes the U-shaped building and its rectangular parking lot, as shown. The floor area of the building is 896 m².

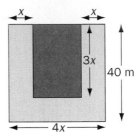

a) What is the value of x, in metres?
b) A parking space requires an area of 24 m², including enough room for access. How many cars can park in the parking lot?

9. Communication A unit fraction, such as $\frac{1}{7}$, is a fraction with 1 as the numerator.
a) Find three different unit fractions that add to 1.
b) Is it possible to have two different unit fractions that add to 1? Explain.

10. Equal sums Copy the diagram. Place the numbers 1, 2, 3, 4, 5, 6, 7, and 8 at the vertices of a cube, so that the sum of the numbers at the vertices of each face is the same.

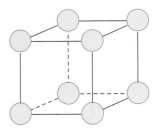

11. Communication Write a problem that can be solved using the guess and check strategy. Have a classmate solve your problem.

Problem Solving: Using the Strategies

1. Congruent pieces The diagram shows one way to divide the grid into two congruent pieces using line segments that connect grid points. Find 12 other ways.

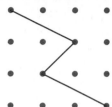

2. Large sum Find the last three digits of the sum $625^{13} + 376^{87}$.

3. Parking cars About how many cars could you park on the grounds surrounding your school?

4. Coins Suppose that you:
• place two identical coins as shown in the diagram
• press firmly on the bottom coin
• roll the top coin around the bottom one until the top coin returns to its original position

a) Predict how many times the rolling coin turns around its centre as it rolls around the stationary coin.
b) Test your prediction.
c) **Communication** Explain your observation.

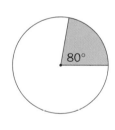

5. Number pattern If the pattern continues, what will be the number directly below 100?

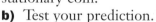

			1			
		2	3	4		
	5	6	7	8	9	
10	11	12	13	14	15	16

6. Arranging blocks In how many different ways can you arrange two identical blue blocks and two identical red blocks in a straight line?

7. Measurement The length, width, and height of a rectangular prism are whole numbers of centimetres. Three faces of the prism have areas of 144 cm², 72 cm², and 32 cm². What are the dimensions of the prism?

8. Abundant numbers The number 12 is the first "abundant number," because it is the smallest whole number for which the sum of its factors, not including itself, is greater than itself.
$$1 + 2 + 3 + 4 + 6 = 16$$
What are the next three abundant numbers?

9. Seating arrangement Four friends—Alexi, Kala, Lisa, and Jamal—are sitting at a round table. The person wearing the red shirt, who is not Alexi or Kala, is sitting between Lisa and the person wearing the blue shirt. The person wearing the green shirt is sitting between Kala and the person wearing the yellow shirt. What colour shirt is each person wearing?

10. Exact change At one stall at the Bargain Flea Market, every item costs a dollar or less, including tax. If you have 3 quarters, 2 dimes, and 5 pennies, how many different prices could you pay with exact change?

11. Rotation A sector with an angle of 80° rotates clockwise about the centre of a circle. The sector moves 80° on each move. How many 80° moves will it take for the sector to arrive back at its original position?

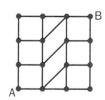

12. Tiling Suppose a road from Toronto to Denver is to be tiled with square tiles that have the same dimensions as processed cheese slices. About how many tiles will be needed if the road is 120 tiles wide?

13. Finding paths In the diagram, the red horizontal, vertical, and diagonal line segments join two points. How many paths are there from A to B that consist of exactly five of these line segments?

CHAPTER 4

Quadratic Functions

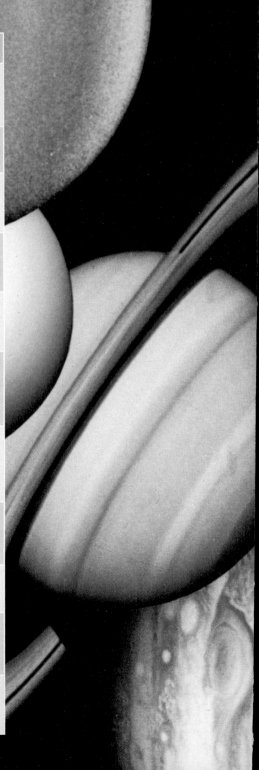

Specific Expectations	Sections
• Identify the effect of simple transformations on the graph and the equation of $y = x^2$, using graphing calculators or graphing software.	4.2
• Explain the role of a, h, and k in the graph of $y = a(x - h)^2 + k$.	4.2 4.3
• Express the equation of a quadratic function in the form $y = a(x - h)^2 + k$, given it in the form $y = ax^2 + bx + c$, using the algebraic method of completing the square.	4.4
• Sketch, by hand, the graph of a quadratic function whose equation is given in the form $y = ax^2 + bx + c$, by completing the square or by expressing in the form $y = ax(x - s) + t$.	4.4 4.5
• Collect data that may be represented by quadratic functions, from secondary sources or from experiments, using appropriate equipment and technology.	4.7 4.8
• Fit the equation of a quadratic function to a scatter plot, using an informal process, and compare the results with the equation of a curve of best fit produced by using graphing calculators or graphing software.	4.7 4.8
• Describe the nature of change in a quadratic function, using finite differences in tables of values, and compare the nature of change in a quadratic function with the nature of change in a linear function.	4.1 4.6
• Report the findings of an experiment in a clear and concise manner, using appropriate mathematical forms, and justify the conclusions reached.	4.7 4.8
• Determine the maximum or minimum value of a quadratic function, using algebraic techniques.	4.4
• Determine the zeros and the maximum or minimum of a quadratic function from its graph, using graphing calculators or graphing software.	4.2 4.3 4.4
• Solve problems related to an application, given the graph or the formula of a quadratic function.	4.2 4.3 4.4

Modelling Math

The Effect of Gravity

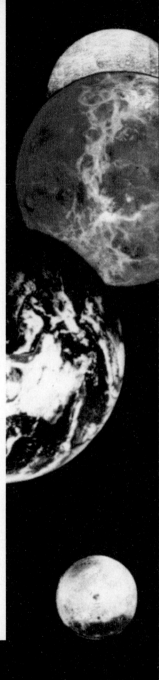

I saac Newton (1642–1727) was a brilliant scientist who made his greatest contributions in branches of physics. After Johannes Kepler (1571–1630) discovered that the planets move in elliptical orbits around the sun, Newton tried to answer some basic questions. What keeps the planets in elliptical orbits? On Earth, what keeps objects from flying into space when they are thrown into the air? Newton's answer was that there is a force called *gravity* that operates between all objects.

A ball is thrown upward from a height of 2 m with an initial velocity of 20 m/s. Its approximate height, *h* metres, after *t* seconds is given by the equation
$$h = -0.5gt^2 + 20t + 2$$

where *g* is a constant that describes the acceleration of gravity. The table gives the approximate value of *g* for three planets.

Planet	Value of g (m/s^2)
Earth	10
Mars	4
Pluto	0.5

For each planet, calculate
a) the maximum height the ball would reach
b) how many seconds the ball would take to reach its maximum height

In the Modelling Math questions on pages 216, 227, and 240, you will solve the above problem and other problems that involve the effect of gravity in different situations.

1. The word *gravity* comes from a Latin word. What is the Latin word, and what is its meaning?

2. How do the designers of amusement park rides incorporate the effect of gravity into their rides?

3. How did the Apollo Moon Program use the effect of gravity on the moon to bring spaceships back to Earth?

Getting Started

Falling Objects

Galileo discovered that, in the absence of resistance from the air or another medium, all objects dropped from equal distances above the Earth reach the ground at the same time. In the absence of resistance, the speed of a falling object increases steadily as it falls, as shown by the approximate values in the table. The rate of increase in the speed is known as the acceleration due to gravity.

Elapsed Time (s)	Total Distance Fallen (m)	Instantaneous Speed (m/s)
0	0	0
1	5	10
2	20	20
3	45	30
4	80	40

The diagram models the motion of a free-falling object.

0 s
⎱ 5 m ⟵ Distance fallen in first second
1 s
⎱ 15 m ⟵ Distance fallen in next second
2 s
⎱ 25 m
3 s
⎱ 35 m
4 s

Notice that, though the speed of the object was 10 m/s at the end of the first second, the object did not fall 10 m in the first second. The reason is that the object was not travelling at 10 m/s for the whole second.

1. Let the total distance fallen be d metres and the elapsed time be t seconds. Use the data in the first two columns of the table to write an equation in the form $d = \blacksquare t^{\blacktriangle}$, where $\blacksquare$ and $\blacktriangle$ represent whole numbers.

2. Use your equation to determine the distance an object falls in

a) 7 s

b) 8 s

c) the 6th second

3. Communication Graph the equation. Is it linear? Explain.

Review of Prerequisite Skills

If you need help with any of the skills named in **purple** below, refer to Appendix A.

1. Evaluating expressions Copy and complete each table of values.

a) $y = 3x - 4$

x	y
5	
3	
0	
–3	
–5	

b) $y = x^2$

x	y
4	
2	
0	
–2	
–4	

c) $y = x^2 - 4x$

x	y
5	
3	
0	
–3	
–5	

d) $y = x^2 + 3x - 5$

x	y
4	
2	
0	
–2	
–4	

2. Evaluating expressions Mentally evaluate each expression for the given values of x.

a) $x^2 + 3$; $x = 2, 4, -2, -4$

b) $2x^2 - 1$; $x = 1, -1, 3, -3$

c) $x^2 + x$; $x = 1, -1, -3, 6$

d) $-x^2 + 2x$; $x = 1, -1, 3, -4$

e) $3x^2 - 4x$; $x = 2, -1, 3, -2$

f) $x^2 - x - 3$; $x = 1, -2, 3, -3$

g) $(x + 2)^2 + 1$; $x = 1, -1, 3, -4$

h) $(x - 1)^2 - 4$; $x = 0, 1, -1, 4$

3. Greatest common factors State the missing factor.

a) $4x^2 + 4x = 4(\rule{2cm}{0.3cm})$

b) $2x^2 - 6x = 2(\rule{2cm}{0.3cm})$

c) $5x^2 + 10x = 5(\rule{2cm}{0.3cm})$

d) $-6x^2 - 12x = -6(\rule{2cm}{0.3cm})$

e) $-3x^2 + 12x = -3(\rule{2cm}{0.3cm})$

f) $-2x^2 - 8x = -2(\rule{2cm}{0.3cm})$

g) $-x^2 + 6x = -(\rule{2cm}{0.3cm})$

h) $-x^2 - 12x = -(\rule{2cm}{0.3cm})$

4. Write each of the following as the square of a binomial.

a) $x^2 + 4x + 4$

b) $x^2 + 6x + 9$

c) $x^2 - 2x + 1$

d) $x^2 - 8x + 16$

e) $x^2 + 20x + 100$

f) $x^2 - 12x + 36$

g) $x^2 - 18x + 81$

h) $x^2 + 22x + 121$

5. Polynomials State the degree of each polynomial.

a) $2x + 1$

b) x^2

c) $y^2 - 3y + 6$

d) $2m^3 + m - 9$

e) $3 - 5x^2 + 10x$

f) $4t^2 + t^4 - 3t$

6. First differences Use first differences to determine whether each relation is linear or non-linear.

a)

x	y
1	2
2	5
3	10
4	17

b)

x	y
1	6
2	11
3	16
4	21

7. Transformations
a) Draw △ABC on grid paper. Then, translate △ABC 4 units to the right and 3 units upward.

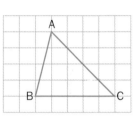

b) Communication Are △ABC and its translation image congruent? Explain.

8. Transformations
a) Draw △PQR and the line m on grid paper. Then, reflect △PQR in the line m.

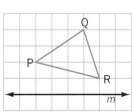

b) Communication Are △PQR and its reflection image congruent? Explain.

A relation is a set of ordered pairs, (x, y).
The following are three relations.
Relation A: $\{(2, 3), (4, 5), (6, 7), (8, 9)\}$
Relation B: $\{(6, 2), (6, 4), (8, 6), (10, 8)\}$
Relation C: $\{(-4, 8), (-2, 4), (0, 0), (2, 4), (4, 8)\}$

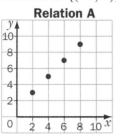

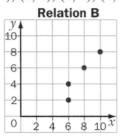

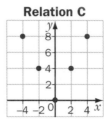

A function is a special relation. A **function** is a set of ordered pairs in which, for every value of x, there is only one value of y.

Relation A, above, is a function because, for every value of x, there is only one value of y.

Relation B is not a function because, when x is 6, there are two values of y, namely 2 and 4.

Relation C is a function. For different values of x, such as 4 and -4, y has the same value, 8. However, for every value of x, there is only one value of y.

Investigation   Complete the Table

The blue whale is the largest animal that has ever roamed our planet. A mature blue whale has a mass of about 150 t and is about 30 m long.

1. The blue whale has a cruising speed of 20 km/h. Copy and complete the table for the distance travelled in different lengths of time by a blue whale at cruising speed.

Time (h)	Distance (km)
2	
	60
	80
	140
	200

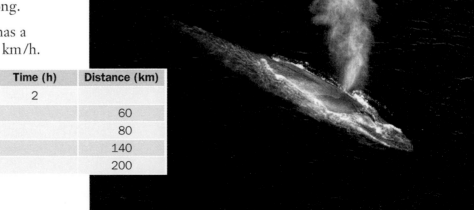

2. Write the relation as a set of ordered pairs, (time, distance).

3. Communication For a blue whale at cruising speed, can there be two different distances travelled in the same length of time? Explain.

4. Communication Is the relation shown in the table a function? Explain.

Example 1   Speed of a Blue Whale
A blue whale has a fleeing speed of about 9 m/s. The equation for the distance travelled, d metres, in a time of t seconds is $d = 9t$.
a) Graph the equation.
b) Is the relation a function? Explain.

Solution
a) Since the distance, d, depends on the time, t, we call d the **dependent variable** and t the **independent variable.**

It is customary to graph the dependent variable versus the independent variable. Graph the distance travelled as a function of the time using paper and pencil, a graphing calculator, or graphing software.

Time (s)	Distance (m)
0	0
1	9
2	18
3	27
4	36

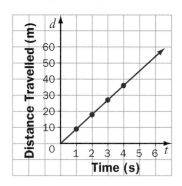

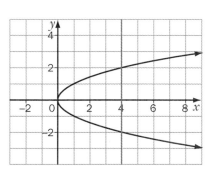

b) The relation is a function because, for every value of t, there is only one value of d.

The graph of a relation can be analyzed to determine if the relation is a function. One method is to use the **vertical line test**. If any vertical line passes through more than one point on the graph, then the relation is not a function.

For the graph shown, the vertical line passes through two points on the graph, namely (4, 2) and (4, −2). When $x = 4$, there are two values for y, 2 and −2. The relation represented by the graph is not a function.

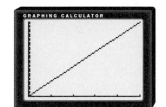

Example 2　Vertical Line Test

Use the vertical line test to determine if each relation is a function.

a)

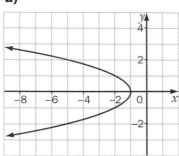

b)

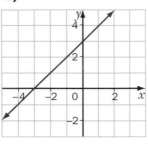

c)

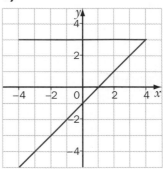

Solution

a) This relation is not a function. A vertical line passes through more than one point.

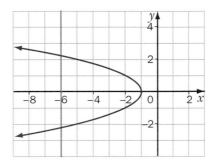

b) This relation is a function. No vertical line passes through more than one point.

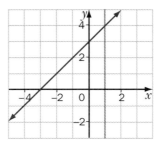

c) This relation is not a function. A vertical line passes through more than one point.

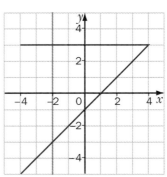

The set of the first elements in a relation is called the **domain** of the relation. For the relation {(2, 3), (4, 5), (6, 7), (8, 9)}, the domain is {2, 4, 6, 8}.

The set of the second elements in a relation is called the **range** of the relation. For the relation {(2, 3), (4, 5), (6, 7), (8, 9)}, the range is {3, 5, 7, 9}.

A function can be defined as a set of ordered pairs in which, for each element in the domain, there is exactly one element in the range.

Example 3   Determining the Domain and Range

Determine the domain and range of each of the following functions.

a)

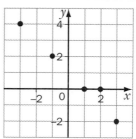

b)

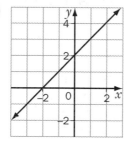

c)

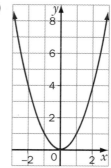

Solution

a) The domain is the set of the first elements.
Domain = {−3, −1, 1, 2, 3}
The range is the set of the second elements.
Range = {4, 2, 0, −2}

b) Since x can be any real number, the domain is the set of real numbers. Since y can be any real number, the range is the set of real numbers.

c) Since x can be any real number, the domain is the set of real numbers. Since the value of y is always greater than or equal to 0, the range is $y \geq 0$.

Key CONCEPTS

1 A function is a set of ordered pairs in which, for every *x*, there is only one *y*.
2 If any vertical line passes through more than one point on the graph of a relation, then the relation is not a function.
3 The set of the first elements in a relation is called the domain. The set of the second elements in a relation is called the range.

Communicate Your Understanding

1. Explain the difference between a relation and a function.

2. Describe how you would determine which of the following relations is a function.

a)

x	y
2	4
1	2
0	1
−1	2
−2	5

b)

x	y
7	6
5	3
5	4
3	1
1	0

c) {(1, 3), (2, 4), (4, 9), (3, 7), (2, 6)}

3. Describe how you would determine which of the following graphs represent functions.

a)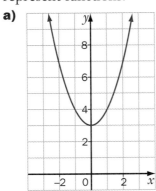

b)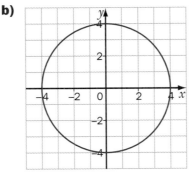

c)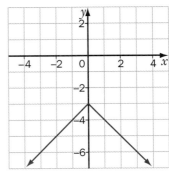

4. Describe how you would determine the domain and range of each of the following functions.

a)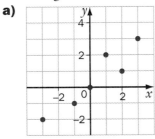

b)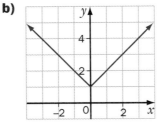

Practice

A

1. State whether each set of ordered pairs represents a function.
a) {(2, 3), (3, 4), (4, 5), (5, 6), (6, 7)}
b) {(5, −3), (6, −4), (7, −5), (8, −6)}
c) {(4, 2), (5, 3), (4, 6), (6, 7)}
d) {(6, 3), (7, 3), (8, 3)}
e) {(7, −1), (8, 0), (9, 1)}
f) {(5, 4), (5, 5), (5, 6), (5, 7)}

2. If $y = 4x - 5$, find the value of y for each of the following values of x.
a) 2   **b)** 7   **c)** 0   **d)** −2   **e)** −4
f) 100   **g)** 0.5   **h)** −0.5   **i)** 1000

3. If $y = 8 - 2x$, find the value of y for each of the following values of x.
a) 1   **b)** 3   **c)** 5   **d)** −3   **e)** 0
f) 10   **g)** 0.5   **h)** −0.1   **i)** 4

4. If $y = x^2 + 5$, find the value of y for each of the following values of x.
a) 2   **b)** 0   **c)** −2   **d)** 10   **e)** −10
f) 0.5   **g)** −0.1

5. If $m = 2n^2 - 4n + 3$, find the value of m for each of the following values of n.
a) 0   **b)** 1   **c)** −2   **d)** 10   **e)** −10
f) 0.5   **g)** 1.5

6. a) Graph the equation $y = 2x + 1$.   **b)** Is the relation a function?

7. State which of the following are graphs of functions.
a)
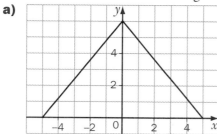
b)
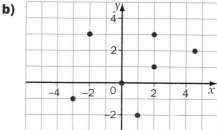
c)
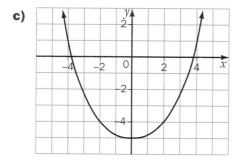
d)
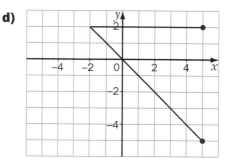

8. State the domain and range of each relation.
a) {(3, 1), (4, −2), (5, 3), (6, 0)}   **b)** {(−3, 2), (−1, 4), (1, 4), (3, 2), (5, 3)}
c) {(−2, 3), (−1, 3), (0, 3), (1, 4)}   **d)** {(−1, 1), (−1, 2), (−1, 3), (−1, 4)}

9. State the domain and range of each relation, and state whether it is a function.

a)

x	y
2	5
1	2
0	1
−1	2
−2	5

b)

x	y
3	1
3	−2
2	0
1	−1
0	−2

10. Determine the domain and range of each of the following relations.

a)
b)
c)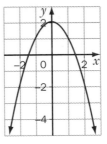
d)

11. The function $y = x^2 + 2$ has a domain $\{-2, -1, 0, 1, 2\}$. Find the range.

Applications and Problem Solving

12. Mach number An aircraft breaks the sound barrier when it flies at about 1200 km/h. This speed is known as Mach 1. The Mach number, M, is given by the function $M = \dfrac{s}{1200}$, where s is the speed of the aircraft in kilometres per hour.
a) What is the value of M when $s = 2400$? when $s = 3000$?
b) Communication In the function defined by the ordered pairs (speed, Mach number), identify the dependent variable and the independent variable. Explain your reasoning.

B

13. Canadian population a) Use the census data in the table to sketch a graph of the population of Canada as a function of the year.
b) Use the graph to estimate the population in 1958.
c) Use the graph to predict the year in which the population will reach 40 million.

Year	Population (millions)
1921	8.8
1931	10.4
1941	11.5
1951	14.0
1961	18.2
1971	21.6
1981	24.3
1991	27.3

14. Communication a) On the same set of axes, graph the functions $y = x$ and $y = x^2$, where x and y are real numbers.
b) For the graph of $y = x$, does x or y have a maximum or minimum value? Explain.
c) For the graph of $y = x^2$, does x or y have a maximum or minimum value? Explain.
d) Describe any other similarities and differences in the graphs.

15. Graph each function. The domain is the set of real numbers. Find the range.
a) $y = 3x - 4$ **b)** $y = x^2 - 2$

16. Algebra If $y = x^2 - 4$, what value(s) of x give each of the following values of y?
a) 0   **b)** 12   **c)** -4 **d)** 7

17. Communication a) Is the set of ordered pairs (n, f) a function, if n is a person's name and f is the person's fingerprints?
b) Reverse the terms of the ordered pairs so that the set of ordered pairs is (f, n). Is the new set of ordered pairs a function? Explain.

18. Communication Is the set of ordered pairs (f, l) a function, if f is the first name of a person in your school and l is the last name of the person? Explain.

19. Communication Explain why the vertical line test works.

C

20. Algebra Write and simplify the equation obtained when the given expression is substituted for x.
a) $y = 4x + 3;\ x = 2a$ **b)** $y = 2 - 3x;\ x = n + 1$
c) $y = x^2 + 1;\ x = m - 1$ **d)** $y = 2x^2 - 3;\ x = 2k + 1$
e) $y = x^2 + 4x - 1;\ x = 3t - 1$ **f)** $y = 3x^2 - 2x + 4;\ x = 3 - 2w$

21. Communication If a linear relation is not a function, what can you state about the graph of the relation? Explain.

22. Gym rental The cost of renting a gym includes an initial fee, plus an additional fee for each hour or part of an hour of use. The rates are shown in the table.

Time (h)	Cost ($)
Up to and including 1	120
Greater than 1; up to and including 2	200
Greater than 2; up to and including 3	280
Greater than 3; up to and including 4	360

The graph of the cost as a function of time is shown.

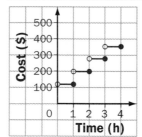

a) Communication Explain why the open and closed dots are used on the graph.
b) Communication The function represented by the graph is known as a **step function**. Explain why.
c) State the domain and range of the function.
d) Write two ordered pairs with the same cost value to represent points on the graph.
e) Write two ordered pairs with different cost values to represent points on the graph.
f) Communication Is it possible to write two different ordered pairs with the same time value to represent points on the graph? Explain.

23. Research Use your research skills to find a rule used to calculate each of the following. Then, sketch the graph of each function.
a) the cost of mailing a first-class letter to an address in Canada as a function of the mass of the letter
b) a taxi fare as a function of the distance travelled

Investigation: Transformations on a Coordinate Grid

1 Translations on a Coordinate Grid

A **translation**, or slide, is a transformation that moves a figure to a new position in the same plane. The diagram shows a translation. △ABC has been translated 5 units to the right and 3 units upward.

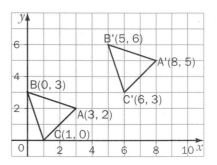

△A′B′C′ is the **translation image** of △ABC. △A′B′C′ has the same size and shape as △ABC. They are congruent triangles.

Notice that A-B-C and A′-B′-C′ read in the same direction, in this case counterclockwise. We say that △ABC and △A′B′C′ have the same **sense**, or **orientation**.

Any point on △ABC can be translated onto the corresponding point on △A′B′C′ by adding 5 to its x-coordinate and adding 3 to its y-coordinate. For example, vertex C(1, 0) is translated onto vertex C′(1 + 5, 0 + 3), or C′(6, 3). Therefore, the translation can be modelled mathematically as the following mapping.

$$(x, y) \rightarrow (x + 5, y + 3)$$

We say that (x, y) maps onto $(x + 5, y + 3)$.

1. Draw each triangle on grid paper. Then, draw the translation image.
a) D(0, 0), E(−4, 0), F(−4, −6)
Translation: 2 units to the right and 4 units upward
b) P(3, 2), Q(−1, 4), R(−3, −5)
Translation: 4 units to the left and 2 units upward
c) U(−2, −1), V(0, 6), W(1, 3)
Translation: 1 unit to the left and 3 units downward
d) F(2, −2), G(−4, 5), H(−1, −3)
Translation: $(x, y) \rightarrow (x + 2, y + 1)$
e) A(−2, 0), B(4, −1), C(2, −4)
Translation: $(x, y) \rightarrow (x + 3, y − 3)$
f) J(2, 2), K(−1, 3), L(−3, −2)
Translation: $(x, y) \rightarrow (x − 3, y − 4)$

2. △RST has been translated 2 units to the right and 4 units upward. The coordinates of the vertices of the image, △R′S′T′, are R′(3, 0), S′(0, 7), and T′(−2, −1). What are the coordinates of R, S, and T?

3. a) △ABC has vertices A(3, 0), B(−1, 5), and C(−3, 1). Draw △ABC on grid paper. Translate △ABC 4 units to the right and 3 units upward. Determine the coordinates of the translation image, △A′B′C′.
b) Translate △A′B′C′ 1 unit to the left and 5 units downward. Determine the coordinates of the translation image, △A″B″C″.
c) What translation would make △A″B″C″ the translation image of △ABC?

2 Reflections on a Coordinate Grid

A **reflection** is a transformation in which a figure is reflected over a **mirror line** or **reflection line**.

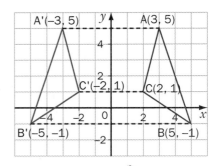

The diagram shows a reflection. △ABC has been reflected in the y-axis. △A′B′C′ is the **reflection image** of △ABC. △A′B′C′ has the same size and shape as △ABC. They are congruent triangles.

Notice that A-B-C and A′-B′-C′ read in opposite directions. The sense of a reflection image is the reverse of the sense of the original figure.

A line segment joining any point on △ABC and its reflection image on △A′B′C′ is perpendicular to the reflection line. Any point and its reflection image are the same distance from the reflection line. For example, vertices A and A′ are both 3 units from the y-axis.

1. Copy each figure onto a grid and draw its reflection image in the x-axis.

a) 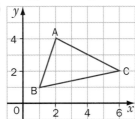 b) 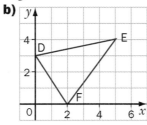 c)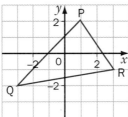

2. Draw each triangle on a grid. Draw the image after a reflection in the y-axis.

a) 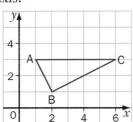 b) 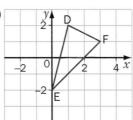 c)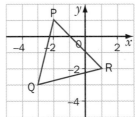

3. Find the coordinates of the image of each point after a reflection in each axis.

	Point	Reflection Line	
		x-axis	y-axis
a)	(2, 3)		
b)	(−1, −2)		
c)	(−3, 2)		
d)	(4, 0)		

4. $\triangle ABC$ has vertices A(1, 1), B(5, 2), and C(3, 6). Draw the image of $\triangle ABC$ after a reflection in the *y*-axis.

5. $\triangle RST$ has vertices R(2, 5), S(−2, 4), and T(−1, −2). Draw the image of $\triangle RST$ after a reflection in the *x*-axis.

6. Communication Name the reflection line for a reflection that can be modelled as each of the following mappings. Explain your reasoning.

a) $(x, y) \rightarrow (−x, y)$ **b)** $(x, y) \rightarrow (x, −y)$

3 Dilatations on a Coordinate Grid

A **dilatation** is a transformation that changes the size of an object. Dilatations are called **enlargements** or **reductions**, depending on the way in which the size is changed. In an enlargement, an object is stretched to give a bigger image. In a reduction, an object is shrunk to give a smaller image.

The diagram shows a dilatation, in this case an enlargement. $\triangle A'B'C'$ is the **dilatation image** of $\triangle ABC$. The coordinates of the vertices of $\triangle ABC$, A(1, 2), B(3, −1), and C(−2, −2), have been multiplied by 3 to give the coordinates of the vertices of $\triangle A'B'C'$, A'(3, 6), B'(9, −3), and C'(−6, −6).

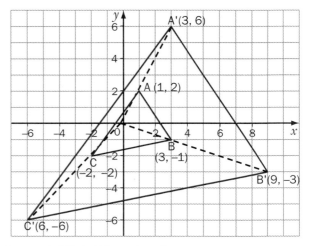

The factor by which the coordinates of the points on a figure are multiplied to give the coordinates of the points on its dilatation image is known as the **scale factor**. For the dilatation of $\triangle ABC$ to give its image, $\triangle A'B'C'$, the scale factor is 3.

$\triangle A'B'C'$ has the same shape but not the same size as $\triangle ABC$. The triangles are said to be **similar**.

A-B-C and A'-B'-C' read in the same direction, in this case clockwise, so $\triangle ABC$ and $\triangle A'B'C'$ have the same sense.

Notice that the straight line drawn from the origin (0, 0) through A passes through A'. Similarly, the straight line drawn from the origin through B passes through B', and the straight line drawn from the origin through C passes through C'. We say that $\triangle ABC$ has been enlarged by a dilatation with **centre** (0, 0).

The dilatation with centre (0, 0) and scale factor 3 can be modelled mathematically as the following mapping.

$$(x, y) \rightarrow (3x, 3y)$$

In general, a dilatation with centre (0, 0) and scale factor k can be modelled mathematically as the following mapping.

$$(x, y) \rightarrow (kx, ky)$$

When $k > 1$, the mapping gives an enlargement.
When $k < 1$, the mapping gives a reduction.

1. A figure is shown with its image to the right. What is the scale factor?

a)

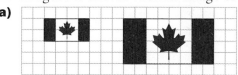

b)

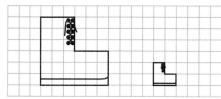

2. Draw the dilatation image of each line segment under the given mapping.

	Line Segment	Mapping
a)	A(3, 2), B(1, 4)	$(x, y) \rightarrow (2x, 2y)$
b)	C(6, 4), D(−2, 2)	$(x, y) \rightarrow \left(\frac{1}{2}x, \frac{1}{2}y\right)$
c)	E(−1, −1), F(1, 2)	$(x, y) \rightarrow (3x, 3y)$
d)	G(9, 3), H(−6, 0)	$(x, y) \rightarrow \left(\frac{1}{3}x, \frac{1}{3}y\right)$

3. △RST has vertices R(2, 3), S(−1, 4), and T(−3, −2). Find the image of △RST under the mapping $(x, y) \rightarrow (3x, 3y)$.

4. Quadrilateral DEFG has vertices D(6, 4), E(−2, 6), F(−4, −4), and G(4, −6). Find the image of quadrilateral DEFG under the mapping $(x, y) \rightarrow \left(\frac{1}{2}x, \frac{1}{2}y\right)$.

5. △PQR has vertices P(−2, 2), Q(−2, −2), and R(2, −2).
a) Draw △PQR on grid paper.
b) Calculate the area of △PQR.
c) Find the image of △PQR, △P′Q′R′, under the mapping $(x, y) \rightarrow (3x, 3y)$.
d) Calculate the area of △P′Q′R′.
e) Find the image of △PQR, △P″Q″R″, under the mapping $(x, y) \rightarrow \left(\frac{1}{2}x, \frac{1}{2}y\right)$.

f) Calculate the area of △P″Q″R″.
g) Write the following ratios.
area △P′Q′R′ : area △PQR
area △P″Q″R″ : area △PQR
h) Communication How is each ratio related to the scale factor that produced the image?

Heritage Day, the birthday of Canada's Maple Leaf flag, is celebrated in February each year. Some celebrations involve the display of large Canadian flags. The largest Canadian flag in the world measures 12.19 m by 24.38 m.

Regulation Canadian flags are twice as long as they are wide. If the width of a Canadian flag is x, then the length is $2x$. The area, y, can be represented by the expression

$$y = 2x \times x$$
$$= 2x^2$$

The equation $y = 2x^2$ is an example of a quadratic function. The word quadratic comes from the Latin word *quadratum*, meaning square.

The simplest quadratic function is $y = x^2$. Its graph is a parabola. Parabolas have a geometric property called **symmetry**. Symmetrical figures are those that can be folded along a fold line such that each half of the figure exactly matches the other half. This fold line is called the **axis of symmetry** of the figure.

The axis of symmetry of a parabola is the reflection line that maps the parabola onto itself. For the graph of $y = x^2$, the axis of symmetry is the y-axis. The equation of the axis of symmetry is $x = 0$.

$y = x^2$

x	y
3	9
2	4
1	1
−1	1
−2	4
−3	9

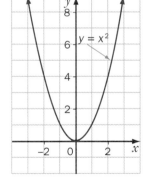

The **vertex**, or turning point, of the parabola is the point at which the graph intersects the axis of symmetry. For $y = x^2$, the coordinates of the vertex are (0, 0).

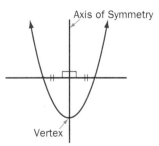

Axis of Symmetry

Vertex

In this section, the effects of two transformations on the basic quadratic function $y = x^2$ will be examined, separately and together.

Investigation · Comparing $y = x^2$ and $y = x^2 + k$

1. Graph the following functions on the same set of axes using a graphing calculator or graphing software.

a) $y = x^2$ **b)** $y = x^2 + 2$ **c)** $y = x^2 - 5$

2. Communication How are the three graphs the same? How are they different?

3. For each graph,
a) use the **Minimum operation** of the graphing calculator, or an equivalent graphing software method, to write the coordinates of the vertex
b) write the equation of the axis of symmetry

4. What translation maps the graph of $y = x^2$ onto the graph of
a) $y = x^2 + 2$?   **b)** $y = x^2 - 5$?

5. Without graphing, write the coordinates of the vertex and the equation of the axis of symmetry for each of the following functions.
a) $y = x^2 + 1$ **b)** $y = x^2 - 3$ **c)** $y = x^2 - 7$ **d)** $y = x^2 + 8$

Investigation · Comparing $y = x^2$ and $y = ax^2$

1. Graph the following functions on the same set of axes using a graphing calculator or graphing software.

a) $y = x^2$ **b)** $y = -x^2$ **c)** $y = 3x^2$

d) $y = -3x^2$ **e)** $y = \dfrac{1}{3}x^2$ **f)** $y = -\dfrac{1}{3}x^2$

2. Communication a) Which graphs open up? Which graphs open down?
b) What determines the direction of the opening?

3. For each graph,
a) use the **Minimum operation** or the **Maximum operation** of the graphing calculator, or an equivalent graphing software method, to write the coordinates of the vertex
b) write the equation of the axis of symmetry

4. What transformation maps
a) $y = x^2$ onto $y = -x^2$?   **b)** $y = 3x^2$ onto $y = -3x^2$?
c) $y = \dfrac{1}{3}x^2$ onto $y = -\dfrac{1}{3}x^2$?

5. Communication How does the shape of the graphs of $y = 3x^2$ and $y = -3x^2$ compare with the shape of the graphs of $y = x^2$ and $y = -x^2$?

6. Communication How does the shape of the graphs of $y = \dfrac{1}{3}x^2$ and $y = -\dfrac{1}{3}x^2$ compare with the shape of the graphs of $y = x^2$ and $y = -x^2$?

1. Use your findings from the previous investigations to predict and sketch the graph of each of the following functions.

a) $y = x^2 + 3$ **b)** $y = -x^2 + 3$

c) $y = 3x^2 - 4$ **d)** $y = -3x^2 + 5$

e) $y = \frac{1}{3}x^2 + 1$ **f)** $y = -\frac{1}{3}x^2 - 2$

2. Communication For each graph from question 1, write
a) the direction of the opening
b) the coordinates of the vertex
c) the equation of the axis of symmetry
d) a description of how the shape compares with the shape of the graphs of $y = x^2$ and $y = -x^2$

3. Use a graphing calculator or graphing software to check your answers to questions 1 and 2.

A **quadratic function** is a function determined by a second degree polynomial. Examples of quadratic functions are
$$y = x^2 \qquad y = 2x^2 + 4 \qquad y = 3x^2 - 2x \qquad y = x^2 + 2x - 7$$

A quadratic function is a function that can be written in the form
$$y = ax^2 + bx + c$$
where a, b, and c are real numbers, and $a \neq 0$.

If the domain is the set of real numbers, the graph of a quadratic function is a parabola. The values of a, b, and c determine where the parabola is located on the coordinate plane, and whether the parabola opens up or down. The vertex of the graph of a quadratic function is either the maximum (highest) point or the minimum (lowest) point on the graph.

Example 1   **Graphing $y = x^2 + k$**
a) Graph $y = x^2 + 3$ and $y = x^2 - 4$. Compare the graphs to the graph of $y = x^2$.
b) Describe each graph in terms of its vertex, axis of symmetry, domain and range, and the maximum or minimum value of the function.

Solution

a) Graph manually using a table of values, or graph using a graphing calculator or graphing software.

$y = x^2$

x	y
3	9
2	4
1	1
0	0
−1	1
−2	4
−3	9

$y = x^2 + 3$

x	y
3	12
2	7
1	4
0	3
−1	4
−2	7
−3	12

$y = x^2 - 4$

x	y
3	5
2	0
1	−3
0	−4
−1	−3
−2	0
−3	5

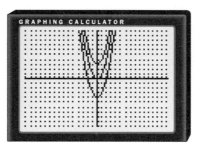

Use the ZSquare instruction to make the scales on the axes equal. Use the format settings to turn the grid on or off.

The graphs of $y = x^2 + 3$ and $y = x^2 - 4$ are congruent to $y = x^2$. All three have the same size and shape, but they are in different positions.

For $y = x^2 + 3$, the y-coordinates are all 3 greater than the corresponding y-coordinates of $y = x^2$. The graph of $y = x^2 + 3$ is the graph of $y = x^2$ translated upward by 3 units.

For $y = x^2 - 4$, the y-coordinates are all 4 less than the corresponding y-coordinates of $y = x^2$. The graph of $y = x^2 - 4$ is the graph of $y = x^2$ translated downward by 4 units.

b) For $y = x^2 + 3$, the vertex is $(0, 3)$. The equation of the axis of symmetry is $x = 0$.
The domain is the set of real numbers, and the range is $y \geq 3$.
The function reaches a minimum value of $y = 3$ when $x = 0$.

For $y = x^2 - 4$, the vertex is $(0, -4)$. The equation of the axis of symmetry is $x = 0$.
The domain is the set of real numbers, and the range is $y \geq -4$.
The function reaches a minimum value of $y = -4$ when $x = 0$.

Example 2　Graphing $y = ax^2$

Graph $y = 2x^2$, $y = \dfrac{1}{2}x^2$, $y = -x^2$, $y = -2x^2$, and $y = -\dfrac{1}{2}x^2$.

Compare the graphs to each other and to the graph of $y = x^2$.

Solution

To graph manually, set up tables of values.

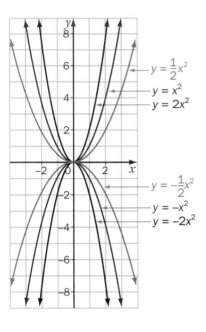

$y = x^2$

x	y
3	9
2	4
1	1
0	0
−1	1
−2	4
−3	9

$y = 2x^2$

x	y
3	18
2	8
1	2
0	0
−1	2
−2	8
−3	18

$y = \dfrac{1}{2}x^2$

x	y
3	4.5
2	2
1	0.5
0	0
−1	0.5
−2	2
−3	4.5

$y = -x^2$

x	y
3	−9
2	−4
1	−1
0	0
−1	−1
−2	−4
−3	−9

$y = -2x^2$

x	y
3	−18
2	−8
1	−2
0	0
−1	−2
−2	−8
−3	−18

$y = -\dfrac{1}{2}x^2$

x	y
3	−4.5
2	−2
1	−0.5
0	0
−1	−0.5
−2	−2
−3	−4.5

Alternatively, graph using a graphing calculator or graphing software.

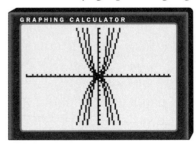

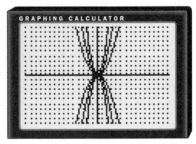

Using the format settings, turn the grid on or off, as you prefer.

The y-coordinates of $y = -x^2$ are opposite to the corresponding y-coordinates of $y = x^2$. The graph of $y = -x^2$ is a reflection of the graph of $y = x^2$ in the x-axis.

For $a > 0$, the parabolas open up, and each vertex is the minimum point on the graph.

For $a < 0$, the parabolas open down, and each vertex is the maximum point on the graph.

In comparison with $y = x^2$, if $a > 1$ or $a < -1$, there is a vertical stretch, and the parabola narrows.

The y-coordinates of $y = 2x^2$ are two times the corresponding y-coordinates of $y = x^2$.

The graph of $y = -2x^2$ is the graph of $y = 2x^2$ reflected in the x-axis, or the graph of $y = x^2$ reflected in the x-axis and then stretched vertically by a scale factor of 2.

In comparison with $y = x^2$, if $-1 < a < 1$, there is a vertical shrink, and the parabola widens.

Recall that $-1 < a < 1$ means that a is less than 1 and greater than -1.

The y-coordinates of $y = \dfrac{1}{2}x^2$ are half the corresponding y-coordinates of $y = x^2$.

The graph of $y = -\dfrac{1}{2}x^2$ is the graph of $y = \dfrac{1}{2}x^2$ reflected in the x-axis, or the graph of $y = x^2$ reflected in the x-axis and then shrunk vertically by a scale factor of $\dfrac{1}{2}$.

Example 3   Graphing $y = ax^2 + k$

Sketch the graph of $y = -2x^2 + 8$ and find
a) the coordinates of the vertex
b) the equation of the axis of symmetry
c) the domain and range
d) the maximum or minimum value
e) any intercepts

Solution

The graph of $y = -2x^2 + 8$ is the graph of $y = -2x^2$ translated 8 units upward.
a) The coordinates of the vertex are $(0, 8)$.
b) The equation of the axis of symmetry is $x = 0$.
c) The domain is the set of real numbers.
The range is $y \le 8$.
d) The graph opens down, so the vertex is the highest point on the graph.
The maximum value of the function is 8 when $x = 0$.
e) The graph intersects the y-axis at $(0, 8)$, so the y-intercept is 8.
The graph appears to cross the x-axis at $(2, 0)$ and $(-2, 0)$, so the x-intercepts are 2 and -2.

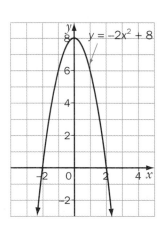

Note that, in Example 3, the Zero operation on a graphing calculator could be used to find the values of the *x*-intercepts. Another graphing calculator method involves displaying a table of values.

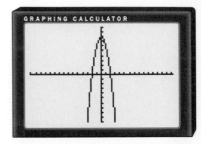
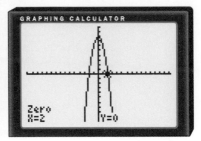

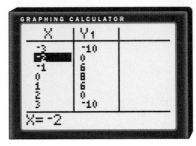

The above examples show that we can visualize the functions by identifying the transformations shown in the general equation.

If *a* < 0, reflection in *x*-axis

$$y = ax^2 + k$$

vertical stretch or shrink

vertical translation

Example 4   St. Louis Gateway Arch

The stainless steel Gateway Arch in St. Louis, Missouri, has the shape of a **catenary**, which is a curve that approximates a parabola. If the curve is graphed on a grid with the origin on the ground directly below the top of the arch, the curve can be modelled by the function

$$h = -0.02d^2 + 192$$

where *h* metres is the height of the arch, and *d* metres is the horizontal distance from the centre of the arch.

a) Graph the shape of the arch.

b) Find the maximum height of the arch.

c) Find the approximate width of the arch at the base.

d) Find the approximate height of the arch at a horizontal distance of 15 m from one end.

Solution

a) Graph the function.

d	h
0	192
20	184
40	160
60	120
80	64
90	30
−20	184
−40	160
−60	120
−80	64
−90	30

$h = -0.02d^2 + 192$

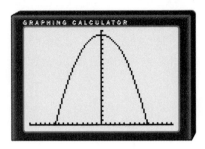

b) Since the origin is directly below the top of the arch, the maximum value of the function gives the maximum height of the arch.

The maximum value is 192, so the maximum height of the arch is 192 m.

c) The width of the arch at the base is the distance from one d-intercept to the other. From the manual graph, the d-intercepts appear to be just less than 100 and just greater than −100, so the width of the arch is close to 200 m. A graphing calculator can give more accurate values for the d-intercepts of about 98 and −98.

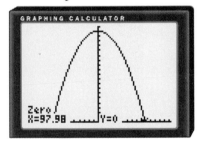

The width of the arch is about 196 m.

d) Because the curve has an axis of symmetry through the vertex, the height of the curve 15 units from either end is the same.

Since the positive d-intercept is about 98, the height of the curve 15 units from this end can be found by evaluating h when d is 98 − 15 or 83.

$$h = -0.02d^2 + 192$$
$$= -0.02(83)^2 + 192$$
$$\doteq 54$$

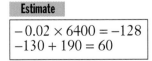

Estimate

$-0.02 \times 6400 = -128$

$-130 + 190 = 60$

So, the height of the arch at a horizontal distance of 15 m from one end is about 54 m.

Key CONCEPTS

1 The table summarizes how parabolas in the form $y = ax^2 + k$ are obtained by transforming the function $y = x^2$.

Operation	Resulting Equation	Transformation
Multiply by a.	$y = ax^2$	Reflects in the x-axis, if $a < 0$.
		Stretches vertically (narrows), if $a > 1$ or $a < -1$.
		Shrinks vertically (widens), if $-1 < a < 1$.
Add k.	$y = ax^2 + k$	Shifts k units upward, if $k > 0$.
		Shifts k units downward, if $k < 0$.

2 Some geometric properties of the parabola $y = ax^2 + k$ are summarized in the following table.

Property	Sign of a	
	positive	negative
Vertex	$(0, k)$	$(0, k)$
Axis of Symmetry	$x = 0$	$x = 0$
Direction of Opening	up	down
Comparison with $y = ax^2$	congruent	congruent

Communicate Your Understanding

1. For each function, describe how you would find the coordinates of the vertex, the equation of the axis of symmetry, the domain and range, and the maximum or minimum value.

a) $y = x^2 + 1$ **b)** $y = -x^2 - 2$
c) $y = 2x^2 + 4$ **d)** $y = -2x^2 - 1$

2. Describe how you would determine the x- and y-intercepts of the parabola $y = 3x^2 - 12$.

3. How can you use symmetry to help draw the graph of a quadratic function using paper and pencil?

4. How can you determine whether the vertex of a parabola is a maximum or minimum without graphing?

5. Is the graph of $y = -x^2$ the same as the graph of $y = (-x)^2$? Explain and justify your reasoning.

Practice

A

1. Sketch the graph of each parabola and state the direction of the opening, the coordinates of the vertex, the equation of the axis of symmetry, the domain and range, and the maximum or minimum value.

a) $y = x^2 + 5$ **b)** $y = x^2 - 2$ **c)** $y = -x^2 - 1$ **d)** $y = -x^2 + 3$

e) $y = 3x^2$ **f)** $y = -4x^2$ **g)** $y = 2 + x^2$ **h)** $y = -1.5x^2$

i) $y = -2x^2 - 3$ **j)** $y = 0.5x^2 + 1$ **k)** $y = -0.5x^2 + 7$ **l)** $y = -3x^2 - 6$

2. Communication Write one sentence that compares each pair of graphs.

a) $y = x^2$ and $y = x^2 - 4$ **b)** $y = -x^2$ and $y = -x^2 + 5$

c) $y = x^2$ and $y = 3x^2$ **d)** $y = -x^2$ and $y = -\frac{1}{3}x^2$

e) $y = 2x^2 + 7$ and $y = 2x^2 - 2$ **f)** $y = 0.25x^2$ and $y = -0.25x^2$

3. The four graphs represent the four equations $y = 2x^2 - 3$, $y = -2x^2 - 3$, $y = 2x^2 + 3$, and $y = -2x^2 + 3$. Match each graph with the correct equation.

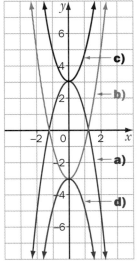

4. Without graphing each function, state the direction of the opening, the coordinates of the vertex, the domain and range, and the maximum or minimum value.

a) $y = -5x^2$ **b)** $y = x^2 - 11.4$

c) $y = -x^2 + 4.7$ **d)** $y = 2x^2 - 3$

e) $y = -2.9x^2 - 8.3$ **f)** $y - 9.9 = 1.6x^2$

g) $3.5 + 2.2x^2 = y$ **h)** $4.3x^2 + y = -0.5$

5. Communication Describe what happens to the point $(2, 4)$ on the graph of $y = x^2$ when each pair of transformations is applied to the parabola in the given order.

a) a vertical stretch of scale factor 2, followed by a vertical translation of 5

b) a reflection in the x-axis, followed by a vertical translation of 3

c) a reflection in the x-axis, followed by a vertical shrink of scale factor $\frac{1}{2}$

d) a vertical translation of -2, followed by a reflection in the x-axis

6. Graph each parabola. State the coordinates of the vertex. Find any intercepts.

a) $y = x^2 - 9$

b) $y = x^2 + 1$

c) $y = -x^2 + 4$

d) $y = 2x^2 - 8$

e) $y = 16 + x^2$

f) $y = 18 - 2x^2$

g) $y = -3 - 3x^2$

h) $y = -5x^2 + 5$

7. Use a graphing calculator or graphing software to determine any x-intercepts, to the nearest tenth.

a) $y = x^2 - 2$

b) $y = -x^2 + 3$

c) $y = x^2 + 6$

d) $y = 2x^2 - 10$

e) $y = 8 - 4x^2$

f) $y = 0.5x^2 - 3$

Applications and Problem Solving

8. Communication If a function of the form $y = ax^2 + k$ has an x-intercept of 7.5, what is the other x-intercept? Explain how you know.

9. Geometry For triangles in which the base and the height are equal,

a) write an equation that relates the area, A, to the height, h

b) graph A versus h

c) find the h- and A-intercepts

d) state the domain and range

 B

10. Write an equation for a parabola with the given vertex and given value of a.

a) $(0, 0)$; $a = 5$

b) $(0, 0)$; $a = -6$

c) $(0, -7)$; $a = -8$

d) $(0, 3)$; $a = 0.2$

11. Find the value of k so that the parabola $y = -2x^2 + k$ passes through the point $(-3, -33)$.

12. Golden Gate Bridge The road on the Golden Gate Bridge is supported by two towers and the two cables that join them. The distance between the towers is 1280 m. Suppose the curve of a cable is graphed on a grid, with the origin on the road at the centre of the bridge. The curve made by the cable is a catenary that can be approximately modelled by the quadratic function

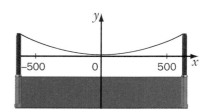

$$h = 0.000\ 37d^2 + 2$$

where h metres is the height of the cable above the road, and d metres is the horizontal distance from the centre of the bridge.

a) Graph the function.

b) What is the distance from the road to the lowest point of the cable?

c) What is the maximum height of the towers above the road, to the nearest ten metres?

d) At a horizontal distance of 200 m from the centre of the bridge, how high is the cable above the road, to the nearest metre?

13. Communication Graph $x + y = 4$ and $y = x^2 - 2$ on the same axes.
a) What are the coordinates of the intersection points?
b) Describe how you found the intersection points.

C

14. Find a and k so that a parabola $y = ax^2 + k$ passes through each pair of points.
a) $(-3, 11)$ and $(4, 18)$
b) $(3, -10)$ and $(-1, -2)$
c) $(1, -1)$ and $(2, 5)$
d) $(-4, -4)$ and $(2, 2)$

15. Patterns In the sequence $-2, 4, 14, 28, \ldots$, the number -2 is in position 1, the number 4 is in position 2, and so on.
a) Write an equation that relates each number, n, to its position, p, in the sequence.
b) Repeat part a) for the sequence $2, -4, -14, -28, \ldots$.
c) Communication How are the graphs of n versus p for the two sequences related?

16. Geometry a) Write an equation that relates the area of a circle, A, to its radius, r.
b) Graph A versus r.
c) Communication Does the graph have an axis of symmetry? Explain.
d) State the domain and range of the function.

17. Measurement The 25 by 16 rectangle contains a square of side length s. The sides of the square are parallel to the sides of the rectangle.

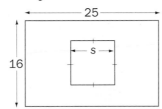

a) Write the area of the shaded region, A, as a function of s.
b) If no part of the square can be outside the rectangle, what is the maximum possible value of s?
c) Graph A versus s.
d) State the domain and range of the function.

18. Communication For quadratic functions of the form $y = ax^2 + k$, where x and y are real numbers, describe any relationships between the values of a and k and
a) the number of y-intercepts
b) the number of x-intercepts

For the equation $y = 0.5x^2$, state **window variables** that produce views of the parabola that resemble the following. Compare your values with your classmates'.

a) a line with a positive slope
b) a line with a negative slope
c) a vertical line

Modelling Math   The Effect of Gravity

For an object dropped from a certain height, the approximate height of the falling object above the ground can be modelled by the function
$$h = -5t^2 + d$$
where h metres is the height t seconds after the object is dropped, and d metres is the height from which it is dropped. Suppose an object is dropped 145 m, the height of the Exchange Tower in Toronto.

a) Graph the function.
b) **Communication** In which quadrant(s) did you graph the function? Explain and justify your reasoning.
c) Use the graph to find how long the object takes to reach the ground, to the nearest tenth of a second.
d) On the moon, the approximate height of a falling object can be modelled by the function
$$h = -0.8t^2 + d$$
If an object is dropped from a height of 145 m, how long does it take to reach the surface of the moon, to the nearest tenth of a second?

Web Connection   www.school.mcgrawhill.ca/resources/

Visit the above web site to find the height of a tall building, in metres. Go to **Math Resources**, then to *MATHPOWER™ 10, Ontario Edition*, to find out where to go next. As described in the Modelling Math problem, above, use the function $h = -5t^2 + d$ to determine the time an object dropped from this height takes to reach the ground, to the nearest tenth of a second.

4.3 Graphing $y = a(x - h)^2 + k$

A quadratic function can be written in several forms. One form is $y = a(x - h)^2 + k$. Writing quadratic functions in this form helps in their analysis.

The Symphony of Fire is the largest offshore fireworks competition in the world. The fireworks are launched from barges anchored in Lake Ontario, close to Toronto. The fireworks are synchronized with a musical soundtrack. Competing countries are judged on the choice of music, the synchronization, and the visual display.

A function that describes the flight of one type of rocket in a fireworks display is
$$h = -4.9(t - 5)^2 + 124$$
where h is the height of the rocket, in metres, and t is the time, in seconds, since it was launched. This function will be used in Example 4.

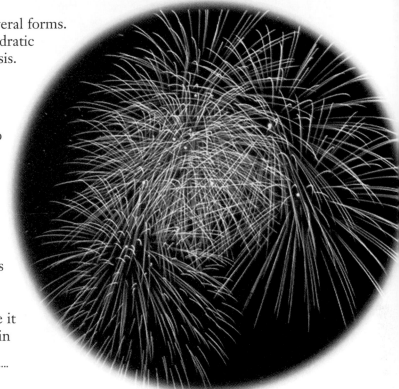

Investigation Compare the Graphs

1. Graph each group of functions on the same set of axes using a graphing calculator, graphing software, or paper and pencil. For each group of functions, complete a table like the one shown.

Group 1: **a)** $y = x^2$ **b)** $y = (x - 4)^2$ **c)** $y = (x + 3)^2$
Group 2: **a)** $y = (x - 4)^2$ **b)** $y = (x - 4)^2 + 2$ **c)** $y = (x - 4)^2 - 3$
Group 3: **a)** $y = (x + 3)^2$ **b)** $y = (x + 3)^2 + 5$ **c)** $y = (x + 3)^2 - 1$

Group 1	Function	Vertex	Axis of Symmetry
a)	$y = x^2$		
b)	$y = (x - 4)^2$		
c)	$y = (x + 3)^2$		

2. For group 1 in question 1, how is the graph of $y = x^2$ translated when x is replaced by
a) $x - 4$? **b)** $x + 3$?

3. Without graphing, write the coordinates of the vertex and the equation of the axis of symmetry for each of the following functions.
a) $y = (x - 7)^2$ **b)** $y = (x + 9)^2$

4. For group 2 in question 1, what translation maps the graph of $y = (x - 4)^2$ onto the graph of
a) $y = (x - 4)^2 + 2$? **b)** $y = (x - 4)^2 - 3$?

5. Without graphing, write the coordinates of the vertex and the equation of the axis of symmetry for each of the following functions.
a) $y = (x - 7)^2 + 6$ **b)** $y = (x - 6)^2 - 5$

6. For group 3 in question 1, what translation maps the graph of $y = (x + 3)^2$ onto the graph of
a) $y = (x + 3)^2 + 5$?   **b)** $y = (x + 3)^2 - 1$?

7. Without graphing, write the coordinates of the vertex and the equation of the axis of symmetry for each of the following functions.
a) $y = (x + 9)^2 + 4$ **b)** $y = (x + 5)^2 - 7$

The graphs of $y = x^2$, $y = x^2 + 5$, $y = (x - 2)^2$, and $y = (x + 3)^2 - 4$ are shown. The graphs of $y = x^2 + 5$, $y = (x - 2)^2$, and $y = (x + 3)^2 - 4$ are congruent to $y = x^2$ but have different positions.

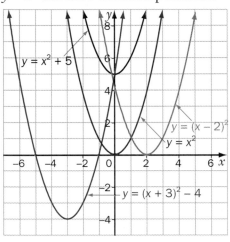

When using a graphing calculator, you may find it easier to keep track by adding one curve at a time to the viewing window and sketching each result.

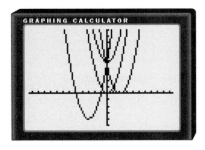

The graph of $y = x^2 + 5$ is the graph of $y = x^2$ translated 5 units upward. The graph of $y = (x - 2)^2$ is the graph of $y = x^2$ translated 2 units to the right. The graph of $y = (x + 3)^2 - 4$ is the graph of $y = x^2$ translated 3 units to the left and 4 units downward.

All quadratic functions can be written in the form $y = a(x - h)^2 + k$.

Function	Function in Form $y = a(x - h)^2 + k$	h	k	Vertex	Axis of Symmetry
$y = x^2$	$y = 1(x - 0)^2 + 0$	0	0	(0, 0)	$x = 0$
$y = x^2 + 5$	$y = 1(x - 0)^2 + 5$	0	5	(0, 5)	$x = 0$
$y = (x - 2)^2$	$y = 1(x - 2)^2 + 0$	2	0	(2, 0)	$x = 2$
$y = (x + 3)^2 - 4$	$y = 1(x + 3)^2 - 4$	-3	-4	(-3, -4)	$x = -3$

For a quadratic function written in the form $y = a(x - h)^2 + k$,
- the coordinates of the vertex are (h, k)
- the equation of the axis of symmetry is $x = h$

Comparing $y = a(x - h)^2 + k$ with $y = x^2$,
- if h is positive, the parabola is translated h units to the right
- if h is negative, the parabola is translated h units to the left
- if k is positive, the parabola is translated k units upward
- if k is negative, the parabola is translated k units downward

Example 1   Graphing When $a > 0$

Sketch the graphs of $y = 2x^2$, $y = 2(x - 4)^2$, and $y = 2(x + 1)^2 + 4$.
Describe each graph in terms of the direction of the opening, the vertex,
the axis of symmetry, the domain and range, and the maximum or minimum
value of the function.

Solution

The graph of $y = 2x^2$ opens up and has the vertex $(0, 0)$.
The equation of the axis of symmetry is $x = 0$.
The domain is the set of real numbers, and the
range is $y \geq 0$.
The function reaches a minimum value of $y = 0$
when $x = 0$.

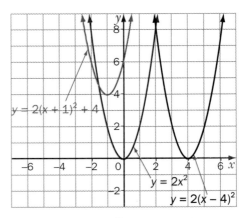

The graph of $y = 2(x - 4)^2$ is the graph of $y = 2x^2$
translated 4 units to the right. The graph of
$y = 2(x - 4)^2$ opens up.
The vertex is $(4, 0)$. The equation of the axis of
symmetry is $x = 4$.
The domain is the set of real numbers, and the
range is $y \geq 0$.
The function reaches a minimum value of $y = 0$
when $x = 4$.

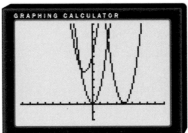

The graph of $y = 2(x + 1)^2 + 4$ is the graph of $y = 2x^2$
translated 1 unit to the left and 4 units upward.
The graph of $y = 2(x + 1)^2 + 4$ opens up.
The vertex is $(-1, 4)$. The equation of the axis of
symmetry is $x = -1$.
The domain is the set of real numbers, and the
range is $y \geq 4$.
The function reaches a minimum value of $y = 4$
when $x = -1$.

Example 2   Graphing When $a < 0$

Sketch the graphs of $y = -3x^2$, $y = -3(x + 2)^2$, and $y = -3(x - 5)^2 - 2$.
Describe each graph in terms of the direction of the opening, the vertex,
the axis of symmetry, the domain and range, and the maximum or minimum
value of the function.

Solution

The graph of $y = -3x^2$ opens down and has the
vertex $(0, 0)$.
The equation of the axis of symmetry is $x = 0$.
The domain is the set of real numbers, and the
range is $y \le 0$.
The function reaches a maximum value of $y = 0$
when $x = 0$.

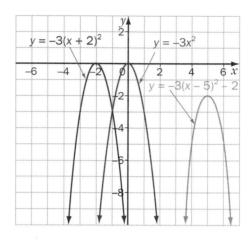

The graph of $y = -3(x + 2)^2$ is the graph of $y = -3x^2$
translated 2 units to the left.
The graph of $y = -3(x + 2)^2$ opens down.
The vertex is $(-2, 0)$. The equation of the axis of
symmetry is $x = -2$.
The domain is the set of real numbers, and the
range is $y \le 0$.
The function reaches a maximum value of $y = 0$
when $x = -2$.

The graph of $y = -3(x - 5)^2 - 2$ is the graph of
$y = -3x^2$ translated 5 units to the right and 2 units
downward.
The graph of $y = -3(x - 5)^2 - 2$ opens down.
The vertex is $(5, -2)$. The equation of the axis
of symmetry is $x = 5$.
The domain is the set of real numbers, and the
range is $y \le -2$.
The function reaches a maximum value of
$y = -2$ when $x = 5$.

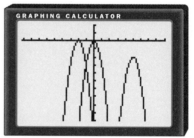

The previous examples show that we can visualize all parabolas,
$y = a(x - h)^2 + k$, by identifying the transformations shown in this
form of the function.

If $a < 0$,
reflection   horizontal
in x-axis   translation
$$y \;=\; a(x \;-\; h)^2 \;+\; k$$
vertical   vertical
stretch   translation
or shrink

Example 3   Locating Intercepts

Sketch the graph of $y = (x + 1)^2 - 4$ and find the intercepts.

Solution

Starting with $y = x^2$, shift the graph 1 unit to the left and 4 units downward to get $y = (x + 1)^2 - 4$.

The graph appears to intersect the x-axis at $(-3, 0)$ and $(1, 0)$, so the x-intercepts appear to be -3 and 1. These values can also be found using the **Zero operation** on a graphing calculator.

The manual graph appears to intersect the y-axis at $(0, -3)$, so the y-intercept appears to be -3. Ways of finding the value on a graphing calculator include **displaying a table** of values or using the **Value operation**. The y-intercept can also be found by substituting 0 for x in the equation.

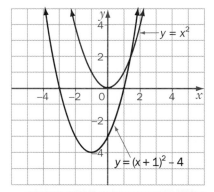

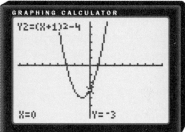

Example 4   Symphony of Fire

The flight of one type of rocket at the Symphony of Fire is described by the function
$$h = -4.9(t - 5)^2 + 124$$
where h is the height of the rocket, in metres, and t is the time, in seconds, since the rocket was fired.

a) What is the maximum height reached by the rocket? How many seconds after it was fired does the rocket reach this height?

b) How high was the rocket above the lake when it was fired?

Solution

a) The function is a parabola in the form $y = a(x - h)^2 + k$, so the vertex is (h, k) or $(5, 124)$.

Since a is negative, the parabola opens down. The vertex is the maximum point on the graph.

So, the rocket reaches a maximum height of 124 m after 5 s.

b) When the rocket was fired, $t = 0$ s.

Substitution into $h = -4.9(t - 5)^2 + 124$ gives
$$
\begin{aligned}
h &= -4.9(0 - 5)^2 + 124 \\
&= -4.9(25) + 124 \\
&= -122.5 + 124 \\
&= 1.5
\end{aligned}
$$

So, the rocket was 1.5 m above the lake when it was fired.

Key CONCEPTS

1 The table summarizes how parabolas in the form $y = a(x - h)^2 + k$ are obtained by transforming the function $y = x^2$.

Operation	Resulting Equation	Transformation
Multiply by *a*.	$y = ax^2$	Reflects in the *x*-axis, if $a < 0$.
		Stretches vertically (narrows), if $a > 1$ or $a < -1$.
		Shrinks vertically (widens), if $-1 < a < 1$.
Replace *x* by $(x - h)$.	$y = a(x - h)^2$	Shifts *h* units to the right, if $h > 0$.
		Shifts *h* units to the left, if $h < 0$.
Add *k*.	$y = a(x - h)^2 + k$	Shifts *k* units upward, if $k > 0$.
		Shifts *k* units downward, if $k < 0$.

2 Some geometric properties of the parabola $y = a(x - h)^2 + k$ are summarized in the following table.

Property	Sign of *a* positive	Sign of *a* negative
Vertex	(h, k)	(h, k)
Axis of Symmetry	$x = h$	$x = h$
Direction of Opening	up	down
Comparison with $y = ax^2$	congruent	congruent

Communicate Your Understanding

1. For each function, describe how you would find the coordinates of the vertex, the equation of the axis of symmetry, and the maximum or minimum value.

a) $y = (x + 5)^2 + 2$ **b)** $y = 3(x - 2)^2 - 4$ **c)** $y = -2(x + 4)^2 + 3$

2. Describe how you would determine the intercepts of the parabola $y = (x - 3)^2 - 4$.

3. Explain whether it is possible for a parabola to have
a) no *y*-intercept   **b)** no *x*-intercepts

Practice

A

1. Sketch each parabola and state the direction of the opening, the coordinates of the vertex, the equation of the axis of symmetry, the domain and range, and the maximum or minimum value.

a) $y = (x + 5)^2$ **b)** $y = -(x + 1)^2$ **c)** $y = (x - 3)^2$

d) $y = (x + 2)^2 + 4$ **e)** $y = -(x - 2)^2 - 5$ **f)** $y = (x + 3)^2 - 5$

g) $y = (x + 6)^2 + 2$ **h)** $y = (x - 5)^2 - 4$ **i)** $y = -(x + 4)^2 + 3$

2. Without sketching each parabola, state the direction of the opening, the coordinates of the vertex, the equation of the axis of symmetry, the domain and range, and the maximum or minimum value.

a) $y = (x - 5)^2$

b) $y = -(x + 4)^2$

c) $y = (x - 2)^2 + 1$

d) $y = -(x + 1)^2 - 2$

3. For each parabola, state the direction of the opening, how the parabola is stretched or shrunk, the coordinates of the vertex, the equation of the axis of symmetry, and the maximum or minimum value.

a) $y = 2(x - 1)^2$

b) $y = -0.5(x + 7)^2$

c) $y = -2(x - 4)^2 + 7$

d) $y = 4(x + 3)^2 - 4$

e) $y = -3(x - 5)^2 + 6$

f) $y = -0.4(x - 8)^2 - 1$

g) $y = \dfrac{1}{3}(x + 6)^2 - 7$

h) $y = 0.5(x + 1)^2 - 5$

i) $y = 2.5(x + 1.5)^2 - 9$

j) $y = -1.2(x - 2.6)^2 + 3.3$

4. The four graphs represent the four equations $y = 3(x - 1)^2 + 2$, $y = 3(x + 1)^2 - 2$, $y = -3(x + 1)^2 + 2$, and $y = -3(x - 1)^2 - 2$. Match each graph with the correct equation.

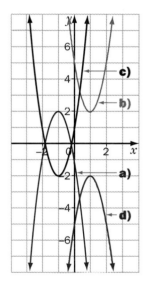

5. Sketch each parabola.

a) $y = (2 + x)^2$

b) $y = 3 + (x - 1)^2$

c) $y - 4 = -2(3 + x)^2$

d) $y + \dfrac{6}{5} = 3(x - 5)^2 + \dfrac{1}{5}$

6. Sketch each parabola and estimate any intercepts.

a) $y = (x - 2)^2$

b) $y = (x + 2)^2 - 9$

c) $y = (x - 3)^2 - 1$

d) $y = -(x + 2)^2 + 1$

7. Determine any x- and y-intercepts by graphing using a graphing calculator or graphing software. Round to the nearest tenth, if necessary.

a) $y = (x + 1)^2 - 3$

b) $y = 2(x - 1)^2 - 4$

c) $y = -4(x - 1)^2 + 1$

d) $y = -5(x + 3)^2 - 2$

e) $y = 0.25(x + 4)^2$

f) $y = -0.5(x + 3)^2 + 2$

Applications and Problem Solving

8. Aerial flares Red aerial miniflares are used by some boaters in an emergency. The flight of one brand of flare, when fired at an angle of 70° to the horizontal, is modelled by the function
$$h = -9(t - 3)^2 + 83$$
where h is the height, in metres, and t is the time, in seconds, since the flare was fired.
a) What is the maximum height of the flare?
b) For how many seconds does the flare burn before it hits the water?

B

9. Write an equation for the parabola with the given vertex and the given value of a.
a) $(7, 0)$; $a = 1$ 　　　　**b)** $(-5, 0)$; $a = -1$
c) $(3, -5)$; $a = 2$ 　　　　**d)** $(6, 7)$; $a = -3$
e) $(-1, -1)$; $a = -0.5$ 　　**f)** $(-8, 9)$; $a = 1.5$

10. Write an equation that defines each parabola.
a) congruent to $y = x^2$; opens up; vertex at $(1, 5)$
b) congruent to $y = x^2$; opens down; vertex at $(-3, 0)$
c) congruent to $y = 3x^2$; minimum at $(4, -2)$
d) congruent to $y = 2x^2$; maximum at $(2, -3)$
e) congruent to $y = 0.4x^2$; opens up; vertex at $(-3, -3)$
f) congruent to $y = 5x^2$; minimum at $(4.5, 0)$
g) congruent to $y = 4x^2$; maximum on the x-axis; axis of symmetry $x = 3$
h) congruent to $y = 2x^2$; minimum value -6; axis of symmetry $x = -5$

11. The vertex of a parabola is $(-2, -4)$. One x-intercept is 7. What is the other x-intercept?

12. Communication The x-intercepts of a parabola are 5 and -7. What is the equation of the axis of symmetry? Explain.

13. Two points on a parabola are $(4, -1)$ and $(-10, -1)$. What is the equation of the axis of symmetry?

14. Baseball The following function gives the height, h metres, of a batted baseball as a function of the time, t seconds, since the ball was hit.
$$h = -6(t - 2.5)^2 + 38.5$$
a) What was the maximum height of the ball?
b) What was the height of the ball when it was hit?
c) How many seconds after it was hit did the ball hit the ground, to the nearest second?
d) Find the height of the ball 1 s after it was hit.

15. Soccer The equation shows the height of a soccer ball, h metres, as a function of the horizontal distance, d metres, the ball travels until it first hits the ground.

$$h = -0.025(d - 20)^2 + 10$$

a) What is the maximum height of the ball?

b) What is the horizontal distance of the ball from the kicker when it reaches its maximum height?

c) How far does the ball travel horizontally from when it is kicked until it hits the ground?

d) What is the height of the ball when it is 10 m horizontally from the kicker?

e) Communication Would an opposing player positioned under the path of the ball 34 m from the kicker be able to head the ball? Explain.

f) If the origin were placed at the vertex of the parabola, what would be the equation of the curve?

16. Touch football A touch football quarterback passed the ball to a receiver 40 m downfield. The path of the ball can be described by the function

$$h = -0.01(d - 20)^2 + 6$$

where h is the height of the ball, in metres, and d is the horizontal distance of the ball from the quarterback, in metres.

a) What was the maximum height of the ball?

b) What was the horizontal distance of the ball from the quarterback at its maximum height?

c) What was the height of the ball when it was thrown? when it was caught?

d) If a defensive back was 2 m in front of the receiver, how far was the defensive back from the quarterback?

e) How high would the defensive back have needed to reach to knock down the pass?

17. a) Sketch the graphs of each pair of functions. Compare the parabolas in each pair.

$y = (x - 1)^2$ and $y = (1 - x)^2$

$y = (x - 4)^2 - 2$ and $y = (4 - x)^2 - 2$

b) Explain your results by expanding $(x - h)^2$ and $(h - x)^2$.

18. Systems of equations a) Graph $y = 3x + 3$ and $y = (x + 2)^2 - 3$ on the same set of axes.

b) What are the coordinates of the intersection points?

c) Communication Describe how you found the intersection points.

19. The functions $y = m(x - 3)^2 + 1$ and $y = n(x - 2)^2 - 3$ are graphed on the same set of axes. How do m and n compare if the graphs both open up and

a) the graphs are congruent?

b) the first graph is narrower than the second?

c) the first graph is wider than the second?

20. Determine the value of k so that the graph of $y = (x + 3)^2 + k$ passes through the point (1, 20).

C

21. Write an equation for the parabola with the given vertex and passing through the given point.
a) vertex (−4, −5); point (−2, −1)
b) vertex (3, 2); point (1, −2)
c) vertex (1, 6); point (3, 2)
d) vertex (−2, 3); point (−1, 6)
e) vertex (−5, −3); point (−3, −11)
f) vertex (6, 4); point (8, 6)

22. Write an equation for each parabola, given the vertex and the y-intercept.
a) vertex (1, 2); y-intercept 4
b) vertex (−2, 3); y-intercept −1
c) vertex (2, −4); y-intercept −2
d) vertex (−4, −1); y-intercept −5

23. Find a and k so that the given points lie on the parabola.
a) $y = a(x − 1)^2 + k$; (2, 6), (3, 12)
b) $y = a(x + 3)^2 + k$; (−5, −8), (1, −20)
c) $y = a(x − 4)^2 + k$; (1, −13), (−1, −45)

24. Communication Describe the graph of $y = a(x − h)^2 + k$ if
a) $h = 0$
b) $k = 0$
c) $h = 0$ and $k = 0$

25. Geometry The area of a square is 3 square units greater than the area of the square shown.
a) Write an equation that relates the area, A, of the larger square to the value of x.
b) Sketch a graph of A versus x for the larger square.
c) What value of x results in the minimum area for the larger square?
d) What is the area of the smaller square when the larger square has its minimum area?

$x − 2$

26. Write the equation of the image of $y = 3(x − 2)^2 + 1$ that results from
a) a reflection in the x-axis
b) a reflection in the y-axis
c) a reflection in the y-axis, followed by a reflection in the x-axis

27. Astronomy British astronomer William Lassell used a telescope he built himself to discover a moon around Neptune in 1846, two moons around Uranus in 1851, and a moon around Saturn in 1858. The mirror from his telescope has a diameter of about 60 cm and a maximum depth of about 0.36 cm. A cross section of the mirror is in the shape of a parabola.
a) Suppose the origin of a coordinate grid is placed at the vertex, the y-axis is the axis of symmetry, and the units on the axes are centimetres. What are the coordinates of each end of the curve?
b) Write an equation for the curve.

60 cm

0.36 cm

c) Move the origin to the end that had two positive coordinates in part a). Write an equation for the curve.
d) Move the origin to the other end of the curve. Write an equation for the curve.
e) Determine the depth of the mirror at a horizontal distance of 20 cm from the vertex.

Technology Extension

For the equation $y = 2(x - 18)^2 + 54$, state window variables that produce views of the parabola that resemble the following. Compare your values with your classmates'.
a) a line with a positive slope
b) a line with a negative slope
c) a vertical line
d) a horizontal line

Modelling Math | **The Effect of Gravity**

The highest Canadian waterfall with a single leap is Hunlen Falls. If an object is thrown straight downward from the height of Hunlen Falls with an initial velocity of 10 m/s, the height of the object above the ground can be approximated by the function
$$d = -5(t + 1)^2 + 258$$
where d metres is the height of the object, and t seconds is the time since the object was thrown.
a) Graph the function.
b) **Communication** Which part of the graph describes the falling object? Explain.
c) What is the height of the falls, in metres?
d) How long does the object take to reach the ground, to the nearest tenth of a second?

Achievement Check
1   2   3   4

A parabolic bridge over a road is 4 m tall, 4 m wide at the base, and 5 m long. Determine the maximum height of a 2-m wide truck that can drive under the bridge. Explain and justify your reasoning.

The Canadian Space Agency (CSA) is involved in such programs as the Canadian Astronaut Program and the Space Science Program. The Space Science Program gives astronauts, such as Julie Payette, access to parabolic flight as part of their training, so that they can become accustomed to weightlessness. A modified DC-9 aircraft is used. It flies in parabolic arcs. One flight of the aircraft includes from 40 to 50 parabolas, each providing astronauts with a simulation of weightless conditions.

The parabolic flight of the aircraft can be modelled by the quadratic function
$$h = -10t^2 + 300t + 9750$$
where h is the altitude of the aircraft, in metres, and t is the time, in seconds, since weightlessness was achieved. This function will be used in Example 4.

The above function is written in the form $y = ax^2 + bx + c$. The analysis of quadratic functions is more convenient in the form $y = a(x - h)^2 + k$. Therefore, a method for rewriting quadratic functions from the form $y = ax^2 + bx + c$ to the form $y = a(x - h)^2 + k$ is useful.

Investigation Look for a Pattern

1. Copy and complete the table by factoring each perfect square trinomial. The first row has been completed for you.

Trinomial, $x^2 + bx + c$	Value of b	Value of c	Factored Form, $(x - h)^2$	Value of h
$x^2 + 6x + 9$	6	9	$(x + 3)^2$	-3
$x^2 + 2x + 1$				
$x^2 + 10x + 25$				
$x^2 - 2x + 1$				
$x^2 - 8x + 16$				
$x^2 - 14x + 49$				

I can't do this

2. Communication The data in each row of the table can be used to write an equation in the form

$$x^2 + bx + c = (x - h)^2$$

If you know the value of b for a perfect square trinomial,
a) how can you find c?   **b)** how can you find h?

3. Use the results from question 1 to copy and complete the following equations for perfect squares. Then, state the value of h.

a) $x^2 + 12x + \blacksquare = (x + \blacktriangle)^2;\ h = \blacktriangledown$ **b)** $x^2 + 16x + \blacksquare = (x + \blacktriangle)^2;\ h = \blacktriangledown$

c) $x^2 - 20x + \blacksquare = (x - \blacktriangle)^2;\ h = \blacktriangledown$ **d)** $x^2 - 4x + \blacksquare = (x - \blacktriangle)^2;\ h = \blacktriangledown$

e) $x^2 + 1.6x + \blacksquare = (x + \blacktriangle)^2;\ h = \blacktriangledown$ **f)** $x^2 - 3x + \blacksquare = (x - \blacktriangle)^2;\ h = \blacktriangledown$

To graph a quadratic function in the form $y = ax^2 + bx + c$, a table of values can be used. For example, the function $y = x^2 + 2x - 3$ can be graphed using the table of values shown. Alternatively, the function can be graphed using a graphing calculator or graphing software.

x	y
-4	5
-3	0
-2	-3
-1	-4
0	-3
1	0
2	5

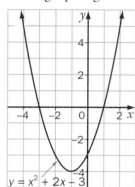

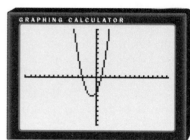

Another method uses the perfect square pattern to change the equation of a quadratic function from the form $y = ax^2 + bx + c$ to the form $y = a(x - h)^2 + k$. The form $y = a(x - h)^2 + k$ can then be used to sketch the graph.

Example 1   **Changing From $y = ax^2 + bx + c$ to $y = a(x - h)^2 + k$**
a) Rewrite the equation $y = x^2 + 6x + 8$ in the form $y = a(x - h)^2 + k$.
b) Sketch the graph. Find the range and any intercepts.

Solution
a) First, determine what must be added to $x^2 + 6x$ to make it a perfect square trinomial. The square of half the coefficient of x is 9. Since 9 must be added to the original function, 9 must also be subtracted to keep the value of the function the same.

$$y = x^2 + 6x + 8$$

Add and subtract the square of half the coefficient of x: $= x^2 + 6x + 9 - 9 + 8$
Group the perfect square trinomial: $= (x^2 + 6x + 9) - 9 + 8$
Write the perfect square trinomial as the square of a binomial: $= (x + 3)^2 - 1$

The equation in the form $y = a(x - h)^2 + k$ is $y = (x + 3)^2 - 1$.

b) The graph is a parabola that is congruent to $y = x^2$.
The graph opens up. The vertex is $(-3, -1)$. The range is $y \geq -1$.
The graph intersects the y-axis at $(0, 8)$, so the y-intercept is 8.
The graph appears to intersect the x-axis at $(-4, 0)$ and $(-2, 0)$,
so the x-intercepts appear to be -4 and -2.
Check the x-intercepts by substituting in $y = x^2 + 6x + 8$.

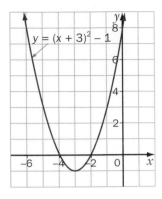

$y = (x + 3)^2 - 1$

For $(-4, 0)$,

L.S. $= y$ **R.S.** $= x^2 + 6x + 8$
$\quad\ = 0 \qquad\quad = (-4)^2 + 6(-4) + 8$
$\qquad\qquad\qquad\ = 16 - 24 + 8$
$\qquad\qquad\qquad\ = 0$
$\qquad\qquad$ L.S. = R.S.

For $(-2, 0)$,

L.S. $= y$ **R.S.** $= x^2 + 6x + 8$
$\quad\ = 0 \qquad\quad = (-2)^2 + 6(-2) + 8$
$\qquad\qquad\qquad\ = 4 - 12 + 8$
$\qquad\qquad\qquad\ = 0$
$\qquad\qquad$ L.S. = R.S.

The x-intercepts are -4 and -2.

Example 2   Completing the Square When $a \neq 1$

a) Express $y = 3x^2 - 12x + 11$ in the form $y = a(x - h)^2 + k$.
b) Sketch the graph. Find the maximum or minimum value of the function.

Solution
a) Factor the coefficient of x^2 from the first two terms.
Then, complete the square as you would for $a = 1$.

$$y = 3x^2 - 12x + 11$$

Group the terms containing x:
Factor the coefficient of x^2 from the first two terms:
Complete the square inside the brackets:
Write the perfect square trinomial as the square of a binomial:
Expand to remove the square brackets:
Simplify:

$$= [3x^2 - 12x] + 11$$
$$= 3[x^2 - 4x] + 11$$
$$= 3[x^2 - 4x + 4 - 4] + 11$$
$$= 3[(x - 2)^2 - 4] + 11$$
$$= 3(x - 2)^2 - 12 + 11$$
$$= 3(x - 2)^2 - 1$$

So, the equation in the form $y = a(x - h)^2 + k$ is $y = 3(x - 2)^2 - 1$.

b) The graph is congruent to $y = 3x^2$.
The graph opens up, and its vertex is $(2, -1)$.
The minimum value is -1 when $x = 2$.

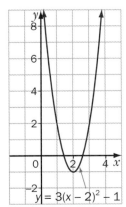

$y = 3(x - 2)^2 - 1$

One way to verify that a parabolic function has been correctly rewritten from the form $y = ax^2 + bx + c$ to the form $y = a(x - h)^2 + k$ is to reverse the process. Another way is to graph both forms in the same viewing window of a graphing calculator. If the two forms are equivalent, you will see only one curve.

Example 3   Completing the Square When *a* is Negative
Find the coordinates of the vertex of the function $y = 6x - 3x^2$.

Solution
Rewrite the equation in the form $y = a(x - h)^2 + k$.

$$y = 6x - 3x^2$$
$$= -3x^2 + 6x$$
$$= [-3x^2 + 6x]$$
$$= -3[x^2 - 2x]$$
$$= -3[x^2 - 2x + 1 - 1]$$
$$= -3[(x - 1)^2 - 1]$$
$$= -3(x - 1)^2 + 3$$

The solution can be modelled graphically.

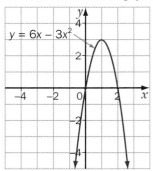

The vertex is (1, 3).

Example 4   Astronaut Training Flights
The parabolic flight of an aircraft used to simulate weightlessness can be modelled by the quadratic equation
$$h = -10t^2 + 300t + 9750$$
where h is the altitude of the aircraft, in metres, and t is the time, in seconds, since weightlessness was achieved. Find
a) the maximum altitude reached by the aircraft
b) the number of seconds the aircraft takes to reach its maximum altitude after weightlessness is achieved
c) the altitude of the aircraft when weightlessness is first achieved
d) the number of seconds the simulation of weightlessness lasts, if weightlessness is lost at the same altitude as it is achieved

Web Connection www.school.mcgrawhill.ca/resources/

To learn more about how astronauts are trained, visit the above web site. Go to **Math Resources,** then to *MATHPOWER*™ *10, Ontario Edition,* to find out where to go next. Write a brief summary of one aspect of the training program.

Solution
Rewrite the equation in the form $y = a(x - h)^2 + k$.

$$h = -10t^2 + 300t + 9750$$
$$= [-10t^2 + 300t] + 9750$$
$$= -10[t^2 - 30t] + 9750$$
$$= -10[t^2 - 30t + 225 - 225] + 9750$$
$$= -10[(t - 15)^2 - 225] + 9750$$
$$= -10(t - 15)^2 + 2250 + 9750$$
$$= -10(t - 15)^2 + 12\ 000$$

The solution can be modelled graphically.

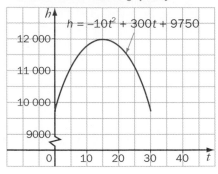

The graph is congruent to $h = -10t^2$.
The graph opens down.
The vertex is (15, 12 000).
a) The aircraft reaches a maximum altitude of 12 000 m.
b) The aircraft takes 15 s to reach its maximum altitude after weightlessness is achieved.
c) Substituting 0 for t in the equation in the form $h = -10t^2 + 300t + 9750$ gives $h = 9750$ when $t = 0$.
So, the aircraft is at an altitude of 9750 m when weightlessness is first achieved.
d) The equation of the axis of symmetry is $t = 15$, and (0, 9750) is one point on the parabola. So, (30, 9750) is another point on the parabola.
The simulation of weightlessness lasts for 30 s.

In some problems involving maximum or minimum values, the function is not given. It must be found from the given information.

Example 5   Theatre Tickets
A theatre company has 300 season ticket subscribers. The board of directors has decided to raise the price of a season ticket from the current price of $400. A survey of the subscribers has determined that, for every $20 increase in price, 10 subscribers would not renew their season tickets.
What price would maximize the revenue from season tickets?

Solution
Let x represent the number of $20 increases.
The cost of a season ticket will be $(400 + 20x)$.
The number of season tickets sold will be $(300 - 10x)$.
The revenue from ticket sales, R, is (number of tickets sold) × (cost per ticket).
So, $R = (300 - 10x)(400 + 20x)$
Find the maximum value of this function.

$$R = (300 - 10x)(400 + 20x)$$
$$= 120\ 000 + 6000x - 4000x - 200x^2$$
$$= -200x^2 + 2000x + 120\ 000$$
$$= -200[x^2 - 10x] + 120\ 000$$
$$= -200[x^2 - 10x + 25 - 25] + 120\ 000$$
$$= -200[(x - 5)^2 - 25] + 120\ 000$$
$$= -200(x - 5)^2 + 5000 + 120\ 000$$
$$= -200(x - 5)^2 + 125\ 000$$

The function reaches a maximum value of 125 000 when $x = 5$.
There should be five $20 increases to maximize the revenue.
$400 + 5(20) = 500$
So, a price of $500 would maximize the revenue from season tickets.

Key CONCEPTS

1 To rewrite a quadratic function $y = ax^2 + bx + c$ in the form $y = a(x - h)^2 + k$, use the steps shown in the following example.

$$y = 2x^2 + 4x + 5$$

Group the terms containing x: $y = (2x^2 + 4x) + 5$
Factor the coefficient of x^2: $y = 2[x^2 + 2x] + 5$
Complete the square inside the brackets: $y = 2[x^2 + 2x + 1 - 1] + 5$
Write the perfect square trinomial
as the square of a binomial: $y = 2[(x + 1)^2 - 1] + 5$
Expand to remove the square brackets: $y = 2(x + 1)^2 - 2 + 5$
Simplify: $y = 2(x + 1)^2 + 3$

2 For a quadratic function in the form $y = ax^2 + bx + c$, find the maximum or minimum value by rewriting the function in the form $y = a(x - h)^2 + k$ to find the vertex, (h, k). The maximum or minimum value of the function is k.

Communicate Your Understanding

1. Describe how you would find the coordinates of the vertex, the equation of the axis of symmetry, and the maximum or minimum value of each function.

a) $y = x^2 + 4x - 3$ **b)** $y = 3x^2 - 6x + 4$ **c)** $y = -2x^2 + 8x - 5$

2. Explain the roles of a, h, and k in the graph of $y = a(x - h)^2 + k$, in comparison with the graph of $y = x^2$.

1. Find the value of c that will make each expression a perfect square trinomial.

a) $x^2 + 14x + c$ **b)** $x^2 - 12x + c$
c) $x^2 - 2x + c$ **d)** $x^2 + 18x + c$
e) $x^2 - 10x + c$ **f)** $x^2 + 20x + c$

2. Write each function in the form $y = a(x - h)^2 + k$. Sketch the graph, showing the coordinates of the vertex, the equation of the axis of symmetry, and the coordinates of two other points on the graph.

a) $y = x^2 + 6x + 3$ **b)** $y = x^2 - 4x - 1$
c) $y = x^2 + 10x + 30$ **d)** $y = x^2 - 2x + 3$
e) $y = 28 + 12x + x^2$ **f)** $y = 12 - 8x + x^2$

3. The six graphs represent the six equations $y = x^2 + 4x$, $y = x^2 - 4x$, $y = -x^2 + 4x$, $y = -x^2 - 4x$, $y = x^2 - 4$, and $y = -x^2 + 4$. Match each graph with the correct equation.

a) 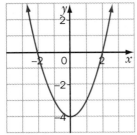 **b)** 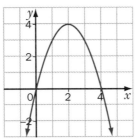 **c)**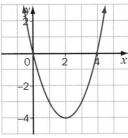

d) 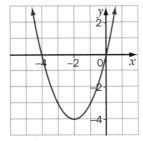 **e)** 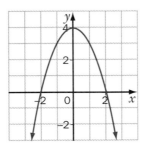 **f)**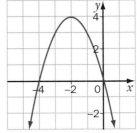

4. Sketch the graph of each function. Show the coordinates of the vertex, the equation of the axis of symmetry, and any intercepts. State the range.

a) $y = x^2 - 2x - 8$ **b)** $y = x^2 - 6x + 10$
c) $y = x^2 + 4x$ **d)** $y = 40 - 12x + x^2$

5. Write each function in the form $y = a(x - h)^2 + k$. Sketch the graph, showing the coordinates of the vertex, the equation of the axis of symmetry, and the coordinates of two other points on the graph.

a) $y = -x^2 + 8x - 11$ **b)** $y = -x^2 - 8x - 7$
c) $y = -x^2 - 4x - 7$ **d)** $y = -2x - x^2$

6. Sketch the graph of each function. Show the coordinates of the vertex, the equation of the axis of symmetry, and any intercepts. State the range.
a) $y = -x^2 - 2x + 3$ **b)** $y = -x^2 - 4x - 12$
c) $y = -x^2 + 8x - 12$ **d)** $y = 10x - 25 - x^2$

7. Without graphing each function, state whether it has a maximum or a minimum. Give the maximum or minimum value of the function.
a) $y = x^2 + 6x + 2$ **b)** $y = -x^2 - 4x + 1$
c) $y = -x^2 + 8x$ **d)** $y = x^2 - 12x + 36$
e) $y = x^2 + 10x - 5$ **f)** $y = 4 - 6x - x^2$
g) $y - 21 = x^2 - 14x$ **h)** $y = 10x - 28 - x^2$

8. Write each function in the form $y = (x - h)^2 + k$. Then, graph the function. Show the coordinates of the vertex and the equation of the axis of symmetry. State the range.
a) $y = 3x^2 + 6x - 8$ **b)** $y = -2x^2 - 12x$
c) $y = 2x^2 - 4x + 5$ **d)** $y = -4x^2 + 8x - 7$
e) $y = 4x^2 - 16x$ **f)** $y = -3x^2 + 12x - 14$

9. State the maximum or minimum value of y and the value of x when it occurs.
a) $y = 2x^2 + 4x + 3$ **b)** $y = -2x^2 + 20x - 44$
c) $y = -4x^2 - 24x - 29$ **d)** $y = -3x^2 + 18x - 28$
e) $y = 5x^2 - 20x + 18$ **f)** $y = 10x^2 - 20x + 12$
g) $y = 8x - 2x^2$ **h)** $y = -4x^2 + 8x - 4$

Applications and Problem Solving

B

10. Find two numbers whose difference is 10 and whose product is a minimum.

11. Find two numbers whose sum is 34 and whose product is a maximum.

12. State the maximum or minimum value of y and the value of x when it occurs.
a) $y = 1.5x^2 + 6x - 8$ **b)** $y = 0.1x^2 + 2x + 1$
c) $y = -0.2x^2 - 2x$ **d)** $y = 1.25x^2 - 5x$
e) $y = -2.5x^2 + 20x - 35$ **f)** $y = -0.003x^2 + 0.6x - 10$
g) $y = 0.5x^2 + x + 2$ **h)** $y = -0.5x^2 + 3x - 5$

13. Sketch the graph of each function. State the coordinates of the vertex.
a) $y = (x + 1)(x + 3)$ **b)** $y = (x + 2)(x - 4)$
c) $y = (2x + 1)(x - 2)$ **d)** $y = -3(x - 1)(x + 3)$

14. Golf The path of the ball for many golf shots can be modelled by a quadratic function. The path of a golf ball hit at an angle of about 10° to the horizontal can be modelled by the function

$$h = -0.002d^2 + 0.4d$$

where h is the height of the ball, in metres, and d is the horizontal distance the ball travels, in metres, until it first hits the ground.
a) What is the maximum height reached by the ball?
b) What is the horizontal distance of the ball from the golfer when the ball reaches its maximum height?
c) What distance does the ball travel horizontally until it first hits the ground?

15. Basketball The path of a basketball shot can be modelled by the equation

$$h = -0.09d^2 + 0.9d + 2$$

where h is the height of the basketball, in metres, and d is the horizontal distance of the ball from the player, in metres.
a) What is the maximum height reached by the ball?
b) What is the horizontal distance of the ball from the player when it reaches its maximum height?
c) How far from the floor is the ball when the player releases it?

16. Brooklyn Bridge The Brooklyn Bridge in New York City is a suspension bridge that crosses the East River and connects Brooklyn to the island of Manhattan. If the origin is placed at the top of one of the cable-support towers, as shown, the shape of a cable that supports the main span can be modelled by the equation

$$h = 0.0008d^2 - 0.384d$$

where h metres represents the height and d metres represents the horizontal distance.

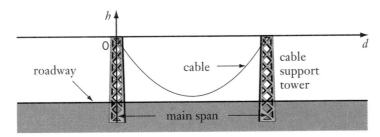

a) What is the vertical distance from the top of a support tower to the lowest point on a cable, to the nearest metre?
b) What is the length of the main span?
c) At a horizontal distance of 50 m from one end of the cable, how far is the cable below the top of the support towers, to the nearest metre?

17. Natural bridge A natural bridge is a stone arch formed over a river or stream. The longest natural bridge in the world is Rainbow Bridge in Utah. If the origin is placed at one end of the arch, the curve of the arch can be modelled by the equation

$$h = -0.0425d^2 + 3.57d$$

where h metres represents the height and d metres represents the horizontal distance.
a) What is the width of the arch at the base?
b) What is the maximum height of the arch, to the nearest metre?
c) At a horizontal distance of 10 m from the vertex, what is the height of the arch, to the nearest metre?

18. Rectangular field A rectangular field is to be enclosed by 400 m of fence.
a) What dimensions will give a maximum area?
b) What is the maximum area?

19. Rectangular corral A farmer wants to make a rectangular corral along the side of a large barn and has enough materials for 60 m of fencing. Only three sides must be fenced, since the barn wall will form the fourth side. What width of rectangle should the farmer use so that the maximum area is enclosed?

20. Fund-raising The Environmental Club sells sweatshirts as a fund-raiser. They sell 1200 shirts a year at $20 each. They are planning to increase the price. A survey indicates that, for every $2 increase in price, there will be a drop of 60 sales a year. What should the selling price be in order to maximize the revenue?

21. Measurement Determine the maximum area of a triangle, in square centimetres, if the sum of its base and its height is 10 cm.

22. Thrown object The top of the R. H. Coats Building in Ottawa is 104 m above the ground. Suppose an object were thrown upward with an initial velocity of 19.6 m/s from this height. The approximate height of the object above the ground, h metres, t seconds after being thrown, would be given by the equation

$$h = -4.9t^2 + 19.6t + 104$$

a) What would be the maximum height of the object above the ground?
b) From the time the object was thrown, how much time would it take to reach the ground, to the nearest second?

23. Communication A parabolic ski is narrower in the middle than it is at the ends. Each edge of the ski is parabolic. Assume that a coordinate grid is placed on the ski as shown.

a) How are the coordinates of the two vertices related?
b) How are the values of a in the equations of the two parabolas related?
c) Use your research skills to find out why parabolic skis are used.

C

24. Communication How is the graph of $y = ax^2 + bx + c$ affected if
a) $a = 0$?
b) $b = 0$?

25. For the function $y = x^2 + 6x + k$, what value(s) of k will result in
a) one x-intercept?
b) two x-intercepts?
c) no x-intercept?

26. For the function $y = -2x^2 + 8x + k$, what value(s) of k will result in
a) one x-intercept?
b) two x-intercepts?
c) no x-intercept?

27. Communication Write a function in the form $y = ax^2 + bx + c$ that meets each of the following sets of conditions. Describe how you found the equation. Have a classmate check that each of your equations meets the conditions.
a) congruent to $y = x^2$, two whole-number x-intercepts, vertex in the fourth quadrant
b) congruent to $y = -x^2$, one positive x-intercept and one negative x-intercept, vertex in the second quadrant
c) congruent to $y = 2x^2$, no x-intercepts, vertex in the first quadrant, y-intercept greater than 20
d) congruent to $y = -0.5x^2$, one x-intercept, y-intercept less than -6

28. Applications research The cross sections of many reflectors and receiving dishes are parabolic. Examples include car headlights, microwave dishes, telescope mirrors, and parabolic microphones. Use your research skills to find out why a parabolic shape is used. Share your findings with your classmates.

For the function $y = -30x^2 + 60x - 52$, state window variables that produce views of the parabola that resemble the following. Compare your values with your classmates'.

a) a line with a positive slope   **b)** a line with a negative slope

c) a horizontal line

$\mathcal{C}$areer $\mathcal{C}$onnection   Business

Canadian businesses are involved in an enormous range of activities. Some businesses produce goods, including cars, clothing, and CDs. Other businesses provide services, including insurance, dental care, and restaurant meals. Though some businesses are large corporations that employ thousands of people, most businesses are small. A small business may employ only a few people or, in some cases, only one person.

To be successful, a business must make a profit by selling goods or services to its customers. Profit is the difference between revenues and costs. The most profitable businesses maximize their revenues and minimize their costs, so that the difference between them is as great as possible.

1. Amusement park An amusement park charges $8 admission and averages 2000 visitors per day. A survey shows that, for each $1 increase in the admission price, 100 fewer people would visit the park.

a) Write an equation to express the revenue, R dollars, in terms of a price increase of x dollars.

b) Find the coordinates of the maximum point of this function.

c) What admission price gives the maximum revenue?

d) How many visitors give the maximum revenue?

2. Communication Explain why there are limits on how a business can maximize profit by

a) charging higher and higher prices

b) making its costs lower and lower

3. Research Use your research skills to describe a successful small business. Describe how the owner(s) maximize revenues and minimize costs to make the business profitable.

4. Research Choose a business career that interests you, such as marketing, hospitality, accounting, or making a product of your choice. Use your research skills to describe the qualifications and training required, and the types of businesses that need people with this background.

A ball is thrown upward from a height of 2 m with an initial velocity of 20 m/s. Its approximate height, h metres, after t seconds is given by the equation

$$h = -0.5gt^2 + 20t + 2$$

where g is a constant that describes the acceleration of gravity. The table gives the approximate value of g for three planets.

Planet	Value of g (m/s^2)
Earth	10
Mars	4
Pluto	0.5

For each planet, determine
a) the maximum height the ball would reach
b) how many seconds the ball would take to reach its maximum height

Achievement Check

1   2   3   4

The side length of a square is 10 cm. Four points on the square are joined to form an inner square, as shown.
a) Find the minimum area of the inner square, in square centimetres.
b) Describe how you could find the minimum area of the inner square for any side length of the outer square.

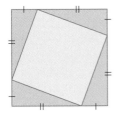

NUMBER POWER

Copy the statements below. Place the digits from 1 to 9 in the boxes to make the statements true. Use the order of operations.

■ × ■ + ■ = 7
■ ÷ ■ + ■ = 7
■ × ■ − ■ = 7

4.5 Investigation: Sketching Parabolas in the Form $y = ax(x - s) + t$

When a quadratic function is written in the form $y = ax(x - s) + t$, two points on the graph of the function can be found by letting $x = 0$ and $x = s$. The coordinates of the vertex can be deduced from these two points.

The following steps show how this method is used to sketch the graph of $y = 2x^2 - 8x + 5$.

$$y = 2x^2 - 8x + 5$$

Step 1 Factor $2x$ from the first two terms: $\quad y = 2x(x - 4) + 5$

Step 2 Substitute 0 for x in $y = 2x(x - 4) + 5$: $\quad y = 2(0)(0 - 4) + 5$
$$y = 5$$

One point on the graph is (0, 5).

Step 3 Substitute 4 for x in $y = 2x(x - 4) + 5$: $\quad y = 2(4)(4 - 4) + 5$
$$y = 5$$

Another point on the graph is (4, 5).

Step 4 Plot the points (0, 5) and (4, 5) on a grid.

Step 5 The graph of $y = 2x^2 - 8x + 5$ is symmetric about the axis of symmetry, which passes through the vertex. Since the points (0, 5) and (4, 5) have the same y-coordinate, they are reflection images of each other in the axis of symmetry. The equation of the axis of symmetry is $x = 2$, so the x-coordinate of the vertex is 2.

Step 6 Substitute 2 for x in $y = 2x^2 - 8x + 5$: $\quad y = 2(2)^2 - 8(2) + 5$
$$= 8 - 16 + 5$$
$$= -3$$

The coordinates of the vertex are (2, –3).

Step 7 Plot the vertex on the grid and draw a smooth curve through the three points.

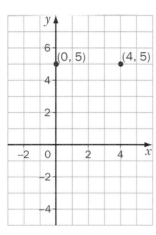

1. Sketch the graph of each of the following quadratic functions by writing it in the form $y = ax(x - s) + t$.

a) $y = x^2 - 4x - 1$ **b)** $y = x^2 - 8x + 6$
c) $y = 3x^2 - 12x + 4$ **d)** $y = 2x^2 - 4x + 3$
e) $y = x^2 + 2x - 5$ **f)** $y = x^2 + 6x + 7$
g) $y = 2x^2 + 12x - 2$ **h)** $y = -x^2 + 4x - 2$
i) $y = -4x^2 + 8x + 1$ **j)** $y = -2x^2 - 4x - 3$

2. Verify that the coordinates of the vertex of the function

$y = ax(x - s) + t$ are $\left(\dfrac{s}{2}, \ t - \dfrac{as^2}{4} \right)$.

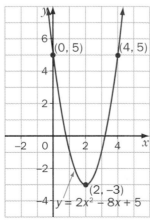

Finite differences are differences found from the *y*-values in tables with evenly spaced *x*-values. **First differences** are calculated by subtracting consecutive *y*-values. **Second differences** are calculated by subtracting consecutive first differences, and so on.

x	y	Difference 1st	Difference 2nd
0	0		
		$1 - 0 = 1$	
1	1		$7 - 1 = 6$
		$8 - 1 = 7$	
2	8		$19 - 7 = 12$
		$27 - 8 = 19$	
3	27		

1 Reviewing Linear Functions, *y* = *mx* + *b*

1. Copy and complete the tables for the following linear functions.

a) $y = 2x + 5$

x	y	1st Difference
0	5	
		$7 - 5 = 2$
1	7	
2		
3		
4		

b) $y = 4x - 2$

x	y	1st Difference
0	−2	
1		
2		
3		
4		

c) $y = -3x + 1$

x	y	1st Difference
0		
1		
2		
3		
4		

2. Communication What is true about the first difference for a linear function?

2 Investigating Quadratic Functions, *y* = *ax*² + *bx* + *c*

1. Copy and complete the tables for the following quadratic functions.

a) $y = x^2 + x + 1$

x	y	Difference 1st	Difference 2nd
0	1		
		2	
1	3		2
		4	
2	7		
3			
4			

b) $y = 2x^2 - x + 5$

x	y	Difference 1st	Difference 2nd
0			
1			
2			
3			
4			

c) $y = 3x^2 + 2x - 1$

x	y	Difference 1st	Difference 2nd
0			
1			
2			
3			
4			

2. Communication For a quadratic function, what is true about
a) the first difference?
b) the second difference?

3. Communication Compare the nature of change in the finite differences for a linear function with the nature of change in the finite differences for a quadratic function.

4. Communication Write a rule for using finite differences to determine whether a function is linear or quadratic.

3 Using Finite Differences

1. Use finite differences to determine whether each function is linear, quadratic, or neither.

a)

x	y
0	4
1	5
2	6
3	7
4	8

b)

x	y
0	−1
1	1
2	3
3	5
4	7

c)

x	y
0	3
1	4
2	7
3	12
4	19

d)

x	y
0	0
1	1
2	8
3	27
4	64

e)

x	y
0	0
1	2
2	6
3	12
4	20

f)

x	y
0	3
1	5
2	7
3	9
4	11

g)

x	y
0	1
1	2
2	4
3	8
4	16

h)

x	y
0	−2
1	−2
2	0
3	4
4	10

i)

x	y
0	−4
2	2
4	8
6	14
8	20

j)

x	y
1	−10
3	0
5	18
7	44
9	78

k)

x	y
−2	10
−1	6
0	2
1	−2
2	−6

l)

x	y
−2	2
−1	1
0	0
1	1
2	2

2. Use inspection or the LinReg (linear regression) instruction of your graphing calculator to write an equation for each linear function in question 1.

3. Use inspection or the QuadReg (quadratic regression) instruction of your graphing calculator to write an equation for each quadratic function in question 1.

4. Letter pattern The first four diagrams in a pattern show asterisks arranged in an m-shape.

a) Copy and complete the table for the four diagrams.

Diagram Number, d	Number of Asterisks, a
1	
2	
3	
4	

b) Use finite differences to determine whether the function is linear or quadratic.

c) Determine an equation of the function by inspection or by using your graphing calculator.

d) How many asterisks will there be in the 15th diagram? the 21st diagram?

e) Which diagram contains 131 asterisks?

5. Square pattern The first four diagrams in a pattern are made up of small green squares and white squares of side length 1 unit.

a) Copy and complete the table for the four diagrams.

Side Length of Large Square, s	Number of Small White Squares, n
2	
3	
4	
5	

b) Use finite differences to determine if the function is linear or quadratic.

c) Determine an equation of the function by inspection or by using your graphing calculator.

d) How many small white squares will there be in a large square of side length 10 units? 25 units?

6. Toothpick pattern The first four diagrams in a pattern show arrangements made from toothpicks.

a) Copy and complete the table for the four diagrams.

Diagram Number, d	Number of Toothpicks, t
1	
2	
3	
4	

b) Use finite differences to determine if the function is linear or quadratic.

c) Determine an equation of the function by inspection or by using your graphing calculator.

d) How many toothpicks would be needed for the arrangement shown in the 15th diagram? the 50th diagram?

7. Square pattern The first five diagrams in a pattern are made up of squares of side length 1 unit.

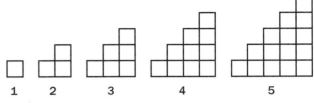

1   2   3   4   5

a) Copy and complete the tables for the five diagrams.

Table 1

Base Length, b	Perimeter, P
1	
2	
3	'
4	
5	

Table 2

Base Length, b	Area, A
1	
2	
3	
4	
5	

b) Use finite differences to determine whether the function shown in each table is linear or quadratic.

c) Determine an equation of each function by using your graphing calculator.

d) Find the perimeter and the area of the diagram of base length 15 units; of base length 30 units.

8. Honeycomb pattern The cross section of a honeycomb can be thought of as a central regular hexagon surrounded by a ring of six more hexagons, surrounded by a ring of twelve more hexagons, and so on. Think of the central hexagon as ring 1, the ring of six hexagons as ring 2, and so on.

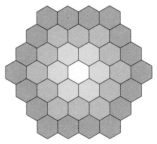

a) Copy and complete the table by recording the total numbers of hexagons in the first ring, the first two rings, the first three rings, and the first four rings.

Total Number of Rings, r	Total Number of Hexagons, h
1	
2	
3	
4	

b) Use finite differences to determine whether the function is linear or quadratic.

c) Determine an equation of the function by using your graphing calculator.

d) Find the total number of hexagons in the first ten rings.

1 Parabolas in the Form $y = ax^2 + k$

Complete parts a) to d) for each of the following tables of values by using the method described for a graphing calculator. Alternatively, use graphing software.

a) Using the STAT EDIT menu, enter the data as two lists.
b) Using the STAT PLOTS menu, draw the scatter plot for the data. Choose suitable window variables, or use the ZoomStat instruction to set them automatically.
c) By entering equations in the Y= editor and graphing them, use trial and error to fit the equation of a quadratic function in the form $y = ax^2 + k$, where a and k are integers, to the scatter plot.
d) Find the equation of the curve of best fit using the QuadReg (quadratic regression) instruction. If necessary, round coefficients and constants to the nearest hundredth. Compare the equation with your result from part c).

1.

x	y
2	6
1	3
0	2
−1	3
−2	6

2.

x	y
2	−7
1	−4
0	−3
−1	−4
−2	−7

3.

x	y
3	5
2	−1
0	−5
−2	−1
−3	3

4.

x	y
5	−22
3	−4
1	3
−2	0
−4	−11

5.

x	y
3	17
1	2
0	0
−2	7
−4	31

2 The Flight of a Cannonball

After Gallileo determined the acceleration due to gravity, as described on page 190, he studied another problem of his day, the flight of a cannonball. The table gives the approximate height of a cannonball for a 6-s flight.

Time, t(s)	Height, h(m)
0	0
1	25
2	40
3	45
4	40
5	25
6	0

1. As described in Investigation 1, enter the data and draw the scatter plot of height versus time.
2. Use trial and error to fit the equation of a quadratic function in the form $y = a(x - h)^2 + k$, where a, h, and k are integers, to the scatter plot.
3. Communication Find the equation of the curve of best fit using quadratic regression. Compare the equation with your result from question 2. Explain any differences.
4. Use your equation to find the height of the cannonball after 2.4 s and 4.6 s.

3 Stopping Distance

The distance a car travels from when the driver applies the brakes until the car comes to a stop is called the stopping distance. The stopping distance is a function of the speed of the car. The table gives the approximate stopping distance for cars travelling at several speeds on dry pavement.
1. As described in Investigation 1, enter the data and draw the scatter plot of stopping distance versus speed.

2. Use trial and error to fit the equation of a quadratic function in the form $y = ax^2$ to the scatter plot.

3. Use your equation to determine the approximate stopping distance, to the nearest metre, if the speed is

a) 60 km/h **b)** 100 km/h

4. Find the equation of the curve of best fit using quadratic regression. Compare the equation with your result from question 2.

5. Use the equation found in question 4 to determine the stopping distance, if the speed is

a) 60 km/h **b)** 100 km/h

Speed (*km*/h)	Stopping Distance (m)
30	13
50	23
70	41
90	67
110	101

4 The Parabolic Dental Arch

Dentists call the shape of the arrangement of human teeth the *parabolic dental arch*. Use the following steps to find an equation for the quadratic function that models your parabolic dental arch.

1. Make an impression of your dental arch by biting a clean piece of paper.

2. Draw a smooth parabolic curve through your impression.

3. Trace your curve onto grid paper. Locate the axes so that the vertex is at the origin and the parabola opens up.

4. Find the coordinates of several points on the parabola.

5. As described in Investigation 1, enter the data and draw the scatter plot.

6. Use trial and error to fit the equation of a quadratic function to the scatter plot.

7. Find the equation of the curve of best fit using quadratic regression. Compare the equation with your result from question 6.

8. Compare your results with your classmates'.

9. Communication Do your upper and lower teeth have different equations for their parabolic dental arches? Explain.

5 Research

1. From secondary sources, such as the Internet or Statistics Canada, collect data that may be represented by quadratic functions.

2. Draw a scatter plot of the data.

3. Use trial and error to fit the equation of a quadratic function to the scatter plot.

4. Find the equation of the curve of best fit using quadratic regression. Compare the equation with your result from question 3.

5. Communication Summarize your findings in a report. Include explanations, tables, graphs, and equations.

1 **Collecting Data From a Rolling Ball**

In this experiment, the motion of a ball rolling up and down a ramp will be measured. The data can be collected with a CBL and a motion detector, or with a CBR.

For this experiment, you will need:
1 CBL unit with motion detector, or 1 CBR unit
1 TI-83 Plus or T1-83 calculator, with a unit-to-unit link cable
a ramp about 2 m long
a variety of balls to roll up the ramp (Do not use soft or felt-covered balls.)

1. Work in pairs.
a) If you use a CBL and motion detector, load and run the RAMP program, and follow the instructions. Before you roll the ball, the program will prompt you to place the ball part way up the ramp and measure its distance from the detector.
b) If you use a CBR, run the RANGER program.
Choose option 1: SETUP/SAMPLE.
Set REAL TIME to NO, TIME (S) to 2, and SMOOTHING to LIGHT.
Move the cursor up to START NOW to collect data.

2. Place the motion detector or CBR at the top of the ramp. Roll a ball up the ramp. Do not roll the ball closer than half a metre from the motion detector. A graph of the motion of the ball will appear on the calculator screen. For a good roll, the graph will have a parabolic shape. You may have to perform the experiment several times to get good results.

3. a) If you used a CBL and motion detector, quit the program. The graph will disappear from the calculator screen. Use the STAT PLOTS menu to draw the scatter plot of distance versus time. Then, use the TRACE instruction to find the approximate coordinates of the vertex of the graph. Round coordinates to the nearest hundredth, if necessary. Use the coordinates of the vertex as the values of h and k in an equation of the form $y = a(x - h)^2 + k$. By entering equations with these values of h and k in the Y= editor, use trial and error to find a value of a for an equation that fits your scatter plot. Then, use the QuadReg (quadratic regression) instruction to find an equation of the curve of best fit.
b) If you used the CBR, go to the main menu of the RANGER program, choose the PLOT menu, and then choose PLOT TOOLS to select a set of

points that defines a parabolic shape. Exclude data points that do not lie on the parabola. Use the TRACE instruction to find the approximate coordinates of the vertex of the scatter plot. Round coordinates to the nearest hundredth, if necessary. Use the coordinates of the vertex as the values of h and k in an equation of the form $y = a(x - h)^2 + k$. By entering equations with these values of h and k in the Y= editor, use trial and error to find a value of a for an equation that fits your scatter plot. Then, use the QuadReg (quadratic regression) instruction to find an equation of the curve of best fit.

4. Communication How does the equation you found by trial and error compare with the equation of the curve of best fit produced using quadratic regression?

5. Communication a) How close did the ball come to the motion detector? **b)** How did you determine this value?

6. Communication If you used the RAMP program for the CBL, why were you first prompted to measure the distance of the ball from the detector when the ball was part way up the ramp?

7. Communication Repeat the experiment using a variety of balls and with the ramp at different angles. Are the shapes of your graphs the same or different? Explain.

8. Communication Summarize your findings from this experiment in a report. Include explanations, tables, graphs, equations, and any calculations you made. Describe any problems you had in doing this experiment, and describe how you overcame them. State and justify any conclusions you reached from the experiment.

2 Collecting Data From Walking

In this activity, a motion detector will record your motion as you move toward it and then away from it. The data can be collected with a CBL and motion detector, or with a CBR.

For this experiment, you will need:
1 CBL unit with motion detector, or 1 CBR unit
1 TI-83 Plus or TI-83 calculator with a unit-to-unit link cable

1. Work in pairs.
a) If you use a CBL unit with a motion detector, load and run the WALK program.
b) If you use a CBR unit, run the RANGER program.
Choose option 1: SETUP/SAMPLE.
Set REAL TIME to NO, TIME (S) to 6, and SMOOTHING to LIGHT.
Move the cursor up to START NOW to collect data.

2. Set the motion detector or CBR on a desk at about waist height. Have one person stand about 3 m away from the unit. The other person will run the program and tell the first person when to begin walking. The walker should walk toward the motion detector for 3 s, and then walk backward to the starting position for 3 s. The walker should not come closer than half a metre from the motion detector. A good set of data will display a parabolic shape when graphed.

3. When you are finished, use the STAT PLOTS menu to draw a scatter plot of distance versus time using the time data in list L_1 and the distance data in list L_2. Use the TRACE instruction on the calculator to find the approximate coordinates of the vertex of the scatter plot. Round coordinates to the nearest hundredth, if necessary. Use the coordinates of the vertex as the values of h and k in an equation of the form $y = a(x - h)^2 + k$. By entering equations with these values of h and k in the Y= editor, use trial and error to find a value of a for an equation that fits your scatter plot. Then, use the QuadReg (quadratic regression) instruction to find an equation of the curve of best fit and store the equation as function Y1 in the Y= editor.

4. Communication How does the equation you found by trial and error compare with the equation of the curve of best fit produced using quadratic regression?

5. Communication How close did the walker come to the motion detector? How did you determine this value?

6. Communication Using the equation you obtained by quadratic regression, find time(s) when you were 2 m from the motion detector. How many solutions are there? Explain why.

7. Repeat the experiment by starting closer to the motion detector and moving more slowly to collect a second set of data. Store the equation you obtain by quadratic regression as function Y2 in the Y= editor.

8. Repeat the experiment again by starting farther back and moving more quickly to collect a third set of data. Store the equation you obtain by quadratic regression as function Y3 in the Y= editor.

9. Communication Using suitable window variables, graph the three equations you obtained by quadratic regression. How do the shapes of the graphs compare? Explain why.

10. Communication Summarize your findings from this experiment in a report. Include explanations, tables, graphs, formulas, and any calculations you made. Describe any problems you had in doing this experiment, and describe how you overcame them. State and justify any conclusions you reached from the experiment.

Rich Problem

Student Tours

The Capital Tour Company offers five-day tours of Ottawa for groups of students. Some of the company's costs per student go down as the number of students increases. Other costs go up, because of room rentals, meals, and the number of vans that are needed.

1. Communication
To determine the profit per student, p dollars, the company uses the function
$$p = -0.6n^2 + 36n - 440$$
where n represents the number of students taking a tour. Write a summary that describes the company profit. Include in your summary
a) the number of students that will give the maximum profit per student
b) the maximum profit per student
c) the least and greatest numbers of students that should be accepted in order for the company to make a profit
d) the least and greatest numbers of students that should be accepted in order for the company to make a profit of at least $90 per student

2. Communication The Capital Tour Company has decided to expand. The function to determine the profit per student, p dollars, has changed to
$$p = -0.2n^2 + 24n - 595$$
where n represents the number of students taking a tour.

Write a summary that describes the new company profit. Include in your summary
a) the number of students that will give the maximum profit per student
b) the maximum profit per student
c) the least and greatest numbers of students that should be accepted in order for the company to make a profit
d) the least and greatest numbers of students that should be accepted in order for the company to make a profit of at least $100 per student

3. Communication Give possible reasons why the company's profit per student might be modelled by a quadratic function of the type given in question 1 or 2.

REVIEW OF Key CONCEPTS

4.1 Functions

Refer to the Key Concepts on page 196.

To determine whether the graph represents a function, use the vertical line test. No vertical line passes through more than one point on the graph. For every value of x, there is only one value of y. The graph represents a function.

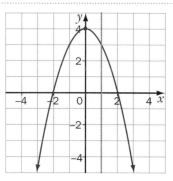

1. State whether each set of ordered pairs represents a function.
a) $\{(2, 5), (4, 3), (6, 1), (8, -1), (9, -2)\}$
b) $\{(3, 2), (5, 6), (6, 8), (3, -2), (6, -4)\}$
c) $\{(2, 3), (2, 2), (2, 1), (2, 0), (2, -1)\}$
d) $\{(8, 1), (7, 1), (-3, 1), (-4, 1)\}$

2. If $y = 2x + 3$, find the value of y for each of the following values of x.
a) 4   **b)** 8   **c)** 0
d) −1   **e)** −4   **f)** 0.5
g) −0.1   **h)** 100   **i)** 5000

3. If $y = 4x^2 - 9$, find the value of y for each of the following values of x.
a) 2   **b)** 3   **c)** −2
d) 0   **e)** −3   **f)** 0.5
g) −0.5   **h)** 10   **i)** 20

4. State whether each of the following is a graph of a function.
a) 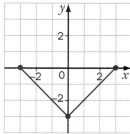   **b)**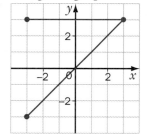

5. State the domain and range of each relation.
a) $\{(0, 4), (1, 5), (2, 6), (3, 7)\}$
b) $\{(-3, 1), (-1, 3), (1, 3), (2, -1)\}$

6. Determine the domain and range of each relation.

a)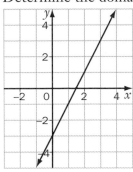

b)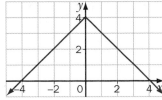

c)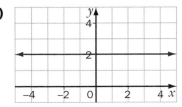

7. Graph each function. The domain is the set of real numbers. Find the range.

a) $y = 2x - 4$

b) $y = x^2 - 1$

4.2 Graphing $y = x^2 + k$, $y = ax^2$, and $y = ax^2 + k$

Refer to the Key Concepts on page 212.

To sketch the graph of $y = 2x^2 - 8$, stretch the graph of $y = x^2$ vertically by a factor of 2. Then, translate 8 units downward.

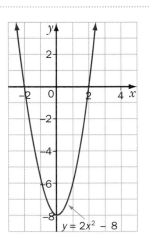

The coordinates of the vertex are $(0, -8)$.
The equation of the axis of symmetry is $x = 0$.
The domain is the set of real numbers.
The range is $y \geq -8$.
The minimum value of the function is -8 when $x = 0$.
The graph crosses the y-axis at $(0, -8)$, so the y-intercept is -8.
The graph appears to cross the x-axis at $(2, 0)$ and $(-2, 0)$, so the x-intercepts are 2 and -2.

8. Communication Write one sentence that compares each pair of graphs.

a) $y = x^2$ and $y = x^2 - 3$ **b)** $y = -x^2$ and $y = -4x^2$

9. Sketch the graph of each parabola and state the direction of the opening, the coordinates of the vertex, the equation of the axis of symmetry, the domain and range, and the maximum or minimum value.

a) $y = x^2 + 4$ **b)** $y = -x^2 - 2$

c) $y = 0.5x^2$ **d)** $y = -3x^2 + 3$

10. Without graphing each function, state the direction of the opening, the coordinates of the vertex, the domain and range, and the maximum or minimum value.

a) $y = -4x^2$ **b)** $y = -x^2 + 3.5$

c) $y = -2x^2 - 7$ **d)** $3 + 0.2x^2 = y$

11. Use a graphing calculator or graphing software to determine any x-intercepts, to the nearest tenth.

a) $y = x^2 - 7$ **b)** $y = -x^2 + 2$

c) $y = x^2 + 1$ **d)** $y = 2x^2 - 9$

12. Xiaoshang Bridge The Xiaoshang Bridge over the Xiaoji River in Henan Province, China, was built in 584 A.D. It is one of the oldest surviving stone arch bridges. Suppose the curve of the arch is graphed on a grid, with the origin on the river directly under the centre of the arch. The arch can be modelled by the function

$$h = -0.06d^2 + 2.13$$

where h metres is the height of the arch, and d metres is the horizontal distance from the centre of the arch.

a) What is the maximum height of the arch?

b) If the ends of the arch are at the level of the river, how wide is the arch, to the nearest metre?

c) At a horizontal distance of 2 m from one end of the arch, how high is the arch, to the nearest tenth of a metre?

4.3 Graphing $y = a(x - h)^2 + k$

Refer to the Key Concepts on page 222.

To sketch the graph of $y = 3(x + 1)^2 - 12$, stretch the graph of $y = x^2$ vertically by a factor of 3. Then, translate 1 unit to the left and 12 units downward.

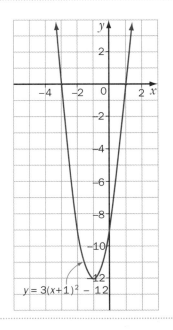

$y = 3(x+1)^2 - 12$

The coordinates of the vertex are $(-1, -12)$.
The equation of the axis of symmetry is $x = -1$.
The domain is the set of real numbers.
The range is $y \geq -12$.
The minimum value of the function is -12 when $x = -1$.
The graph crosses the y-axis at $(0, -9)$, so the y-intercept is -9. The graph appears to cross the x-axis at $(1, 0)$ and $(-3, 0)$, so the x-intercepts are 1 and -3.

13. Sketch each parabola and state the direction of the opening, how the parabola is stretched or shrunk, if at all, the coordinates of the vertex, the equation of the axis of symmetry, the domain and range, and the maximum or minimum value.

a) $y = -2(x - 3)^2 + 1$
b) $y = (x + 7)^2 - 2$
c) $y = 0.5(x + 1)^2 + 5$
d) $y = -(x + 3)^2 - 1$

14. Without sketching each parabola, state the direction of the opening, how the parabola is stretched or shrunk, if at all, the coordinates of the vertex, the equation of the axis of symmetry, the domain and range, and the maximum or minimum value.

a) $y = (x + 1)^2 - 1$
b) $y = -4(x - 1)^2$
c) $y = -2(x - 4)^2 - 3$
d) $y = 0.25(x + 2)^2 + 1$

15. Sketch each parabola and find the coordinates of the vertex, the maximum or minimum value, any intercepts, and two other points on the graph.

a) $y = (x - 3)^2$
b) $y = (x + 2)^2 - 4$
c) $y = 2(x - 3)^2 - 8$
d) $y = -(x + 2)^2 + 9$

16. Use a graphing calculator or graphing software to determine any x-intercepts, to the nearest tenth.

a) $y = (x + 2)^2 - 5$
b) $y = -2(x - 1)^2 + 3$

17. Baseball The height, h metres, of a batted baseball as a function of the time, t seconds, since the ball was hit can be modelled by the function
$$h = -2.1(t - 2.4)^2 + 13$$
a) What was the maximum height of the ball?
b) What was its height when it was hit, to the nearest tenth of a metre?
c) How many seconds after it was hit did the ball hit the ground, to the nearest tenth of a second?
d) What was the height of the ball, to the nearest tenth of a metre, 1 s after it was hit?

4.4 Graphing $y = ax^2 + bx + c$ by Completing the Square

Refer to the Key Concepts on page 233.

18. Find the value of c that will make each expression a perfect square trinomial.

a) $x^2 + 8x + c$
b) $x^2 - 14x + c$

19. Write each function in the form $y = a(x - h)^2 + k$. Sketch the graph, showing the coordinates of the vertex, the equation of the axis of symmetry, and the coordinates of two other points on the graph.

a) $y = x^2 + 4x + 1$
b) $y = x^2 - 10x + 15$
c) $y = -x^2 - 6x - 5$
d) $y = 3 - 4x - x^2$

20. Sketch the graph of each function. Show the coordinates of the vertex and the equation of the axis of symmetry. State the range.

a) $y = x^2 + 6x$

b) $y = x^2 - 8x + 12$

c) $y + 9 = -x^2 - 4x$

d) $y = 15 + 8x + x^2$

21. Find the coordinates of the vertex.

a) $y = 2x^2 - 4x + 6$

b) $y = 3x^2 - 12x + 7$

c) $y = -2x^2 - 8x - 11$

d) $y = -3x^2 - 12x - 9$

e) $y = 4x^2 + 40x + 98$

f) $y = -3x^2 + 18x - 22$

22. Use a graphing calculator or graphing software to determine any x-intercepts. Round to the nearest tenth, if necessary.

a) $y = x^2 + 2x - 3$

b) $y = 4x^2 - 12x + 3$

23. Integers Find two integers whose difference is 12 and whose product is a minimum.

24. Rectangular fence A rectangular field is to be enclosed by 600 m of fence.

a) What dimensions will give the maximum area?

b) What is the maximum area?

4.5 Sketching Parabolas in the Form $y = ax(x - s) + t$

Refer to steps 1–7 on page 241.

25. Sketch the graph of each of the following quadratic functions by writing it in the form $y = ax(x - s) + t$.

a) $y = x^2 - 6x + 8$

b) $y = x^2 + 8x + 12$

c) $y = 2x^2 - 4x - 6$

d) $y = -3x^2 + 12x - 7$

4.6 Finite Differences

1 In tables with evenly spaced x-values, first differences are calculated by subtracting consecutive y-values, and second differences are calculated by subtracting consecutive first differences.

2 For a linear function, the first difference is a constant. For a quadratic function, the second difference is a constant.

26. Use finite differences to determine whether each function is linear, quadratic, or neither.

a)

x	y
1	3
2	5
3	7
4	9

b)

x	y
1	-3
2	-2
3	2
4	9

c)

x	y
1	0
2	1
3	8
4	27

d)

x	y
2	4
4	18
6	40
8	70

27. Letter pattern Each diagram shows asterisks arranged in an X-shape.
a) Write an equation in the form $n = \blacksquare$ that relates the number of asterisks, n, to the diagram number, d.
b) Predict the number of diagrams in the 20th diagram.
c) Which diagram contains 201 asterisks?

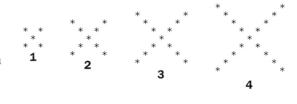

28. Triangle pattern The diagrams show the first four right triangles in a pattern.
a) Use a graphing calculator to write an equation of the form $A = \blacksquare$ that relates the area, A, of each triangle to the diagram number, d.
b) What is the area of the 15th triangle in the pattern?

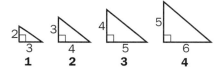

4.7–4.8 Equations of Parabolas of Best Fit

To fit an equation of a quadratic function to a scatter plot using a graphing calculator,
a) use the STAT EDIT menu to enter the data as two lists
b) use the STAT PLOTS menu to draw the scatter plot
c) enter possible equations in the Y= editor, and use trial and error to fit an equation of a quadratic function to the scatter plot
d) compare the result from step c) with the equation of the curve of best fit found by using the QuadReg (quadratic regression) instruction.

29. Draw a scatter plot for each table of values, and use trial and error to fit an equation of a quadratic function to each scatter plot. Compare the result with the quadratic equation of the curve of best fit produced by a graphing calculator or graphing software. Round coefficients and constants to the nearest hundredth, if necessary.

a)

x	y
2	1
1	-2
0	-3
-1	-2
-2	1

b)

x	y
4	-15
2	-4
0	1
-2	-3
-4	-17

c)

x	y
2	-8
1	-3
0	0
-1	-1
-2	-8

Chapter Test

1. State whether each set of ordered pairs represents a function.
a) $\{(2, 4), (3, 5), (7, 9), (2, -5), (3, -7)\}$
b) $\{(5, 4), (4, 3), (3, 2), (2, 1), (1, 0)\}$
c) $\{(-1, 6), (0, -6), (1, -6), (2, -6)\}$

2. Sketch the graph of each parabola and state the direction of the opening, the coordinates of the vertex, the equation of the axis of symmetry, the domain and range, and the maximum or minimum value.
a) $y = x^2 - 1$ **b)** $y = -x^2 + 5$

3. Use a graphing calculator or graphing software to determine any x-intercepts, to the nearest tenth.
a) $y = x^2 + 3$ **b)** $y = -x^2 + 10$ **c)** $y = 8 - 3x^2$

4. Without sketching each parabola, state the direction of the opening, how the parabola is stretched or shrunk, if at all, the coordinates of the vertex, the equation of the axis of symmetry, the domain and range, and the maximum or minimum value.
a) $y = (x + 3)^2 - 1$ **b)** $y = -2(x - 5)^2 - 2$ **c)** $y = -0.5(x + 2)^2 + 3$

5. Use a graphing calculator or graphing software to determine any x-intercepts, to the nearest tenth.
a) $y = 2(x + 2)^2 - 9$ **b)** $y = -(x - 2)^2 + 3$

6. Write each function in the form $y = a(x - h)^2 + k$. Sketch the graph, showing the coordinates of the vertex, the equation of the axis of symmetry, and the coordinates of two other points on the graph.
a) $y = x^2 + 8x + 8$ **b)** $y = -x^2 - 10x - 4$

7. Sketch the graph of each function. Show the coordinates of the vertex, the equation of the axis of symmetry, and any intercepts. State the range.
a) $y = x^2 - 10x$ **b)** $y = -x^2 - 6x - 10$

8. Find the coordinates of the vertex.
a) $y = 2x^2 + 12x + 13$ **b)** $y = -3x^2 + 24x - 50$

9. Sketch the graph of each of the following quadratic functions by writing it in the form $y = ax(x - s) + t$.
a) $y = x^2 - 8x + 5$ **b)** $y = -2x^2 + 4x - 3$

10. Use finite differences to determine whether each function is linear, quadratic, or neither.

a)

x	y
0	-1
1	1
2	7
3	17

b)

x	y
2	0
4	4
6	8
8	12

c)

x	y
1	1
2	16
3	81
4	256

11. Flare The height, h metres, of a flare as a function of the time, t seconds, since the flare was fired from a boat, can be modelled by the function

$$h = -5.25(t - 4)^2 + 86$$

a) What was the maximum height of the flare?
b) What was its height when it was fired?
c) How many seconds after it was fired did the flare hit the water, to the nearest second?

12. Riverboat cruise The captain of a riverboat cruise charges $36 per person, including lunch. The cruise averages 300 customers a day. The captain is considering increasing the price. A survey of customers indicates that for every $2 increase, there would be 10 fewer customers. What increase in price would maximize the revenue?

13. Rectangle pattern The diagrams show the first four rectangles in a pattern.
a) Write an equation of the form $A = \blacksquare$ that relates the area, A, of each rectangle to its width, w.
b) Find the area of the 25th rectangle in the pattern.

14. Draw a scatter plot for each table of values, and use trial and error to fit an equation of a quadratic function to each scatter plot. Compare the result with the quadratic equation of the curve of best fit produced by a graphing calculator or graphing software.

a)

x	y
2	2
1	-1
0	-2
-1	-1
-2	2

b)

x	y
3	-5
1	2
0	3
-1	2
-3	-7

Achievement Check

1   2   3   4

A cattle farmer wants to build a rectangular fenced enclosure divided into three rectangular pens, as shown in the diagram. A total length of 120 m of fencing material is available. Find the overall dimensions of the enclosure that will make the total area a maximum. Explain and justify your reasoning.

Diagrams can be useful for simplifying and solving problems of many types, including design, navigation, and scheduling problems.

For their final assignment, ten media students must write reviews of three television commercials. Each commercial is to run continuously for 10 min. To allow time for changeovers, 15-min time slots are needed. The commercials each student has chosen to review are shown in the table. Design a possible schedule for showing all the commercials in the minimum number of time slots, starting at 13:00. All students must be able to see their chosen commercials, so there must be no conflicts.

Commercial	Student									
	1	2	3	4	5	6	7	8	9	10
A	X			X				X	X	
B		X		X		X				X
C	X	X					X	X	X	
D			X		X	X				X
E	X		X		X		X		X	
F		X		X		X		X		X
G			X		X		X			

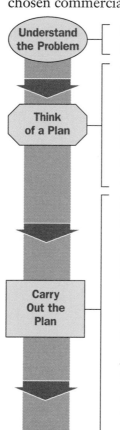

Understand the Problem

1. What information are you given?
2. What are you asked to do?

Think of a Plan

Represent each commercial by a point. Since Student 1 wants to review commercials A, C, and E, join these points as shown in Figure 1 to indicate that these commercials cannot be shown at the same time. Complete the network by connecting the points that represent the commercials each of the other students wants to review, as shown in Figure 2.

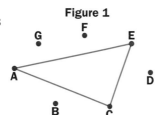

Figure 1

Carry Out the Plan

Now put a symbol at each point to represent a time slot. Because connected points represent commercials that cannot be shown at the same time, no two connected points can have the same symbol. Use the least possible number of symbols, as shown in Figure 3.

Since four different symbols are used, four time slots are needed. Commercials A and G will be shown at the same time, as will B and E, and C and D.

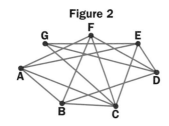

Figure 2

A possible schedule is as follows.
□ Commercials A and G: 13:00 to 13:15
△ Commercials B and E: 13:15 to 13:30
○ Commercials C and D: 13:30 to 13:45
◇ Commercial F: 13:45 to 14:00

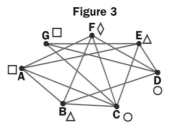

Figure 3

Look Back

At what times will Student 3 see the commercials?
Can all the students review the commercials they want?
Is there another possible schedule?
Is there another way to solve the problem?

Use a Diagram

1. Draw a diagram to represent the situation.
2. Use the diagram to solve the problem.
3. Check that the answer is reasonable.

Applications and Problem Solving

1. Film schedule Seven film students must write reviews of three short films, each lasting one-half hour. The films the seven students have chosen are shown in the table.

	Student						
Film	1	2	3	4	5	6	7
A	X		X	X		X	
B	X				X	X	X
C		X		X		X	X
D		X			X		
E	X	X	X	X			X
F			X		X		

Set up a schedule for showing the films in the minimum number of time periods, starting at 13:00. Allow 10 min for changeovers between time periods. All students must be able to see their three films, so there can be no conflicts.

2. Travel routes There are six towns in Galleragas County—Alliston, Bevan, Dunstan, Clearwater, Flagstaff, and Gaston. Only the following pairs of towns are joined by roads.

Alliston is 25 km from Flagstaff.
Bevan is 32 km from Gaston.
Dunstan is 28 km from Flagstaff.
Clearwater is 19 km from Bevan.
Gaston is 33 km from Flagstaff.
Alliston is 24 km from Bevan.
Dunstan is 19 km from Alliston.
Clearwater is 27 km from Flagstaff.

Draw a map showing possible locations of the towns. Then, find the shortest route from
a) Alliston to Gaston
b) Clearwater to Dunstan
c) Gaston to Bevan if you must go through Flagstaff
d) Flagstaff to Alliston if you must go through Bevan

3. Pool deck The diagram shows the outdoor pool at Lakeview Park. A cement deck 2 m wide surrounds the outside edge of the pool. Calculate the area of the deck.

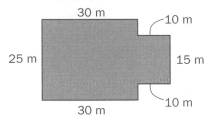

4. Basketball league There are six teams in a summer basketball league. Each team plays four games against each of the other teams. How many games are played?

5. Floor tiles Sarah wants to cover the floor of a kitchen with 20-cm square tiles. The floor is 3 m by 4 m. How many tiles does she need?

6. Decorating Ari has to paint the ceiling and walls of a room in his house. The room is 5 m long and 4 m wide. The ceiling height is 2.5 m. There are two doors, each measuring 1 m by 2 m. There are three windows, each measuring 1 m by 1.5 m. The windows and doors will not be painted. The room will get two coats of paint. One litre of paint covers 10 m². How many litres of paint should Ari buy?

7. Sightseeing Tara left her hotel to sightsee in Ottawa. She walked four blocks north, three blocks east, one block south, four blocks east, six blocks north, five blocks west, two blocks south, and six blocks west. How many blocks and in which directions should Tara walk to get back to her hotel in the shortest distance?

8. Communication Write a scheduling problem like the one shown in the example. Have a classmate solve your problem.

Problem Solving: Work Backward

In some problems, you are given an end result and asked to find a fact or condition that leads to the result. For this type of problem, working backward is a useful problem solving strategy.

Hailie, Monique, and Elena played a dice game. In the preliminary round, each player rolled two dice and added the two numbers rolled to give an initial number of points. Then, in each regular round, each player rolled one die. The person who rolled the lowest number in a regular round gave each of the other players enough points to double that player's points. In the event of a tie for lowest score, the round was repeated to decide a single loser. In the first three regular rounds, Hailie lost, and then Elena lost, and finally Monique lost. After the third regular round, Hailie had 8 points, Monique had 10 points, and Elena had 4 points. How many points did each player score in the preliminary round by rolling two dice?

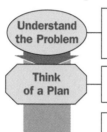

Understand the Problem

1. What information are you given?
2. What are you asked to find?
3. Do you need an exact or an approximate answer?

Think of a Plan

Set up a table and start with the number of points each player had at the end of the third round. Then, work backward.

Carry Out the Plan

At the end of the third round, the points for each player were as shown.

After Round	Points		
	Hailie	Monique	Elena
3	8	10	4

Monique was the last to lose, and she had to double the points of each of the other players. Since Hailie had 8 points, she must have had 4 points before Monique lost. Similarly, Elena must have had 2 points before Monique lost. Monique gave away a total of 6 points after she lost. So, at the end of the second round, before Monique lost, the points were as shown.

After Round	Points		
	Hailie	Monique	Elena
3	8	10	4
2	4	16	2

Elena lost the second round, so she gave Hailie 2 points and Monique 8 points. Elena gave away 10 points. At the end of the first round, before Elena lost, the points were as shown.

After Round	Points		
	Hailie	Monique	Elena
3	8	10	4
2	4	16	2
1	2	8	12

Hailie lost the first round, so she gave Monique 4 points and Elena 6 points. Hailie gave away 10 points. At the end of the preliminary round, before Hailie lost, the points were as shown.

So, in the preliminary round, Hailie scored 12 points, Monique scored 4 points, and Elena scored 6 points by rolling two dice.

After Round	Points		
	Hailie	Monique	Elena
3	8	10	4
2	4	16	2
1	2	8	12
Preliminary	12	4	6

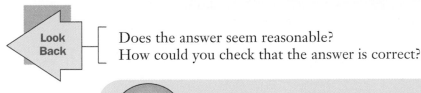

Does the answer seem reasonable?
How could you check that the answer is correct?

Work Backward
1. Start with what you know.
2. Work backward to get an answer.
3. Check that your answer is reasonable.

Applications and Problem Solving

1. Dice game Scott, Ivan, and Enzo played the dice game described in the example. Ivan lost the first regular round. Then, Scott lost a round. Then, Enzo lost two rounds in a row. After these 4 rounds, Scott had 12 points, Ivan had 8 points, and Enzo had 1 point. How many points did each player score in the preliminary round?

2. Coin collecting Miki is a coin collector. She bought a rare coin from another collector. She paid the collector $750 in cash and borrowed the money for the balance. The loan was for one year at an annual interest rate of 8%. Her monthly payments were $247.50. How much did Miki pay the collector for the coin?

3. Transformations When the following transformations are applied to a point A in the given order, the final result is the point B(3, −2). Find the coordinates of point A.
  a reflection in the *x*-axis
  a horizontal translation of −1
  a vertical stretch of scale factor 2
  a vertical translation of 6
  a reflection in the *y*-axis

4. Photocopying A photocopier was set to enlarge an original to 150% of its dimensions. A diagram was enlarged, the result was enlarged, and the new result was enlarged. The dimensions of the final result were 20.25 cm by 13.5 cm. What were the dimensions of the original diagram?

5. Chess tournament In a chess tournament, each player played a game in the first round. The losers dropped out. This process continued until a winner was declared. Jasmin won the tournament by winning 8 games. How many people were in the tournament?

6. Itinerary You are a travel agent. A local newspaper reporter will cover the United Nations Anniversary celebrations in New York City. The special session of the General Assembly will take place at the United Nations building on the fourth Tuesday in October. The session will start at 16:00 and end at 18:00. It will be followed by a reception for dignitaries and the press from 18:00 to 20:00. There is a press briefing at 15:00 on the day before the session. Your task is to use commercial transportation to get the reporter to the press briefing, the special session, and the reception, so that the reporter is away from home for as little time as possible. The reporter will look after hotel reservations and any taxis to and from airports, bus terminals, or train stations. Design an itinerary for the trip.

7. Communication Design a dice game similar to the one described in the example. Give a classmate the rules and the final number of points for each player. Have your classmate find the number of points each player scored in the preliminary round.

8. Communication Write another problem that can be solved by working backward. Have a classmate solve your problem.

1. Telephone keypad A telephone keypad is shown. The distance between the centre of the 1 button and the centre of the 2 button is 2 cm. The distance between the centre of the 1 button and the centre of the 4 button is 2 cm. To enter the following number, what is the minimum distance your finger would have to travel, to the nearest centimetre?
1-726-567-2194

```
1  2  3
4  5  6
7  8  9
*  0  #
```

2. Average ages The average age of the students in a group was 15. The average age of the teachers in the same group was 45. The average age of the whole group was 19. What was the smallest possible number of people in the group?

3. Chess tournament The contestants in a chess tournament were numbered from 1 to 18. When the players were paired for the first game, the sum of the two numbers for each pair was a perfect square. What were the pairings for the first game?

4. International travel You are leaving Calgary at 13:00 on a Friday to fly to Zurich, Switzerland, via Toronto. If your plane averages 850 km/h, and you stop for 1 h in Toronto, at about what time on what day will you land in Zurich?

5. Transformations Draw a square. Rotate the square 45° about one corner and draw the new square. Then, rotate the square another 45° in the same direction about the same corner and draw the next square. Continue the procedure until the square is returned to its original position.
a) How many squares are in the final diagram?
b) How many triangles are there?

6. Making change What is the most money you can have in $1 coins, $2 coins, $5 bills, $10 bills, $20 bills, and $50 bills, and still not be able to make change for a $100 bill?

7. Number puzzle Copy the diagram. Place one of the digits 1, 2, 3, 4, 5, and 6 in each square to make the multiplication true.

8. Lunch meeting Tia, Jane, Fran, and Marta are friends who meet every Friday for lunch. Their occupations are teacher, lawyer, carpenter, and police officer. Each woman has a pet—a dog, a cat, a parrot, or a turtle. Copy and complete the table. Use the clues to match the woman with her occupation and the pet she owns.
• Tia owns the turtle.
• Fran and the carpenter play baseball.
• The dog owner and the teacher do not play baseball.
• Tia is not the teacher or the police officer.
• Marta sat across from the parrot owner and the dog owner at lunch.
• The lawyer does not play baseball.

	tea	law	car	pol	dog	cat	par	tur
Tia								
Jane								
Fran								
Marta								
dog								
cat								
par								
tur								

9. Communication Estimate the total number of CDs owned by the high school students in your province. Explain and justify your answer.

Cumulative Review: Chapters 3 and 4

Chapter 3

1. Simplify.
a) $(3x^2 + 4x - 2) + (x^2 - 5x + 4)$
b) $(2y^2 - 8y + 7) - (5y^2 - 6y - 2)$

2. Expand and simplify.
a) $3(2m - n) - 2(m + 3n)$
b) $4p(p + 2) + 3p(2p - 5)$
c) $2w(w^2 + w - 3) - 3w(2w^2 + 1)$
d) $(2x + 1)(3x - 1)$
e) $(5z + 1)(z - 2) + (4z - 3)(2z + 3)$
f) $(y + 3)(2y^2 - 5y - 4)$

3. Expand and simplify.
a) $(4x + 1)(4x - 1)$
b) $(2m + n)^2$
c) $(y - 4)^2 - (y + 2)(y - 2)$
d) $4(t + 1)^2 + 2(2t + 1)(2t - 1)$

4. Factor.
a) $14x^2 - 7x$
b) $5yz^2 - 35yz + 10y^2z$
c) $x(y - 3) - 4(y - 3)$
d) $2mn + 3mp - 4n - 6p$

5. Factor.
a) $x^2 - 12x + 20$
b) $y^2 + 3y - 18$
c) $x^2 - 81$
d) $6y^2 + 11y + 4$
e) $25a^2 - b^2$
f) $n^2 - 6n + 9$
g) $49b^2 - 28b + 4$

6. Factor fully.
a) $2s^2 + 14s - 16$
b) $9x^2 + 24x + 12$
c) $ax^2 + 6ax + 9a$
d) $40c^2 - 10d^2$

7. Calculator screen On one model of graphing calculator, the area of the screen can be represented by the expression $8x^2 + 10x - 25$.
a) Factor the expression $8x^2 + 10x - 25$ to find binomials that represent the dimensions of the screen.
b) If x represents 17 mm, what are the dimensions of the screen, in millimetres?

Chapter 4

1. For each parabola, state the direction of the opening, how the parabola is stretched or shrunk, if at all, the coordinates of the vertex, the equation of the axis of symmetry, the domain and range, and the maximum or minimum value.
a) $y = -2x^2$
b) $y = x^2 - 3$
c) $y = (x + 3)^2$
d) $y = -(x - 2)^2 + 1$
e) $y = 0.5(x - 4)^2 + 3$
f) $y = -3(x + 5)^2 - 2$

2. Use a graphing calculator or graphing software to determine any x-intercepts, to the nearest tenth.
a) $y = x^2 - 5$
b) $y = -2(x + 3)^2 + 6$

3. Write each function in the form $y = a(x - h)^2 + k$. Sketch the graph. Show the coordinates of the vertex, the equation of the axis of symmetry, and the coordinates of two other points on the graph.
a) $y = x^2 + 4x - 2$
b) $y = 3x^2 - 6x + 7$

4. Sketch the graphs of the following. Show the coordinates of the vertex and any intercepts.
a) $y = x^2 - 4x$
b) $y = -x^2 + 2x + 8$

5. Sketch the graph of the function $y = x^2 - 6x + 3$ by writing it in the form $y = ax(x - s) + t$.

6. Use finite differences to determine whether each function is linear, quadratic, or neither.

a) x	y	b) x	y	c) x	y
2	4	1	−1	2	0
3	8	2	5	4	4
4	16	3	13	6	8
5	28	4	29	8	12

7. Admission fee A museum has an admission fee of $14 and averages 300 visitors per day. The museum board decides to raise the fee. Research indicates that for every $1 increase, there would be 10 fewer visitors per day. What admission fee would maximize the revenue?

Specific Expectations	Sections
• Solve quadratic equations by factoring and by using graphing calculators or graphing software.	5.1 5.2
• Interpret real and non-real roots of quadratic equations geometrically as the x-intercepts of the graph of a quadratic function.	5.1 5.2
• Sketch, by hand, the graph of a quadratic function whose equation is given in the form $y = ax^2 + bx + c$ by locating the x-intercepts if the equation is factorable.	5.3
• Solve quadratic equations, using the quadratic formula.	5.4
• Determine the zeros of a quadratic function, using algebraic techniques.	5.2 5.3 5.4
• Solve problems related to an application, given the formula of a quadratic function.	5.1 5.2 5.4

Modelling Math

The Motion of Airborne Objects

The motion of an airborne baseball can be modelled using a quadratic function. The function $h = -5t^2 + 20t + 1$ models the height, h metres, of a baseball as a function of the time, t seconds, since it was struck. The ball hit the ground before a fielder could catch it.

a) How long was the baseball in the air?
b) For how many seconds was the height of the baseball at least 16 m?

In the Modelling Math questions on pages 277, 286, and 295, you will solve the above problems and other problems that involve the motion of airborne objects.

1. List possible factors that might affect how long a baseball is in the air after it is hit.

2. List other sports in which the length of time a ball spends in the air is important. Explain why.

3. List some jumping events in which the length of time an athlete spends in the air is important. For each event, describe how the athlete can affect the length of time spent in the air.

Getting Started

Ocean Waves

For ocean waves, the wavelength is the distance from one wave crest to the next.

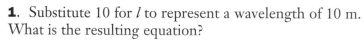

In deep water, the speed of a wave, s metres per second, is approximately related to the wavelength, l metres, by the following equation.
$$s^2 = 1.6l$$

1. Substitute 10 for l to represent a wavelength of 10 m. What is the resulting equation?

2. What values of s satisfy your equation from question 1?

3. **Communication** Which of the values of s that you found in question 2 has no meaning for the speed of a wave? Explain.

4. What is the speed of a wave with a wavelength of 10 m?

5. Find the speed of a wave with a wavelength of
a) 2.5 m   **b)** 22.5 m   **c)** 0.9 m

Review of Prerequisite Skills

If you need help with any of the skills named in **purple** below, refer to Appendix A.

1. Evaluating expressions Evaluate for $x = 2$, $y = 1$, and $z = 3$.
a) $5x - y + 2z$
b) $4xz - 3y + 9$
c) $2(4x + 7y)$
d) $yz - xz + xyz$
e) $5(z - x - y)$
f) $3y^2 + 4z^2 - 2x^2$
g) $3y(7 + 8z)$
h) $(xyz)^2$

2. Evaluating expressions Evaluate for $a = -3$, $b = -1$, and $c = 2$.
a) $2ac - 5b$
b) $6a - 2b - 3c$
c) $4a(2b - c)$
d) $ab - bc - ac$
e) $2a^2 + 3b^2 - c^2$
f) $(a - b)(b - c)$
g) $(a + b - c)^2$
h) $4ab^2c - 15$

3. Solving equations Solve and check.
a) $4x + 3 = x - 45$
b) $3y + 16 = y - 28$
c) $3(x - 4) - 6 = 5x - 12$
d) $4(2w - 1) - (w - 5) = 15$
e) $2(1 - 3x) - 2(4x - 5) = -2$
f) $0 = 5 - 3(t - 5) + 4(2 - t)$
g) $4 - (x - 3) + 2(3x - 5) = 7$
h) $3(2x + 1) - 2(1 - x) = 5$
i) $\dfrac{x}{2} + 1 = \dfrac{x}{3}$
j) $\dfrac{x}{3} - \dfrac{x}{4} = \dfrac{1}{2}$

4. Common factoring Factor.
a) $4x^2 + 8x$
b) $3x^2 - 3x$
c) $6x^2 + 4x - 8$
d) $5x^2 - 20x + 10$

5. Factor, if possible.
a) $x^2 + 7x + 12$
b) $x^2 - 7x + 10$
c) $y^2 - 2y - 8$
d) $t^2 + 3t + 10$
e) $r^2 - 16$
f) $w^2 - 25$
g) $z^2 + 10z + 25$
h) $x^2 - 14x + 49$
i) $t^2 - t - 12$
j) $w^2 + 2w - 24$
k) $x^2 + 100$
l) $w^2 + 3w - 88$
m) $x^2 - 4x - 45$
n) $y^2 - 2y + 1$
o) $z^2 + 7z - 30$
p) $t^2 + 11t + 28$
q) $w^2 - 14w + 40$
r) $x^2 + 6x - 27$
s) $y^2 - y - 20$

6. Factor, if possible.
a) $2x^2 + 7x + 3$
b) $6t^2 - 7t - 3$
c) $2y^2 - 7y + 5$
d) $10x^2 - x - 2$
e) $3z^2 - 3z - 4$
f) $4x^2 - 9$
g) $4x^2 - 12x + 9$
h) $2w^2 + 9w + 10$
i) $3t^2 - 11t + 10$
j) $3x^2 - 11x - 20$
k) $9y^2 + 6y + 1$
l) $36x^2 + 1$
m) $6w^2 + w - 1$
n) $4x^2 + 20x + 25$
o) $25n^2 - 1$

7. Evaluating radicals Evaluate, if possible.
a) $\sqrt{49}$
b) $\sqrt{-9}$
c) $\sqrt{121}$
d) $\sqrt{25 + 56}$
e) $\sqrt{36 - 20}$
f) $\sqrt{64 - 28}$
g) $\sqrt{16 + 4(12)}$
h) $\sqrt{10^2 - 36}$
i) $\sqrt{7^2 + 32}$
j) $\sqrt{3^2 - 4(2)(-2)}$
k) $\sqrt{8^2 - 4(3)(-3)}$
l) $\sqrt{7^2 - 4(2)(3)}$

Canada's rich history in soccer includes the gold medal at the 1904 Olympic Games in St. Louis. Today, many Canadians play professional soccer around the world. Many others play in amateur leagues.

The path of one kick of a soccer ball can be modelled by the function

$$h = -0.025d^2 + d$$

where h metres is the height of the ball, and d metres is the horizontal distance of the ball from the place on the ground where it was kicked. One way to find the horizontal distance the ball travels before it first hits the ground is to graph the function and find the d-intercepts.

Since the height of the ball is 0 m when it is kicked and when it hits the ground, we can substitute 0 for h. When the ball is kicked and when it first hits the ground, the following equation is true.

$$-0.025d^2 + d = 0$$

So, another way to find the horizontal distance the ball travels before it first hits the ground is to solve this equation. This solution will be shown in Example 4.

The equation $-0.025d^2 + d = 0$ is an example of a **quadratic equation.** Quadratic equations are equations in the form $ax^2 + bx + c = 0$, where a, b, and c are real numbers and $a \neq 0$.

The graph of the quadratic function $y = ax^2 + bx + c$ represents all the ordered pairs (x, y) that satisfy the function. When solving the quadratic equation $ax^2 + bx + c = 0$, we are interested only in the values of x that make the expression $ax^2 + bx + c$ equal to zero.

1. Graph $y = 2x - 4$ and $y = x^2 - 2x - 3$ on the same set of axes using paper and pencil, a graphing calculator, or graphing software. Find the x-intercept(s) for each graph.

2. Communication For the linear function $y = 2x - 4$, a related linear equation is $2x - 4 = 0$. For which point on the graph of $y = 2x - 4$ is the x-coordinate the solution to $2x - 4 = 0$? Explain.

3. Communication For the quadratic function $y = x^2 - 2x - 3$, a related quadratic equation is $x^2 - 2x - 3 = 0$. For which points on the graph of $y = x^2 - 2x - 3$ are the x-coordinates solutions to $x^2 - 2x - 3 = 0$? Explain.

4. a) Graph $y = x^2 + x - 6$.
b) Find the x-intercepts.
c) Do the x-intercepts satisfy the equation $x^2 + x - 6 = 0$?

5. Solve each quadratic equation by graphing.
a) $x^2 - 2x - 8 = 0$ **b)** $x^2 + 3x - 4 = 0$ **c)** $x^2 + 2x + 1 = 0$

The solutions of the quadratic equation $ax^2 + bx + c = 0$ are known as the **zeros** of the quadratic function $y = ax^2 + bx + c$. The real zeros are the x-intercepts of the parabola $y = ax^2 + bx + c$, since the value of y is zero for points on the x-axis. The x-intercepts are called the real solutions, or real **roots**, of the quadratic equation.

Example 1 Solving by Graphing
Solve $x^2 - 6x + 8 = 0$ by graphing.

Solution 1 Graphing-Calculator Method
Graph the related quadratic function $y = x^2 - 6x + 8$.

The values of the x-intercepts can be found using the Zero operation or by displaying a table of values.

The x-intercepts are the real zeros of the function $y = x^2 - 6x + 8$, since $y = 0$ for these values of x.

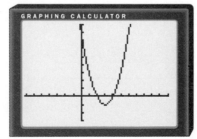

So, $x^2 - 6x + 8 = 0$ when $x = 2$ or $x = 4$.

Solution 2   Paper-and-Pencil Method

Use a table of values to draw the graph of the related quadratic function $y = x^2 - 6x + 8$.

x	y
0	8
1	3
2	0
3	-1
4	0
5	3
6	8

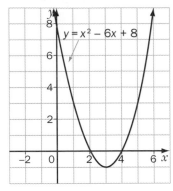

The graph intersects the x-axis at (2, 0) and (4, 0). The x-intercepts are the real zeros of the function $y = x^2 - 6x + 8$, since $y = 0$ for these values of x. So, $x^2 - 6x + 8 = 0$ when $x = 2$ or $x = 4$.

Check for Solution 1 and Solution 2.

For $x = 2$,

L.S. $= x^2 - 6x + 8$ **R.S.** $= 0$
$= (2)^2 - 6(2) + 8$
$= 4 - 12 + 8$
$= 0$

For $x = 4$,

L.S. $= x^2 - 6x + 8$ **R.S.** $= 0$
$= (4)^2 - 6(4) + 8$
$= 16 - 24 + 8$
$= 0$

The roots of the equation $x^2 - 6x + 8 = 0$ are 2 and 4.

The equation in Example 1 has two different or distinct roots. Some quadratic equations do not have distinct roots.

Example 2   Two Equal Roots

Solve $x^2 - 6x = -9$ by graphing.

Solution

Rewrite the equation in the form $ax^2 + bx + c = 0$.
$$x^2 - 6x = -9$$
So, $x^2 - 6x + 9 = 0$

Graph the related quadratic function $y = x^2 - 6x + 9$.
The graph meets the x-axis at one point, (3, 0).
The x-intercept is 3, so the root is 3.

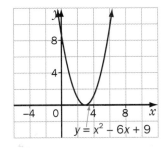

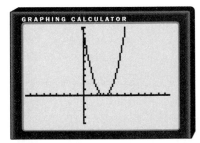

In Example 2, there are actually two roots. Each root equals 3. In this situation, an equation is said to have a **double root**.

Example 3   No Real Roots

Solve $2x^2 + x + 2 = 0$ by graphing.

Solution

Graph the related quadratic function
$y = 2x^2 + x + 2$.
The graph of the function does not
intersect the x-axis.
The quadratic equation has no real roots.

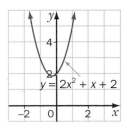

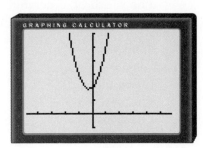

The following graphs show the three possible outcomes when solving a
quadratic equation.

two distinct real roots   *two equal real roots*   *no real roots*

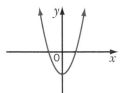 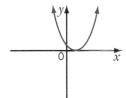 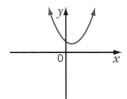

Example 4   Soccer

The function $h = -0.025d^2 + d$ models the height, h metres, of one kick of a
soccer ball as a function of the horizontal distance, d metres, from the place
on the ground where the ball was kicked. By graphing, find the horizontal
distance the ball travels before it first hits the ground.

Solution

Solve the equation $-0.025d^2 + d = 0$ by graphing the function
$h = -0.025d^2 + d$.

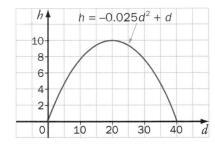

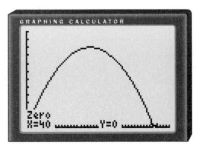

The d-intercepts are $(0, 0)$ and $(40, 0)$.
The roots of the equation are 0 and 40.
The ball was kicked at $d = 0$. It hits the ground at $d = 40$.
So, the ball travels a horizontal distance of 40 m before it first hits
the ground.

Example 5   Measurement

The width of a rectangle is 2 m less than the length. The area of the rectangle is 48 m^2. Find the dimensions of the rectangle.

Solution

Let the length be x.
Then, the width is $x - 2$.
The area is $x(x - 2)$.
The area is known to be 48 m^2.

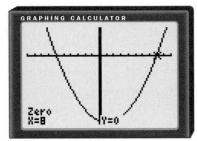

So, $x(x - 2) = 48$
$$x^2 - 2x = 48$$
$$x^2 - 2x - 48 = 0$$

Graph the function $A = x^2 - 2x - 48$.

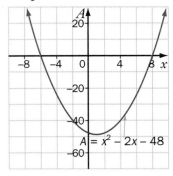

The graph intersects the x-axis at $(-6, 0)$ and $(8, 0)$, so the x-intercepts are -6 and 8.
The roots of the equation are -6 and 8.
The length of a rectangle cannot be negative, so the root -6 is said to be inadmissible and is rejected.

The length of the rectangle is 8 m, and the width is $8 - 2$ or 6 m.

Check.
The width is 2 m less than the length: $8 - 6 = 2$
The area is 48 m^2: $8 \times 6 = 48$

CONCEPTS

1 The solutions to the quadratic equation $ax^2 + bx + c = 0$ are the x-intercepts of the quadratic function $y = ax^2 + bx + c$.

2 There are three possible results when solving a quadratic equation.

a) two distinct real roots   **b)** two equal real roots   **c)** no real roots

Communicate Your Understanding

1. Explain why the x-intercepts of a quadratic function are the solutions to a quadratic equation.

2. Describe how you would solve each of the following quadratic equations by graphing.

a) $x^2 - 4x - 5 = 0$ **b)** $-2x^2 + x = -6$ **c)** $x^2 = -4x - 4$

Practice

A

1. Solve by graphing. Check real solutions.

a) $x^2 + x - 6 = 0$ **b)** $x^2 - 5x + 4 = 0$
c) $x^2 - 4 = 0$ **d)** $x^2 + x + 1 = 0$
e) $x^2 - x - 2 = 0$ **f)** $x^2 + 3x - 4 = 0$
g) $x^2 + 6x + 9 = 0$ **h)** $x^2 - 5x = 0$

2. Solve by graphing.

a) $3x + x^2 = 0$ **b)** $x^2 + 3x = 4$
c) $-x^2 + 3x = 0$ **d)** $9 - x^2 = 0$
e) $-x^2 - 1 = 0$ **f)** $x^2 = 5 - 4x$
g) $-2 = x - x^2$ **h)** $-x^2 + 3x = 2$
i) $x + 3 = -x^2$ **j)** $4 - 4x = -x^2$

3. Solve graphically using a graphing calculator or graphing software. Round each answer to the nearest tenth, if necessary.

a) $2x^2 - x - 3 = 0$ **b)** $2x^2 - 5x - 3 = 0$
c) $4x^2 - 11x + 9 = 0$ **d)** $4x^2 + 4x + 1 = 0$
e) $-2x^2 + 5x = 0$ **f)** $-3x^2 - 7x + 5 = 0$
g) $6x^2 - 5x - 4 = 0$ **h)** $9a^2 - 48a + 64 = 0$
i) $40x^2 = 10 - 9x$ **j)** $3 = 2x + 7x^2$
k) $0.5x^2 - x - 3 = 0$ **l)** $0.02x^2 - 0.03x + 7 = 0$
m) $1.07x^2 + 3.5x = 0$ **n)** $-0.36n^2 - 1 = 1.2n$

Applications and Problem Solving

Solve problems 4–15 using a graphing calculator or graphing software.

4. Measurement The width of a rectangle is 1 m less than the length. The area is 72 m². Find the width and the length.

B

5. Football During a field goal attempt, the function $h = -0.02d^2 + 0.9d$ models the height, h metres, of a football in terms of the horizontal distance, d metres, from where the ball was kicked. Find the horizontal distance the ball travels until it first hits the ground.

6. Measurement The length of a rectangle is 5 cm greater than twice the width. The area is 33 cm^2. Find the dimensions.

7. Measurement The hypotenuse of a right triangle measures 10 m. One of the other two sides is 2 m longer than the third side. Find the unknown side lengths.

8. Measurement The hypotenuse of a right triangle has a length of 13 cm. The sum of the lengths of the other two sides is 17 cm. Find the unknown side lengths.

9. Measurement The height of a triangle is 2 m more than the base. The area is 17.5 m^2. Find the length of the base.

10. Fenced field The area of a rectangular field is 2275 m^2. The field is enclosed by 200 m of fencing. What are the dimensions of the field?

11. Basketball court The width of a basketball court is 1 m more than half the length. If the area of the court is 364 m^2, find the length and the width.

12. Measurement The diagonal of a rectangle is 8 cm. The length of the rectangle is 1.6 cm more than the width. Find the dimensions of the rectangle.

13. Integers The sum of the squares of two consecutive even integers is 452. Find the integers.

14. Canadian flag The Unity Flag is one of the largest Canadian flags. The length is twice the width, and the area is 167.2 m^2. Find the dimensions of the Unity Flag, to the nearest tenth of a metre.

15. Integers The sum of the squares of three consecutive positive integers is 194. Find the integers.

16. Solve by graphing.

a) $(x - 2)^2 - 1 = 0$

b) $(x + 1)^2 - 4 = 0$

c) $(x + 2)^2 + 1 = 0$

d) $(x - 3)^2 = 0$

e) $-1(1 - x)^2 = 0$

f) $4(x + 1)^2 - 1 = 0$

g) $0 = -2(p - 1)^2$

h) $0.1(q + 3)^2 = 1.6$

17. Factored form **a)** The left side of the equation $(x - 4)(x + 3) = 0$ is in factored form. Expand and simplify the left side.
b) Solve the resulting equation by graphing.
c) Communication How are the roots of the equation related to the two numerical terms in the factored form of the equation?

C

18. For what values of c will the equation $x^2 + c = 0$ have
a) two distinct real roots?
b) two equal real roots?
c) no real roots?

19. For what values of c will the equation $x^2 + 14x + c = 0$ have
a) two equal roots?
b) two distinct real roots?
c) no real roots?

20. For what values of b will the equation $x^2 + bx + 25 = 0$ have
a) two equal real roots?
b) two distinct real roots?
c) no real roots?

21. Communication For the equation $x^2 + bx = 0$,
a) what value of b will give two equal real roots?
b) when there are two distinct real roots, what does one of them always equal? How is the other root related to b?

22. For the quadratic function $y = x^2 - 9$, determine the values of x such that
a) $y \geq 7$ **b)** $y \leq 16$

Modelling Math | **The Motion of Airborne Objects**

The function $h = -0.04d^2 + 0.8d$ models the height of a soccer ball, h metres, in terms of the horizontal distance, d metres, from where the ball was kicked on the ground. How far does the ball travel horizontally through the air until it first hits the ground?

W O R D   P O W E R

Lewis Carroll invented a word game called doublets. The object of the game is to change one word to another by changing one letter at a time. You must form a real word each time you change a letter. The best solution has the fewest steps. Change the word RING to the word BELL by changing one letter at a time.

Any quadratic equation can be written in the form $ax^2 + bx + c = 0$, where $a \neq 0$.
In the equation $x^2 + 3x + 2 = 0$, $a = 1$, $b = 3$, and $c = 2$.
The equation $2x^2 = 5$ can be written as $2x^2 - 5 = 0$.
In this case, $a = 2$, $b = 0$, and $c = -5$.

Recall that, when a number is multiplied by zero, the result is always zero. For example, $3 \times 0 = 0$, $0 \times (-7) = 0$, and $0 \times 0 = 0$.

The **zero product property** states that, if the product of two real numbers is zero, then one or both of the numbers must be zero.

Thus, if $ab = 0$, then $a = 0$, or $b = 0$, or $a = 0$ and $b = 0$.

You will be able to solve some quadratic equations by writing them in the form $ax^2 + bx + c = 0$, and then factoring and setting each factor equal to zero.
For the equation $x^2 + 2x - 3 = 0$, factoring results in the equation $(x + 3)(x - 1) = 0$.
Thus, $x + 3 = 0$ or $x - 1 = 0$
$\qquad\quad x = -3$ or $\quad x = 1$

Investigation **Solve an Equation**

Maureen Griffin and Heather Landymoore won a bronze medal for Canada in the team épée fencing event at the Pan-American Games in Mar Del Plata, Argentina. Épée competitions are held on a rectangular strip whose length is 12 m greater than its width. The area of the strip is 28 m^2.

1. a) Let the width be x metres. Write an expression for the length in terms of x.
b) Write an expression for the area in terms of x.
c) Write an equation that relates the known area to the expression you wrote in part b).
d) Write your equation in the form $ax^2 + bx + c = 0$.

2. Factor the left side of the equation from question 1d).

3. a) Solve the equation for x.
b) State the width and the length of the strip.

4. Solve each of the following equations by factoring.
a) $x^2 + 5x + 6 = 0$ **b)** $x^2 - 3x - 4 = 0$ **c)** $x^2 + 2 = 3x$

Example 1   Solving by Factoring, a = 1
Solve and check $x^2 + 7x + 12 = 0$.

Solution

$$x^2 + 7x + 12 = 0$$

Factor the left side: $\quad (x + 4)(x + 3) = 0$

Use the zero product property: $\quad x + 4 = 0 \quad$ or $\quad x + 3 = 0$

$$x = -4 \quad \text{or} \quad x = -3$$

Check.

For $x = -4$,

L.S. $= x^2 + 7x + 12 \qquad$ **R.S.** $= 0$

$\quad = (-4)^2 + 7(-4) + 12$

$\quad = 16 - 28 + 12$

$\quad = 0$

$\qquad$ L.S. = R.S.

For $x = -3$,

L.S. $= x^2 + 7x + 12 \qquad$ **R.S.** $= 0$

$\quad = (-3)^2 + 7(-3) + 12$

$\quad = 9 - 21 + 12$

$\quad = 0$

$\qquad$ L.S. = R.S.

The solutions are -4 and -3.

You can model the solution by graphing $y = x^2 + 7x + 12$.

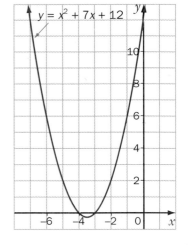

Example 2   Solving by Factoring, a ≠ 1
Solve and check $2x^2 + 3 = 5x + 1$.

Solution

$$2x^2 + 3 = 5x + 1$$

Write in the form $ax^2 + bx + c = 0$: $\quad 2x^2 - 5x + 2 = 0$

Factor the left side: $\quad (2x - 1)(x - 2) = 0$

Use the zero product property: $\quad 2x - 1 = 0 \ $ or $\ x - 2 = 0$

$$2x = 1 \quad \text{or} \quad x = 2$$

$$x = \frac{1}{2}$$

Check.

For $x = \frac{1}{2}$,

L.S. $= 2x^2 + 3 \quad$ **R.S.** $= 5x + 1$

$\quad = 2\left(\frac{1}{2}\right)^2 + 3 \qquad = 5\left(\frac{1}{2}\right) + 1$

$\quad = 2\left(\frac{1}{4}\right) + 3 \qquad = 2\frac{1}{2} + 1$

$\quad = 3\frac{1}{2} \qquad\qquad = 3\frac{1}{2}$

$\qquad$ L.S. = R.S.

For $x = 2$,

L.S. $= 2x^2 + 3 \qquad$ **R.S.** $= 5x + 1$

$\quad = 2(2)^2 + 3 \qquad = 5(2) + 1$

$\quad = 2(4) + 3 \qquad = 10 + 1$

$\quad = 11 \qquad\qquad = 11$

$\qquad$ L.S. = R.S.

You can model the solution by graphing $y = 2x^2 - 5x + 2$.

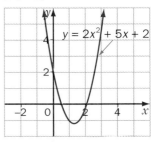

The roots are $\frac{1}{2}$ and 2.

If $c = 0$, a quadratic equation simplifies to $ax^2 + bx = 0$. In this case, one of the roots is 0.

Example 3   Solving by Factoring When $c = 0$

Solve $3x^2 + 5x = 0$.

Solution

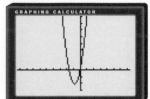

You can model the solution by graphing $y = 3x^2 + 5x$.

$$3x^2 + 5x = 0$$

Remove the common factor: $\quad x(3x + 5) = 0$

Use the zero product property: $\quad x = 0 \quad$ or $\quad 3x + 5 = 0$

$$3x = -5$$
$$x = -\frac{5}{3}$$

The roots are 0 and $-\frac{5}{3}$.

Example 4   Solving by Factoring When $b = 0$

Solve $2x^2 - 18 = 0$.

Solution

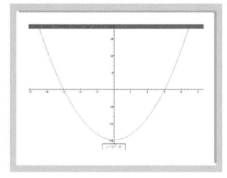

You can model the solution by graphing $y = 2x^2 - 18$.

$$2x^2 - 18 = 0$$

Divide both sides by 2: $\qquad \dfrac{2x^2}{2} - \dfrac{18}{2} = \dfrac{0}{2}$

$$x^2 - 9 = 0$$

Factor the left side: $\qquad (x + 3)(x - 3) = 0$

Use the zero product property: $\quad x + 3 = 0 \quad$ or $\quad x - 3 = 0$

$$x = -3 \quad \text{or} \quad x = 3$$

The solutions are -3 and 3.

Example 5   Solving Equations With Fractions

Solve and check $\dfrac{x^2}{6} - \dfrac{4x}{3} = -2$.

Solution

First, clear the fractions by multiplying by the lowest common denominator (LCD).

$$\frac{x^2}{6} - \frac{4x}{3} = -2$$

Multiply both sides by the LCD, 6: $\quad 6 \times \left(\dfrac{x^2}{6}\right) - 6 \times \left(\dfrac{4x}{3}\right) = 6 \times (-2)$

Simplify: $\qquad\qquad\qquad\qquad\qquad\qquad x^2 - 8x = -12$

Write in the form $ax^2 + bx + c = 0$: $\qquad x^2 - 8x + 12 = 0$

Factor the left side: $\qquad\qquad\qquad\qquad (x - 6)(x - 2) = 0$

Use the zero product property: $\quad x - 6 = 0 \quad$ or $\quad x - 2 = 0$

$$x = 6 \qquad \text{or} \qquad x = 2$$

Check.

For $x = 6,$

L.S. $= \dfrac{x^2}{6} - \dfrac{4x}{3}$ **R.S.** $= -2$

$= \dfrac{6^2}{6} - \dfrac{4(6)}{3}$

$= 6 - 8$

$= -2$

   L.S. = R.S.

For $x = 2,$

L.S. $= \dfrac{x^2}{6} - \dfrac{4x}{3}$ **R.S.** $= -2$

$= \dfrac{2^2}{6} - \dfrac{4(2)}{3}$

$= \dfrac{2}{3} - \dfrac{8}{3}$

$= -2$

   L.S. = R.S.

The roots are 2 and 6.

Example 6   Framing a Picture

A picture that measures 10 cm by 5 cm is to be surrounded by a mat before being framed. The width of the mat is to be the same on all sides of the picture. The area of the mat is to be twice the area of the picture. What is the width of the mat?

Solution

Draw a diagram. Let the width of the mat be w cm.
Write and solve an equation to find w.
The dimensions of the picture plus the mat are $(10 + 2w)$ by $(5 + 2w)$.
The total area is 3×50 or 150 cm^2.
So, $(10 + 2w)(5 + 2w) = 150$

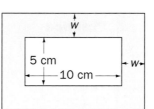

	$(10 + 2w)(5 + 2w) = 150$
Expand the left side:	$50 + 20w + 10w + 4w^2 = 150$
Simplify:	$4w^2 + 30w = 100$
Write in the form $ax^2 + bx + c = 0$:	$4w^2 + 30w - 100 = 0$
Divide both sides by 2:	$2w^2 + 15w - 50 = 0$
Factor the left side:	$(2w - 5)(w + 10) = 0$
Use the zero product property:	$2w - 5 = 0 \quad\text{or}\quad w + 10 = 0$
	$w = \dfrac{5}{2} \quad\text{or}\quad w = -10$

The width cannot be negative, so the root -10 is inadmissible and is rejected.
So, $w = \dfrac{5}{2}$
The width of the mat is 2.5 cm.

Check.
The overall dimensions of the mat and the picture are
$10 + 2(2.5)$ by $5 + 2(2.5)$, or 15 cm by 10 cm.
The total area is 15×10 or 150 cm^2.
The area of the mat is $150 - 50$ or 100 cm^2, which is twice the area
of the picture.

Key CONCEPTS

To solve a quadratic equation by factoring,
a) write the equation in the form $ax^2 + bx + c = 0$
b) factor $ax^2 + bx + c$
c) use the zero product property
d) solve the two resulting equations to find the roots
e) check your solutions

Communicate Your Understanding

1. If the product of two factors is zero, what must be true of the factors?

2. Can $x(x - 3) = 0$ be solved by dividing both sides of the equation by x? Explain.

3. Describe how you would solve each equation by factoring.
a) $x^2 - 2x - 15 = 0$ **b)** $2x^2 - x = 1$ **c)** $2x^2 + 3x = 0$

d) $x^2 = 49$ **e)** $\dfrac{x^2}{4} + \dfrac{x}{2} = 2$

Practice

A

1. Solve.
a) $(x + 1)(x + 2) = 0$ **b)** $(x + 3)(x - 1) = 0$
c) $(x - 5)(x - 5) = 0$ **d)** $(x - 2)(x + 3) = 0$
e) $(2x + 1)(x - 3) = 0$ **f)** $(3x + 4)(2x - 1) = 0$
g) $x(x + 9) = 0$ **h)** $x(4 - x) = 0$

2. Write each equation in the form $ax^2 + bx + c = 0$.
a) $x^2 - 6 = 2x$ **b)** $2y^2 - 3y = -2$ **c)** $3(z^2 + 1) = -4z$
d) $(x + 1)^2 = 4$ **e)** $4m^2 = 3m$ **f)** $2(x^2 - 1) = x$

3. Write each equation in the form $ax^2 + bx + c = 0$.

a) $\dfrac{x^2}{2} - \dfrac{3x}{2} = -1$ **b)** $\dfrac{x^2}{2} + \dfrac{x}{3} = 1$ **c)** $\dfrac{x^2}{8} + \dfrac{5x}{4} = -2$

4. Solve and check.
a) $n^2 + 7n + 12 = 0$ **b)** $y^2 - 3y + 2 = 0$ **c)** $x^2 - x - 6 = 0$
d) $a^2 - 8a + 16 = 0$ **e)** $0 = p^2 + 2p - 35$ **f)** $m^2 - 7m = 18$

5. Solve and check.
a) $2a^2 + 3a - 2 = 0$ **b)** $3s^2 - 4s + 1 = 0$ **c)** $2t^2 + 11t + 5 = 0$
d) $3x^2 + 7x - 6 = 0$ **e)** $0 = 4m^2 - 4m - 3$ **f)** $10y^2 - 16y = -6$

6. Solve and check.
a) $x^2 + 2x = 0$ **b)** $y^2 - 3y = 0$ **c)** $3m^2 + 2m = 0$
d) $5n^2 - 8n = 0$ **e)** $5t^2 - 20t = 0$ **f)** $0 = 4x + 3x^2$

7. Solve.

a) $x^2 - 25 = 0$

b) $y^2 + 12 = 48$

c) $n^2 + 4 = 20$

d) $m^2 - 7.5 = 92.5$

e) $1.3 = x^2 + 0.3$

f) $1.25 + z^2 = 1.5$

g) $2x^2 - 32 = 0$

h) $3x^2 + 2 = 29$

i) $4x^2 + 5 = 21$

j) $125 = 3y^2 - 22$

8. Solve.

a) $x^2 - 2x - 11 = 4$

b) $w^2 + 30 = 9 + 10w$

c) $3p^2 + 8p - 9 = 2p$

d) $4t^2 = 12t - 9$

e) $5r^2 = 2r$

f) $(x - 6)^2 - 8x = 0$

g) $(a + 4)^2 = 4$

h) $(b - 3)^2 = 9$

9. Solve.

a) $x^2 + \dfrac{9x}{2} - \dfrac{5}{2} = 0$

b) $\dfrac{x^2}{4} - x - 3 = 0$

c) $\dfrac{x^2}{6} + 2x + \dfrac{10}{3} = 0$

d) $\dfrac{x^2}{9} - \dfrac{x}{3} = 2$

e) $\dfrac{x^2}{2} + \dfrac{7x}{4} = 0$

f) $\dfrac{x^2}{4} - \dfrac{x}{3} = \dfrac{1}{3}$

10. Solve.

a) $\dfrac{z^2 - 1}{5} = 7$

b) $2 = \dfrac{4 + x^2}{10}$

c) $\dfrac{3y^2 + 7}{2} = 5$

d) $\dfrac{1 - 5n^2}{4} = -31$

Applications and Problem Solving

11. Measurement The area of the rectangle shown in the diagram is 36 cm². What are its dimensions?

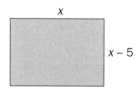

12. Framing a photograph A photograph measuring 12 cm by 8 cm is to be surrounded by a mat before framing. The width of the mat is to be the same on all sides of the photograph. The area of the mat is to equal the area of the photograph. Find the width of the mat.

B

13. Numbers Two numbers differ by 6. If the numbers are squared and then added, the result is 146. What are the numbers?

14. Integers Two consecutive integers are added. The square of their sum is 361. What are the integers?

15. Numbers The product of two consecutive even numbers is 288. What are the numbers?

16. Integers When the square of an integer is added to ten times the integer, the sum is zero. What is the integer?

17. Integers Three times the square of an integer is 432. Find the integer.

18. Integers Eighteen more than the square of an integer is 43. What is integer?

19. Tenpin bowling A tenpin bowling lane is 17 m longer than it is wide. The area of the lane is 18 m^2. What are the dimensions of the lane?

20. Provinces Adding 19 to the square of the number of provinces in South Africa gives the square of the number of provinces in Canada. How many provinces are there in South Africa?

21. Carpets A rectangular carpet and a square carpet have equal areas. The square carpet has a side length of 4 m. The length of the rectangular carpet is 2 m less than three times its width. Find the dimensions of the rectangular carpet.

22. Measurement The hypotenuse of a right triangle is 17 cm long. Another side of the triangle is 7 cm longer than the third side. Determine the unknown side lengths.

23. Geometry A regular polygon with n sides has $\dfrac{n(n-3)}{2}$ diagonals. Find the number of sides of a regular polygon that has 44 diagonals.

24. Measurement The surface area of a cube is 384 cm^2. Find the length of one edge.

25. Measurement Find the dimensions of both squares in each diagram. The area of the shaded region is given in each case.

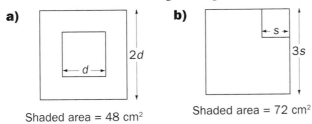

a)

2d

d

Shaded area = 48 cm²

b)

s

3s

Shaded area = 72 cm²

26. Area rug An area rug has a central 5 m by 3 m rectangle in a mosaic pattern, with a plain border of uniform width around it. The total area of the rug is 24 m^2. Find the width of the border.

27. Currency In Britain, people refer to their paper money as notes. A five-pound note is worth 5 pounds sterling. The length of a five-pound note is 5 mm less than twice the width. The area is 9450 mm².
a) Find the dimensions of a five-pound note.
b) Communication How do the dimensions compare with those of a Canadian $20 bill?

28. Communication a) Solve the equation $x^2 + 6x + 9 = 0$ by graphing. How many roots do there appear to be?
b) Solve the same equation by factoring. How many roots are there? How are they related?

29. Solve.

a) $\dfrac{x+1}{2} + \dfrac{x-1}{3} = x^2$

b) $\dfrac{5x+1}{4} - \dfrac{2x-1}{2} = x^2$

30. Solve.
a) $2x(x - 2) + x(x + 1) = 0$
b) $x(2x - 3) + 4(x + 1) = 2(3 + 2x)$
c) $k^2 + (k + 1)^2 + (k + 2)^2 = 29$
d) $(2z + 1)(2z - 1) + 12 = 4(z + 5) - 10$
e) $3(x - 2)(x + 1) - 2(x - 1)^2 = 4$
f) $5g(g - 4) + 48 = 2g(g + 3)$
g) $2y(y - 1) - y(y - 2) - 9 = 0$
h) $(2n + 3)^2 = (3n + 2)^2$
i) $2(x + 1)(x + 2) - 4(x - 1)^2 = 0$

C

31. Solve for x.
a) $x^2 + 5xy + 4y^2 = 0$

b) $2x^2 - 5xy - 3y^2 = 0$

c) $4x^2 - 4xy + y^2 = 0$

d) $\dfrac{2x^2}{5} + \dfrac{7xy}{10} - \dfrac{y^2}{5} = 0$

e) $5x^2 + xy = 0$

f) $3x^2 - 7xy = 0$

32. Communication a) Write a quadratic equation whose roots are −2 and 3.
b) Is it possible to write another quadratic equation with the same roots? Explain.

33. Write a quadratic equation in the form $ax^2 + bx + c = 0$ with roots p and q.

34. If −3 is one root of the equation $3x^2 + mx + 3 = 0$,
a) what is the value of m?
b) what is the other root?

35. Communication Write quadratic equations that have the following roots. Describe your method and justify your reasoning.
a) two roots that equal the same negative integer
b) two distinct roots that are positive integers
c) two distinct roots, one a positive fraction and the other a negative integer

Career Connection Archaeology

Archaeology is the scientific study of the objects that remain from past cultures. These objects, such as tools, ornaments, and bones, give clues about how people lived. Archaeologists use aerial photographs, maps, and historical records to decide where to look for objects. The search usually involves digging up a site. To record where each object is found, archaeologists divide the site into a grid of congruent squares before beginning to dig.

1. The diagram shows a site divided into a grid of 16 squares. The side length of each small square on the grid is represented by x.
a) If the area of the grid is 144 m^2, write and solve an equation to find the side length of each small square.
b) A site divided into a 10 by 10 grid has an area of 400 m^2. Find the side length of each small grid square.

2. Research Use your research skills to investigate
a) the training needed to become an archaeologist
b) the organizations that employ archaeologists

Modelling Math The Motion of Airborne Objects

An object is thrown upward at a speed of 9 m/s from a height of 2 m. The function $h = -5t^2 + 9t + 2$ models the approximate height of the object, h metres, above the ground in terms of the time, t seconds, since the object was thrown.
a) Substitute the value of h when the object hits the ground.
b) By factoring, solve the resulting equation to find the time the object takes to hit the ground.

LOGIC POWER

You have an empty 7-L pail, an empty 3-L pail, and a 10-L pail full of water. There are no volume markings on the pails. In one pouring, you can fill or empty a pail by pouring water from one pail to another. What is the smallest number of pourings needed to get 5 L of water in the 10-L pail and 5 L of water in the 7-L pail?

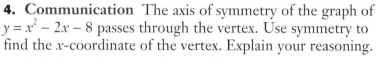

5.3 Investigation: Graphing Quadratic Functions by Factoring

If a quadratic equation of the form $ax^2 + bx + c = 0$ can be solved by factoring, then the x-intercepts of the quadratic function $y = ax^2 + bx + c$ can be found. The coordinates of the vertex can be deduced from the x-intercepts.

1. The x-intercepts of a quadratic function are the x-coordinates of the points where the graph crosses the x-axis, or where $y = 0$. For the function $y = x^2 - 2x - 8$, let $y = 0$ and solve the resulting quadratic equation by factoring.

2. What are the x-intercepts?

3. On a grid, plot the points where the graph crosses the x-axis.

4. Communication The axis of symmetry of the graph of $y = x^2 - 2x - 8$ passes through the vertex. Use symmetry to find the x-coordinate of the vertex. Explain your reasoning.

5. Substitute the x-coordinate of the vertex in $y = x^2 - 2x - 8$ to find the y-coordinate of the vertex.

6. Plot the vertex on the grid and draw a smooth curve through the three points.

7. Sketch the graphs of the following quadratic functions by factoring to find the x-intercepts, and then deducing the coordinates of the vertex.
a) $y = x^2 - 8x + 12$
b) $y = x^2 - 2x - 3$
c) $y = x^2 + 10x + 21$
d) $y = x^2 + 4x$
e) $y = x^2 - 6x + 5$
f) $y = x^2 - 6x - 7$
g) $y = x^2 - 8x$
h) $y = x^2 - 2x - 35$

8. Communication Could you use the above method for sketching the graph of $y = ax^2 + bx + c$ when $ax^2 + bx + c$ is a perfect square? Explain.

Canadians Phillipe LaRoche and Lloyd Langlois won silver and bronze medals for Canada in the freestyle skiing aerials competition at the Winter Olympics in Lillehammer, Norway. In this competition, jumpers are judged in three categories: air, form, and landing. In the air category, points are awarded for the takeoff, height, and distance.

The path of one skier from the top of the kicker (ramp) to the landing point can be modelled by the function

$$h = -0.2d^2 + 2.5d + 8$$

where h is the height in metres above the landing point, and d is the horizontal distance from the kicker.

Since $h = 0$ when the skier lands, solving the equation

$$-0.2d^2 + 2.5d + 8 = 0$$

gives the horizontal distance from the kicker to the landing point, as will be shown in Example 4.

This equation and all other quadratic equations can be solved using the **quadratic formula**. For a quadratic equation in the form $ax^2 + bx + c = 0$, $a \neq 0$, the quadratic formula is written as follows.

$$x = \frac{-b \pm \sqrt{b^2 - 4ac}}{2a}$$

The symbol $\pm$ is read as "plus or minus," so the formula means that

$$x = \frac{-b + \sqrt{b^2 - 4ac}}{2a} \quad \text{or} \quad x = \frac{-b - \sqrt{b^2 - 4ac}}{2a}$$

1. Copy and complete the following table.

Equation	$b^2 - 4ac$	$\sqrt{b^2 - 4ac}$	$x = \dfrac{-b + \sqrt{b^2 - 4ac}}{2a}$	$x = \dfrac{-b - \sqrt{b^2 - 4ac}}{2a}$
a) $x^2 + 6x + 8 = 0$				
b) $x^2 + 3x + 2 = 0$				
c) $x^2 + 8x + 15 = 0$				
d) $x^2 + 7x + 12 = 0$				

2. Solve each equation in the table by factoring.
3. Compare the roots found by factoring with the roots found using the quadratic formula.
4. Use the quadratic formula to solve the following quadratic equations.
   a) $x^2 + 5x + 6 = 0$ **b)** $x^2 + x - 12 = 0$ **c)** $x^2 + 2x - 8 = 0$

Recall that you can solve an equation by performing the same operations on both sides. To solve the quadratic equation $x^2 = 25$ for x, you can take the square root of both sides.

$$x^2 = 25$$
$$\pm\sqrt{x^2} = \pm\sqrt{25}$$
$$\pm x = \pm 5$$

There seem to be four cases to consider, but we can show that there are only two.

$x = 5$ or $x = -5$ or $-x = 5$ or $-x = -5$
$\qquad\qquad\qquad\qquad\quad x = -5 \qquad\quad x = 5$

Thus, the two cases are $x = 5$ or $x = -5$, which can be written as $x = \pm 5$. This information is used in the following method for deriving the quadratic formula.

$$ax^2 + bx + c = 0$$

Multiply both sides by $4a$: $4a^2x^2 + 4abx + 4ac = 0$

Subtract $4ac$ from both sides: $4a^2x^2 + 4abx = -4ac$

Add b^2 to both sides to complete
the square on the left side: $4a^2x^2 + 4abx + b^2 = b^2 - 4ac$

Write the perfect square trinomial
as the square of a binomial: $(2ax + b)^2 = b^2 - 4ac$

Take the square root of both sides: $2ax + b = \pm\sqrt{b^2 - 4ac}$

Subtract b from both sides: $2ax = -b \pm\sqrt{b^2 - 4ac}$

Divide both sides by $2a$: $x = \dfrac{-b \pm\sqrt{b^2 - 4ac}}{2a}$

Example 1   Rational Roots
Solve $3x^2 + 5x - 2 = 0$.

Solution
For $3x^2 + 5x - 2 = 0$, $a = 3$, $b = 5$, and $c = -2$.
Substitute these values into the quadratic formula.

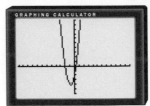

The solution can be modelled graphically.

$$x = \frac{-b \pm \sqrt{b^2 - 4ac}}{2a}$$
$$= \frac{-5 \pm \sqrt{5^2 - 4(3)(-2)}}{2(3)}$$
$$= \frac{-5 \pm \sqrt{25 + 24}}{6}$$
$$= \frac{-5 \pm \sqrt{49}}{6}$$
$$= \frac{-5 \pm 7}{6}$$

So, $x = \dfrac{-5 + 7}{6}$ or $x = \dfrac{-5 - 7}{6}$
$\qquad = \dfrac{2}{6} \qquad\qquad = -\dfrac{12}{6}$
$\qquad = \dfrac{1}{3} \qquad\qquad = -2$

The roots are $\dfrac{1}{3}$ and -2.

To use the quadratic formula, rewrite quadratic equations in the form
$ax^2 + bx + c = 0$, if necessary.

Example 2   Irrational Roots
Solve $x^2 - 3x = -1$. Express answers as
a) exact roots   **b)** approximate roots, to the nearest hundredth

Solution
Write $x^2 - 3x = -1$ in the form $ax^2 + bx + c = 0$.
$x^2 - 3x + 1 = 0$
a) For $x^2 - 3x + 1 = 0$, $a = 1$, $b = -3$, and $c = 1$.

The solution can be modelled graphically.

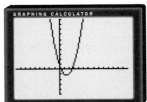

$$x = \frac{-b \pm \sqrt{b^2 - 4ac}}{2a}$$
$$= \frac{-(-3) \pm \sqrt{(-3)^2 - 4(1)(1)}}{2(1)}$$
$$= \frac{3 \pm \sqrt{5}}{2}$$

The exact roots are $\dfrac{3 + \sqrt{5}}{2}$ and $\dfrac{3 - \sqrt{5}}{2}$.

b) $x = \dfrac{3+\sqrt{5}}{2}$ or $x = \dfrac{3-\sqrt{5}}{2}$

$\qquad \doteq 2.62 \qquad\qquad \doteq 0.38$

The approximate roots are 2.62 and 0.38, to the nearest hundredth.

Example 3   Non-Real Roots
Solve $x^2 - 2x + 3 = 0$.

Solution
For $x^2 - 2x + 3 = 0$, $a = 1$, $b = -2$, and $c = 3$.

$$x = \dfrac{-b \pm \sqrt{b^2 - 4ac}}{2a}$$

$$= \dfrac{-(-2) \pm \sqrt{(-2)^2 - 4(1)(3)}}{2(1)}$$

$$= \dfrac{2 \pm \sqrt{4-12}}{2}$$

$$= \dfrac{2 \pm \sqrt{-8}}{2}$$

The solution can be modelled graphically. Since the solutions are not real, the graph does not cross the x-axis.

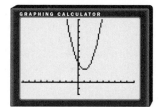

Since no real number is the square root of a negative number, there are no real solutions.

Example 4   Freestyle Aerials
Solve the equation $-0.2d^2 + 2.5d + 8 = 0$ for d, the horizontal distance from the kicker to the landing point, to the nearest metre.

Solution
For $-0.2d^2 + 2.5d + 8 = 0$, $a = -0.2$, $b = 2.5$, and $c = 8$.

$$d = \dfrac{-b \pm \sqrt{b^2 - 4ac}}{2a}$$

$$= \dfrac{-2.5 \pm \sqrt{(2.5)^2 - 4(-0.2)(8)}}{2(-0.2)}$$

$$= \dfrac{-2.5 \pm \sqrt{6.25 + 6.4}}{-0.4}$$

$$= \dfrac{-2.5 \pm \sqrt{12.65}}{-0.4}$$

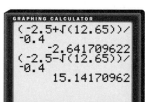

So, $d \doteq -3$ or $d \doteq 15$

Since the distance is positive, the root -3 is inadmissible and is rejected.
The horizontal distance from the kicker to the landing point is 15 m, to the nearest metre.

Key CONCEPTS

1 To solve a quadratic equation using the quadratic formula, write the equation in the form $ax^2 + bx + c = 0$, $a \neq 0$.

2 The quadratic formula is $x = \dfrac{-b \pm \sqrt{b^2 - 4ac}}{2a}$.

Communicate Your Understanding

1. Describe the three methods you know for solving quadratic equations. Describe the advantages and disadvantages of each method.

2. State the method you would use to solve each of the following quadratic equations. Explain why you chose each method.
a) $x^2 - 7x + 12 = 0$ **b)** $x^2 + 6x + 9 = 0$ **c)** $x^2 - 5x + 1 = 0$
d) $2x^2 + 7x + 3 = 0$ **e)** $2x^2 - x = -4$

Practice

A

1. Solve using the quadratic formula. Check your solutions.
a) $x^2 + 6x + 5 = 0$ **b)** $x^2 + 2x - 8 = 0$ **c)** $x^2 - 2x - 3 = 0$
d) $x^2 - 12x + 35 = 0$ **e)** $x^2 + 4x + 4 = 0$ **f)** $y^2 - 2y + 1 = 0$

2. Solve using the quadratic formula.
a) $2x^2 - 3x + 1 = 0$ **b)** $5x^2 - 14x - 3 = 0$ **c)** $2x^2 - 5x - 12 = 0$
d) $9x^2 - 6x + 1 = 0$ **e)** $8x^2 + 6x - 9 = 0$ **f)** $6x^2 - x = 2$
g) $4x^2 - 9 = 0$ **h)** $0 = 4x^2 + 16x + 15$ **i)** $2x^2 - 5x = 0$
j) $3w^2 + 11w = -10$

3. Solve using the quadratic formula. Express answers as exact roots and as approximate roots, to the nearest hundredth.
a) $x^2 + 5x + 2 = 0$ **b)** $x^2 - 3x - 1 = 0$ **c)** $x^2 - x - 3 = 0$
d) $x^2 + 7x + 2 = 0$ **e)** $x^2 - 5x - 2 = 0$ **f)** $z^2 - z - 4 = 0$
g) $0 = x^2 + x - 7$ **h)** $a^2 - a = 5$ **i)** $2x^2 + 3x - 7 = 0$
j) $3x^2 - x - 1 = 0$ **k)** $2x^2 + x - 5 = 0$ **l)** $0 = -3x^2 + 3x + 1$

Applications and Problem Solving

4. Peace Tower a) Find the width, in metres, of the Canadian flag on the Peace Tower in Ottawa by solving the equation $8w^2 + 18w - 81 = 0$.
b) The height of the Peace Tower is 90 m. If an object is thrown downward from this height at 5 m/s, the approximate time, t seconds, the object takes to reach the ground can be found by solving the equation $-5t^2 - 5t + 90 = 0$. Find the time taken, to the nearest tenth of a second.

B

5. Solve. Express answers as integers or as decimals, to the nearest tenth.

a) $5x^2 = 8x$

b) $2x^2 + 3x = 5x^2 - 1$

c) $\dfrac{x^2}{2} - x - \dfrac{5}{2} = 0$

d) $2c(c - 3) = 7$

e) $(n - 4)(n - 2) = 12$

f) $2(x - 2)(x + 1) - (x + 3) = 0$

g) $(6x - 1)(x + 5) = 15x - 9$

h) $(3x - 1)(x - 4) = (2x - 5)(x + 2)$

i) $(2d + 3)(d - 2) = (d + 9)(d - 3) + 16$

j) $3g^2 - (5g + 1)(2g - 3) = 3$

6. Solve. Round answers to the nearest hundredth.

a) $0.1x^2 + 0.4x - 0.3 = 0$

b) $0.25x^2 - x - 1.5 = 0$

c) $0.17y^2 - 0.2y = 0.03$

d) $1.2n^2 = 1.4n + 1$

e) $0.1 = -2.2x^2 - 2.4x$

f) $0.04a^2 + 0.1a + 0.05 = 5$

7. Natural bridge Sipapu Natural Bridge is in Utah. Find the horizontal distance, in metres, across this natural arch at the base by solving the equation $-0.04x^2 + 3.28x = 0$.

8. Hedge maze The world's largest hedge maze is in the grounds of an English country house known as Longleat. The rectangular maze has 2.7 km of paths flanked by 16 180 yew trees. The length of the rectangle is 60 m more than the width. The area of the rectangle is 6496 m². What are the dimensions of the rectangle?

9. Measurement The hypotenuse of a right triangle measures 20 cm. The sum of the lengths of the other two sides is 28 cm. Find the lengths of these two sides.

10. Lidless box A rectangular piece of tin 50 cm by 40 cm is made into a lidless box of base area 875 cm² by cutting squares of equal sizes from the corners and bending up the sides. Find

a) the side length of each removed square

b) the volume of the box

11. Measurement The length and width of a rectangle are 6 m and 4 m. When each dimension is increased by the same amount, the area of the new rectangle is 50 m². Find the dimensions of the new rectangle, to the nearest tenth of a metre.

12. Skating rink A rectangular skating rink measures 40 m by 20 m. It is to be doubled in area by extending each side by the same amount. Determine how much each side should be extended, to the nearest tenth of a metre.

13. Measurement A triangle has a height of 6 cm and a base of 8 cm. If the height and the base are both decreased by the same amount, the area of the new triangle is 20 cm². What are the base and height of the new triangle, to the nearest tenth of a centimetre?

14. Television screens The size of a television screen or a computer monitor is usually stated as the length of the diagonal. A screen has a 38-cm diagonal. The width of the screen is 6 cm more than the height. Find the dimensions of the screen, to the nearest tenth of a centimetre.

15. Cropping a photograph If part of a photograph is used to fill an available space in a book or magazine, the photograph is said to be cropped. A photograph that was originally 15 cm by 10 cm is cropped by removing the same width from the top and the left side. Cropping reduces the area by 46 cm^2. What are the dimensions of the cropped photograph?

16. Estimation a) Estimate the side length of a square that has the same area as a circle of radius 10 cm.
b) Check your estimate by finding the side length of the square, to the nearest hundredth of a centimetre.

17. Retail sales A sporting goods store sells 90 ski jackets in a season for $200 each. Each $10 decrease in the price would result in five more jackets being sold.
a) Find the number of jackets sold and the selling price to give revenues of $17 600 from sales of ski jackets.
b) What is the lowest price that would produce revenues of at least $15 600? How many jackets would be sold at this price?

18. Measurement The height of a triangle is 2 units more than the base. The area of the triangle is 10 square units. Find the base, to the nearest hundredth.

C

19. Pattern Two points can be connected by a maximum of one line segment. Three non-collinear points can be connected by a maximum of three line segments.
a) Find the maximum number of line segments that can connect four non-collinear points; five non-collinear points.
b) Write an equation of the form $s = $ ■ that relates the maximum number of line segments, s, to the number of non-collinear points, p.
c) Find the number of non-collinear points that can be connected by a maximum of 55 line segments.
d) Communication Is it possible for a set of non-collinear points to be connected by a maximum of 40 line segments? Explain.

20. Communication If a quadratic equation can be solved by factoring, what do you know about $b^2 - 4ac$?

21. Communication If a quadratic equation appears to have one root, that is, it has two equal real roots, what do you know about $b^2 - 4ac$?

22. Measurement A cylinder has a height of 5 cm and a surface area of 100 cm^2. Find the radius of the cylinder, to the nearest tenth of a centimetre.

23. Communication Describe the roots of the equation $ax^2 + bx + c = 0$ in each of the following situations. Explain and justify your reasoning, and give examples to support your answers.
a) $b^2 - 4ac$ is less than zero
b) $b^2 - 4ac = 0$
c) $b^2 - 4ac$ is a perfect square
d) $b^2 - 4ac$ is greater than zero but is not a perfect square

24. Solve each equation for x.
a) $2x^2 + 17xy + 8y^2 = 0$
b) $x^2 + 2xy - y^2 = 0$

25. Communication Write two problems that can be solved using quadratic equations. Check that the roots of each equation are real. Then, have a classmate solve your problems.

Modelling Math | The Motion of Airborne Objects

The function $h = -5t^2 + 20t + 1$ models the height, h metres, of a baseball as a function of the time, t seconds, since it was hit. The ball hit the ground before a fielder could catch it. Use the quadratic formula to solve the following problems.
a) How long was the baseball in the air, to the nearest tenth of a second?
b) For how many seconds was the height of the ball at least 16 m?

Achievement Check

1 2 3 4

A bakery sells 50 loaves a day of a particular bread at $1.50 a loaf. Research indicates that, for every 10¢ increase in the price, two fewer loaves would be sold. An equation for the daily revenue is $R = -0.2x^2 + 2x + 75$, where x represents the number of 10¢ increases.
a) Use this equation to find the number of 10¢ increases that will result in a daily revenue of $80.00.
b) What is the new price of a loaf of bread?
c) What price for a loaf of bread would give a daily income of at least $79.20?

Technology Extension: Solving Quadratic Equations

A graphing calculator or a computer can be programmed to solve a quadratic equation.

1 Using a Graphing Calculator Program

The graphing calculator program, which is suitable for a TI-83 or TI-83 Plus calculator, solves a quadratic equation in the form $Ax^2 + Bx + C = 0$.

```
PROGRAM:SOLVQUAD
:Disp "ENTER COEFFICIENTS"
:Prompt A, B, C
:(B²–4AC)→D
:If D≥0
:Then
:Disp (-B+√(D))/(2A), (-B–√(D))/(2A)
:Else
:Disp "NO REAL SOLUTION"
```

1. Communication Describe what each line of the program does.

2. Enter the program into your graphing calculator using the **PRGM key** and the **PRGM NEW menu**. Using the **PRGM EXEC menu**, execute the program to solve each of the following.

a) $x^2 + 3x + 6 = 0$ **b)** $4x^2 - 9x + 2 = 0$

c) $2x^2 + 3x = -1$ **d)** $5x^2 = 4x$

e) $2x^2 + 6.8x - 0.7 = 0$ **f)** $\dfrac{x^2}{4} - \dfrac{x}{4} = \dfrac{3}{2}$

3. Use the program to solve each of the following. Round solutions to the nearest hundredth, if necessary.

a) $x^2 + 5x - 11 = 0$

b) $5x^2 + 6x + 2 = 0$

c) $\dfrac{2x^2}{3} = \dfrac{3x}{7}$

2 Using Preprogrammed Calculators

Some calculators, such as the TI-92 and TI-92 Plus, are preprogrammed with the capability to solve quadratic equations algebraically. The screen display shows how such a calculator can be used.

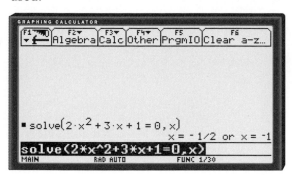

Complete the following using the solve function of a preprogrammed calculator.

1. Solve.

a) $x^2 - 3x - 4 = 0$ **b)** $x^2 + 3x - 10 = 0$

c) $x^2 + 6x + 5 = 0$ **d)** $y^2 - 7y + 6 = 0$

e) $x^2 - 16x + 64 = 0$ **f)** $n^2 - 0.49 = 0$

g) $2x^2 + x = 1$ **h)** $6p^2 - 5p - 6 = 0$

i) $7x^2 = -3x$ **j)** $(3x + 4)(x + 1) = 2$

k) $0.1x^2 + 0.2x - 1.5 = 0$ **l)** $2.7s^2 + 8.1s = 10.8$

m) $\dfrac{x^2}{2} - \dfrac{x}{3} = \dfrac{4}{3}$ **n)** $\dfrac{x^2 + 1}{5} + \dfrac{1 - x^2}{3} = x$

o) $\dfrac{4z^2}{3} - 3(z^2 - 5) = \dfrac{z - 3}{2}$

2. Solve.

a) $x^2 + 4x - 7 = 0$ **b)** $a^2 - 6a + 4 = 0$

c) $x^2 - 5x = -2$ **d)** $2x^2 + 7x - 12 = 0$

e) $3t^2 + 5t + 1 = 0$ **f)** $0.3x^2 - 2.3 = 1.2x$

g) $1.5k^2 + 6.2k - 11 = 0$ **h)** $(x + 2)(x - 3) = 5$

i) $5(2x^2 - 5) = -2(4 - x)$ **j)** $\dfrac{w^2}{4} + \dfrac{w}{2} = 1$

k) $\dfrac{x + 7}{5} - \dfrac{3 - x}{2} = \dfrac{x^2}{4}$ **l)** $\dfrac{3b - 4}{6} - \dfrac{3b^2}{4} = 2(2b - 3)$

3. a) Solve $x^2 + 2x + 13 = 0$ algebraically with paper and pencil.

b) Communication Try to solve $x^2 + 2x + 13 = 0$ algebraically with your graphing calculator. Explain the result.

Rich Problem

The Golden Ratio

The **golden ratio** is a number that is usually represented by the Greek letter phi (ϕ). This is the first letter in the name of Phidias, a Greek sculptor who used the golden ratio extensively in his work. The number ϕ satisfies the following proportion.

$$\frac{1}{\phi} = \frac{\phi}{1+\phi}$$

The golden ratio can be represented by a **golden rectangle**, in which the ratio of the length to the width is ϕ. Many people have found the shape of a golden rectangle esthetically pleasing, and it has been widely used in art and architecture. For example, the golden rectangle can be found in the abstract art of the Dutch painter Piet Mondrian, 1872–1944. The work shown is called *Place de la Concorde*.

Dallas Museum of Art, Foundation for the Arts Collection, gift of the James H. and Lillian Clark Foundation

A golden rectangle has dimensions that satisfy the following proportion.

$$\frac{w}{l} = \frac{l}{w+l}$$

To find the golden ratio, let the width, w, of the rectangle be 1 unit. Then,

$$\frac{1}{l} = \frac{l}{1+l}$$

Multiplying by the common denominator $l(1 + l)$ gives
$$1 + l = l^2$$
$$\text{or } l^2 - l - 1 = 0$$

1 Determining ø

1. For the equation $l^2 - l - 1 = 0$, the exact value of the positive root, is the exact value of ϕ.

a) Solve the equation to find the exact value of ϕ.

b) Find the approximate value of ϕ, to the nearest thousandth.

2. Use the approximate value of ϕ to identify golden rectangles in Piet Mondrian's *Place de la Concorde*.

2 Geometry and ø

1. The base of the square ABCD has been bisected at E. With centre E and radius EC, an arc is drawn to cut AB extended at F. Let the length AB be 2 units.

Verify that $\dfrac{AF}{AB} = \phi$.

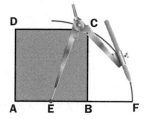

2. Communication A **golden triangle** is an isosceles triangle in which the ratio of the length of one of the equal sides to the length of the base is the golden ratio. Describe how you could modify the construction method in question 1 to construct a golden triangle. Explain your reasoning.

3 Fibonacci Numbers and ø

1. Sequence The Fibonacci sequence of numbers begins with 1, 1, . . . Each subsequent term is found by adding the two terms before it.

$$1, 1, 2, 3, 5, 8, 13, 21, . . .$$

The ratios of consecutive pairs of Fibonacci numbers converge to the golden ratio, ϕ.

The ratio of the two consecutive Fibonacci numbers 13 and 21

gives $\dfrac{21}{13} = 1.615\ 384. . .$, which correctly shows the first three digits of ϕ.

Which two consecutive Fibonacci numbers correctly show the first six digits of ϕ?

2. The following continued fraction also converges to the golden ratio.

$$1 + \cfrac{1}{1 + \cfrac{1}{1 + \ldots}}$$

a) Simplify. $1 + \cfrac{1}{1 + \cfrac{1}{1 + 1}}$

b) Simplify. $1 + \cfrac{1}{1 + \cfrac{1}{1 + \cfrac{1}{1 + 1}}}$

c) Communication Describe how numbers found in the simplification of the continued fraction are related to the Fibonacci numbers.

d) Write the continued fraction that equals $\dfrac{13}{8}$.

3. Sequence Suppose the first two terms of a sequence are natural numbers chosen at random, and subsequent terms are found using the same rule used in the Fibonacci sequence.

a) Write the first 10 terms of the sequence that begins 2, 5, . . .

b) Determine the ratio of each pair of successive terms. To what value do the ratios converge?

c) Repeat parts a) and b) for a sequence that begins with two natural numbers of your choice.

4 ø in Architecture, and Design

1. Parthenon The Parthenon is in Athens, Greece. The width of the Parthenon and its height at the apex are approximately in the golden ratio. If the width is about 29 m, what is its height at the apex, to the nearest metre?

2. Great Pyramid The Great Pyramid of Cheops has a height of 146 m. The square base has a side length of 230 m. How does the slant height of a face compare with half the side length of the base?

3. Canadian money A Canadian $5 bill measures 152 mm by 70 mm. Compare the length of a diagonal of the bill, AC, with the length of a diagonal of half the bill, BC.

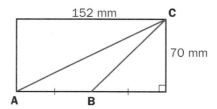

Web Connection   www.school.mcgrawhill.ca/resources/

To learn more about the golden ratio and the Fibonacci sequence, visit the above web site. Go to **Math Resources**, then to *MATHPOWER™ 10, Ontario Edition*, to find out where to go next. Describe an example of the golden ratio and an example of the Fibonacci sequence in nature.

REVIEW OF *Key* CONCEPTS

5.1 **Solving Quadratic Equations by Graphing**

Refer to the Key Concepts on page 275.

To solve $x^2 + 2x - 3 = 0$ by graphing, graph the related quadratic function $y = x^2 + 2x - 3$ using paper and pencil, a graphing calculator, or graphing software.

Find the values of the x-intercepts.

x	y
2	5
1	0
0	−3
−1	−4
−2	−3
−3	0
−4	5

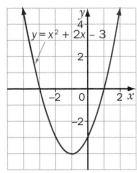

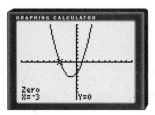

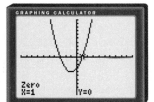

The graph intersects the x-axis at (1, 0) and (−3, 0).
The roots of the equation $x^2 + 2x - 3 = 0$ are 1 and −3.

1. Solve by graphing.
a) $x^2 - 2x - 3 = 0$
b) $x^2 + x - 2 = 0$
c) $x^2 - 9 = 0$
d) $-x^2 - 3x + 4 = 0$
e) $x^2 - 2x + 1 = 0$
f) $x^2 + 6x = -5$
g) $x^2 = 5x$

2. Solve graphically using a graphing calculator or graphing software.
Round each answer to the nearest tenth, if necessary.
a) $2x^2 + x - 3 = 0$
b) $-3x^2 + 7x - 2 = 0$
c) $-x^2 + 2 = 3x$

3. Measurement The length of a rectangle is 2 cm more than the width.
The area is 24 cm². What are the dimensions of the rectangle?

Refer to the Key Concepts on page 282.

To solve $x^2 - 3x = 4$ by factoring, first write the equation in the form $ax^2 + bx + c = 0$.

$$x^2 - 3x - 4 = 0$$

Factor the left side: $\qquad\qquad (x - 4)(x + 1) = 0$

Use the zero product property: $\quad x - 4 = 0 \quad$ or $\quad x + 1 = 0$

$$x = 4 \qquad \text{or} \qquad x = -1$$

The roots are 4 and −1.

4. Solve by factoring.
a) $x^2 + 3x - 28 = 0$
b) $y^2 - 5y + 6 = 0$
c) $g^2 + 7g + 10 = 0$
d) $x^2 + 8x + 16 = 0$
e) $2x^2 - 7x - 30 = 0$
f) $9x^2 - 4 = 0$
g) $2x^2 + 5x = 3$
h) $2n^2 = 27 - 15n$
i) $8k^2 - 3k = 0$
j) $18 + m^2 = 82$
k) $\dfrac{x^2}{6} - x + \dfrac{4}{3} = 0$

l) $\dfrac{x^2}{2} - \dfrac{x}{2} = -\dfrac{1}{8}$

(handwritten work:)
$(x - 7)(x + 4) = 0$
$x - 7 = 0 \qquad x + 4 = 0$
$x = 7 \qquad x = -4$

$(y - 3)(y - 2)$
$y - 3 = 0 \qquad y - 2 = 0$
$y = 3 \qquad y = 2$

5. Curling The playing surface in the game of curling is a rectangular sheet of ice with an area of about 225 m². The width is about 40 m less than the length. Find the approximate dimensions of the playing surface.

The coordinates of the vertex and two other points can be used to sketch the graph of a quadratic function. The coordinates can be found by factoring.

To sketch the graph of $y = x^2 - 4x - 5$, solve $x^2 - 4x - 5 = 0$ to find the x-intercepts.

$$x^2 - 4x - 5 = 0$$
$$(x - 5)(x + 1) = 0$$
$$x - 5 = 0 \quad \text{or} \quad x + 1 = 0$$
$$x = 5 \quad \text{or} \quad x = -1$$

The x-intercepts are 5 and -1.

Plot the points $(5, 0)$ and $(-1, 0)$.
Since the two x-intercepts are reflection images of each other in the axis of symmetry, the x-coordinate of the vertex is 2.
Substitute 2 for x in $y = x^2 - 4x - 5$ to find the y-coordinate of the vertex.

$$y = x^2 - 4x - 5$$
$$= 2^2 - 4(2) - 5$$
$$= -9$$

The coordinates of the vertex are $(2, -9)$.

Plot the vertex on the grid and draw a smooth curve through the three points.

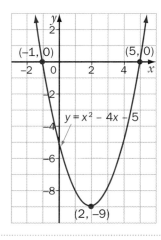

6. Sketch the graphs of the following quadratic functions by factoring to locate the x-intercepts, and then finding the coordinates of the vertex.

a) $y = x^2 + 6x + 8$ **b)** $y = x^2 - 2x - 15$
c) $y = x^2 - 8x$ **d)** $y = x^2 + 2x - 8$
e) $y = x^2 - 4x - 5$ **f)** $y = x^2 - 4x + 3$

Refer to the Key Concepts on page 292.

To use the quadratic formula to solve $2x^2 + 5x - 12 = 0$, substitute $a = 2$, $b = 5$, and $c = -12$ into the quadratic formula.

$$x = \frac{-b \pm \sqrt{b^2 - 4ac}}{2a}$$
$$= \frac{-5 \pm \sqrt{5^2 - 4(2)(-12)}}{2(2)}$$
$$= \frac{-5 \pm \sqrt{25 + 96}}{4}$$
$$= \frac{-5 \pm \sqrt{121}}{4}$$
$$= \frac{-5 \pm 11}{4}$$

So, $x = \dfrac{-5 + 11}{4}$ or $x = \dfrac{-5 - 11}{4}$
$$\qquad = \frac{6}{4} \qquad\qquad = -\frac{16}{4}$$
$$\qquad = \frac{3}{2} \qquad\qquad = -4$$

The roots are $\dfrac{3}{2}$ and -4.

7. Solve using the quadratic formula.
a) $x^2 - 7x + 12 = 0$ **b)** $x^2 - 3x + 5 = 0$
c) $n^2 + n - 42 = 0$ **d)** $x^2 - 1 = 0$
e) $2x^2 + 3x = 0$ **f)** $4x^2 - 12x + 9 = 0$
g) $7g^2 + 2 = 9g$ **h)** $4m^2 = 3 + 4m$

8. Solve using the quadratic formula. Express answers as exact roots and as approximate roots, to the nearest hundredth.
a) $x^2 + 5x - 3 = 0$ **b)** $k^2 - 9k = 1$
c) $8w^2 = 2 - 3w$ **d)** $3 = 5x + 3x^2$

9. Solve, to the nearest hundredth.
a) $6x^2 + x - 4 = 0$ **b)** $1.2x^2 + 0.5x - 0.3 = 0$

10. Measurement A rectangle has a perimeter of 46 cm and an area of 120 cm². Find its dimensions by writing an equation and using the quadratic formula to solve it.

Chapter Test

1. Solve by graphing. Check real solutions.
   a) $x^2 + 2x - 8 = 0$ **b)** $x^2 - 9 = 0$ **c)** $x^2 - 4x + 4 = 0$
   d) $x^2 + 6x = 0$ **e)** $x^2 + 3 = -2x$ **f)** $-x^2 + 2x - 1 = 0$

2. Solve by factoring, and check.
   a) $q^2 + 2q - 15 = 0$ **b)** $w^2 + 24 = 11w$ **c)** $2k^2 + 7k = 4$
   d) $9x^2 = 3x + 2$ **e)** $2x^2 = 3x$ **f)** $12x^2 - 3 = 0$

   g) $x^2 + 2x = -1$ **h)** $x^2 + 11 = 155$ **i)** $x^2 - \dfrac{3x}{2} + \dfrac{1}{2} = 0$

3. Sketch the graphs of the following quadratic functions by factoring to find the x-intercepts, and then deducing the coordinates of the vertex.
   a) $y = x^2 + 6x + 5$ **b)** $y = x^2 + 4x - 5$

4. Solve using the quadratic formula.
   a) $y^2 - 3y - 18 = 0$ **b)** $x^2 - 8x = -16$ **c)** $2x^2 + 8 + 8x = 0$
   d) $3x^2 - 17x = 0$ **e)** $9x^2 - 4 = 0$ **f)** $2x^2 + 2x = -1$
   g) $0 = 18w^2 + 9w - 2$ **h)** $12d^2 = 5d + 3$ **i)** $2 = -7p - 5p^2$

5. Solve using the quadratic formula. Express answers as exact roots and as approximate roots, to the nearest hundredth.
   a) $x^2 + 5x - 7 = 0$ **b)** $0 = 4t^2 + 9t + 3$ **c)** $3x^2 - x = 7$

6. **Daily journal** The area of the front cover of a daily journal is 273 cm^2, and the length is 8 cm greater than the width. What are the dimensions of the cover?

7. **Landscaping** A rectangular lawn measuring 8 m by 4 m is surrounded by a flower bed of uniform width. The combined area of the lawn and the flower bed is 165 m^2. What is the width of the flower bed?

Achievement Check

1   **2**   **3**   **4**

Markita wants to fence a rectangular plot of land along the shore of a lake. Only three sides must be fenced, since the lake will form the fourth side. Markita has 100 m of fencing, and she wants the plot of land to have an area of 500 m^2. Find the dimensions of the plot of land, to the nearest tenth of a metre. Explain and justify your solution.

Problem Solving: Solve a Simpler Problem

Many problems can be solved more easily if they are broken down into smaller problems.

Some cities in Ontario, including Hamilton and Toronto, have neighbourhoods in which the streets run east-west and north-south. Tony lives in Hamilton. His home is three blocks west and three blocks south of his school. In how many different ways can he walk to school, if he walks only east and north?

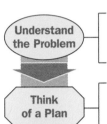
Understand the Problem

1. What information are you given?
2. What are you asked to find?
3. Do you need an exact or an approximate answer?

Think of a Plan

Find how many possible routes there are for parts of the walk from his home to his school. Use the results to solve the complete problem.

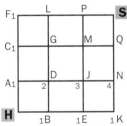

Carry Out the Plan

Draw a grid that shows the positions of Tony's home, H, and his school, S. There is only 1 way for Tony to get to A, to C, and to F. Mark this information on the grid. Similarly, there is only 1 way for him to get to B, to E, and to K.

Since there is 1 way to A and 1 way to B, there are 2 ways to D.
Since there is 1 way to E and 2 ways to D, there are 3 ways to J.
Since there is 1 way to K and 3 ways to J, there are 4 ways to N.

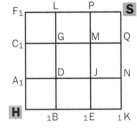

Complete the grid to find the total number of ways in which Tony can walk from his home to his school.

The completed grid shows that Tony can walk to school in 20 different ways, if he walks only east and north.

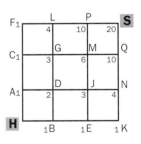

Look Back

How could you check the answer?
Is there another way to solve the problem?

Solve a Simpler Problem

1. Break the problem into smaller parts.
2. Solve the problem.
3. Check that your answer is reasonable.

Applications and Problem Solving

1. Taxi routes The streets in a town run north-south and east-west, as shown. How many ways are there for a taxi to get from A to B if the taxi travels only north and east?

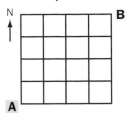

2. Bus routes A town is separated into two parts by a bridge at M. How many routes are there for a bus to get from B to A if the bus travels only south and west?

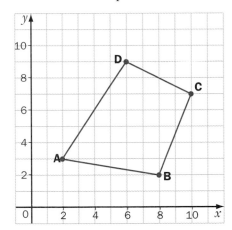

3. Measurement Quadrilateral ABCD has vertices A(2, 3), B(8, 2), C(10, 7), and D(6, 9). Find the total area of quadrilateral ABCD.

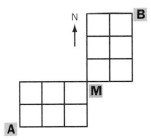

4. Measurement Quadrilateral WXYZ has vertices W(2, 3), X(3, −1), Y(1, −3), and Z(−4, 2). Find the area of the quadrilateral.

5. Measurement Pentagon DEFGH has vertices D(2, 3), E(7, 2), F(11, 5), G(9, 10), and H(4, 8). Find the area of the pentagon.

6. E-shapes Each figure is made from squares of side length 1 unit.

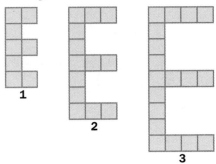

a) What is the area of the 50th figure?
b) What is the perimeter of the 39th figure?

7. Toothpicks Each figure is made using toothpicks.

a) If the pattern continues, how many toothpicks are needed for the 5th figure? the 6th figure?
b) Write an expression for the number of toothpicks in terms of the figure number, n. Write the expression in the form $n(n + \blacksquare)$, where $\blacksquare$ is a whole number.
c) Use the expression from part b) to find the number of toothpicks in the 50th figure.
d) If the pattern continues, how many small squares are in the 5th figure? the 6th figure?
e) Write an expression for the number of small squares in terms of the figure number, n.
Write the expression in the form $\dfrac{n(n + \bullet)}{\blacktriangle}$, where $\bullet$ and $\blacktriangle$ are whole numbers.
f) Use the expression from part e) to find the number of small squares in the 50th figure.

8. Communication Write a problem that can be solved by solving a simpler problem. Have a classmate solve your problem.

Using a table or a spreadsheet is a powerful way to organize and manipulate data to solve problems.

Nasif opened a boutique in a shopping mall to sell perfume and cologne. During the first month, his business lost $750. The profit that month could be expressed as –750. In the next month, Nasif's business lost $650, an improvement in performance of $100. At the end of the second month, the net financial position of the business could be expressed as –1400, since it had lost a total of $1400. The performance continued to improve by $100 each month for the first 20 months.

a) In which month did the net financial position first become positive?

b) Write a quadratic function that describes the net financial position in terms of the number of months.

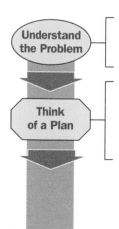

Understand the Problem

1. What information are you given?
2. What are you asked to find?
3. Do you need an exact or an approximate answer?

Think of a Plan

Use a table or a spreadsheet to calculate the profit and the net financial position at the end of each month. Use the maximum or minimum value of the net financial position to find the equation of the function.

a)

Month	Profit ($)	Net Financial Position ($)	Month	Profit ($)	Net Financial Position ($)
1	–750	–750	11	250	–2750
2	–650	–1400	12	350	–2400
3	–550	–1950	13	450	–1950
4	–450	–2400	14	550	–1400
5	–350	–2750	15	650	–750
6	–250	–3000	16	750	0
7	–150	–3150	17	850	850
8	–50	–3200	18	950	1800
9	50	–3150	19	1050	2850
10	150	–3000	20	1150	4000

The net financial position first became positive in the 17th month.

b) The vertex is at the minimum value, –3200, of the function. The vertex is $(8, -3200)$, so $h = 8$ and $k = -3200$. Substitute for h and k in $n = a(m - h)^2 + k$, where n is the net financial position, and m is the number of months.

$$n = a(m - 8)^2 - 3200$$

The parabola crosses the m-axis at $(16, 0)$, so substitute 16 for m and 0 for n to find the value of a.

$$n = a(m - 8)^2 - 3200$$
$$0 = a(16 - 8)^2 - 3200$$
$$0 = 64a - 3200$$
$$3200 = 64a$$
$$50 = a$$

The function is $n = 50(m - 8)^2 - 3200$.

The solution can be modelled graphically.

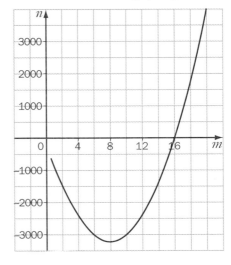

Does the answer seem reasonable?
How could you verify the assumption that the function is quadratic?
Is there another way to find the equation of the function?
How could you set up a computer spreadsheet to calculate the net financial position values shown in the table?

Use a Table or Spreadsheet

1. Organize the given information in a table or spreadsheet.
2. Complete the table or spreadsheet.
3. Find the answer from the table or spreadsheet.
4. Check that your answer is reasonable.

Applications and Problem Solving

1. Business Priya and Gustav opened a store to sell clothing and equipment to campers, hikers, rock climbers, and cross-country skiers. Priya and Gustav projected that the business would lose $2100 in the first month, and $1900 in the second month. They thought that the business would continue to improve by $200/month for the first two years.
a) Make a table of values showing the net financial position at the end of each month.
b) In which month would the net financial position of the business first become positive?
c) Write an equation to describe the net financial position as a function of the number of months.

2. Business Priya and Gustav revised their projections from question 1. They thought they could work more and cut expenses to change their improvement in performance from $200/month to $250/month for the first two years. They assumed that the business would still lose $2100 in the first month. Repeat question 1 using the new projections. Find how many months sooner the net financial position of the business would first become positive.

3. Vending machine The items in a vending machine all sell for $1.00, $1.50, $2.00, or $3.00. The machine can accept quarters, loonies, and toonies. How many combinations of coins must the machine be programmed to accept?

4. Chess Some versions of chess do not use the usual 8 by 8 chessboard. Find the total number of squares of all sizes on each of the following chessboards.
a) Capablanca's chess, played on a 10 by 8 board
b) wildebeest chess, played on an 11 by 10 board

5. Gravity A rock was fired into the air. Without the effect of gravity, it would have travelled upward 49 m every second. However, its height at the end of the first second was 4.9 m less than 49 m. In each second after the first, the rock travelled upward 9.8 m less than in the previous second.
a) Make a table of values showing the height of the rock at the end of each second.
b) After how many seconds was the rock at its maximum height?
c) What was the maximum height?
d) Write an equation describing the height of the rock as a function of the time since it was fired.
e) What are the domain and range of this function?

6. Measurement How many scalene triangles, with side lengths that are whole numbers of centimetres, have no side longer than 10 cm?

7. Summer jobs During the summer, Tara earns $12/h cutting lawns and $16/h painting houses. In how many different ways can she earn $432 in a week, if she works a whole number of hours at each job?

8. Communication Ray earns $3000/month, after taxes and other deductions. He decides to save for a car by saving 25% of the total money he has on payday each month. At the end of the first month, he saves 25% of $3000 or $750. At the end of the second month, he has the $3000 he receives on payday, plus the $750 he already saved, so he increases his total savings to 25% of $3750. He continues in this way for ten more months. Is this a good way to save for a car? Explain.

9. Communication Write a problem that can be solved using a table or spreadsheet. Have a classmate solve your problem.

Problem Solving: Using the Strategies

1. Dart board A dart that lands on a regulation dart board can score a whole number of points from 1 to 20, or double or triple each number. If the dart hits the bulls-eye, it can score 25 or 50 points.

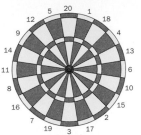

Pierre threw three darts. One missed the board, but Pierre scored a total of 35 points with the other two darts. In how many different ways could he have scored 35 points with two darts?

2. Measurement The first rectangle is 3 m long and 2 m wide. The second is 4 m long and 3 m wide. The third is 5 m long and 4 m wide. Find the area of the shaded region.

3. Names Four students have the first names Tim, Trip, Terry, and Thomas. Their middle names are Bob, Bill, Bevan, and Brooks. Their last names are Sol, Sand, Stone, and Silver. Each student has a different number of letters in each of his names. None of Terry's names has 6 letters. The name Bill does not belong to Tim or Sol. What is the full name of each student?

4. Descending numbers In a **descending number**, such as 743, each digit is greater than the digit on the right. How many descending numbers are there between 500 and 600?

5. Painted prism A rectangular prism made up of 1-cm cubes has dimensions of 3 cm by 4 cm by 5 cm. If the faces of the prism are painted orange, how many cubes have orange paint on 1 face?

6. Population Estimate the percent of the North American population that lives within a day's drive from your school.

7. Statistics If you list the digits used to write the numbers from 1 to 100, what is
a) the median digit? **b)** the mode digit?

8. Communication Naomi is in Paris, France, on business. She needs to arrange a conference call with two colleagues. One is at head office in Vancouver. The other is in Sydney, Australia. For what time of day, Paris time, should Naomi arrange the call? Explain.

9. Number puzzle Each letter in the box represents a different number. The sums of four columns and four rows are given. Find the missing sums.

A	A	A	C	B	25
B	A	B	B	C	17
C	B	B	C	A	20
C	C	D	C	A	24
D	A	A	D	D	■
21	25	19	20	■	

10. Congruence The diagram shows one way to cut the figure into four congruent pieces using straight lines. Find three other ways.

11. Bowling After the preliminary games in a bowling tournament, bowler A is ranked first, B is second, C is third, and D is fourth. These four bowlers have a playoff. In the first playoff game, D bowls against C. The loser gets the fourth-place prize, and the winner bowls against B in the second game. The loser of the second game gets the third-place prize, and the winner bowls against A in the final game. The loser of the final game gets the second-place prize, and the winner gets the first-place prize. In how many different orders can A, B, C, and D finish the playoff?

12. Communication One year, about 45 000 cyclists took part in the 71-km Tour de l'Île de Montréal. If all the bicycles had been placed end to end, would they have stretched the entire length of the tour? Explain your reasoning and state your assumptions.

CHAPTER

6 Trigonometry

Specific Expectations	Sections
• Determine the properties of similar triangles through investigation, using dynamic geometry software.	6.1
• Describe and compare the concepts of similarity and congruence.	6.2
• Solve problems involving similar triangles in realistic situations.	6.2
• Define the formulas for the sine, the cosine, and the tangent of angles, using the ratios of sides in right triangles.	6.3 6.4 6.5
• Determine the measures of the sides and angles in right triangles, using the primary trigonometric ratios.	6.3 6.4 6.5 6.6 6.7
• Solve problems involving the measures of sides and angles in right triangles.	6.3 6.4 6.5 6.6 6.7
• Determine the height of an inaccessible object in the environment around the school, using the trigonometry of right triangles.	6.3 6.7
• Determine, through investigation, the relationships between the angles and sides in acute triangles, using dynamic geometry software.	6.8
• Calculate the measures of sides and angles in acute triangles, using the sine law and cosine law.	6.9 6.10
• Describe the conditions under which the sine law or the cosine law should be used in a problem.	6.9 6.10
• Solve problems involving the measures of sides and angles in acute triangles.	6.9 6.10
• Describe the application of trigonometry in science or industry.	6.6 6.7

Modelling Math

Measuring Inaccessible Heights and Widths

Trigonometry is a branch of mathematics that is used to find the measures of sides and angles in triangles. Surveyors, architects, navigators, and engineers are just a few of the people who use trigonometry.

Similar triangles can be used to calculate unknown heights or widths of objects. Trigonometry, which is based on the properties of similar triangles, can also be used. In some cases, the objects are accessible, which means that you could measure them instead of doing calculations. In other cases, the objects are inaccessible, which means that you cannot measure them and must calculate any unknown dimensions.

Dimensions of inaccessible objects include the heights of mountains, the widths of canyons, and the heights of flagpoles on the tops of buildings. For example, Mount Robson is the highest peak in the Canadian Rockies. The diagram shows the measurements that a surveyor made to find the height of Mount Robson above sea level. What is the height of Mount Robson, to the nearest metre?

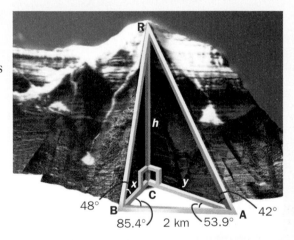

In the Modelling Math questions on pages 325, 333, 359, and 368, you will solve the above problem and other problems that involve inaccessible heights and widths.

1. What instruments do surveyors use?
2. Why do cities and towns employ surveyors?
3. What are some of the possible measurements that surveyors need to determine?

Getting Started

Using the Pythagorean Theorem

1. Spirals Calculators and computers can give only approximate values for some square roots, such as $\sqrt{2}, \sqrt{3}, \sqrt{5},$ and $\sqrt{6}$, because each of these roots is irrational, that is, a non-terminating, non-repeating decimal. Yet these real numbers do exist, and their magnitudes can be represented precisely by line segments. Spirals contain lengths that can be represented by square roots. Examples of naturally occurring spirals are found in chambered nautilus shells, sunflowers, and pineapples.

a) Find the lengths of the unknown sides in the spiral shown in the diagram. Leave your answers in radical form.

b) If the pattern continues, what will be the value of k?

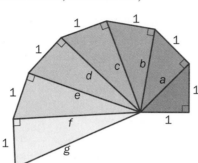

2. Measurement Calculate the length of the unknown side, to the nearest tenth of a unit.

a)

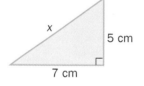

x, 5 cm, 7 cm

b)

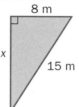

8 m, x, 15 m

c)

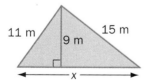

11 m, 9 m, 15 m, x

d)

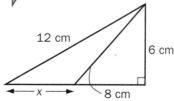

12 cm, 6 cm, x, 8 cm

3. Geoboard The diagram shows one way to divide a 3-pin-by-3-pin geoboard into two non-congruent polygonal regions, with vertices on the pins.

a) Sketch the five other different ways to divide the geoboard into two non-congruent polygonal regions, with vertices on the pins.

b) If the vertical and horizontal distance between two pins is 1 unit, calculate the exact perimeter of each polygonal region. Express any irrational numbers in radical form.

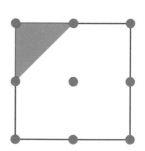

Review of Prerequisite Skills

If you need help with any of the skills named in **purple** below, refer to Appendix A.

1. Solving proportions Solve for x. Express each answer as a fraction in lowest terms.

a) $\dfrac{x}{7} = \dfrac{11}{35}$

b) $\dfrac{2}{3} = \dfrac{7}{x}$

c) $\dfrac{3}{4} = \dfrac{x}{6}$

d) $\dfrac{2}{x} = \dfrac{8}{5}$

e) $11 = \dfrac{2}{x}$

f) $\dfrac{6}{x} = 9$

g) $x:3 = 8:5$

h) $2:x = 4:3$

i) $4:5 = x:7$

j) $8:20 = 6:x$

2. Solving proportions Solve for x. Express each answer as a decimal. Round to the nearest hundredth, if necessary.

a) $\dfrac{x}{4.3} = 7.1$

b) $21.78 = \dfrac{x}{1.27}$

c) $\dfrac{5.6}{x} = 4.2$

d) $8.9 = \dfrac{3.3}{x}$

e) $\dfrac{x}{2.4} = \dfrac{1.6}{8}$

f) $\dfrac{3.6}{x} = \dfrac{9}{0.3}$

g) $\dfrac{3}{0.5} = \dfrac{1.5}{x}$

h) $\dfrac{0.72}{0.4} = \dfrac{x}{1.4}$

i) $x:3.8 = 2.5:2$

j) $3.2:0.4 = 9.6:x$

k) $1.75:x = 4.5:0.7$

l) $2.8:3.5 = x:8.2$

3. Congruent triangles List the corresponding equal parts in each pair of congruent scalene triangles.

a) $\triangle ABC \cong \triangle DEF$

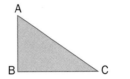

b) $\triangle PQR \cong \triangle XYZ$

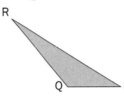

4. Angle properties Find the missing angle measures.

a)

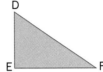

b)

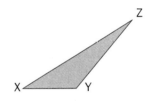

c)

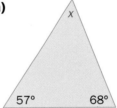

d)

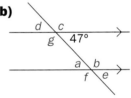

e)

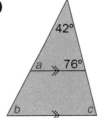

f)

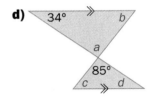

Technology: Investigating Similar Triangles Using *The Geometer's Sketchpad*®

Similar triangles have the same shape but not necessarily the same size. In this investigation, you will determine the properties of similar acute triangles.

1. Construct an acute triangle ABC.

2. Construct a point, D, on side AC.

3. With point D and line segment BC selected, choose the Parallel Line command from the Construct menu to create a line through D parallel to BC.

4. Construct the point of intersection of this line with side AB. Label this point E.

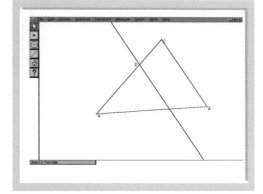

5. Hide the line, highlight points A, D, and E, and choose the Segment command from the Construct menu. There are now two triangles, △ABC and △AED. △ABC and △AED are similar. They have the same shape but not the same size.

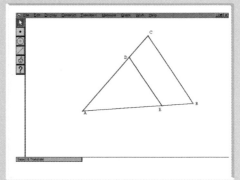

6. Measure the corresponding angles, ∠CAB and ∠DAE, ∠ACB and ∠ADE, and ∠ABC and ∠AED.

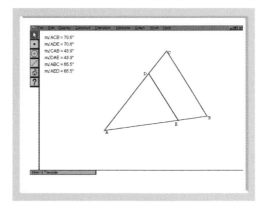

7. How do the measures of the corresponding angles compare?

8. Is this property preserved if any of the original vertices, A, B, or C, is dragged to a new position?

9. Measure the lengths of the corresponding sides, DE and BC, DA and CA, and AE and AB.

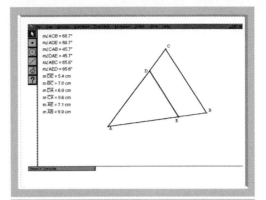

10. Choose the Calculate command from the Measure menu to open a calculator window. Click on the length of DE from the top left corner of the screen, followed by the division button (/) in the calculator window, and finally the length of BC. Click on OK in the calculator window to display the ratio DE:BC. Similarly, calculate the ratios DA:CA and AE:AB.

11. How do the ratios of the corresponding sides compare? Is this property preserved if any of the original vertices, A, B, or C, is dragged to a new position?

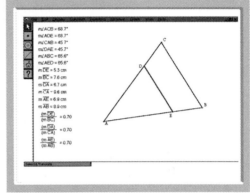

12. For convenience, drag point D to a location that makes the ratio of the corresponding sides a decimal that terminates in the first decimal place. Express this ratio in fraction form.

13. Choose the Area command from the Measure menu to measure the areas of △AED and △ABC.

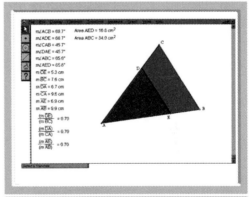

14. Calculate the ratio of the areas, area △AED:area △ABC. Express this ratio in fraction form.

15. Communication What is the relationship between the ratio of the areas and the ratio of the lengths of the corresponding sides?

16. Communication Summarize your findings about angle measures, side lengths, and areas in similar triangles.

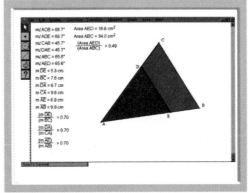

A statue of a polar bear in Cochrane, Ontario, symbolizes the town's northerly location and the Polar Bear Express train, which runs north from Cochrane to Moosonee, on the shores of James Bay. The length of the statue is about 5 m. A real polar bear has a length of about 2.5 m.

The statue of the polar bear is the same shape as, or is similar to, a real polar bear. **Similar figures** have the same shape, but not necessarily the same size.

Investigation **Use the Diagrams**

1. In the similar triangles ABC and DEF, determine the measures of the side lengths and the measures of the unknown angles.
Copy and complete the table.

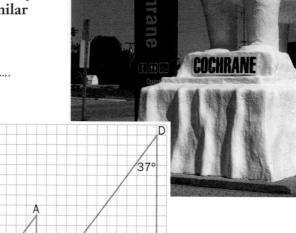

△ABC		△DEF	
∠A =	AB =	∠D =	DE =
∠B =	BC =	∠E =	EF =
∠C =	AC =	∠F =	DF =

2. How do the measures of the corresponding angles compare?

3. Find the ratios of the lengths of the corresponding sides, AB:DE, BC:EF, and AC:DF.

4. How do the ratios of the corresponding sides compare?

5. Calculate the area of each triangle.

6. Find the ratio of the area of △ABC to the area of △DEF.

7. How does the ratio of the areas compare with the ratio of the corresponding sides?

8. Communication a) In what way are △ABC and △DEF the same as congruent triangles?
b) In what way are they different from congruent triangles?

9. What is the ratio of the lengths of corresponding sides in congruent triangles?

10. Communication a) △DEF is an enlargement of △ABC. Explain why.
b) What is the scale factor?

$\triangle$KLM and $\triangle$TUV are similar. We write
$\triangle$KLM ~ $\triangle$TUV. This means that
• the corresponding angles are equal
$\angle$K = $\angle$T $\qquad$ $\angle$L = $\angle$U $\qquad$ $\angle$M = $\angle$V
• the ratios of the corresponding sides are equal
$$\frac{KL}{TU} = \frac{LM}{UV} = \frac{KM}{TV} \quad \text{or} \quad \frac{m}{v} = \frac{k}{t} = \frac{l}{u}$$
• the ratio of the areas is equal to the ratio of
the squares of the corresponding sides

$$\frac{\text{area} \triangle KLM}{\text{area} \triangle TUV} = \frac{m^2}{v^2} = \frac{k^2}{t^2} = \frac{l^2}{u^2}$$

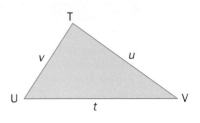

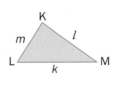

Because congruent triangles, such as $\triangle$PQR and
$\triangle$WXY, have the same size and the same shape,
• the corresponding angles are equal
$\angle$P = $\angle$W $\qquad$ $\angle$Q = $\angle$X $\qquad$ $\angle$R = $\angle$Y
• the corresponding sides are equal, so the ratio
of corresponding sides is 1
PQ = WX $\qquad$ QR = XY $\qquad$ PR = WY

so $\dfrac{PQ}{WX} = \dfrac{QR}{XY} = \dfrac{PR}{WY} = 1$ or $\dfrac{r}{y} = \dfrac{p}{w} = \dfrac{q}{x} = 1$

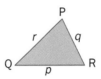

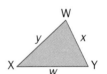

• the areas are equal, so the ratio of the areas is 1
area $\triangle$PQR = area $\triangle$WXY

so $\dfrac{\text{area} \triangle PQR}{\text{area} \triangle WXY} = 1$

Example 1 Finding Side Lengths
$\triangle$BCD ~ $\triangle$EFG. Find the values of e and c.

Solution
Since the triangles are similar, the ratios of the
corresponding sides are equal.

$$\frac{BC}{EF} = \frac{CD}{FG} = \frac{BD}{EG} \quad \text{or} \quad \frac{d}{g} = \frac{b}{e} = \frac{c}{f}$$

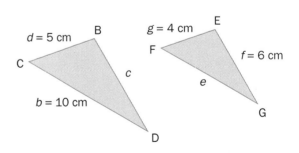

Substitute known values: $\dfrac{5}{4} = \dfrac{10}{e} = \dfrac{c}{6}$

Take the ratios two at a time.
Solve the proportions using the cross-product rule.

$\dfrac{5}{4} = \dfrac{10}{e}$ $\qquad\qquad\qquad$ $\dfrac{5}{4} = \dfrac{c}{6}$

$5 \times e = 10 \times 4$ $\qquad\qquad$ $5 \times 6 = c \times 4$

$5e = 40$ $\qquad\qquad\qquad$ $30 = 4c$

$e = 8$ $\qquad\qquad\qquad$ $7.5 = c$

So, e is 8 cm, and c is 7.5 cm.

Example 2   Finding Areas

$\triangle ABC \sim \triangle DEF$. $AB = 8$ cm and $DE = 12$ cm.
The area of $\triangle DEF$ is 54 cm². Find the area of $\triangle ABC$.

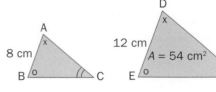

Solution

AB and DE are corresponding sides.
The ratio of the corresponding sides is

$$\frac{AB}{DE} = \frac{8}{12}$$

$$= \frac{2}{3}$$

The ratio of the areas of the triangles is $\frac{2^2}{3^2}$, or $\frac{4}{9}$.

$$\frac{\text{area } \triangle ABC}{\text{area } \triangle DEF} = \frac{4}{9}$$

Let the area of $\triangle ABC$ be x.
Write and solve a proportion.

$$\frac{x}{54} = \frac{4}{9}$$

Use equivalent ratios.   or   Use the cross-product rule.

$$\frac{x}{54} = \frac{4 \times 6}{9 \times 6} \qquad\qquad 9 \times x = 54 \times 4$$

$$\frac{x}{54} = \frac{24}{54} \qquad\qquad\qquad 9x = 216$$

$$x = 24 \qquad\qquad\qquad\qquad x = 24$$

The area of $\triangle ABC$ is 24 cm².

Example 3   Showing and Using Similarity

a) Show why $\triangle ABC$ is similar to $\triangle EDC$.
b) Find the lengths x and y.

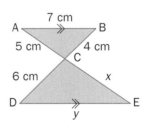

Solution

a) Since AB ∥ DE,

$$\angle A = \angle E \qquad \text{(alternate angles)}$$
$$\angle B = \angle D \qquad \text{(alternate angles)}$$
$$\angle ACB = \angle ECD \qquad \text{(opposite angles)}$$

Since the corresponding pairs of angles are equal,
$\triangle ABC \sim \triangle EDC$

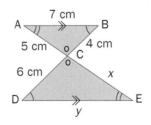

b) Since △ABC ~ △EDC, the ratios of the corresponding sides are equal.

$$\frac{x}{5} = \frac{6}{4} \qquad \frac{y}{7} = \frac{6}{4}$$
$$4 \times x = 5 \times 6 \qquad 4 \times y = 7 \times 6$$
$$4x = 30 \qquad 4y = 42$$
$$x = 7.5 \qquad y = 10.5$$

So, x is 7.5 cm and y is 10.5 cm.

Similar triangles can be used to measure distances that are difficult to measure directly.

Example 4   River Width

The diagram shows how surveyors can lay out two triangles to find the width of a river. Use the triangles to calculate the width of the river, DE.

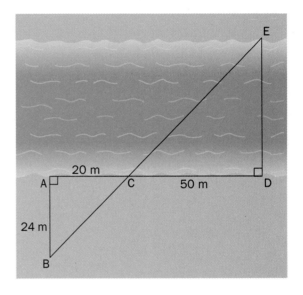

Solution

If △ABC is similar to △DEC, you can write ratios of corresponding sides to find DE.
In △ABC and △DEC,
∠CAB = ∠CDE   (both 90°)
∠ACB = ∠DCE   (opposite angles)
If two angles in one triangle are equal to two angles in another triangle, the third angles in each triangle must be equal.
∠ABC = ∠DEC

Since corresponding angles are equal,
△ABC ~ △DEC

Since the triangles are similar, the ratios of corresponding sides are equal.

$$\frac{AC}{DC} = \frac{AB}{DE}$$
$$\frac{20}{50} = \frac{24}{DE}$$
$$20 \times DE = 50 \times 24$$
$$20 \times DE = 1200$$
$$DE = 60$$

The width of the river is 60 m.

If △ABC and △DEF are similar,

a) the corresponding pairs of angles are equal

$$\angle A = \angle D \qquad \angle B = \angle E \qquad \angle C = \angle F$$

b) the ratios of the corresponding sides are equal

$$\frac{a}{d} = \frac{b}{e} = \frac{c}{f}$$

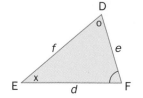

c) the ratio of their areas is equal to the ratio of the squares of their corresponding sides

$$\frac{\text{area } \triangle ABC}{\text{area } \triangle DEF} = \frac{a^2}{d^2} = \frac{b^2}{e^2} = \frac{c^2}{f^2}$$

Communicate Your Understanding

1. Describe and compare the concepts of similarity and congruence.

2. △ABC ~ △DEF. The area of △ABC is 8 cm². Describe how you would find

a) the unknown side lengths

b) the area of △DEF

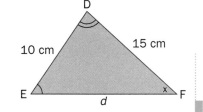

Practice

A

1. The triangles in each pair are similar. Find the unknown side lengths.

a)

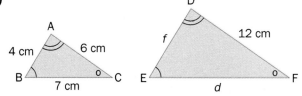

b)

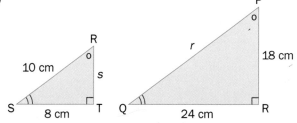

c)

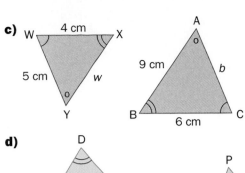

d)

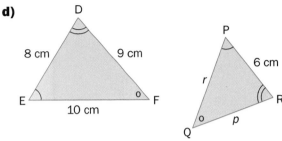

e)

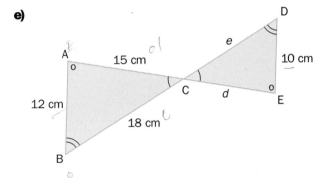

2. Find x.

a)

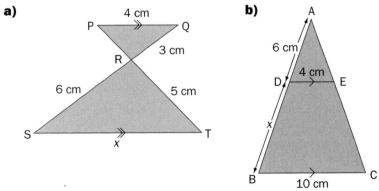

b)

3. △PQR ~ △STU. PQ = 12 cm and ST = 9 cm.
The area of △STU is 72 cm². Find the area of △PQR.

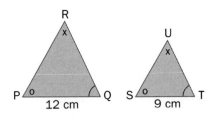

4. a) Show why △PQR is similar to △STR.
b) Find the lengths x and y.

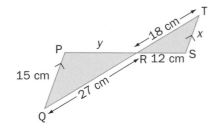

Applications and Problem Solving

5. Shadows A 5-m flagpole casts a 4-m shadow at the same time of day as a building casts a 30-m shadow. How tall is the building?

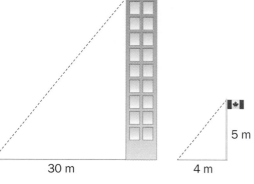

6. Lake length Surveyors have laid out triangles to find the length of a lake. Calculate this length, AB.

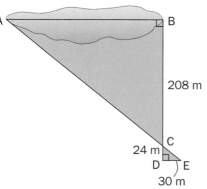

B

7. Communication Malik thinks that two triangles on a page look similar. Describe two different methods he could use to find out if the triangles are similar. Explain your reasoning.

8. Flower garden Serena made a scale drawing of her triangular flower garden. Two sides of her garden are 5 m and 6 m long, and form an angle of 40°. Serena drew a 40° angle on paper, marked points at 10 cm and 12 cm on the arms, and joined these points. She measured the third side to be 9.5 cm. How long is the third side of the garden?

9. Tree height To find the height of a tree, Sarah placed a mirror on the ground 15 m from the base of the tree. She walked backward until she could see the top of the tree in the centre of the mirror. At that position she was 1.2 m from the mirror and her eyes were 1.4 m from the ground. Find the height of the tree.

10. Communication △ABC and △DEF are similar. The ratio of their corresponding sides is 3:5. What is the ratio of their perimeters? Explain.

11. Communication Are all isosceles triangles similar? Are some isosceles triangles similar? Explain, using diagrams where necessary, and justify your reasoning.

12. Communication Are all equilateral triangles similar? Explain and justify your reasoning.

13. Communication △PQR and △LMN are similar. Can they be congruent? Explain and justify your answer.

14. Communication △PQR and △LMN are congruent. Are they similar? Explain and justify your answer.

C

15. The areas of two similar triangles are 72 cm² and 162 cm². What is the ratio of the lengths of their corresponding sides?

Modelling Math **Measuring Inaccessible Heights and Widths**

Surveyors have laid out these triangles to calculate the width of a canyon. Find this width, to the nearest metre.

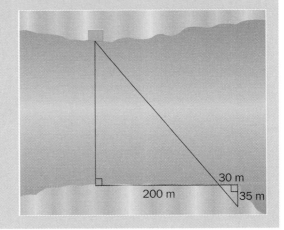

Achievement Check

1 2 3 4

△ABC is shown in the diagram. What are the measures of the sides and angles of another triangle, △DEF, in each of the following situations? Explain and justify your reasoning.
a) △ABC and △DEF are congruent.
b) △ABC and △DEF are similar but not congruent.
c) △ABC and △DEF are similar, and △DEF has an area of 120 cm².

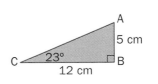

If you stand outside a building and look at an upstairs window, the angle that your line of sight makes with the horizontal is known as the **angle of elevation**.

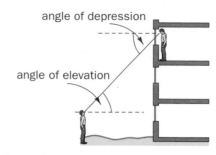

angle of depression

angle of elevation

If someone is standing at the window and looking down at you, the angle that the person's line of sight makes with the horizontal is known as the **angle of depression**.

A popular tourist attraction in Ottawa is the Peace Tower, which rises from the Centre Block of the Parliament Buildings. From a point on the ground 30 m from the base of the tower, the angle of elevation of the top of the tower is 72°. The height of the tower can be calculated using a branch of mathematics called **trigonometry**, as will be shown in Example 4.

The word trigonometry comes from two Greek terms, *trigonon*, meaning triangle, and *metrikos*, meaning measure. The study of trigonometry involves triangle measurements. A **trigonometric ratio** is the ratio of the lengths of two sides in a right triangle.

When working with right triangles to find trigonometric ratios, the sides are given special names in relation to the acute angle being considered.

For ∠A in right △ABC, AB is the hypotenuse, BC is the side opposite ∠A, and AC is the side adjacent to ∠A.

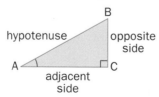

For ∠B in right △ABC, AB is the hypotenuse, AC is the side opposite ∠B, and BC is the side adjacent to ∠B.

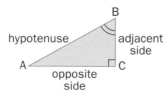

Investigation   Compare the Ratios

1. Four nested right triangles are drawn on grid paper.
a) Copy and complete the table. Express each ratio in decimal form.

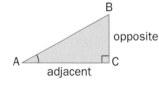

Triangle	△ABC	△ADE	△AFG	△AHI
Ratio	$\dfrac{BC}{AC} =$	$\dfrac{DE}{AE} =$	$\dfrac{FG}{AG} =$	$\dfrac{HI}{AI} =$

b) How do the ratios compare?

2. Communication Explain why △ABC, △ADE, △AFG, and △AHI are similar.

3. Which angle is common to all four triangles?

4. Communication The ratio you found is called the **tangent ratio** for the common angle. Explain the meaning of the tangent ratio by describing the positions of the two sides in each ratio in relation to the common angle.

5. Find the tangent ratio for ∠C in each of the following triangles. Express each answer in fraction form.

a)
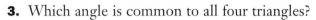
B, 5 cm, C, A, 9 cm

b)
C 12 cm D
7 cm
B

c)
E 7 cm C
6 cm
D

For any acute angle A in a right triangle, the tangent ratio is

$$\text{tangent } A = \frac{\text{length of the side opposite } \angle A}{\text{length of the side adjacent to } \angle A}$$

This definition is abbreviated to

$$\tan A = \frac{\text{opposite}}{\text{adjacent}}$$

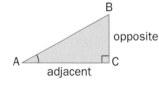

In the above investigation, you found that the value of the tangent ratio for a given angle depends only on the measure of the angle. The value of the tangent ratio does not depend on the size of the right triangle in which the angle is found. An acute angle of a given measure has a unique tangent ratio.

If you know the degree measure of an angle, the TAN key on your calculator can be used to find the tangent ratio for the angle.

Example 1   Finding Tangent Ratios

Find the tangent ratio, to the nearest thousandth, for each angle.

a) $40°$ **b)** $55°$ **c)** $73°$ **d)** $89°$

Solution

a) $\tan 40° \doteq 0.839$

If you get a different value, check the mode settings to make sure that your calculator is in degree mode.

b) $\tan 55° \doteq 1.428$
c) $\tan 73° \doteq 3.271$
d) $\tan 89° \doteq 57.290$

If you know the tangent ratio of an angle, the TAN^{-1} key on your calculator can be used to find the degree measure of the angle.

Example 2   Finding Angle Measures

Find each angle measure, to the nearest degree, for each tangent ratio.

a) $\tan A = 1.782$ **b)** $\tan B = 0.509$
c) $\tan C = 6.895$ **d)** $\tan D = 0.063$

Solution

a) If $\tan A = 1.782$
$\angle A \doteq 61°$

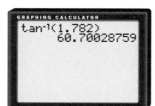

b) If $\tan B = 0.509$
$\angle B \doteq 27°$

c) If $\tan C = 6.895$
$\angle C \doteq 82°$

d) If $\tan D = 0.063$
$\angle D \doteq 4°$

Example 3   Finding Two Acute Angles
In △PQR, find
a) tan P and ∠P   **b)** tan R and ∠R

Solution

$$\tan = \frac{\text{opposite}}{\text{adjacent}}$$

a) $\tan P = \dfrac{5}{8}$

$\quad\quad \angle P \doteq 32°$

b) $\tan R = \dfrac{8}{5}$

$\quad\quad \angle R \doteq 58°$

Example 4   Peace Tower
From a point on the ground 30 m from the foot of the
Peace Tower, the angle of elevation of the top of the tower
is 72°. Find the height of the tower, to the nearest metre.

Solution
From the diagram,

$$\tan 72° = \frac{h}{30}$$
$$30 \tan 72° = h$$
$$92 \doteq h$$

The height of the
tower is 92 m, to the
nearest metre.

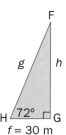

Example 5   Finding Side Lengths
In △JKL, find the length of KL, to the nearest metre.

Solution

$$\tan K = \frac{10}{KL}$$
$$\tan 30° = \frac{10}{KL}$$
$$KL \tan 30° = 10$$
$$KL = \frac{10}{\tan 30°}$$
$$KL \doteq 17$$

The length of KL is 17 m, to the nearest metre.

For any acute angle A in a right triangle, the tangent ratio is

$$\text{tangent A} = \frac{\text{length of the side opposite } \angle A}{\text{length of the side adjacent to } \angle A}$$

or $\tan A = \dfrac{\text{opposite}}{\text{adjacent}}$

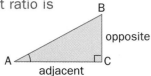

Communicate Your Understanding

1. Explain why the value of the tangent ratio for a given angle depends only on the measure of the angle and not on the size of the right triangle.

2. Describe how you would use a tangent ratio to calculate the length of t.

3. Describe how you would use a tangent ratio to calculate the measure of $\angle B$.

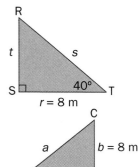

Practice

1. Find tan A and tan C in each triangle. Round answers to the nearest thousandth, if necessary

a)

b)
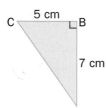

2. Find each of the following, to the nearest thousandth.
a) tan 15° **b)** tan 62° **c)** tan 5°
d) tan 30° **e)** tan 82° **f)** tan 45°

3. Find $\angle B$, to the nearest degree.
a) tan B = 0.600 **b)** tan B = 0.833 **c)** tan B = 3.025

4. Find $\angle W$, to the nearest degree.
a) $\tan W = \dfrac{4}{5}$ **b)** $\tan W = \dfrac{6}{7}$ **c)** $\tan W = \dfrac{7}{4}$ **d)** $\tan W = \dfrac{15}{9}$

5. Calculate tan C in each triangle.

a)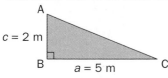

b)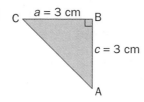

6. Calculate tan D, ∠D, tan E, and ∠E. Round each angle measure to the nearest degree.

a)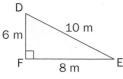

b)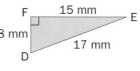

7. Find the value of x, to the nearest tenth of a metre.

a)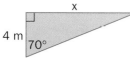

b)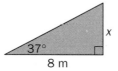

c)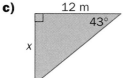

d)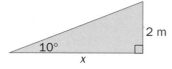

e)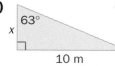

f)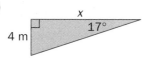

8. Find the value of x, to the nearest tenth of a metre.

a)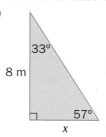

b)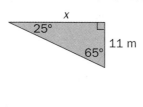

Applications and Problem Solving

9. In a right triangle, the side adjacent to an angle of 23° is 12 cm long. How long is the side opposite the 23° angle, to the nearest tenth of a centimetre?

10. In a right triangle, the side opposite the 53° angle is 4 cm long. How long is the side adjacent to the 53° angle, to the nearest centimetre?

B

11. Ladder When a ladder is rested against a tree, the foot of the ladder is 1 m from the base of the tree and forms an angle of 64° with the ground. How far up the tree does the ladder reach, to the nearest tenth of a metre?

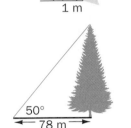

12. Tall tree One of Canada's tallest trees is a Douglas fir on Vancouver Island. The angle of elevation measured by an observer who is 78 m from the base of the tree is 50°. How tall is this tree, to the nearest metre?

13. Roof rafters The angle of inclination of the rafters of the roof of a house is 26°. The roof support is 3 m high. How wide is the house, to the nearest metre?

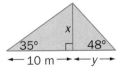

14. Schoolyard Pietra walked diagonally across a rectangular schoolyard 45 m by 65 m. To the nearest degree, at what angle with respect to the longer side did she walk?

15. Stairs Comfortable stairs have a slope of $\frac{3}{4}$. What angle do the stairs make with the horizontal, to the nearest degree?

16. Skylon Tower From a point 50 m from the base of the Skylon Tower in Niagara Falls, the angle of elevation of the top of the tower is 78°. Find the height of the tower, to the nearest metre.

17. Measurement Find the length of x, then the length of y, to the nearest tenth of a metre.

18. Measurement Find the length of x, to the nearest tenth of a centimetre, then the measure of $\angle y$, to the nearest degree.

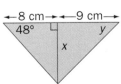

C

19. Linear equations The graph of the line $y = x + 2$ is shown.
a) Find the measure of the acute angle that the line $y = x + 2$ makes with the x-axis.
b) Find the measure of the acute angle that the line $y = x - 3$ makes with the x-axis.
c) Find the measure of the acute angle that the line $y = -x + 4$ makes with the x-axis.

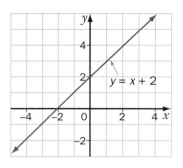

20. Prince Shoal lighthouse The light on the Prince Shoal lighthouse is 25 m above the water level. From a position beside the light, the angle of depression of a sailboat is 12°. How far is the sailboat from the lighthouse, to the nearest metre?

21. Communication Write a problem similar to questions 9 and 10. Have a classmate solve it.

Modelling Math   Measuring Inaccessible Heights and Widths

Choose three objects around your school that are too tall for you to measure their heights directly. Your choices might include the school building, a flagpole, or a street lamp. To calculate each height, measure the angle of elevation of the top of the object from a point that is a known distance horizontally from the bottom of the object. Then, use the tangent ratio. Describe how you found the angle of elevation. Suggest ways in which you could make the calculated height more accurate.

LOGIC POWER

There are two red disks and two blue disks on the grid. Each disk can move in an L-shape. No two disks can occupy the same square at the same time. Therefore, the disk in the top left corner can move either one square to the right and two squares down or one square down and two squares to the right. Find the minimum number of moves it takes to switch the positions of the red disks with those of the blue disks.

Parasailing is becoming a popular summer water sport in Canada. A parasail is designed to be towed behind a boat. The parasailor snaps into a harness, signals the driver of the boat to start, takes a few steps, and then is lifted into the air. The height that the parasailor reaches depends on the length of the towrope and the angle that the towrope makes with the water, as will be shown in Example 5.

Investigation **Compare the Ratios**

1. Four nested right triangles are drawn on grid paper.

a) Use the Pythagorean Theorem to calculate the lengths of DE, CE, BE, and AE. Then, copy and complete the table. Express each ratio in decimal form.

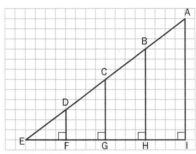

Triangle	△EDF	△ECG	△EBH	△EAI
Ratio	$\dfrac{DF}{DE} =$	$\dfrac{CG}{CE} =$	$\dfrac{BH}{BE} =$	$\dfrac{AI}{AE} =$

b) How do the ratios compare?

2. Which angle is common to all four triangles?

3. **Communication** The ratio you found is called the **sine ratio** for the common angle. Explain the meaning of the sine ratio by describing the positions of the two sides in each ratio in relation to the common angle.

4. Find the sine ratio for ∠B in each of the following triangles. Express each answer in fraction form in lowest terms.

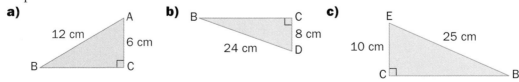

a) 12 cm, 6 cm   **b)** 24 cm, 8 cm   **c)** 10 cm, 25 cm

For any acute angle A in a right triangle, the sine ratio is

$$\text{sine A} = \frac{\text{length of the side opposite } \angle A}{\text{length of the hypotenuse}}$$

This definition is abbreviated to

$$\sin A = \frac{\text{opposite}}{\text{hypotenuse}}$$

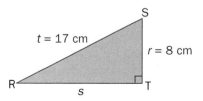

Like the tangent ratio, the sine ratio for a given angle depends only on the measure of the angle. The value of the sine ratio does not depend on the size of the right triangle in which the angle is found. An acute angle of a given measure has a unique sine ratio.

If you know the degree measure of an angle, the SIN key on your calculator can be used to find the sine ratio for the angle.

Example 1　Finding Sine Ratios
Find the sine ratio, to the nearest thousandth, for each angle.
a) 75°　　　　**b)** 52°　　　　**c)** 17°　　　　**d)** 90°

Solution
a) sin 75° ≐ 0.966

b) sin 52° ≐ 0.788
c) sin 17° ≐ 0.292
d) sin 90° = 1.000

If you know the sine ratio of an angle, the SIN⁻¹ key on your calculator can be used to find the degree measure of the angle.

Example 2　Finding Angle Measures
In △RST, find sin R and ∠R.

Solution

$$\sin = \frac{\text{opposite}}{\text{hypotenuse}}$$

$$\sin R = \frac{8}{17}$$

$$\angle R \doteq 28°$$

Example 3   Finding Side Lengths

In △JKL, find the length of JK, to the nearest tenth of a centimetre.

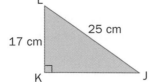

Solution 1   Using the Sine Ratio

$$\sin J = \frac{17}{25}$$

$$\angle J \doteq 43°$$

Therefore, $\angle L = 180° - 43° - 90°$

$$= 47°$$

$$\sin L = \frac{JK}{25}$$

$$\sin 47° = \frac{JK}{25}$$

$$25 \sin 47° = JK$$

$$18.3 \doteq JK$$

The length of JK is 18.3 cm, to the nearest tenth of a centimetre.

Solution 2   Using the Pythagorean Theorem

$$JK^2 + LK^2 = JL^2$$

$$JK^2 + 17^2 = 25^2$$

$$JK^2 = 25^2 - 17^2$$

$$JK = \sqrt{25^2 - 17^2}$$

$$\doteq 18.3$$

The length of JK is 18.3 cm, to the nearest tenth of a centimetre.

Example 4   Finding Side Lengths

In △ABC, find the length of c, to the nearest tenth of a metre.

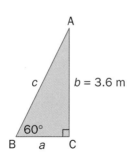

Solution

$$\sin 60° = \frac{3.6}{c}$$

$$c \sin 60° = 3.6$$

$$c = \frac{3.6}{\sin 60°}$$

$$\doteq 4.2$$

The length of c is 4.2 m, to the nearest tenth of a metre.

Example 5   Parasailing

The towrope pulling a parasailor is 90 m long. A crew member on the boat estimates that the angle between the towrope and the water is about 40°. Find the height of the parasailor above the water, to the nearest 10 m.

Solution

In △PBW,

$$\sin 40° = \frac{PW}{90}$$
$$90 \sin 40° = PW$$
$$60 \doteq PW$$

The parasailor is 60 m above the water, to the nearest 10 m.

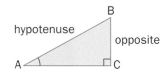

Key CONCEPTS

For any acute angle A in a right triangle, the sine ratio is

$$\text{sine } A = \frac{\text{length of the side opposite } \angle A}{\text{length of the hypotenuse}}$$

or $\sin A = \dfrac{\text{opposite}}{\text{hypotenuse}}$

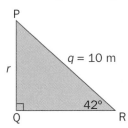

Communicate Your Understanding

1. Explain why the value of the sine ratio for a given angle depends only on the measure of the angle and not on the size of the right triangle.

2. Describe how you would use a sine ratio to calculate the length of *r*.

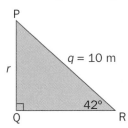

3. Describe how you would use a sine ratio to calculate the measure of ∠F.

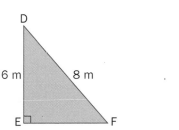

1. Find sin A and sin C in each triangle. Round answers to the nearest thousandth, if necessary.

a)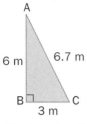

b)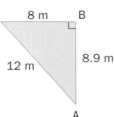

2. Find each of the following, to the nearest thousandth.

a) sin 45°   **b)** sin 60°   **c)** sin 37°

d) sin 25°   **e)** sin 0°   **f)** sin 89°

3. Find ∠J, to the nearest degree.

a) sin J = 0.503   **b)** sin J = 0.952   **c)** sin J = 0.712

d) sin J = 0.303   **e)** sin J = 0.998   **f)** sin J = 0.101

4. Find ∠B, to the nearest degree.

a) $\sin B = \dfrac{2}{3}$ **b)** $\sin B = \dfrac{3}{4}$ **c)** $\sin B = \dfrac{1}{2}$

d) $\sin B = \dfrac{2}{5}$ **e)** $\sin B = \dfrac{1}{8}$ **f)** $\sin B = \dfrac{7}{9}$

5. Calculate sin T in each triangle. Then, find ∠T, to the nearest degree.

a)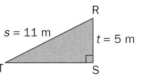

b)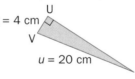

6. Find the value of x, to the nearest tenth of a centimetre.

a)

b)

c)

d)

e)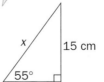

f)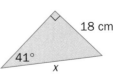

Applications and Problem Solving

7. In △PQR, ∠Q = 90°, and PR = 20 cm. Find PQ, to the nearest tenth of a centimetre, if ∠R = 41°.

8. In △DEF, find ∠F, to the nearest degree, if DE = 15 cm, DF = 18 cm, and ∠E = 90°.

9. In △ABC, ∠B = 90°. If AB = 10 cm and ∠C = 38°, find the length of AC, to the nearest tenth of a centimetre.

B

10. Parasailing The towrope pulling a parasailor is 70 m long. A boat crew member estimates that the angle between the towrope and the water is about 30°. Find the height of the parasailor above the water, to the nearest 10 m.

11. Garden hoe A 1.5-m hoe rests against the side of a garden shed. The angle the handle of the hoe forms with the ground is 71°. How far up the wall of the shed does the hoe reach, to the nearest tenth of a metre?

12. △ABC is an isosceles triangle. The height of the triangle is 3 cm, and the two acute angles at its base are each 56°. How long are the two equal sides, to the nearest tenth of a centimetre?

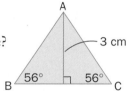

13. Splintered tree A tree is splintered by lightning 2 m up its trunk, so that the top part of the tree touches the ground. The angle the top of the tree forms with the ground is 70°. Before it was splintered, how tall was the tree, to the nearest tenth of a metre?

14. a) Evaluate sin 39° with a calculator. Round your answer to the nearest thousandth.
b) Use the diagram to write the ratio represented by your answer to part a).
c) What is the length of *a* in terms of *c*?
d) What is the length of *c* in terms of *a*?

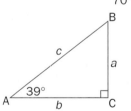

C

15. Measurement Find the length of *x*, then the length of *y*, to the nearest tenth of a centimetre.

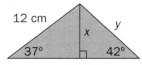

16. Measurement Find the length of *x*, to the nearest tenth of a metre, then the measure of ∠*y*, to the nearest degree.

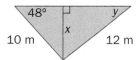

17. Communication Write a problem similar to question 7, 8, or 9. Have a classmate solve it.

To mark the fifteenth Commonwealth Games, held in Victoria, the world's tallest totem pole *The Spirit of Nations* was erected at Songhees Point on Victoria Harbour. Unlike most totem poles, which are stabilized by sinking them into the ground, *The Spirit of Nations* required anchor lines because it sat on rock. The lengths of the anchor lines will be calculated in Example 4.

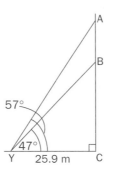

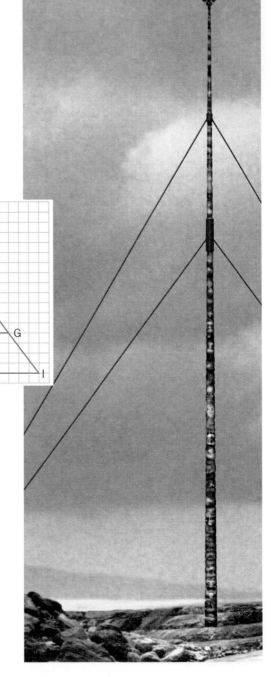

Investigation Compare the Ratios

1. Four nested right triangles are drawn on grid paper.

a) Determine the lengths of the line segments AC, AE, AG, and AI. Then, copy and complete the table. Express each ratio in decimal form.

Triangle	△ABC	△ADE	△AFG	△AHI
Ratio	$\dfrac{BC}{AC} =$	$\dfrac{DE}{AE} =$	$\dfrac{FG}{AG} =$	$\dfrac{HI}{AI} =$

b) How do the ratios compare?

2. Communication Explain why ∠ACB, ∠AED, ∠AGF, and ∠AIH are equal.

3. Communication Explain why △ABC, △ADE, △AFG, and △AHI are similar.

4. Communication The ratio you found is called the **cosine ratio** for ∠ACB, ∠AED, ∠AGF, and ∠AIH. Explain the meaning of the cosine ratio by describing the positions of the two sides in each ratio in relation to ∠ACB, ∠AED, ∠AGF, and ∠AIH.

5. Find the cosine ratio for ∠D in each of the following triangles. Express each answer as a fraction in lowest terms.

a)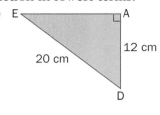

b)

c)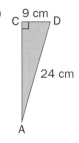

For any acute angle A in a right triangle, the cosine ratio is

$$\text{cosine A} = \frac{\text{length of the side adjacent to } \angle A}{\text{length of the hypotenuse}}$$

This definition is abbreviated to

$$\cos A = \frac{\text{adjacent}}{\text{hypotenuse}}$$

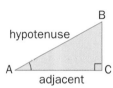

Like the tangent and sine ratios, the cosine ratio for a given angle depends only on the measure of the angle. The value of the cosine ratio does not depend on the size of the right triangle in which the angle is found. An acute angle of a given measure has a unique cosine ratio.

If you know the degree measure of an angle, the COS key on your calculator can be used to find the cosine ratio for the angle.

Example 1   Finding Cosine Ratios
Find the cosine ratio, to the nearest thousandth, for each angle.

a) 42°   **b)** 9°   **c)** 20°   **d)** 90°

Solution
a) cos 42° ≐ 0.743

```
GRAPHING CALCULATOR
cos(42)
       .7431448255
```

b) cos 9° ≐ 0.988
c) cos 20° ≐ 0.940
d) cos 90° = 0.000

If you know the cosine ratio of an angle, the $\cos^{-1}$ key on your calculator can be used to find the degree measure of the angle.

Example 2   Finding Angle Measures
In $\triangle BDE$, find $\cos B$ and $\angle B$.

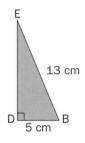

E

13 cm

D   B
5 cm

Solution

$$\cos = \frac{\text{adjacent}}{\text{hypotenuse}}$$

$$\cos B = \frac{5}{13}$$

$$\angle B \doteq 67°$$

GRAPHING CALCULATOR
cos⁻¹(5/13)
          67.38013505

Example 3   Finding Side Lengths
In $\triangle WXY$, find the length of w, to the nearest centimetre.

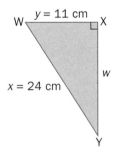

W $y = 11$ cm   X

w

$x = 24$ cm

Y

Solution 1   Using the Cosine Ratio

$$\cos W = \frac{11}{24}$$

$$\angle W \doteq 63°$$

Since $\angle W = 63°$ and $\angle X = 90°$, $\angle Y = 27°$.

$$\cos Y = \frac{w}{24}$$

$$\cos 27° = \frac{w}{24}$$

$$24 \cos 27° = w$$

$$21 \doteq w$$

GRAPHING CALCULATOR
24cos(27)
          21.38415658

The length of w is 21 cm, to the nearest centimetre.

Solution 2   Using the Pythagorean Theorem

$$y^2 + w^2 = x^2$$

$$11^2 + w^2 = 24^2$$

$$w^2 = 24^2 - 11^2$$

$$w = \sqrt{24^2 - 11^2}$$

$$\doteq 21$$

GRAPHING CALCULATOR
√(24²−11²)
          21.33072901

The length of w is 21 cm, to the nearest centimetre.

Example 4   The Spirit of Nations

Calculate the lengths of the anchor lines AY and BY, to the nearest tenth of a metre.

Solution

In △AYC,   In △BYC,

$$\cos 57° = \frac{25.9}{AY}$$ $$\cos 47° = \frac{25.9}{BY}$$

$$AY \cos 57° = 25.9$$ $$BY \cos 47° = 25.9$$

$$AY = \frac{25.9}{\cos 57°}$$ $$BY = \frac{25.9}{\cos 47°}$$

$$AY \doteq 47.6$$ $$BY \doteq 38.0$$

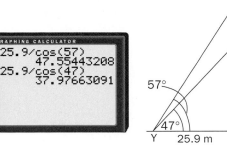

GRAPHING CALCULATOR
```
25.9/cos(57)
            47.55443208
25.9/cos(47)
            37.97663091
```

So, the length of AY is 47.6 m and the length of BY is 38.0 m, to the nearest tenth of a metre.

Key CONCEPTS

For any acute angle A in a right triangle, the cosine ratio is

$$\text{cosine } A = \frac{\text{length of the side adjacent to } \angle A}{\text{length of the hypotenuse}}$$

$$\text{or } \cos A = \frac{\text{adjacent}}{\text{hypotenuse}}$$

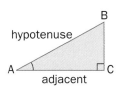

Communicate Your Understanding

1. Explain why the value of the cosine ratio for a given angle depends only on the measure of the angle and not on the size of the right triangle.

2. Describe how you would use the cosine ratio to calculate the length of x.

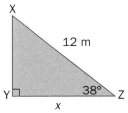

3. Describe how you would use the cosine ratio to calculate the measure of $\angle C$.

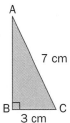

Practice

1. Calculate cos A and cos C in each triangle. Round answers to the nearest thousandth, if necessary.

a)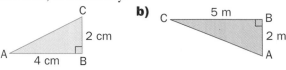

b)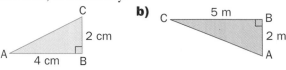

2. Find each of the following, to the nearest thousandth.

a) cos 30°   **b)** cos 45°   **c)** cos 60°   **d)** cos 89°

e) cos 0°   **f)** cos 5°   **g)** cos 19°   **h)** cos 83°

3. Find ∠P, to the nearest degree.

a) cos P = 0.343   **b)** cos P = 0.887   **c)** cos P = 0.621

d) cos P = 0.019   **e)** cos P = 0.731   **f)** cos P = 0.524

4. Find ∠Q, to the nearest degree.

a) $\cos Q = \dfrac{1}{6}$ **b)** $\cos Q = \dfrac{5}{11}$ **c)** $\cos Q = \dfrac{5}{9}$

d) $\cos Q = \dfrac{7}{8}$ **e)** $\cos Q = \dfrac{15}{16}$ **f)** $\cos Q = \dfrac{3}{14}$

5. Calculate cos T in each triangle. Then, find ∠T, to the nearest degree.

a)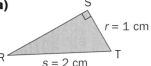

b)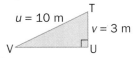

6. Find *x*, to the nearest tenth of a centimetre.

a)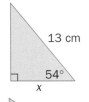

b)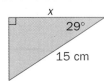

c)

d)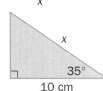

e)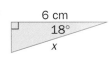

f)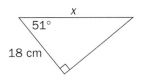

Applications and Problem Solving

7. The side adjacent to the 74° angle in a right triangle is 6 cm long. How long is the hypotenuse, to the nearest tenth of a centimetre?

8. The hypotenuse of a right triangle is 10 cm long. How long is the side adjacent to the 21° angle, to the nearest tenth of a centimetre?

B

9. Ladder A ladder leans against a vertical wall and makes an angle of 65° with the ground. The foot of the ladder is 2 m from the base of the wall. Calculate the length of the ladder, to the nearest tenth of a metre.

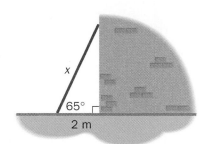

10. Kite A kite string is 35 m long. The angle the string makes with the ground is 50°. To the nearest metre, how far from the person holding the string is a person standing directly under the kite?

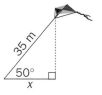

11. Find all the angles in $\triangle$WXY, to the nearest degree.

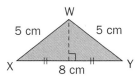

C

12. Communication a) Select three different values for an angle x between 0° and 90°. For each value of x, evaluate the expression $(\sin x)^2 + (\cos x)^2$.

b) Use the results from part a) to write a conjecture.

c) Verify your conjecture from part b) by simplifying

$$\left(\frac{\text{opposite}}{\text{hypotenuse}}\right)^2 + \left(\frac{\text{adjacent}}{\text{hypotenuse}}\right)^2.$$

13. Measurement Find the length of x, then the length of y, to the nearest tenth of a metre.

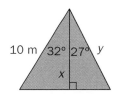

14. Measurement Find the length of x, to the nearest tenth of a centimetre, then the measure of $\angle y$, to the nearest degree.

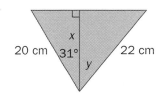

15. Use trigonometric ratios to verify that $\tan A = \dfrac{\sin A}{\cos A}$.

16. Communication Write a problem similar to questions 7 and 8. Have a classmate solve it.

Investigation Study the Diagram

The diagram shows some measurements for a right triangle ABC, whose hypotenuse models one side of the Leaning Tower of Pisa.

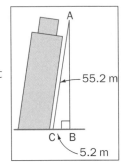

1. Communication a) Describe two different methods you could use to calculate the angle that the tower makes with the ground.
b) Use a method of your choice to complete the calculations. Round your answer to the nearest degree.

2. Communication a) Describe two different methods you could use to calculate the vertical height of the top of the tower above the ground.
b) Use a method of your choice to complete the calculations. Round your answer to the nearest tenth of a metre.

3. Of the unknown angles and sides in △ABC, which one have you not yet found? Determine its value.

To **solve** a right triangle means to find all the unknown sides and unknown angles.

Example 1 Solving a Right Triangle, Given Two Sides
Solve △ABC. Find side lengths to the nearest tenth of a centimetre and angles to the nearest degree.

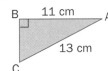

Solution
The cosine ratio can be used to calculate ∠A.

$$\cos A = \frac{11}{13}$$
$$\angle A \doteq 32°$$
$$\angle C = 180° - 32° - 90°$$
$$= 58°$$

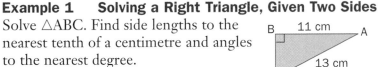

The sine ratio or the Pythagorean Theorem can be used to find the length of BC.

Using the sine ratio, $\dfrac{BC}{13} = \sin 32°$
$$BC = 13 \sin 32°$$
$$\doteq 6.9$$

The length of BC is 6.9 cm, to the nearest tenth of a centimetre.
∠A is 32° and ∠C is 58°, to the nearest degree.

Example 2 Solving a Right Triangle, Given a Side and an Angle

Solve △DEF. Find side lengths to the nearest tenth of a centimetre.

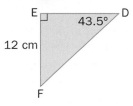

Solution

$\angle F = 180° - 43.5° - 90°$
$\quad\ = 46.5°$

The sine ratio can be used to find the length of DF.

$$\sin 43.5° = \frac{12}{DF}$$
$$DF \sin 43.5° = 12$$
$$DF = \frac{12}{\sin 43.5°}$$
$$DF \doteq 17.4$$

The tangent ratio or the Pythagorean Theorem can be used to find the length of DE.

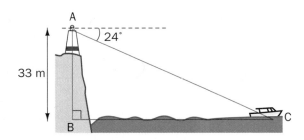

Using the tangent ratio, $\quad \tan 43.5° = \frac{12}{DE}$
$$DE \tan 43.5° = 12$$
$$DE = \frac{12}{\tan 43.5°}$$
$$DE \doteq 12.6$$

$\angle F$ is 46.5°, DF is 17.4 cm, and DE is 12.6 cm, to the nearest tenth of a centimetre.

Example 3 Lighthouse

A lighthouse sits at the top of a sheer cliff. The top of the lighthouse is 33 m above sea level. The angle of depression to sight a small fishing boat at sea is 24°. How far from the base of the cliff is the fishing boat, to the nearest metre?

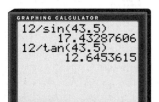

Solution

In △ABC, $\angle BAC = 90° - 24°$
$\quad\quad\quad\quad\quad = 66°$

The length of BC can be found from the tangent ratio.

$$\tan 66° = \frac{BC}{33}$$
$$33 \tan 66° = BC$$
$$74 \doteq BC$$

The fishing boat is 74 m from the base of the cliff, to the nearest metre.

1 To use trigonometry to solve a right triangle, given the measure of one acute angle and the length of one side, find

a) the measure of the third angle using the angle sum in the triangle

b) the measure of a second side using sine, cosine, or tangent ratios

c) the measure of the third side using a sine, cosine, or tangent ratio, or the Pythagorean Theorem

2 To use trigonometry to solve a right triangle, given the lengths of two sides, find

a) the measure of one angle using its sine, cosine, or tangent ratio

b) the measure of the third angle using the angle sum in the triangle

c) the measure of the third side using a sine, cosine, or tangent ratio, or the Pythagorean Theorem

Communicate Your Understanding

1. Explain what it means to solve a right triangle.

2. Describe how you would use trigonometry to solve △RST.

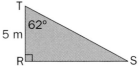

3. Describe how you would use trigonometry to solve △DEF.

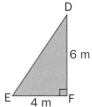

Practice

 A

1. Solve each triangle. Round each side length to the nearest tenth of a unit, and each angle to the nearest degree.

a)

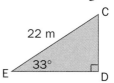

b)

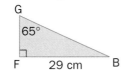

c)

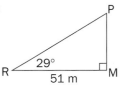

d)

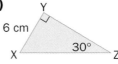

e)

f)

2. Find all the unknown angles, to the nearest degree, and all the unknown side lengths, to the nearest tenth of a unit.

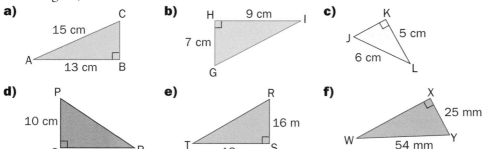

a) 15 cm, C, A, 13 cm, B

b) H, 9 cm, I, 7 cm, G

c) K, 5 cm, J, 6 cm, L

d) P, 10 cm, Q, 11 cm, R

e) R, 16 m, T, 18 m, S

f) X, 25 mm, W, 54 mm, Y

Applications and Problem Solving

3. Lighthouse Peggy's Cove Lighthouse, in Nova Scotia, is possibly the most photographed lighthouse in the world. The observation deck is about 20 m above sea level. From the observation deck, the angle of depression of a boat is 6°. How far is the boat from the lighthouse, to the nearest metre?

B

4. Kite A kite is 32 m above the ground. The angle the kite string makes with the ground is 39°. How long is the kite string, to the nearest metre?

5. Roller coaster The world's fastest roller coaster is at Six Flags Magic Mountain. At the start, riders are shot forward and then up a tower. They then begin the backward descent. The cars reach a speed of 160 km/h in 7 s during the descent. From a point 100 m from the foot of the tower, the angle of elevation of the top of the tower is 52°. Find the height of the tower, to the nearest metre.

6. Tall building Montréal's Marathon building is 195 m tall. From a point level with, and 48 m from, the base of the building, what is the angle of elevation of the top of the building, to the nearest degree?

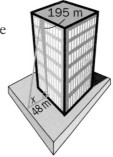

7. Totem pole Ropes are used to pull a totem pole upright. Then, the ropes are anchored in the ground to hold the pole until the hole is filled. One of the ropes holding this totem pole is 18 m long and forms an angle of 48° with the ground. Find, to the nearest metre,
a) the height of the totem pole
b) how far the anchor point is from the base of the totem pole

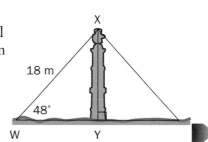

8. Flagpole The two guy wires supporting a flagpole are each anchored 7 m from the flagpole and form an angle of 52° with the ground. What is the total length of guy wire, to the nearest metre, needed to support this flagpole?

9. Two CN Towers Edmonton's CN Tower is a highrise office building. From a point 35 m from the base of the building and level with the base, the angle of elevation of the top is 72.5°.
a) Find the height of Edmonton's CN Tower, to the nearest metre.
b) Toronto's CN Tower is a tourist attraction, with a height of 555 m. How many times as tall as Edmonton's CN Tower is Toronto's CN Tower?
c) Communication Edmonton's CN Tower has 27 storeys. If an office building were the height of Toronto's CN Tower, how many storeys would you expect it to have? Explain.

10. Coast guard A coast guard patrol boat is 14.8 km east of the Brier Island lighthouse. A disabled yacht is 7.5 km south of the lighthouse.
a) How far is the patrol boat from the yacht, to the nearest tenth of a kilometre?
b) At what angle south of due west, to the nearest degree, should the patrol boat travel to reach the yacht?

C

11. Highway signs A sign shows that a hill has a grade of 9%. What angle does the hill make with the horizontal, to the nearest tenth of a degree?

12. Communication a) When you are standing without shoes on, what is the height of your eyes above the ground, to the nearest centimetre?
b) Calculate the angle of depression, to the nearest degree, you would use to look at a point on the ground 5 m in front of you.
c) Would the answer to part b) be greater or less for a person taller than you? Explain.

13. Communication a) Use right triangles ABC and DEF to copy and complete the table. Leave all ratios in fraction form.

Triangle	Angle x			Angle (90° − x)		
	tan	sin	cos	tan	sin	cos
ABC						
DEF						

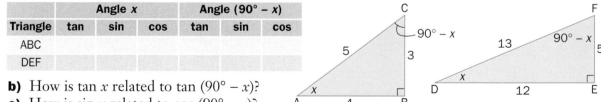

b) How is tan x related to tan (90° − x)?
c) How is sin x related to cos (90° − x)?
d) How is cos x related to sin (90° − x)?
e) Explain the relationships in parts a), b), and c).

$\mathscr{C}$areer $\mathscr{C}$onnection Industry

The word *industry* describes the production of all goods and services. Primary industries, such as iron-ore mining or logging, involve the mining or harvesting of raw materials. Secondary industries, such as car manufacturing, make finished goods from raw materials. Other industries, such as banking, dentistry, or home renovation, are known as service industries. Most Canadian workers are employed in service industries.

1. A home-renovation company installs windows in houses so that the windows receive the maximum amount of sun in the winter and the minimum amount of sun in the summer. In St. John's, Newfoundland, the angle of elevation of the sun at noon on the longest day of the year is 66°. On the shortest day of the year, the angle of elevation of the sun at noon is 19°. A house is being constructed with a window that is 2 m tall and faces south. The top of the window is 0.5 m below the overhang, as shown in the diagram.

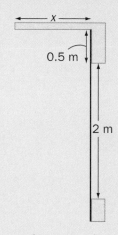

a) What length, *x*, should the company make the overhang, to the nearest tenth of a metre, so that the window receives no direct sunlight at noon on the longest day of the year?

b) Use the length you calculated in part a) to determine how much of the window will receive direct sunlight at noon on the shortest day of the year.

c) The angle of elevation of the sun at noon on the longest day of the year can be found by subtracting your latitude from 90° and adding 23.5°. The angle of elevation of the sun at noon on the shortest day of the year can be found by subtracting your latitude from 90° and subtracting 23.5°. Repeat parts a) and b) for a 2-m tall, south-facing window in your community.

2. Communication Use your research skills to describe another application of trigonometry in industry.

The historic lighthouse at Cape Spear, Newfoundland, stands on a cliff on the easternmost point of the North American continent. The lighthouse operated from 1836 to 1955. From a point 155 m offshore, the angle of elevation of the foot of the lighthouse is 26° and the angle of elevation of the top of the lighthouse is 29°.

Investigation   Use a Diagram

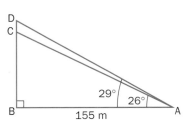

1. The diagram represents the above information. What is represented by

a) the line segment CD?

b) the line segment BC?

2. a) In △ABC, use trigonometry to write an equation that expresses BC in terms of ∠BAC and AB.

b) Calculate BC, to the nearest tenth of a metre.

3. a) In △ABD, use trigonometry to write an equation that expresses BD in terms of ∠BAD and AB.

b) Calculate BD, to the nearest tenth of a metre.

4. What is the height of the lighthouse, to the nearest tenth of a metre?

5. Communication What is the angle of depression of point A from the top of the lighthouse? Explain.

Web Connection   www.school.mcgrawhill.ca/resources/

To learn more about Canadian lighthouses, visit the above web site.
Go to **Math Resources,** then to *MATHPOWER™ 10, Ontario
Edition,* to find out where to go next. Use data for one lighthouse to
write a trigonometry problem. Have a classmate solve your problem.

Example 1   Cloud Height at Night

Many pilots flying from small airports follow visual flight rules.
Under these rules, an aircraft can take off only if the visibility is
5 km or greater, and the cloud height is 300 m or higher. Airport
managers determine the cloud height visually during the day. To
determine the cloud height at night, many small airports have a
spotlight that shines on the clouds.

The angle the light beam makes with the ground is 70°. An
observer, located on the ground 300 m from the light, measures
the angle of elevation of the point where the light shines on the
clouds. Suppose the angle of elevation of this point is 60°, and
the light and the observer are on opposite sides of the point.
Find the cloud height, to the nearest metre.

Solution

Draw and label a diagram. Let h represent the cloud height.

Mark the given data on the diagram. From the data, $\angle ADB = 30°$
and $\angle CDB = 20°$.

Since $x + y = 300$, use the two right triangles to write
equations that express x and y in terms of h.

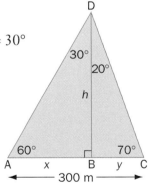

In $\triangle ABD$,

$$\frac{x}{h} = \tan 30°$$
$$x = h \tan 30°$$

But

In $\triangle BCD$,

$$\frac{y}{h} = \tan 20°$$
$$y = h \tan 20°$$

$$x + y = 300$$

so $h \tan 30° + h \tan 20° = 300$
and $h(\tan 30° + \tan 20°) = 300$

$$h = \frac{300}{\tan 30° + \tan 20°}$$
$$h \doteq 319$$

The cloud height is 319 m, to the nearest metre.

Example 2   Confederation Bridge

The Confederation Bridge spans the Northumberland Strait and joins New Brunswick and Prince Edward Island. From one point in the strait, the angle of elevation of the highest point on the bridge is 27°. From a point 100 m closer to the bridge, the angle of elevation is 73°. How high is the bridge, to the nearest metre?

Solution

Draw and label a diagram. Let h represent the height of the bridge. Mark the given data on the diagram. From the data, $\angle BAD = 63°$ and $\angle CAD = 17°$.

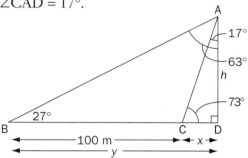

Since $y - x = 100$, use the two right triangles to write equations that express x and y in terms of h.

In $\triangle ABD$,

$$\frac{y}{h} = \tan 63°$$
$$y = h \tan 63°$$

In $\triangle ACD$,

$$\frac{x}{h} = \tan 17°$$
$$x = h \tan 17°$$

But
$$y - x = 100$$
so $h \tan 63° - h \tan 17° = 100$
and $h(\tan 63° - \tan 17°) = 100$

$$h = \frac{100}{\tan 63° - \tan 17°}$$
$$h \doteq 60$$

The height of the bridge is 60 m, to the nearest metre.

To solve a problem involving two right triangles using trigonometry,
a) draw and label a diagram showing the given information, and the length or angle measure to be found
b) identify the two triangles that can be used to solve the problem, and plan how to use each triangle
c) solve the problem and show each step in your solution
d) write a concluding statement giving the answer

Communicate Your Understanding

1. Describe how you would find the length x in each of the following diagrams.

a)

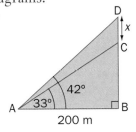

b)

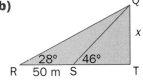

c)

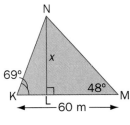

Practice

A

1. Find EF, to the nearest tenth of a metre.

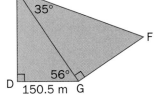

2. Find UV, to the nearest tenth of a metre.

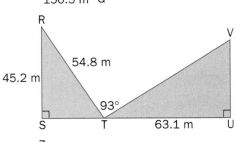

3. Find YZ, to the nearest tenth of a metre.

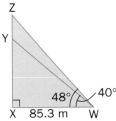

4. Find BC, to the nearest metre.

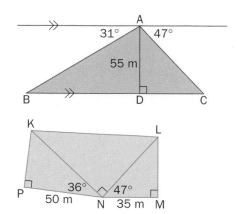

5. Find KL, to the nearest metre.

6. Find PQ, to the nearest metre.

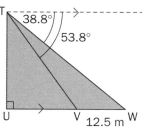

7. Find RS, to the nearest metre.

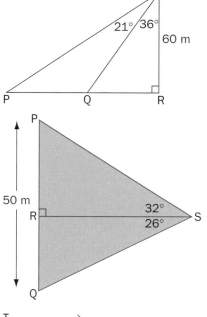

8. Find TU, to the nearest tenth of a metre.

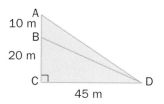

9. Find the measure of ∠ADB, to the nearest degree.

10. Find the measure of ∠WXZ, to the nearest tenth of a degree.

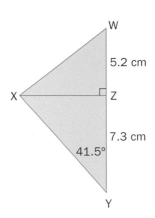

Applications and Problem Solving

B

11. Height of a building From the window of one building, Sam finds the angle of elevation of the top of a second building is 41° and the angle of depression of the bottom is 54°. The buildings are 56 m apart. Find, to the nearest metre,
a) the height of the second building
b) the height Sam is above the ground

12. Horseshoe Falls From the bridge of a boat on the Niagara River, the angle of elevation of the top of the Horseshoe Falls is 64°. The angle of depression of the bottom of the Falls is 6°. If the bridge of the boat is 2.8 m above the water, calculate the height of the Horseshoe Falls, to the nearest tenth of a metre.

13. Capilano Suspension Bridge The Capilano Suspension Bridge in North Vancouver is the world's highest footbridge of its kind. The bridge is 140 m long. From the ends of the bridge, the angles of depression of a point on the river under the bridge are 41° and 48°. How high is the bridge above the river, to the nearest metre?

14. Surveying A surveyor uses an instrument called a theodolite to measure angles vertically and horizontally. To measure the height of an inaccessible cliff, a surveyor sets up the theodolite at E and measures ∠DEF to be 56.7°. Then, the baseline EG is laid off perpendicular to EF. The length of EG is 74.6 m, and ∠EGF measures 49.1°.
a) Find DF, to the nearest tenth of a metre.
b) If the theodolite is 1.6 m tall, what is the height of the cliff?

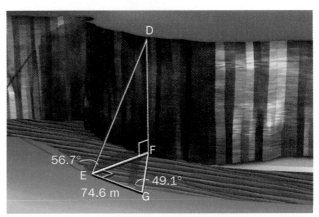

15. Whooping crane The whooping crane is Canada's tallest bird. When the angle of elevation of the sun decreases from 30° to 25°, the length of a whooping crane's shadow increases by 62 cm. How tall is the whooping crane, to the nearest centimetre?

16. Lovett Lookout In heavily forested areas, a fire-watch system is usually maintained during dry periods. The system consists of a chain of lookout towers, often supplemented by small aircraft and by satellite photographs. The system is linked by radio to a central office, which can dispatch fire fighting crews. Lovett Lookout is in Northern Alberta and has a height of 24 m. From the top of the lookout, a ranger sees two fires. One is at an angle of depression of 6° and the other at an angle of depression of 4°. The fires and the tower are in a straight line. Find the distance between the fires, to the nearest metre, if they are
a) on the same side of the tower
b) on opposite sides of the tower

17. Pont du Gard aqueduct The Pont du Gard is an aqueduct that crosses the River Gard near Nîmes in France. From one point on the river, the angle of elevation of the top of the aqueduct is 43.6°. From a point 30 m farther away from the aqueduct, the angle of elevation is 31.2°. Find the height of the aqueduct, to the nearest metre.

C

18. Aircraft speed An Airbus A320 aircraft is cruising at an altitude of 10 000 m. The aircraft is flying in a straight line away from Chandra, who is standing on the ground. If she sees the angle of elevation of the aircraft change from 70° to 33° in one minute, what is its cruising speed, to the nearest kilometre per hour?

19. Pendulum When a pendulum swings 40° from the vertical, the bob moves 20 cm horizontally and 7.3 cm vertically. What is the length of the pendulum, to the nearest centimetre?

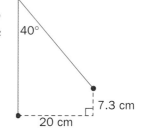

20. Measurement In a regular octagon, AB is a diagonal and CD joins the midpoints of two opposite sides. The side length of the octagon is 4 cm. To the nearest tenth of a centimetre, find
a) AB   **b)** CD

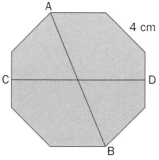

21. Communication Write a problem that involves the use of two right triangles. Have a classmate solve your problem.

The Canadian Space Agency governs the Space Science Program. Space science includes five major areas of study: space life sciences, solar-terrestrial relations, atmospheric sciences, space astronomy, and microgravity sciences. The information gathered by satellites is an important part of space science research.

1. The angle of elevation of an orbiting satellite from tracking station Alpha is 67° and from tracking station Bravo is 58°. The two tracking stations are 1700 km apart on Earth.
a) What is the height of the satellite, to the nearest kilometre, if it is in position S_1?
b) What is the height of the satellite, to the nearest kilometre, if it is in position S_2?
c) Communication What assumptions have you made?

S_2 S_1

Bravo   Alpha

2. Communication Use your research skills to describe another application of trigonometry in science.

Modelling Math   Measuring Inaccessible Heights and Widths

Determine the height of an inaccessible object around your school. The bottom of the object should be well above the height of your head, so that you cannot measure the height of the top or the bottom of the object. Measure the angle of elevation of the top of the object, and the angle of elevation of the bottom of the object, from a point that is a known distance horizontally from the bottom of the object. Then, use your knowledge of how to solve problems involving two right triangles to find the height of the inaccessible object. Suggest ways in which you could make the calculated height more accurate.

Achievement Check
1 2 3 4

At the bottom of a ski lift, there are two vertical poles. One is 15 m tall, and the other is 10 m tall. The ground between the poles is level, and the bases of the poles are 8 m apart. The poles are connected by two straight wires. Each wire runs from the top of one pole to the bottom of the other.
a) What angle does each wire make with the ground?
b) How high above the ground do the wires intersect, to the nearest tenth of a metre? Explain and justify your reasoning.

1 Angle Measures and Side Lengths

In this investigation, you will determine the relationship between the measures of angles and the lengths of sides in acute triangles.

1. Construct any acute triangle ABC.

2. Measure the lengths of the sides and the degree measures of the angles.

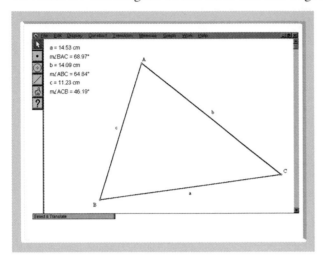

3. **a)** Which side is the longest?
b) Which angle is the largest?
c) Where are the longest side and the largest angle located with respect to each other in the triangle?

4. **a)** Which side is the shortest?
b) Which angle is the smallest?
c) Where are the shortest side and the smallest angle located with respect to each other in the triangle?

5. Drag one of the vertex points of the triangle so that a different side is the longest and a different side is the shortest.
a) Where are the longest side and the largest angle located with respect to each other in the triangle?
b) Where are the shortest side and the smallest angle located with respect to each other in the triangle?
c) Compare your answers to parts a) and b) with your answers to questions 3c) and 4c).

6. **Communication** Write a statement summarizing the relationships you have found for side lengths and angle measures in acute triangles.

2 Ratios of Side Lengths and Sines of Opposite Angles

In this investigation, you will determine the relationship between the ratio of side lengths and the ratio of the sines of their opposite angles in acute triangles.

1. Construct any acute triangle ABC.

2. Measure the lengths of the three sides and the measures of the three angles.

3. a) For any two of the sides, choose the Calculate command from the Measure menu to calculate the ratio of their lengths, as described in question 10 on page 317.
b) Using the same feature, calculate the ratio of the sines of the angles that are opposite the sides you used in part a). You will need to choose the sin[x] command from the Functions pop-up menu in the calculator dialog box. Be sure to put the sines of the opposite angles in the same order you used for the sides in part a).

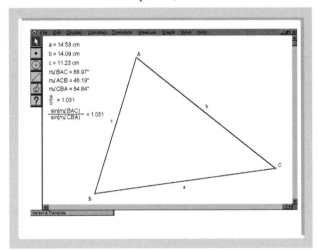

c) What do you notice about the two ratios?

4. Select a different pair of sides and their opposite angles. Repeat question 3. Do you get the same result as you did in question 3c)?

5. If any of the vertices of the acute triangle are dragged to a new location, is the relationship preserved?

6. Communication Write a statement summarizing the relationship you have found between the ratio of side lengths and the ratio of the sines of their opposite angles in acute triangles.

7. Do you get the same results if you use the cosine ratio instead of the sine ratio?

8. Do you get the same results if you use the tangent ratio instead of the sine ratio?

The Joint Astronomy Centre operates two telescopes on the summit of Mauna Kea in Hawaii. They are the United Kingdom Infrared Telescope and the James Clerk Maxwell Telescope. Canada, the Netherlands, and the United Kingdom share the use and the costs of the telescopes.

Investigation   Interpret the Diagram

The classical way to find the height of a mountain uses a theodolite, which measures horizontal and vertical angles.

To find the height of Mauna Kea, a surveyor finds the length of a baseline AB. A and B are at the same altitude, and, in this case, AB is 6 km. C is the summit of the mountain. D is directly below the summit and is at the same altitude as A and B.

Standing at A, the surveyor points the theodolite at B and then at C. In this case, the theodolite gives the horizontal angle BAD as 42° and the angle of elevation CAD as 33°.

Standing at B, the surveyor points the theodolite at A and then at C. In this case, the theodolite gives the horizontal angle ABD as 53° and the angle of elevation CBD as 37.8°.

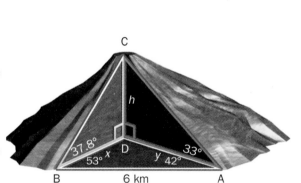

1. Communication Why are △CDA and △CDB right triangles?

2. A triangle that is not right-angled is either acute or obtuse. Is △ABD right-angled, acute, or obtuse?

3. Communication In △ABD, is each of the following lengths greater than, less than, or equal to the length AB? Explain.
a) length x **b)** length y

4. Communication How could the height h be calculated
a) if the length x was known?
b) if the length y was known?

In an acute triangle, when two angles and a side are given, the other sides can be found using the sine law, which can be developed as follows.

In △ABC, draw AD perpendicular to BC. AD is the altitude or height, h, of △ABC.

In △ABD, $\dfrac{h}{c} = \sin B$ 　　 In △ACD, $\dfrac{h}{b} = \sin C$

$h = c \sin B$ 　　　　　　 $h = b \sin C$

Then, 　　　　 $c \sin B = b \sin C$

Divide both sides by bc: 　$\dfrac{c \sin B}{bc} = \dfrac{b \sin C}{bc}$

Simplify: 　　　　　 $\dfrac{\sin B}{b} = \dfrac{\sin C}{c}$

Drawing the altitude from C and repeating the steps gives $\dfrac{\sin A}{a} = \dfrac{\sin B}{b}$.

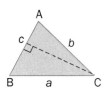

Combining the results gives two forms of the sine law.

$$\frac{\sin A}{a} = \frac{\sin B}{b} = \frac{\sin C}{c} \quad \text{or} \quad \frac{a}{\sin A} = \frac{b}{\sin B} = \frac{c}{\sin C}$$

Example 1　　Two Angles and a Side

In △RST, ∠S = 83°, $r = 53$ m, and ∠T = 26°. Solve the triangle. Round each side length to the nearest metre.

Solution

First, determine the measure of ∠R.

∠R = 180° − 83° − 26°

　　 = 71°

Use the sine law to find s and t.

$$\frac{s}{\sin S} = \frac{r}{\sin R}$$

$$\frac{s}{\sin 83°} = \frac{53}{\sin 71°}$$

$$s = \frac{53 \sin 83°}{\sin 71°}$$

$$s \doteq 56$$

$$\frac{t}{\sin T} = \frac{r}{\sin R}$$

$$\frac{t}{\sin 26°} = \frac{53}{\sin 71°}$$

$$t = \frac{53 \sin 26°}{\sin 71°}$$

$$t \doteq 25$$

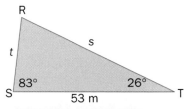

In △RST, ∠R = 71°, $s = 56$ m, and $t = 25$ m.

Example 2   Two Sides and an Opposite Angle

In acute $\triangle DEF$, $\angle F = 35°$, $f = 42$ m, and $d = 64$ m.
Solve the triangle. Round each length to the nearest metre
and each angle measure to the nearest degree.

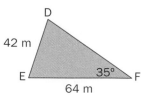

42 m

E   35°   F

64 m

D

Solution

Use the sine law to find the measure of $\angle D$.

$$\frac{\sin D}{d} = \frac{\sin F}{f}$$

$$\frac{\sin D}{64} = \frac{\sin 35°}{42}$$

$$\sin D = \frac{64 \sin 35°}{42}$$

$$\angle D \doteq 61°$$

GRAPHING CALCULATOR
64sin(35)/42
        .8740212363
sin⁻¹(Ans)
        60.92935008

*Ans in the calculator display
indicates the last answer. To
include the last answer at the
cursor location, press the 2nd
key and then the (−) key.*

Determine the measure of $\angle E$.

$$\angle E = 180° - 35° - 61°$$
$$= 84°$$

Use the sine law to find e.

$$\frac{e}{\sin E} = \frac{f}{\sin F}$$

$$\frac{e}{\sin 84°} = \frac{42}{\sin 35°}$$

$$e = \frac{42 \sin 84°}{\sin 35°}$$

$$e \doteq 73$$

GRAPHING CALCULATOR
42sin(84)/sin(35
)
        72.82363249

In $\triangle DEF$, $\angle D = 61°$, $\angle E = 84°$, and $e = 73$ m.

Example 3   Height of Mauna Kea

The diagram shows the measurements a surveyor
used to calculate the height of Mauna Kea.
a) Find h, to the nearest metre.
b) If the elevation of A, B, and D is 1077 m,
what is the height of Mauna Kea?

Solution

a) Find the measure of $\angle BDA$.

$$\angle BDA = 180° - 53° - 42°$$
$$= 85°$$

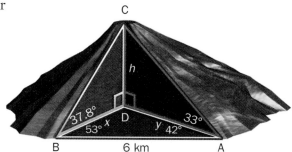

C

h

37.8°

53° x   D   y 42°

33°

B   6 km   A

Use the sine law to find y.

$$\frac{y}{\sin DBA} = \frac{AB}{\sin BDA}$$

$$\frac{y}{\sin 53°} = \frac{6000}{\sin 85°}$$

$$y = \frac{6000 \sin 53°}{\sin 85°}$$

$$\doteq 4810$$

In $\triangle ACD$, $\dfrac{h}{4810} = \tan 33°$

$$h = 4810 \tan 33°$$

$$\doteq 3124$$

So, h is 3124 m, to the nearest metre.

b) Since the elevation of A, B, and D is 1077 m, the height of Mauna Kea is 3124 + 1077, or 4201 m.

Key CONCEPTS

1 There are two forms of the sine law.

$$\frac{a}{\sin A} = \frac{b}{\sin B} = \frac{c}{\sin C} \quad \text{or} \quad \frac{\sin A}{a} = \frac{\sin B}{b} = \frac{\sin C}{c}$$

2 The sine law can be used to solve an acute triangle when given:
a) the measures of two angles and any side
b) the measures of two sides and an angle opposite one of these sides

Communicate Your Understanding

1. Explain what it means to solve an acute triangle.

2. Describe how you would solve acute $\triangle ABC$.

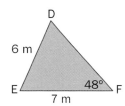

3. Describe how you would solve acute $\triangle DEF$.

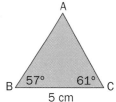

Practice

A

1. Find the length of the indicated side, to the nearest metre.

a)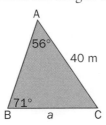

b)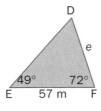

c)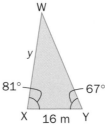

2. For each of the following acute triangles, find the measure of the indicated angle, to the nearest degree.

a)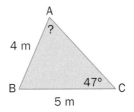

b)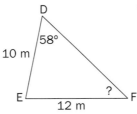

c)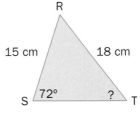

3. Find the indicated quantity, to the nearest tenth.
a) In $\triangle ABC$, $\angle B = 38.2°$, $\angle C = 65.6°$, and $b = 54$ cm. Find c.
b) In $\triangle DEF$, $\angle D = 71.5°$, $d = 7.4$ m, and $\angle E = 30.2°$. Find f.
c) In $\triangle GHK$, $\angle G = 44.1°$, $k = 9.5$ cm, and $\angle H = 78.4°$. Find h.
d) In acute $\triangle RST$, $\angle T = 56.5°$, $t = 8.2$ m, $r = 9.3$ m. Find $\angle R$.
e) In acute $\triangle JKL$, $\angle K = 64.3°$, $k = 22$ cm, $l = 19$ cm. Find $\angle L$.
f) In acute $\triangle PQR$, $\angle Q = 53.7°$, $q = 35$ m, $r = 28$ m. Find $\angle P$.

4. Solve each of the following triangles. Round each answer to the nearest whole number, if necessary.

a)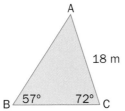

b)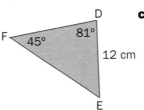

c)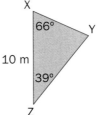

5. Solve each of the following acute triangles. Round each answer to the nearest whole number, if necessary.

a)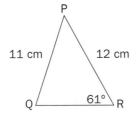

b)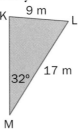

c)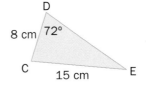

Applications and Problem Solving

6. Inaccessible cliff To measure the height, AB, of an inaccessible cliff, a surveyor records the data shown. Find the height of the cliff, to the nearest metre.

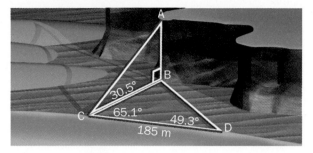

7. Measurement Find the perimeter of isosceles △RST, to the nearest centimetre.

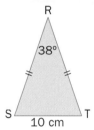

8. Surveying A field is in the shape of a triangle. Label the triangle ABC. A surveyor determines that the length of side AB is 620 m. Using a theodolite, the surveyor finds that ∠A is 56.8° and ∠B is 60.4°. Find the perimeter of the field, to the nearest metre.

9. Measurement In △ABC, ∠B = 51°, ∠C = 63°, and a = 80 m.
a) Find c, to the nearest metre.
b) Draw an altitude to BC from A.
c) Find the length of the altitude, h, to the nearest metre.
d) Calculate the area of the triangle, to the nearest square metre.

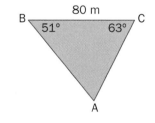

10. Measurement The longest side of a triangle is 50 cm. The measures of two angles in the triangle are 42° and 64°. Find the lengths of the other two sides, to the nearest centimetre.

11. Communication Use the sine law to explain why the two equal sides of an isosceles triangle must be opposite the two equal angles.

12. Communication a) Use the sine law to find x, to the nearest tenth.
b) Use the sine ratio to find x, to the nearest tenth.
c) Explain why the two methods are equivalent in a right triangle.

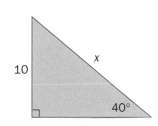

13. Ferry crossings Two hotels are located on the same side of a river. The hotels are on the bank of the river and are 400 m apart. Across the river is the dock for two ferries to bring tourists to the hotels. The angles made by the riverbank and the lines drawn from the hotels to the dock, D, are shown.

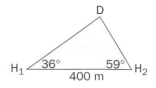

a) How far is each hotel from the dock, to the nearest metre?
b) What is the width of this part of the river, to the nearest metre?

14. Heron's formula A surveyor recorded the data shown for the triangular plot of land ABC.

a) Heron's formula states that the area of a triangle is given

by $\text{Area} = \sqrt{s(s-a)(s-b)(s-c)}$

where the semiperimeter, $s = \dfrac{1}{2}(a + b + c)$.

Use Heron's formula to find the area of the plot of land, to the nearest square metre.

b) Communication Use a different method to determine the area of the plot of land. Explain and justify your reasoning.

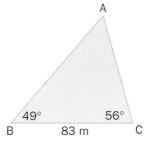

Modelling Math | Measuring Inaccessible Heights and Widths

As described on page 313, the diagram shows the measurements that a surveyor made to find the height of Mount Robson above sea level. The points A, B, and C are all at the same elevation, 1200 m. The summit of the mountain is represented by R, and the point C is directly below R. What is the height of Mount Robson, to the nearest metre?

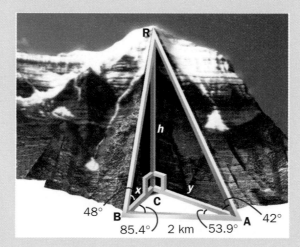

Investigation | Use the Diagram

Around 700 B.C., engineers on the Greek island of Sámos constructed a tunnel through Mount Kastron to bring water from one side of the mountain to a city on the other side. This feat was amazing because the digging teams started at opposite ends and met at the centre, with only a small error.

A way for a surveyor to find the length of the tunnel, XY, is to select a point Z and measure ∠Z and the lengths x and y.

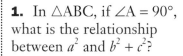

1. In △ABC, if ∠A = 90°, what is the relationship between a^2 and $b^2 + c^2$?

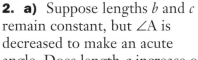

2. a) Suppose lengths b and c remain constant, but ∠A is decreased to make an acute angle. Does length a increase or decrease?
b) What is the relationship between a^2 and $b^2 + c^2$ when ∠A is acute?

3. a) Suppose lengths b and c remain constant, but ∠A is increased to make an obtuse angle. Does length a increase or decrease?
b) What is the relationship between a^2 and $b^2 + c^2$ when ∠A is obtuse?

4. A surveyor examining the tunnel through Mount Kastron selected a point 5000 m from one end of the tunnel and 5500 m from the other end.

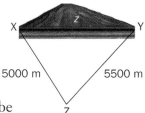

a) If ∠Z was 90°, what would be the length of the tunnel, to the nearest metre?
b) The surveyor found that ∠Z was actually 10°. Is the length of the tunnel greater than or less than the length you found in part a)?
c) Estimate the length of the tunnel.

5. Communication Can you use the sine law to find the actual length of the tunnel? Explain.

Some acute triangles that cannot be solved using the sine law can be solved using the cosine law, which can be developed as follows.

In $\triangle ABC$, draw CD perpendicular to AB.
CD is the altitude, h, of $\triangle ABC$.
Let AD $= x$.
Then, BD $= c - x$.

In $\triangle ACD$, $b^2 = h^2 + x^2$

and $\dfrac{x}{b} = \cos A$

$\quad x = b \cos A$

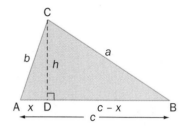

In $\triangle BCD$, $a^2 = h^2 + (c - x)^2$
Expand: $\qquad = h^2 + c^2 - 2cx + x^2$
Rearrange: $\quad\ = c^2 + (h^2 + x^2) - 2cx$

Substituting b^2 for $(h^2 + x^2)$ and $b \cos A$ for x gives
$$a^2 = c^2 + b^2 - 2c(b \cos A)$$
$$= c^2 + b^2 - 2cb \cos A$$
$$= b^2 + c^2 - 2bc \cos A$$

Deriving similar equations that include cos B and cos C gives three forms of the cosine law.
$$a^2 = b^2 + c^2 - 2bc \cos A$$
$$b^2 = a^2 + c^2 - 2ac \cos B$$
$$c^2 = a^2 + b^2 - 2ab \cos C$$

Example 1   Given Two Sides and the Contained Angle
In $\triangle ABC$, $\angle B = 42°$, $a = 52$ m, and $c = 36$ m.
Find b, to the nearest metre.

Solution
Use the cosine law.
$$b^2 = a^2 + c^2 - 2ac \cos B$$
$$= 52^2 + 36^2 - 2(52)(36) \cos 42°$$
$$b \doteq 35$$

The length b is 35 m, to the nearest metre.

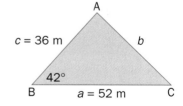

The cosine law can also be used to find the measure of an angle of a triangle when the lengths of the three sides are known. To do this, the formula can be solved for the cosine value.

$$a^2 = b^2 + c^2 - 2bc \cos A$$

Rearrange:

$$2bc \cos A = b^2 + c^2 - a^2$$

Divide both sides by $2bc$:

$$\cos A = \frac{b^2 + c^2 - a^2}{2bc}$$

Similarly

$$\cos B = \frac{a^2 + c^2 - b^2}{2ac}$$

and

$$\cos C = \frac{a^2 + b^2 - c^2}{2ab}$$

Example 2   Given Three Sides

In $\triangle DEF$, $d = 62$ cm, $e = 51$ cm, and $f = 48$ cm.
Find each angle of the triangle, to the nearest degree.

Solution

Use the cosine law to find $\angle F$.

$$\cos F = \frac{d^2 + e^2 - f^2}{2de}$$
$$= \frac{62^2 + 51^2 - 48^2}{2(62)(51)}$$
$$\angle F \doteq 49°$$

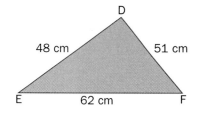

Use the cosine law or the sine law to find $\angle D$.

Using the cosine law,

$$\cos D = \frac{e^2 + f^2 - d^2}{2ef}$$
$$= \frac{51^2 + 48^2 - 62^2}{2(51)(48)}$$
$$\angle D \doteq 77°$$

Using the sine law,

$$\frac{\sin D}{d} = \frac{\sin F}{f}$$
$$\frac{\sin D}{62} = \frac{\sin 49°}{48}$$
$$\sin D = \frac{62 \sin 49°}{48}$$
$$\angle D \doteq 77°$$

$$\angle E = 180° - 49° - 77°$$
$$= 54°$$

In $\triangle DEF$, $\angle D = 77°$, $\angle E = 54°$, and $\angle F = 49°$, to the nearest degree.

Example 3   Solving a Triangle

In △RST, ∠R = 72°, s = 12 m, and t = 10 m. Solve the triangle. Round each answer to the nearest whole number, if necessary.

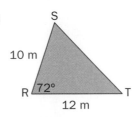

Solution

Use the cosine law to find r.

$r^2 = s^2 + t^2 - 2st \cos R$

$\quad = 12^2 + 10^2 - 2(12)(10)(\cos 72°)$

$r \doteq 13$

Use the sine law to find ∠T.

$\dfrac{\sin T}{t} = \dfrac{\sin R}{r}$

$\dfrac{\sin T}{10} = \dfrac{\sin 72°}{13}$

$\sin T = \dfrac{10 \sin 72°}{13}$

$\angle T \doteq 47°$

$\angle S = 180° - 72° - 47°$

$\quad = 61°$

In △RST, r = 13 m, ∠T = 47°, and ∠S = 61°.

Example 4   Tunnel Through Mount Kastron

Find the length of the tunnel, XY, to the nearest metre.

Solution

Use the cosine law to find z.

$z^2 = x^2 + y^2 - 2xy \cos Z$

$\quad = 5500^2 + 5000^2 - 2(5500)(5000) \cos 10°$

$z \doteq 1042$

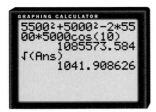

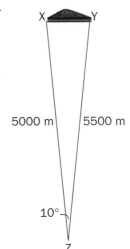

The tunnel is 1042 m long, to the nearest metre.

1 There are two forms of the cosine law.

$$a^2 = b^2 + c^2 - 2bc \cos A \quad \text{or} \quad \cos A = \frac{b^2 + c^2 - a^2}{2bc}$$

2 The cosine law can be used to solve an acute triangle when given:
a) the measures of two sides and the contained angle
b) the measures of three sides

Communicate Your Understanding

1. Describe how you would solve acute △ABC.

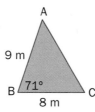

2. Describe how you would solve acute △DEF.

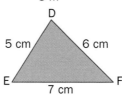

3. When solving a triangle, describe the conditions under which
a) the sine law is used to find the first measurement
b) the cosine law is used to find the first measurement

Practice

A

1. Find the missing side length, to the nearest tenth of a unit.

a)

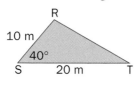

b)

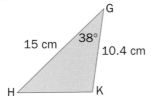

2. Find the indicated angle, to the nearest degree.

a)

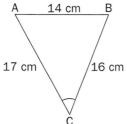

b)

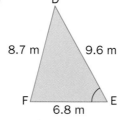

3. Find the indicated quantity, to the nearest tenth of a unit.
a) In $\triangle PQR$, $p = 15.3$ m, $q = 18.2$ m, and $\angle R = 70.5°$. Find r.
b) In $\triangle UVW$, $u = 10.3$ cm, $v = 11.4$ cm, and $w = 12.5$ cm. Find $\angle V$.
c) In $\triangle BCD$, $b = 10.8$ cm, $c = 22.1$ cm, and $d = 22.1$ cm. Find $\angle B$.
d) In $\triangle KLM$, $k = 36.5$ m, $m = 51.4$ m, and $\angle L = 72.1°$. Find l.

4. Solve each triangle. Round each calculated value to the nearest tenth of a unit, if necessary.

a)

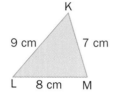

b)

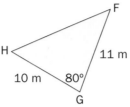

c) In $\triangle IJK$, $i = 10.5$ m, $j = 11.8$ m, and $k = 12.5$ m.
d) In $\triangle TUW$, $w = 25.4$ cm, $u = 34.2$ cm, and $\angle T = 43.1°$.

Applications and Problem Solving

5. Space shuttle The tops of the solid rocket boosters used to launch the space shuttle are cones of diameter 3.7 m and slant height 5.4 m. Find the angle that the curved surface of the cone makes with a diameter, to the nearest tenth of a degree.

6. Navigation Two ships left Parry Sound and sailed into Georgian Bay at the same time. One travelled at 16 km/h on a course of 277°. The other travelled at 14 km/h on a course of 230°. How far apart were the ships after two hours, to the nearest tenth of a kilometre?

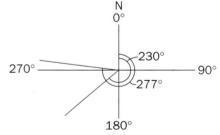

7. Triathlon The three phases of a triathlon involve swimming, cycling, and running, in that order. The distances for each phase can vary. For a triathlon held in Hawaii each year, competitors swim in the ocean, bicycle 112 km, and run 41.8 km. In the diagram, S is the start of the swim, and F is the finish. A surveyor used the dimensions shown to calculate the length SF across the bay.
a) Find the distance the athletes swim in the Hawaiian triathlon, to the nearest metre.
b) Communication What assumptions have you made?

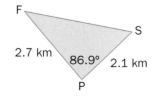

8. Measurement Given the side lengths in △RST, find the area of the triangle, to the nearest square metre.

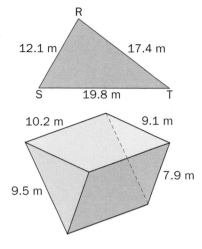

9. Measurement Find the volume of the right prism, to the nearest cubic metre.

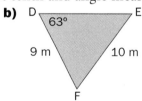

10. Measurement In △ABC, $a = 32$ cm, $b = 35$ cm, and $c = 29$ cm. Find the measure of the largest angle, to the nearest degree.

11. Communication Explain whether you can use the sine law to find p in △PQR when given $\angle P = 47°$, $q = 9$ m, and $r = 11$ m.

12. Communication Explain whether you can use the cosine law to find r in △RST when given $\angle T = 53°$, $t = 15$ m, and $s = 14$ m.

13. Sine or cosine law Determine whether the sine law or the cosine law should be used first to solve each triangle. Then, solve the triangle. Round side lengths to the nearest tenth and angle measures to the nearest degree.

a)

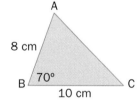

b)

c)

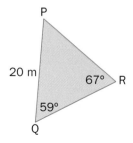

d)

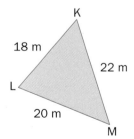

14. Coordinate geometry Solve △ABC with vertices A(2, 1), B(7, 4), and C(1, 5). Round each calculated value to the nearest tenth of a unit.

15. Communication The Pythagorean Theorem can be thought of as a special case of the cosine law. Explain why.

16. Algebra Use the cosine law to show that each angle of an equilateral triangle must measure 60°.

17. Communication Try to solve a triangle with side lengths 3 cm, 8 cm, and 4 cm using the cosine law. What do you find? Explain why.

Achievement Check

1 2 3 4

△ABC represents a plot of land.
a) List all of the possible unknown quantities that you could be required to determine for this plot of land.
b) If you were a surveyor, and you had to determine all of the unknown quantities you listed, which ones would you measure and which ones would you calculate? Explain and justify your reasoning.

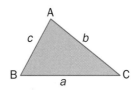

PATTERN POWER

In diagram 1, there is one $1 \times 1 \times 1$ cube, so the total number of cubes is 1. In diagram 2, there are eight $1 \times 1 \times 1$ cubes and one $2 \times 2 \times 2$ cube, so the total number of cubes is 9.

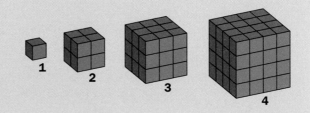

1. What is the total number of cubes in
a) diagram 3?   **b)** diagram 4?

2. Communication Describe the pattern in the total numbers of cubes.

3. Use the pattern to predict the total number of cubes in
a) diagram 5   **b)** diagram 6

Technology Extension: Graphing Calculator Programs

1 The Sine Law

The graphing calculator program shows how to calculate
the length of a side of a triangle using the sine law.
A is the unknown side length.
B is the given length.
X is the measure of the angle opposite B.
Y is the measure of the angle opposite A.

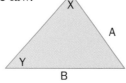

PROGRAM:SINES
:ClrHome
:Prompt B,X,Y
:Bsin(Y)/sin(X)→A
:Disp A

1. Communication Describe what each line of the program does.

2. Using the **PRGM NEW menu**, enter the program into your graphing calculator.
Using the **PRGM EXEC menu**, execute the program to find the unknown side
length, A, in each of the following triangles, to the nearest tenth of a unit.

a)

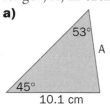

b)

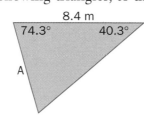

2 The Cosine Law

The graphing calculator program shows how to calculate
the length of a side of a triangle using
the cosine law.
A is the unknown side length.
B and C are the given side lengths.
X is the measure of the contained
angle, opposite side A.

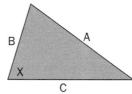

PROGRAM:COSINES
:ClrHome
:Prompt B,C,X
:√(B^2+C^2−2BCcos(X))→A
:Disp A

1. Communication Describe what each line of the program does.

2. Using the **PRGM NEW menu**, enter the program into your graphing calculator.
Using the **PRGM EXEC menu**, execute the program to find the unknown side
length, A, in each of the following triangles, to the nearest tenth of a unit.

a)

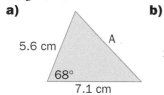

b)

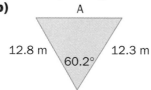

3. Suppose that side lengths A, B, and C are given, but angle measure X is unknown.
a) Modify the program to find the unknown angle measure, X.
b) Check that your program gives the correct angle measures in a triangle with side lengths
of 10.8 m, 11.4 m, and 12.5 m.

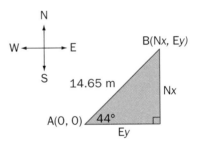

Rich Problem

An Archaeological Site

When archaeologists begin an excavation at a new site, they place a main stake as a reference point and establish a baseline. The baseline usually runs north-south, but sometimes it must be adjusted to fit the constraints of the location. Once the main stake at (0, 0) and the baseline are established, points in the dig can be described as ordered pairs that involve directions.

Many distances between points cannot be measured directly because of the topography or because objects, such as trees or boulders, are in the way. In these cases, archaeologists measure angles and distances with a transit and then use trigonometric ratios to determine the distances.

For example, the coordinates of point B can be determined as follows, to the nearest hundredth.

$$\sin 44° = \frac{Nx}{14.65}$$
$$Nx = 14.65 \sin 44°$$
$$\doteq 10.18$$

$$\cos 44° = \frac{Ey}{14.65}$$
$$Ey = 14.65 \cos 44°$$
$$\doteq 10.54$$

The coordinates of B are (N10.18, E10.54), to the nearest hundredth.

When the ground is not flat, archaeologists determine angles of elevation and unknown distances with a stadia rod and a transit. Horizontal distances can then be calculated. Note that measurements made with the transit take into account the height of the instrument.

For example, the westerly distance of C from A(0, 0) can be found, to the nearest hundredth of a metre, as follows.

$$\cos 4.2° = \frac{AB}{50.70}$$
$$AB = 50.70 \cos 4.2°$$
$$\doteq 50.56$$

Therefore, the westerly distance of C from A(0, 0) is 50.56 m, to the nearest hundredth of a metre.

The coordinates of C are (0, W50.56).

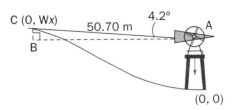

1 Discovery Harbour

Gina is an archaeology student working on a dig at Discovery Harbour. Use her sketch map to determine the coordinates of the stakes at points B, C, D, E, and F, to the nearest hundredth. This part of the site is flat.

Web Connection www.school.mcgrawhill.ca/resources/

Visit the above web site to learn about a Canadian archaeological site. Go to **Math Resources,** then to *MATHPOWER™ 10, Ontario Edition,* to find out where to go next. Write a short description of a Canadian archaeological site and what it shows about Canadian history.

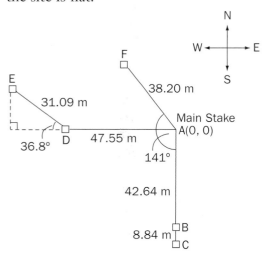

2 The Bayfield Complex

In another part of the site, the land slopes up uniformly at a 5.5° angle from south to north. Gina's team found an artifact at a location that they marked as point G on their sketch plan. Use the plan to determine the coordinates of G, to the nearest hundredth. Explain and justify your reasoning.

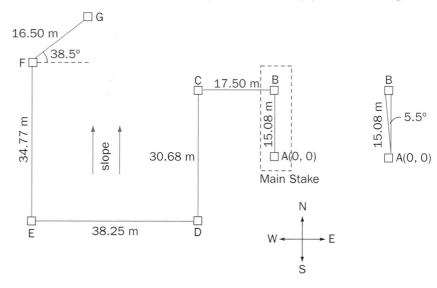

6.1–6.2 Similar Triangles

Refer to the Key Concepts on page 322.

$\triangle ABC \sim \triangle DEF$. The area of $\triangle ABC$ is 15 m^2.
To find the length d, use the equal ratios of corresponding sides.

$$\frac{c}{f} = \frac{a}{d}$$
$$\frac{5}{8} = \frac{7}{d}$$
$$d \times 5 = 8 \times 7$$
$$5d = 56$$
$$d = 11.2$$

The length d is 11.2 m.

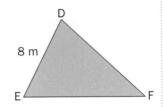

To find the area of $\triangle DEF$, use the equal
ratios of the squares of corresponding sides.

$$\frac{\text{area}\,\triangle ABC}{\text{area}\,\triangle DEF} = \frac{5^2}{8^2}$$

Let the area of $\triangle DEF$ be x.

$$\frac{15}{x} = \frac{25}{64}$$
$$64 \times 15 = x \times 25$$
$$960 = 25x$$
$$38.4 = x$$

The area of $\triangle DEF$ is 38.4 m^2.

1. The pairs of triangles are similar. Find the unknown side lengths.

a)

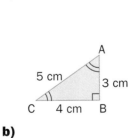

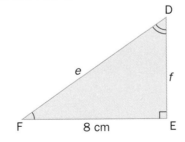

b)

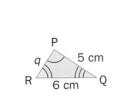

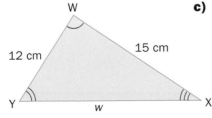

c)

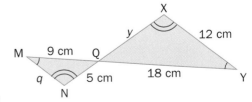

2. Surveying Use the dimensions of the surveyors' triangles to find the width of the river, to the nearest metre.

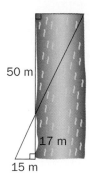

50 m

17 m

15 m

3. $\triangle PQR \sim \triangle KLM$. $PQ = 4$ cm and $KL = 6$ cm. The area of $\triangle PQR$ is 12 cm². Find the area of $\triangle KLM$.

Q · R
4 cm
x
P

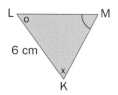

L · M
6 cm
x
K

6.3 The Tangent Ratio

Refer to the Key Concepts on page 330.

To calculate the measure of $\angle Z$, to the nearest degree, use the tangent ratio.

$\tan Z = \dfrac{3}{8}$

$\angle Z \doteq 21°$

$\angle Z$ is 21°, to the nearest degree.

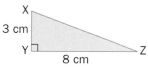

X
3 cm
Y
8 cm
Z

To calculate the length q, to the nearest tenth of a metre, use the tangent ratio.

$\tan 48° = \dfrac{q}{20}$

$20 \tan 48° = q$

$22.2 \doteq q$

The length q is 22.2 m, to the nearest tenth of a metre.

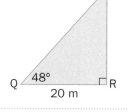

P
48°
Q
20 m
R

4. Find the measure of $\angle A$, to the nearest degree.

a)

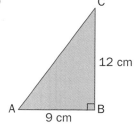

C
12 cm
A
9 cm
B

b)

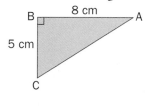

B
8 cm
A
5 cm
C

5. Find x, to the nearest tenth of a centimetre.

a)

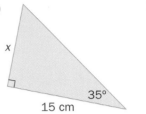

15 cm, 35°, x

b)

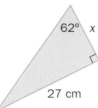

62° x, 27 cm

6. One Canada Square The tallest building in London, England, has the address "One Canada Square." From a point on the ground 70 m from the foot of the building, the angle of elevation of the top of the building is 74°. Find the height of the building, to the nearest metre.

6.4 The Sine Ratio

Refer to the Key Concepts on page 337.

To calculate the measure of ∠B, to the nearest degree, use the sine ratio.

$$\sin B = \frac{7}{16}$$

$$\angle B \doteq 26°$$

∠B is 26°, to the nearest degree.

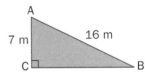

To calculate the length f, to the nearest tenth of a metre, use the sine ratio.

$$\sin 36° = \frac{f}{15}$$
$$15 \sin 36° = f$$
$$8.8 \doteq f$$

The length f is 8.8 m, to the nearest tenth of a metre.

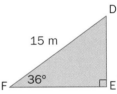

7. Find the measure of ∠D, to the nearest degree.

a)

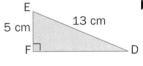

E, 5 cm, 13 cm, F, D

b)

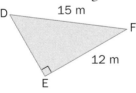

D, 15 m, F, 12 m, E

8. Find x, to the nearest tenth of a metre.

a)

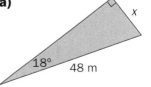

x, 18°, 48 m

b)

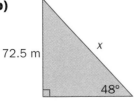

72.5 m, x, 48°

6.5 The Cosine Ratio

Refer to the Key Concepts on page 343.

To calculate the measure of ∠D, to the nearest degree, use the cosine ratio.

$$\cos D = \frac{8}{15}$$

$$\angle D \doteq 58°$$

∠D is 58°, to the nearest degree.

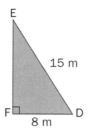

To calculate the length c, to the nearest tenth of a metre, use the cosine ratio.

$$\cos 27° = \frac{c}{12}$$

$$12 \cos 27° = c$$

$$10.7 \doteq c$$

The length c is 10.7 m, to the nearest tenth of a metre.

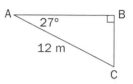

9. Find the measure of ∠Q, to the nearest degree.

a)

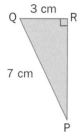

b)

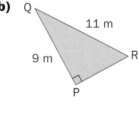

10. Find x, to the nearest unit.

a)

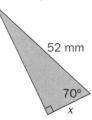

b)

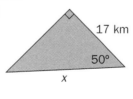

Refer to the Key Concepts on page 348.

To solve $\triangle ABC$, where $\angle B = 90°$, $\angle A = 56°$, and $b = 12$ cm, find the unknown angle and use trigonometric ratios to find the unknown side lengths, to the nearest tenth of a centimetre.

$$\angle C = 180° - 90° - 56°$$
$$= 34°$$

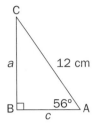

$$\sin 34° = \frac{c}{12} \qquad \cos 34° = \frac{a}{12}$$
$$12 \sin 34° = c \qquad 12 \cos 34° = a$$
$$6.7 \doteq c \qquad 9.9 \doteq a$$

$\angle C = 34°$, $c = 6.7$ cm, and $a = 9.9$ cm.

To solve $\triangle DEF$, where $\angle E = 90°$, $e = 8$ cm, and $d = 6$ cm, use trigonometric ratios to find another angle, to the nearest degree, and the third side, to the nearest tenth of a centimetre. Find the third angle.

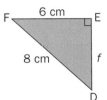

$$\sin D = \frac{6}{8}$$
$$\angle D \doteq 49°$$

$$\cos 49° = \frac{f}{8}$$
$$8 \cos 49° = f$$
$$5.2 \doteq f$$

$$\angle F = 180° - 90° - 49°$$
$$= 41°$$

$\angle D = 49°$, $\angle F = 41°$, and $f = 5.2$ cm.

11. Solve each triangle. Round each side length to the nearest tenth of a unit and each angle to the nearest degree.

a)
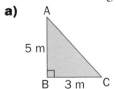

b)
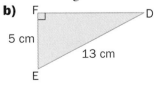

c)

d)
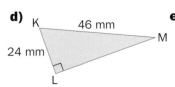

e)
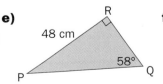

f)
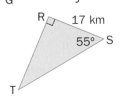

12. Road gradient When a road has a 10% gradient, it means that the road rises 10 m for every 100 m of horizontal distance travelled. What is the angle of inclination of the road, to the nearest degree?

13. Ballooning If you were in a hot air balloon 500 m above North Bay, at what angle of depression would you look at a point on the ground 800 m horizontally from the balloon?

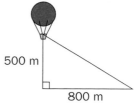

500 m

800 m

14. Flagpole A flagpole casts a shadow of 28 m when the sun's rays make an angle of 25° with the ground. How tall is the flagpole, to the nearest metre?

15. Escalator The world's longest escalator is in the subway system in St. Petersburg, Russia. The escalator is 330.7 m long and rises a vertical distance of 59.7 m. What is the angle of elevation of the top of the escalator when viewed from the bottom, to the nearest degree?

6.7 Problems Involving Two Right Triangles

Refer to the Key Concepts on page 355.

To find the length e in $\triangle$CDE, find $\angle$DCE by first finding $\angle$BCA in $\triangle$ABC.

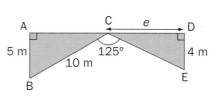

In $\triangle$ABC,

$$\sin BCA = \frac{5}{10}$$
$$= \frac{1}{2}$$
$$\angle BCA = 30°$$

In $\triangle$CDE,
$$\angle DCE = 180° - 125° - 30°$$
$$= 25°$$

$$\tan 25° = \frac{4}{e}$$
$$e \tan 25° = 4$$
$$e = \frac{4}{\tan 25°}$$
$$e \doteq 8.6$$

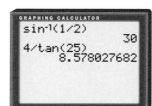

GRAPHING CALCULATOR
sin⁻¹(1/2)
                    30
4/tan(25)
          8.578027682

16. Find AB, to the nearest centimetre.

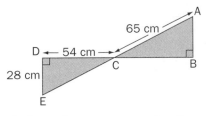

17. For each of the following, find the length h, to the nearest tenth of a metre.

a)

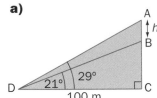

b)

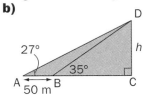

c)

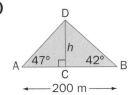

18. Railway bridge The High Level Bridge, a railway bridge that crosses the Oldman River, is over 1 km long. From one point on the river, the angle of elevation of the top of the bridge is 62.6°. From a point 20 m closer to the bridge, the angle of elevation of the top of the bridge is 72.8°. How high is the bridge above the river, to the nearest metre?

19. Model rockets Hobbyists often compete with their model rockets to determine which rocket flies the highest. On one test launch, a rocket was fired vertically upward. The angle of elevation to the top of the flight was measured from two points that were 20 m apart, on the same side of the launch site, and collinear with it. The angles measured at the two points were 66° and 37°. How high did the rocket fly, to the nearest metre?

6.8–6.9 The Sine Law

Refer to the Key Concepts on page 365.

To solve △RST, where $\angle R = 67°$, $\angle S = 41°$, and $r = 8$ cm, find the third angle and use the sine law to find the other two sides, to the nearest tenth of a centimetre.

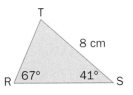

$$\angle T = 180° - 67° - 41°$$
$$= 72°$$

$$\frac{s}{\sin S} = \frac{r}{\sin R} \qquad \frac{t}{\sin T} = \frac{r}{\sin R}$$

$$\frac{s}{\sin 41°} = \frac{8}{\sin 67°} \qquad \frac{t}{\sin 72°} = \frac{8}{\sin 67°}$$

$$s = \frac{8\sin 41°}{\sin 67°} \qquad t = \frac{8\sin 72°}{\sin 67°}$$

$$s \doteq 5.7 \qquad t \doteq 8.3$$

$\angle T = 72°$, $s = 5.7$ cm, and $t = 8.3$ cm.

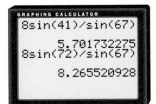

20. In $\triangle$KLM, $\angle$K = 54°, $\angle$L = 61°, and k = 23.3 m. Find l, to the nearest tenth of a metre.

21. In $\triangle$PQR, $\angle$Q = 73°, $\angle$R = 45°, and p = 28.3 cm. Find r, to the nearest tenth of a metre.

22. Solve each of the following triangles. Round side lengths to the nearest tenth of a unit and angles to the nearest degree.

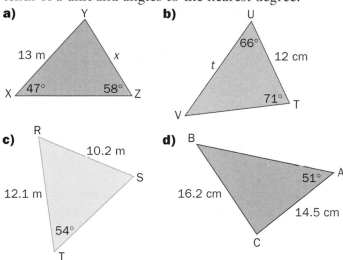

a)

b)

c)

d)

23. Covered bridge The world's longest covered bridge crosses the Saint John River at Hartland, New Brunswick. From two points, X and Y, 100 m apart on the same side of the river, the lines of sight to the far end of the bridge, Z, make angles of 85.6° and 79.8° with the river bank, as shown. What is the length of the bridge, b, to the nearest ten metres?

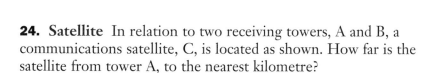

24. Satellite In relation to two receiving towers, A and B, a communications satellite, C, is located as shown. How far is the satellite from tower A, to the nearest kilometre?

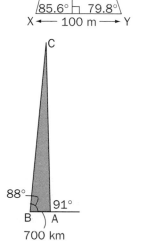

Refer to the Key Concepts on page 373.

To solve △ABC, where ∠C = 63°, a = 7 cm, and
b = 6 cm, use the cosine law to find the third side, to
the nearest tenth of a centimetre, and then find the
other two angles, to the nearest degree.

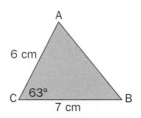

$c^2 = a^2 + b^2 - 2ab \cos C$
$\quad = 7^2 + 6^2 - 2(7)(6)(\cos 63°)$
$c \doteq 6.8$

$\dfrac{\sin A}{a} = \dfrac{\sin C}{c}$

$\dfrac{\sin A}{7} = \dfrac{\sin 63°}{6.8}$

$\sin A = \dfrac{7 \sin 63°}{6.8}$

$\quad \angle A \doteq 67°$

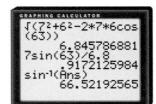

$\angle B = 180° - 63° - 67°$
$\quad = 50°$

c = 6.8 cm, ∠A = 67°, and ∠B = 50°.

25. In △ABC, a = 14.3 m, c = 16.4 m, and ∠B = 72°. Find b, to the nearest
tenth of a metre.

26. In △CDE, c = 4.8 cm, d = 5.3 cm, and e = 4.5 cm. Find ∠D, to the
nearest degree.

27. Solve the following triangles. Round side lengths to the nearest tenth
of a metre and angles to the nearest degree.

a)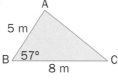

b)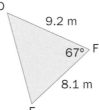

28. Solve the following triangles. Round angles to the nearest degree.

a)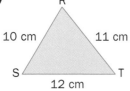

b)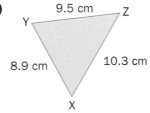

29. Lake length The points B and C are located at each end of a small lake. Point A is on land. The distances from A to B and A to C, and the measure of ∠BAC, are shown. Find the length of the lake, BC, to the nearest metre.

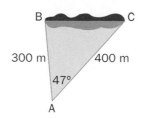

30. Boating Two pleasure boats left Hamilton harbour at the same time. One travelled at 10 km/h on a course of 47°. The other travelled at 8 km/h on a course of 79°. How far apart were the boats after 45 min, to the nearest tenth of a kilometre?

31. Sine or cosine law Determine whether the sine law or the cosine law should be used first to solve each triangle. Then, solve the triangle. Round side lengths to the nearest tenth of a unit and angles to the nearest degree.

a)

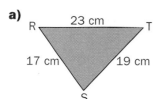

b)

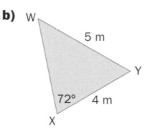

c)

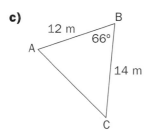

d)

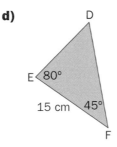

Chapter Test

1. △RST ~ △PQW. Find the unknown side lengths.

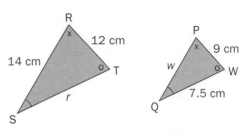

2. △ABC ~ △KLM. AB = 8 cm and KL = 10 cm. The area of △KLM is 40 cm². Find the area of △ABC.

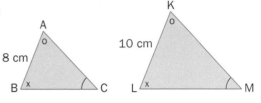

3. Find *p*, to the nearest tenth of a metre.

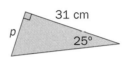

4. Find *m*, to the nearest tenth of a kilometre.

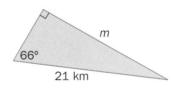

5. Find *w*, to the nearest tenth of a centimetre.

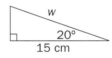

6. Solve each of the following triangles. Round each side length to the nearest tenth of a unit and each angle to the nearest degree.

a)

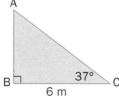

b)

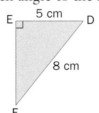

7. Find the length *h*, to the nearest tenth of a metre.

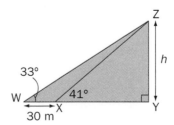

8. Solve each of the following triangles. Round each side length to the nearest tenth of a unit and each angle to the nearest degree.

a)
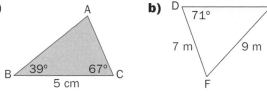

b)
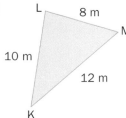

c)
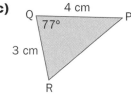

d)
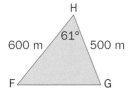

9. Ambassador Bridge The span of a bridge is the distance between its supports. A helicopter is hovering above the longest span of the Ambassador Bridge, which connects Windsor and Detroit. The distances to the ends of the longest span and the angle between the lines of sight are as shown. What is the length of the longest span of the bridge, FG, to the nearest ten metres?

11. Giant rock Percé Rock is a popular tourist attraction on the shore of the Gaspé Peninsula. To find its height, measurements were taken at low tide, as shown in the diagram. What is the height of Percé Rock, to the nearest metre?

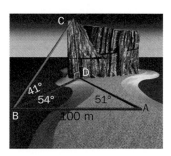

Achievement Check

 1 2 3 4

A ferry takes 3 h to make the trip from Anchorville to Cold Cove. A service is being added from Anchorville to Bayswater. How long will the trip take, to the nearest minute?

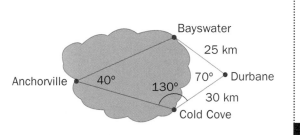

Problem Solving: Using the Strategies

1. Equilateral triangles Use an isometric grid with the dimensions shown. How many different-sized equilateral triangles can you make on the grid?

2. Whole numbers The difference between the squares of two consecutive whole numbers is 63. What are the numbers?

3. Measurement A kite is a quadrilateral with two pairs of adjacent sides equal. If a kite has diagonals that are 10 cm and 12 cm long, what is the area of the kite?

4. Clock hands A clock's minute hand is 10 cm long, and its hour hand is 7 cm long. Find the total distance moved by the tips of both hands in a 24-h period.

5. Measurement Three identical rectangles are placed as shown to form a large rectangle. The area of the large rectangle is 1536 m².
a) Find the dimensions of each of the small rectangles.
b) Find the area of the square that has the same perimeter as the large rectangle.

c) Two diagonals have been drawn to make ∠ABC. Find the measure of ∠ABC, to the nearest degree.

7. Communication
A valuable gold coin that had been stolen was recovered, along with seven counterfeit copies that had been placed in the same box. If the counterfeit coins are all identical and are slightly lighter than the real coin, how can the real coin be found with only two weighings on a balance scale?

8. Congruence Copy the diagram. Show two ways of dividing the square along grid lines into 4 congruent parts, so that each part contains exactly one **X**.

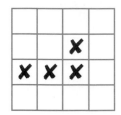

9. School reunion Five friends—three women and two men—met at a school reunion. The men were Smith and Wong. The women were Bevan, Lee, and Kostash. Their occupations were biologist, farmer, accountant, writer, and baker. Each one lived in a different city: London, England; Vancouver; Paris, France; Toronto; and Melbourne, Australia. Use the information to determine the occupation and city of residence for each person.
• Mr. Smith is not the baker.
• The five friends are Ms. Bevan, Mr. Wong, the woman who lives in Paris, the man who lives in Vancouver, and the biologist who lives in Melbourne.
• The accountant and Ms. Lee live outside Canada but not in Melbourne.
• Ms. Bevan does not live in London and is not the woman writer.

10. Dominoes a) How many dominoes are there in a double-six set of dominoes?
b) How many spots are there on a double-six set of dominoes?

11. Area of Canada a) About how many times could you handwrite the following sentence on pages with a total area that equals the area of Canada?
  Canada is the world's second-largest country, after Russia.
b) About how many years would you take to write the sentence this many times?

12. Fresh water Which Canadian province has
a) the most fresh water?
b) the most fresh water per person?

Chapter 5

1. Solve by graphing.
a) $x^2 - 2x - 8 = 0$
b) $x^2 - 9 = 0$
c) $x^2 - 6x + 9 = 0$
d) $x^2 + 5x = 0$
e) $x^2 + 2x + 3 = 0$

2. Solve by factoring, and check.
a) $x^2 + 3x - 18 = 0$
b) $x^2 - 8x + 7 = 0$
c) $2x^2 + 5x - 12 = 0$
d) $3x^2 - 10x - 8 = 0$
e) $2x^2 - 5x = 0$
f) $x^2 - 16 = 0$
g) $x^2 - 2x + 1 = 0$
h) $9x^2 - 1 = 0$

3. Solve using the quadratic formula. Round answers to the nearest tenth, if necessary.
a) $x^2 + 2x - 4 = 0$ **b)** $x^2 - 3x + 1 = 0$
c) $2x^2 + x - 3 = 0$ **d)** $3x^2 - 8x + 2 = 0$
e) $4x^2 + 7x = 0$ **f)** $2x^2 + x + 1 = 0$

4. Sketch the graphs of the following quadratic functions by factoring to locate the x-intercepts and finding the coordinates of the vertex.
a) $y = x^2 - 6x + 8$ **b)** $y = x^2 - 6x$
c) $y = x^2 + 4x - 5$ **d)** $y = x^2 + 6x - 7$

5. Numbers One number is 5 greater than another number. If the numbers are squared and then added, the result is 233. What are the numbers?

6. Measurement The area of a triangle is 24 cm². Its height is 2 cm more than its base. Determine the base and the height.

7. Garden A rectangular garden is 10 m long and 5 m wide. It is to be tripled in area by extending each side by the same amount. Determine how much each side should be extended.

Chapter 6

1. $\triangle ABC \sim \triangle DEF$. Find the lengths of the unknown sides.

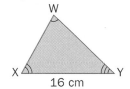

2. $\triangle PQR \sim \triangle WXY$. QR = 12 cm and XY = 16 cm. The area of $\triangle WXY$ is 80 cm². Find the area of $\triangle PQR$.

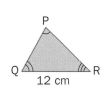

3. Solve the following triangles. Round each side length to the nearest tenth of a centimetre and each angle to the nearest degree.
a) In $\triangle PQR$, $\angle Q = 90°$, $\angle R = 38°$, and $p = 12$ cm.
b) In $\triangle WXY$, $\angle X = 90°$, $x = 10$ cm, and $w = 7$ cm.

4. Building From a point 20 m from the base of a building, the angle of elevation of the top of the building is 72°. How tall is the building, to the nearest metre?

5. Find the value of h, to the nearest tenth of a metre.

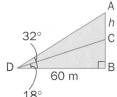

6. Solve the following triangles. Round each side length to the nearest tenth of a unit and each angle to the nearest degree.
a) In $\triangle DEF$, $\angle D = 58°$, $\angle E = 53°$, and $d = 8$ cm.
b) In $\triangle RST$, $\angle R = 73°$, $r = 8$ m, and $t = 6$ m.
c) In $\triangle ABC$, $\angle A = 68°$, $b = 5$ cm, and $c = 7$ cm.
d) In $\triangle WXY$, $w = 11$ m, $x = 10$ m, and $y = 14$ m.

Cumulative Review: Chapters 1–6

Chapter 1 Linear Systems

1. Solve each system by graphing. Check your solutions.

a) $y = x + 2$
$y = 4 - x$

b) $y = x + 6$
$y = 2 - x$

c) $2x - y = 1$
$x - y = -3$

d) $2x - y + 9 = 0$
$x + y - 3 = 0$

2. Without graphing, determine whether each system has one solution, no solution, or infinitely many solutions.

a) $y = -5x - 8$
$x + 3y = 4$

b) $x - 5y = 3$
$2x - 10y = -3$

c) $2x - y = -4$
$3x + 2y = -20$

d) $y = 4 - 3x$
$6x + 2y = 8$

3. Solve each system by substitution. Check each solution.

a) $x - 2y = 4$
$2x - 3y = 7$

b) $y = 2x + 3$
$4x + 5y = 8$

4. Solve each system by elimination. Check each solution.

a) $3x + 8y = -3$
$5x + 8y = -5$

b) $11m + 3n = 25$
$-11m + 7n = -15$

c) $3x - 4y = 10$
$2x - 3y = 7$

d) $4x - 5y = -22$
$5x + 6y = -3$

e) $\dfrac{x}{3} - \dfrac{y}{2} = 7$
$\dfrac{x}{2} + \dfrac{y}{5} = 1$

f) $0.4x - 0.3y = 2.2$
$0.3x + 0.2y = 0.8$

5. Measurement The perimeter of a rectangle is 50 cm. The length is 7 cm more than the width. Find the dimensions of the rectangle.

6. Investing Amy invested $20 000, part in bonds that paid 3% per annum and the remainder in term deposits that paid 5% per annum. The total interest after one year was $760. How much did she invest at each rate?

7. Nitric acid solutions A lab technician needs to make 60 mL of 32% nitric acid solution. The acid solutions available are 20% nitric acid solution and 40% nitric acid solution. How many millilitres of each solution should be mixed to make the 32% solution?

Chapter 2 Analytic Geometry

8. Find the length of the line segment joining each pair of points. Express each answer to the nearest tenth of a unit.

a) (2, 5) and (5, 7)

b) (0, 3) and (−6, 0)

c) (−1, −3) and (−2, −4)

d) (−1.6, 1.5) and (2.4, −0.5)

9. Find the coordinates of the midpoint of each line segment, given the endpoints.

a) M(−2, 2), P(4, 8)

b) A(3, 3), J(−9, 3)

10. The midpoint of AB is M(−2, 1). If one endpoint is A(−7, 3), what are the coordinates of B?

11. Write an equation for the circle with centre (0, 0) and radius 15.

12. Determine the radius of a circle with centre (0, 0) and equation $x^2 + y^2 = 100$.

13. Measurement A rectangle has vertices Q(5, 6), R(5, −3), S(1, −3), and T(1, 6). Find
a) the perimeter
b) the area

14. △ABC has vertices A(3, 5), B(−1, 3), and C(1, −1).
a) Classify the triangle by side length.
b) Determine the perimeter of the triangle, to the nearest tenth of a unit.
c) Verify that the line segment joining the midpoints of AB and AC is parallel to BC and one-half the length of BC.

15. Quadrilateral WXYZ has vertices W(3, 3), X(−4, 2), Y(−3, −4), and Z(4, −3).
a) Verify that quadrilateral WXYZ is a parallelogram.
b) Verify that the diagonals of the parallelogram bisect each other.

16. △DEF has vertices D(−2, 4), E(0, −2), and F(6, 2). Determine
a) an equation for DG , the median from D to EF
b) an equation for FC, the altitude from F to DE
c) an equation for AB, the right bisector of DF

17. Find the shortest distance from the point (1, 3) to the line $y = x − 4$, to the nearest tenth.

Chapter 3 Polynomials

18. Simplify.
a) $(4x − 3) + (5x + 4)$
b) $(2x^2 − 3x + 4) − (x^2 + 4x − 1)$
c) $(−4x^2)(2x)$
d) $(−6x^3yz^2)(−2xy^2z)$
e) $\dfrac{36a^2b^3}{−6ab}$
f) $\dfrac{−40a^2b^4c^2}{−10ab^2c}$

19. Expand and simplify.
a) $3(x + 5) + 4(x − 3)$
b) $5(t + 7) − 9(t − 2)$
c) $3x(2x − 4) − x(x + 5)$
d) $4(x^2 − 2x + 5) − (2x^2 + 3x − 2)$

20. Find the product.
a) $(x − 5)(x + 7)$
b) $(4y − 3)(3y − 1)$
c) $(2m − 3)(3m + 1)$
d) $(3x + 4)(2x − 7)$

21. Expand and simplify.
a) $2(3x − 2)(3x + 2)$
b) $4(2x + 1)(x − 5)$
c) $3(y + 2)(y − 3) + 2(y − 4)(y + 1)$
d) $2(2x − 3)(x + 4) − (4x + 1)(x + 2)$

22. Expand.
a) $(x + 2)^2$
b) $(x − 5)(x + 5)$
c) $(2y − 3)(2y + 3)$
d) $(4y + 3)^2$
e) $(3x − 1)^2$
f) $(5x − 2y)(5x + 2y)$

23. Expand and simplify.
a) $(x − 4)(x + 4) + 2(x + 1)^2$
b) $(t − 3)^2 − (t + 7)(t − 7)$
c) $2(2x + 1)^2 − (4x − 3)(4x + 3)$

24. Factor, if possible.
a) $7x + 42$
b) $4x^2 − 28x$
c) $6xy − 7st$
d) $14r^2t − 7rt + 21rt^2$
e) $x(y + 4) − 2(y + 4)$
f) $2x(m + n) + 3(m + n)$
g) $xy − 12 + 4x − 3y$

25. Factor, if possible.
a) $x^2 + 7x + 12$
b) $y^2 + y − 6$
c) $k^2 + k + 1$
d) $x^2 − 2x − 15$
e) $y^2 + 10y + 21$
f) $x^2 − 11x + 18$

26. Factor fully.
a) $2x^2 − 6x − 8$
b) $3x^2 + 12x + 9$

27. Factor, if possible.
a) $3x^2 + 5x − 2$
b) $2y^2 + 11y + 12$
c) $4x^2 + 8x + 5$
d) $4x^2 − 10x + 3$

28. Factor fully.
a) $4x^2 + 6x − 10$
b) $18x^2 − 30x + 12$

29. Factor, if possible.
a) $x^2 − 16$
b) $y^2 + 10y + 25$
c) $x^2 + 9$
d) $x^2 − 6x + 9$
e) $4x^2 − 4x + 1$
f) $9x^2 − 16y^2$

30. Factor fully.
a) $7x^2 − 7$
b) $5x^2 − 20x + 20$

Chapter 4 Quadratic Functions

31. Determine whether each set of ordered pairs represents a function.
a) {(2, 3), (3, 4), (4, 5), (5, 6)}
b) {(1, 2), (2, 2), (3, 2), (4, 2)}
c) {(6, 7), (7, 9), (6, 10), (7, 11)}

32. Sketch the graph of each parabola and state the direction of the opening, how the parabola is stretched or shrunk, if at all, the coordinates of the vertex, the equation of the axis of symmetry, the domain and range, and the maximum or minimum value.
a) $y = 3x^2$
b) $y = -x^2 + 5$
c) $y = -(x - 1)^2 - 3$
d) $y = 3(x + 4)^2$
e) $y = 2(x + 3)^2 - 4$
f) $y = -0.5(x + 7)^2 + 2$

33. Baseball The path of a baseball after a batter hit a pop-up can be modelled by the following function. For this function, h metres is the height of the ball and d metres is the horizontal distance of the ball from home plate, where it was hit.
$$h = -0.07(d - 10)^2 + 8$$
a) What was the maximum height of the ball?
b) What was the horizontal distance of the ball from home plate when it reached its maximum height?
c) What was the height of the ball when it was hit?
d) If the ball was caught 19.5 m from home plate, how far off the ground was the infielder's glove when the ball was caught, to the nearest tenth of a metre?
e) If no one had caught the ball, what would its horizontal distance from home plate have been when it hit the ground, to the nearest tenth of a metre?

34. Determine any x-intercepts, to the nearest tenth, using a graphing calculator or graphing software.
a) $y = x^2 - 7$
b) $y = -(x + 2)^2 + 5$

35. Write each function in the form $y = a(x - h)^2 + k$. Sketch the graph showing the coordinates of the vertex, the equation of the axis of symmetry, and the coordinates of two other points on the graph.
a) $y = x^2 - 8x + 3$
b) $y = -2x^2 + 4x - 5$

36. Sketch the graph of the following showing the coordinates of the vertex and any intercepts.
a) $y = x^2 + 6x$
b) $y = -x^2 + 6x - 8$

37. Sketch the graph of the following quadratic functions by writing them in the form $y = ax(x - s) + t$, finding two points on the graph, and deducing the coordinates of the vertex.
a) $y = x^2 - 6x + 3$
b) $y = 2x^2 - 8x + 7$

38. Fencing A rectangular field is to be enclosed by 800 m of fencing.
a) What dimensions will give the maximum area?
b) What is the maximum area?

39. Use finite differences to determine whether each function is linear, quadratic, or neither.

a)

x	y
2	1
3	0
4	−1
5	−2

b)

x	y
0	−2
1	0
2	6
3	24

c)

x	y
0	8
1	7
2	4
3	−1

40. Draw a scatter plot for each table of values by entering the data as two lists in your graphing calculator. Use trial and error to fit the graph of an equation of a quadratic function to the scatter plot. Compare the equation you found to the equation of the curve of best fit produced by using the quadratic regression feature on your calculator.

a)

x	y
2	7
1	4
0	3
−1	4
−2	7

b)

x	y
3	5
2	1
0	−4
−2	0
−3	5

c)

x	y
3	−6
2	−2
0	2
−2	−3
−3	−8

Chapter 5 Quadratic Equations

41. Solve by graphing.
a) $x^2 + x - 12 = 0$
b) $x^2 - 8x + 15 = 0$
c) $x^2 + 4x + 4 = 0$
d) $x^2 - 7x = 0$
e) $x^2 - 1 = 0$

42. Solve by factoring, and check.
a) $x^2 - 8x - 9 = 0$ **b)** $x^2 + 7x + 6 = 0$
c) $x^2 - 121 = 0$ **d)** $x^2 - 6x + 9 = 0$
e) $2x^2 + 3x = 0$ **f)** $4x^2 - 9 = 0$
g) $2x^2 - 13x + 20 = 0$ **h)** $3x^2 + 8x - 3 = 0$

43. Integers The sum of the squares of three consecutive integers is 194. What are the integers?

44. Measurement The hypotenuse of a right triangle is 26 cm. The sum of the other two sides is 34 cm. Find the lengths of the other two sides of the triangle.

45. Sketch the graphs of the following quadratic functions by factoring to locate the x-intercepts and finding the coordinates of the vertex.
a) $y = x^2 - 4x - 12$ **b)** $y = x^2 - 10x + 9$

46. Solve using the quadratic formula. Round answers to the nearest tenth, if necessary.
a) $x^2 - 3x - 18 = 0$ **b)** $3x^2 + 10x = 0$
c) $3x^2 - x - 4 = 0$ **d)** $2x^2 + 7x + 1 = 0$
e) $x^2 + 2x + 8 = 0$ **f)** $2x^2 - 9 = 0$

47. A rectangular building that measures 100 m by 80 m is to be surrounded by a lawn of uniform width. The area of the lawn must equal the area of the building. Find the width of the lawn, to the nearest tenth of a metre.

Chapter 6 Trigonometry

48. $\triangle$RST ~ $\triangle$WXY.
a) Find the lengths of the unknown sides.

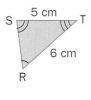
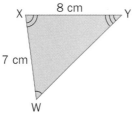

b) The area of $\triangle$WXY is 27.5 cm^2. Calculate the area of $\triangle$RST, to the nearest tenth of a square centimetre.

49. Solve each of the following triangles. Round each side length to the nearest tenth and each angle to the nearest degree.
a) In $\triangle$ABC, $\angle B = 90°$, $\angle A = 47°$, and $b = 15$ cm.
b) In $\triangle$DEF, $\angle D = 90°$, $e = 8$ m, and $f = 12$ mm.

50. Building From a point 35 m from the base of a building, the angle of elevation of the top of the building is 65°. How tall is the building, to the nearest metre?

51. Find BD, to the nearest metre.

52. Solve each of the following acute triangles. Round each side length to the nearest tenth and each angle to the nearest degree.
a) In $\triangle$WXY, $\angle W = 52°$, $\angle X = 70°$, and $w = 20$ cm.
b) In $\triangle$PQR, $\angle R = 68°$, $r = 15$ m, and $q = 16$ m
c) In $\triangle$ABC, $\angle B = 55°$, $a = 11$ cm, and $c = 14$ cm.
d) In $\triangle$JKL, $j = 23$ m, $k = 27$ m, and $l = 29$ m.

53. Measurement A plot of land is in the shape of a triangle. Two of the angles measure 48° and 74°. The length of the side between them is 90 m.

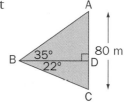

a) Calculate the perimeter of the plot, to the nearest metre.
b) Calculate the area of the plot, to the nearest square metre.

54. Measurement The sides of a triangle measure 15 cm, 17 cm, and 18 cm. Find the measure of the largest angle, to the nearest degree.

A Review of Prerequisite Skills

Adding polynomials

To add $2x + 5y - 4$, add the like terms.
$3x - 2y - 5$

$$2x + 5y - 4$$
$$3x - 2y - 5$$
$$\overline{5x + 3y - 9}$$

1. Add.

a) $3x + 2y + 5$
$4x + 3y + 7$

b) $3x - 4y - 5$
$6x - 2y - 7$

c) $x^2 + 6x - 4$
$2x^2 - 4x + 8$

d) $3a^2 - a + 2$
$2a^2 + 4a - 1$

e) $2y^2 + y - 3$
$3y^2 - y + 2$

f) $-6a + 2b + 4$
$4a - 3b - 7$

Angle properties

To find the measure of x, recall that the sum of the interior angles of a triangle is 180°.

$$x + 72° + 67° = 180°$$
$$x + 139° = 180°$$
$$x = 180° - 139°$$
$$x = 41°$$

When a transversal intersects two parallel lines:

a) the alternate angles are equal

b) the corresponding angles are equal

c) the co-interior angles are supplementary

$x + y = 180°$

To find the measures of x, y, and z, use the fact that, since AC || EF, the alternate angles are equal.
∠BEF = ∠ABE (alternate angles)
   $x = 54°$
∠BFE = ∠CBF (alternate angles)
   $z = 73°$

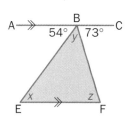
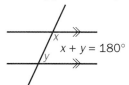

$$x + y + z = 180°$$
$$54° + y + 73° = 180°$$
$$y + 127° = 180°$$
$$y = 180° - 127°$$
$$y = 53°$$

1. Find the missing angle measures.

a)

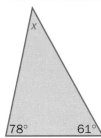

b)

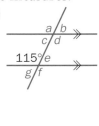

c)

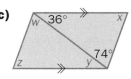

d)

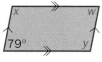

Common factoring

To factor the expression $10y^2 + 8y$, determine the greatest common factor of both terms. Refer to greatest common factors in this appendix.

$$10y^2 = 2 \times 5 \times y \times y$$
$$8y = 2 \times 2 \times 2 \times y$$

The greatest common factor is $2y$.

The second factor is $\dfrac{10y^2}{2y} + \dfrac{8y}{2y}$ or $5y + 4$.

The factors of $10y^2 + 8y$ are $2y$ and $5y + 4$.
Therefore, $10y^2 + 8y = 2y(5y + 4)$.

1. State the missing factor.

a) $6x + 8y = 2(\blacksquare)$ **b)** $2x^2 - 5x = x(\blacksquare)$ **c)** $4abc + 10ab = 2ab(\blacksquare)$

d) $8a^3 - 12a^2 = 4a^2(\blacksquare)$ **e)** $-5ab - 10c = -5(\blacksquare)$ **f)** $-4x^2 + 8x = -4x(\blacksquare)$

2. Factor.

a) $5y + 15$ **b)** $24x - 16$ **c)** $4ab + 6a$ **d)** $3x^2 - 18x$

e) $2x^2 + 4x - 6$ **f)** $6x^3 - 3x^2 + 9x$ **g)** $8ab^2 + 4ab + 12a^2b$ **h)** $10y^3 - 10$

Congruent triangles

Congruent triangles have the same shape and the same size. When two triangles are congruent, their corresponding angles and corresponding sides are equal.
$\triangle ABC$ is congruent to $\triangle DEF$.
The following corresponding parts are equal.

$\angle A = \angle D$ $AB = DE$

$\angle B = \angle E$ $AC = DF$

$\angle C = \angle F$ $BC = EF$

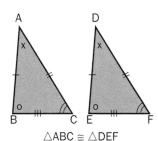

$\triangle ABC \cong \triangle DEF$

1. List the corresponding equal parts in each pair of congruent scalene triangles.

a)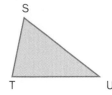

b)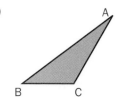

Evaluating expressions

To evaluate the expression $4x^2 - 5y$ for $x = 2$ and $y = -3$, substitute 2 for x and -3 for y in the expression. Then simplify using the order of operations.

$$4x^2 - 3y = 4(2)^2 - 5(-3)$$
$$= 4(4) - 5(-3)$$
$$= 16 + 15$$
$$= 31$$

1. Evaluate for $x = 3$, $y = 2$, and $z = 1$.

a) $3x + 4$
b) $2x + 4y - 3z$
c) $3(x + z)$
d) $x^2 - y^2 + z^2$
e) $3xy - yz + 2$
f) $2y^2 + x$
g) $3(4z + 3y)$
h) $2z(x - 2y)$
i) $3y^2 - 2x^2 + 3z^2$
j) $x(z - 4y)$
k) $(yz)^2$
l) $4(x - y - z)$

2. Evaluate for $x = -2$, $y = 3$, and $z = -1$.

a) $x + y - z$
b) $4x + 3y$
c) $5x + 3z - 4y$
d) $3xyz - 6$
e) $4yz - x$
f) $xy + yz - xz$
g) $x^2 + y^2 - z^2$
h) $3(2z - x)$
i) $(x + y)(y - z)$
j) $(xyz)^3$
k) $2z(4y - 3x)$
l) $2z^2 - 3y^2 - 4x^2$

To complete the table of values for $y = x^2 - 5x$, substitute the given values for x in $x^2 - 5x$ and determine y.

$y = x^2 - 5x$

x	y
-2	
0	
2	

When $x = 2$, $y = (2)^2 - 5(2)$
$= 4 - 10$
$= -6$
When $x = 0$, $y = (0)^2 - 5(0)$
$= 0 - 0$
$= 0$
When $x = -2$, $y = (-2)^2 - 5(-2)$
$= 4 + 10$
$= 14$

$y = x^2 - 5x$

x	y
-2	-6
0	0
2	14

3. Copy and complete each table of values.

a) $y = x + 4$

x	y
2	
1	
0	
−1	
−2	

b) $y = 2x - 3$

x	y
2	
1	
0	
−1	
−2	

c) $y = -x + 5$

x	y
4	
2	
0	
−2	
−4	

d) $y = x^2 + 1$

x	y
2	
1	
0	
−1	
−2	

e) $y = x^2 + 2x$

x	y
2	
1	
0	
−1	
−2	

f) $y = x^2 - 2x + 4$

x	y
4	
2	
0	
−2	
−4	

Evaluating radicals

Since $7 \times 7 = 49$, $\sqrt{49} = 7$.

Since $0.4 \times 0.4 = 0.16$, $\sqrt{0.16} = 0.4$.

1. Evaluate.

a) $\sqrt{4}$ **b)** $\sqrt{25}$ **c)** $\sqrt{0.81}$ **d)** $\sqrt{1.21}$

e) $\sqrt{0.09}$ **f)** $\sqrt{0.01}$ **g)** $\sqrt{225}$ **h)** $\sqrt{1.69}$

To evaluate $\sqrt{56}$, to the nearest tenth, use a calculator.

$\sqrt{56} \doteq 7.483314774$

so $\sqrt{56} = 7.5$, to the nearest tenth.

2. Evaluate, to the nearest tenth.

a) $\sqrt{44}$ **b)** $\sqrt{129}$ **c)** $\sqrt{3422}$ **d)** $\sqrt{20.5}$

e) $\sqrt{89.4}$ **f)** $\sqrt{747}$ **g)** $\sqrt{65\,771}$ **h)** $\sqrt{0.7}$

Expanding expressions

To expand $3x(x - 4)$, use the distributive property.

$3x(x - 4) = 3x(x - 4)$
$ = 3x^2 - 12x$

1. Expand.

a) $2(x + 3)$ **b)** $3(x + y - 7)$ **c)** $5(a - b + c)$

d) $-2(5a - 4)$ **e)** $-(2x - y)$ **f)** $x(x + 6)$

g) $2x(3x + 7)$ **h)** $x(x^2 - x + 5)$ **i)** $-3a(a^2 + 2a - 1)$

Exponent rules

To multiply powers with the same base, add the exponents.

$$x^2 \times x^3 = x^{2+3}$$
$$= x^5$$

To divide powers with the same base, subtract the exponents.

$$x^5 \div x^2 = x^{5-2}$$
$$= x^3$$

To raise a power to a power, multiply the exponents.

$$(x^2)^4 = x^{2 \times 4}$$
$$= x^8$$

1. Simplify, using the exponent rules. Express each answer in exponential form.

a) $2^2 \times 2^5$ **b)** $3^6 \times 3^4$ **c)** $4^2 \times 4^3 \times 4^2$ **d)** $5^3 \times 5^2 \times 5$

e) $2^5 \div 2^3$ **f)** $3^7 \div 3^4$ **g)** $4^6 \div 4$ **h)** $(2^3)^2$

i) $(3^4)^3$ **j)** $y^4 \times y^7$ **k)** $z^3 \times z^3$ **l)** $y^5 \div y^4$

m) $z^8 \div z^2$ **n)** $(x^3)^5$ **o)** $(y^2)^8$ **p)** $3x^4 \times 2x^3$

q) $(-2y^3)(-4y^4)$ **r)** $-10m^7 \div (-2m^3)$ **s)** $(3y^3)^2$ **t)** $(-2x^3)^3$

First differences

First differences are calculated from tables of values in which the x-coordinates are evenly spaced. First differences are found by subtracting consecutive y-coordinates.

If the first differences are constant, the relation is linear. If the first differences are not constant, the relation is non-linear.

This relation is linear.

x	y	1st Difference
1	3	
		5 – 3 = 2
2	5	
		7 – 5 = 2
3	7	
		9 – 7 = 2
4	9	

This relation is non-linear.

x	y	1st Difference
1	1	
		4 – 1 = 3
2	4	
		9 – 4 = 5
3	9	
		16 – 9 = 7
4	16	

1. Use first differences to determine whether each relation is linear or non-linear.

a)

x	y
1	5
2	8
3	11
4	14

b)

x	y
1	7
2	5
3	3
4	1

c)

x	y
1	2
2	5
3	10
4	17

d)

x	y
1	2
2	6
3	10
4	14

Graphing equations

To graph the line $x + y = 6$ using a table of values, choose suitable values for x, say $\{5, 3, 1, -1\}$. Complete a table of values by finding the value of y for each value of x.

$x + y = 6$

x	y
5	1
3	3
1	5
-1	7

Plot the points on a grid and draw a line through the points.

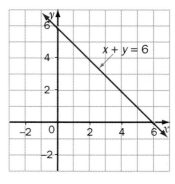

$x + y = 6$

1. Graph each equation using a table of values.

a) $x + y = 4$ **b)** $x - y = 2$ **c)** $y = x + 2$ **d)** $y = 2x + 1$

To graph $x + 2y = 6$ using the intercepts, find the points where the graph of $x + 2y = 6$ crosses the x- and y-axes.
To find the x-intercept, let $y = 0$.

$x + 2y = 6$
$x + 2(0) = 6$
$\quad\quad x = 6$

One point on the line is $(6, 0)$.
To find the y-intercept, let $x = 0$.

$x + 2y = 6$
$0 + 2y = 6$
$\quad\quad y = 3$

Another point on the line is $(0, 3)$.
Plot the points on a grid.
Draw a line through the points.

2. Graph each equation using the intercepts.

a) $x + y = 3$ **b)** $x - y = 4$ **c)** $4x + y = 8$ **d)** $2x - 5y = 10$

To graph $y = x + 3$ using the slope and y-intercept, first find the point where the graph crosses the y-axis.
Since the y-intercept is 3, plot the point (0, 3).
The slope is 1. Use the slope to find another point on the line.
Draw the graph.

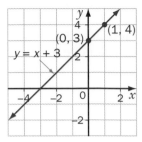

3. Graph each equation using the slope and y-intercept.
a) $y = x + 3$ **b)** $y = -x - 4$ **c)** $y = 2x + 3$ **d)** $y = 3x - 1$

To find the point of intersection of the lines $y = x - 3$ and $y = 5 - x$, graph the lines on the same set of axes.
The coordinates of the point of intersection are (4, 1).

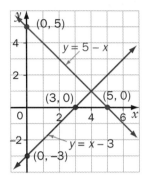

4. Graph each pair of lines and find the coordinates of the point of intersection.
a) $y = x - 4$ and $y = 8 - x$ **b)** $y = x + 3$ and $y = 7 - x$
c) $y = x - 6$ and $y = 2 - x$ **d)** $y = x + 5$ and $y = 3 - x$

Greatest common factors

To determine the greatest common factor (GCF) of $4c^2d$ and $6cd^3$, write each expression as a product. Then write the factors common to both.
$4c^2d = 2 \times 2 \times c \times c \times d$
$6cd^3 = 2 \times 3 \times c \times d \times d \times d$
The GCF of $4c^2d$ and $6cd^3$ is $2 \times c \times d$ or $2cd$.

1. Determine the greatest common factor of each pair.
a) $4x, 10x$ **b)** $12y, 8y$ **c)** $15z, 10z$ **d)** $30a, 20a$
e) $6x^2, 14x$ **f)** $14ab, 7abc$ **g)** $12x^3, 18x^2$ **h)** $9ab^2c, 7a^2bc$

2. Determine the greatest common factor of each set.
a) $4ab, 2abc, 6a$ **b)** $3xyz, 9yz, 12xy$ **c)** $8x^3, 20x^2, 24x^4$
d) $15mn^2, 18m^2n, 12mn$ **e)** $10rt^3, 15r^2t^2, 20r^3t^4$ **f)** $9rs, 18ab, 27xy$

Lengths of line segments

The length of any line segment is a positive number.
To find the length of the horizontal line segment joining (3, 5) and (−4, 5), subtract the x-coordinates.

$$3 - (-4) = 3 + 4 \quad \text{or} \quad -4 - 3 = -7$$
$$= 7$$

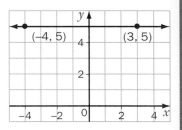

The length of the horizontal line segment joining (3, 5) and (−4, 5) is 7 units.

To find the length of the vertical line segment joining (2, −4) and (2, 7), subtract the y-coordinates.

$$-4 - 7 = -11 \quad \text{or} \quad 7 - (-4) = 7 + 4$$
$$= 11$$

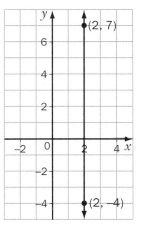

The length of the vertical line segment joining (2, −4) and (2, 7) is 11 units.

1. Find the length of the line segment joining each of the following pairs of points.
a) (8, 7) and (2, 7)   **b)** (5, 1) and (9, 1)   **c)** (3, 8) and (3, 2)
d) (5, 1) and (5, 9)   **e)** (2, 4) and (−5, 4)   **f)** (1, 7) and (1, −6)
g) (−4, −3) and (−8, −3)   **h)** (−2, 5) and (−2, −7)   **i)** (6, 3) and (0, 3)
j) (−6, −7) and (−6, 0)   **k)** (−6, 4) and (8, 4)   **l)** (−7, −9) and (−7, −3)

Like terms

Like terms have exactly the same variables raised to exactly the same exponents. An expression is in simplest form when there are no like terms.
To simplify $x^2 + 5x - 7 - 2x + 4 + 3x^2$, collect like terms.
$$x^2 + 5x - 7 - 2x + 4 + 3x^2 = x^2 + 3x^2 + 5x - 2x - 7 + 4$$
$$= 4x^2 + 3x - 3$$

1. Simplify by collecting like terms.
a) $4x + 7x - 5x$ **b)** $2y - 6 + 3y - 8$ **c)** $2x + 3y - 2 + x - 4y - 5$
d) $3a - 2b + 4c - 3b + a$ **e)** $x^2 - 2x - 7x - 3 - 3x^2$ **f)** $3 - t^2 + 8t - 7 - 6t - t$
g) $3x + 2y - 5 - 3 + x + 7y$ **h)** $3y^2 - 4y^2 - 11y + 3 - 7y$ **i)** $15 - 4t - 5t - t^2 - t^2 - t$

Polynomials

The degree of a polynomial in one variable is the highest power of the variable in any one term.

For the polynomial $3x^2 - 2x + 7$ the highest power, 2, is contained in the term $3x^2$.

$3x^2 - 2x + 7$ is a second-degree polynomial.

1. State the degree of each polynomial.

a) $4x - 3$ **b)** x^3 **c)** $4 - 2y^2 - 5y$

d) $6m^2 - m^3 - 2$ **e)** $2x + 7 - 5x^4$ **f)** $2 - 4t^5 - 3t^3 + 9t$

Pythagorean Theorem

To find the length of d in the right triangle, to the nearest tenth of a unit, use the Pythagorean Theorem. This states that, in a right triangle, the square of the length of the hypotenuse is equal to the sum of the squares of the lengths of the other two sides.

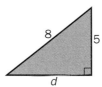

$$d^2 + 5^2 = 8^2$$
$$d^2 + 25 = 64$$
$$d^2 = 64 - 25$$
$$d^2 = 39$$
$$d = \sqrt{39}$$
$$d \doteq 6.244997998$$

The length of d is 6.2 units, to the nearest tenth of a unit.

1. In each right triangle, find the unknown side length, to the nearest tenth of a unit.

a)

b)

c)

d)

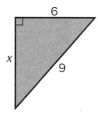

e)

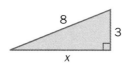

f)

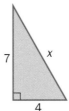

Simplifying expressions

To simplify $3(x + 2) - (x - 4)$, remove brackets and collect like terms.

$$3(x + 2) - (x - 4) = 3(x + 2) - 1(x - 4)$$
$$= 3x + 6 - x + 4$$
$$= 2x + 10$$

1. Simplify.
a) $5x + 2(x + 7)$
b) $3(2a - 7) + 3a$
c) $4(x - 3) - 2x$
d) $-5(y - 3) + 6$
e) $2(t + 4) + 3(t - 4)$
f) $8(y - 3) - (y + 6)$
g) $-4(z + 3) - 2(z - 2)$
h) $7(2 - w) - (w - 3)$
i) $6(x - 4) + 2(3 + x)$

2. Simplify.
a) $(3x + 4y) + (2x + 3y)$
b) $(4r - 3s) + (r + 4s)$
c) $(3p + 5q) - (4p - q)$
d) $2(x - 3y) + 3(6x - y)$
e) $4(3a + 5b) - (7a - b)$
f) $-4(c - 5d) + 3c - d$
g) $4a - b + 3c - 2(a + b - c)$
h) $3(x + y - 2z) + 7x - 5$
i) $6x + 4(2x + 3y - z) + 5y$

Slope

To find the slope of the line passing through the points $(-2, 1)$ and $(3, 5)$, use the formula for slope.

$$m = \frac{y_2 - y_1}{x_2 - x_1}$$
$$= \frac{5 - 1}{3 - (-2)}$$
$$= \frac{4}{5}$$

1. Find the slope of the line passing through each of the following pairs of points.
a) $(0, 0)$ and $(2, 6)$
b) $(0, 0)$ and $(4, 2)$
c) $(1, 2)$ and $(3, 6)$
d) $(2, 5)$ and $(3, 7)$
e) $(3, 0)$ and $(0, 6)$
f) $(-3, 5)$ and $(2, 6)$
g) $(-4, 2)$ and $(5, 2)$
h) $(-3, -4)$ and $(-1, -8)$
i) $(5, -7)$ and $(3, -10)$

Parallel lines have the same slope. The slope of the line parallel to $y = 2x + 3$ is 2.
The product of the slopes of perpendicular lines is -1.

The slope of the line perpendicular to $y = 2x + 3$ is $-\frac{1}{2}$, since $2 \times -\frac{1}{2} = -1$.

2. State the slope of a line parallel to and a line perpendicular to each of the following lines.
a) $y = 3x + 5$
b) $y = -2x - 4$
c) $y = -x + 7$
d) $y = \frac{1}{4}x - 4$
e) $y = -\frac{2}{3}x + 1$
f) $y = \frac{4}{5}x - 6$

Solving equations

To solve $2x - 3 = 11$, isolate the variable.

$$2x - 3 = 11$$

Add 3 to both sides: $\quad 2x - 3 + 3 = 11 + 3$

Simplify: $\qquad\qquad\qquad 2x = 14$

Divide both sides by 2: $\quad \dfrac{2x}{2} = \dfrac{14}{2}$

Simplify: $\qquad\qquad\qquad x = 7$

To check, substitute 7 for x in the original equation.

L.S. $= 2x - 3 \qquad$ **R.S.** $= 11$
$\quad = 2(7) - 3$
$\quad = 14 - 3$
$\quad = 11$

Since L.S. = R.S., the solution is $x = 7$.

1. Solve and check.

a) $3x + 2 = 11$ $\qquad$ **b)** $2x - 5 = 7$ $\qquad$ **c)** $5x - 2 = -17$
d) $4x - 7 = 9$ $\qquad$ **e)** $1 - 2x = 15$ $\qquad$ **f)** $8 + 7x = -6$
g) $3x + 4 = 2x + 5$ $\qquad$ **h)** $5x + 7 = 3x - 9$ $\qquad$ **i)** $2x - 3 = 5x + 9$

To solve $3(x - 2) = 9$, expand to remove the brackets.

$$3(x - 2) = 9$$

Expand: $\qquad\qquad\qquad 3x - 6 = 9$

Add 6 to both sides: $\quad 3x - 6 + 6 = 9 + 6$

Simplify: $\qquad\qquad\qquad 3x = 15$

Divide both sides by 3: $\quad \dfrac{3x}{3} = \dfrac{15}{3}$

Simplify: $\qquad\qquad\qquad x = 5$

To check, substitute 5 for x in the original equation.

L.S. $= 3(x - 2) \qquad$ **R.S.** $= 9$
$\quad = 3(5 - 2)$
$\quad = 3(3)$
$\quad = 9$

Since L.S. = R.S., the solution is $x = 5$.

2. Solve and check.

a) $2(x + 4) = 10$ $\qquad$ **b)** $4(x - 1) = 16$ $\qquad$ **c)** $6(x - 5) + 7 = 1$
d) $5(x + 1) = -15$ $\qquad$ **e)** $2(x - 3) = 3(x + 1)$ $\qquad$ **f)** $5(x - 3) = 3(x + 7)$
g) $7(x + 2) - 3(x - 4) = 30$ $\qquad$ **h)** $5(x - 2) + 3(x - 1) = 3$ $\qquad$ **i)** $7(x + 6) - (x + 7) = -1$

To solve $\dfrac{x-1}{3} = \dfrac{2x-3}{5}$, eliminate fractions by multiplying by the lowest common denominator, 15.

$$\frac{x-1}{3} = \frac{2x-3}{5}$$

Multiply both sides by 15: $\qquad 15 \times \dfrac{x-1}{3} = 15 \times \dfrac{2x-3}{5}$

Simplify: $\qquad\qquad\qquad\quad 5(x-1) = 3(2x-3)$

Expand: $\qquad\qquad\qquad\qquad 5x - 5 = 6x - 9$

Add 5 to both sides: $\qquad\quad 5x - 5 + 5 = 6x - 9 + 5$

Simplify: $\qquad\qquad\qquad\qquad\quad 5x = 6x - 4$

Subtract $6x$ from both sides: $\quad 5x - 6x = 6x - 4 - 6x$

Simplify: $\qquad\qquad\qquad\qquad\quad -x = -4$

Divide both sides by -1: $\qquad\qquad x = 4$

To check, substitute 4 for x in the original equation.

L.S. $= \dfrac{x-1}{3}$ $\qquad$ **R.S.** $= \dfrac{2x-3}{5}$

$\qquad = \dfrac{4-1}{3}$ $\qquad\qquad\qquad = \dfrac{2(4)-3}{5}$

$\qquad = \dfrac{3}{3}$ $\qquad\qquad\qquad\quad = \dfrac{5}{5}$

$\qquad = 1$ $\qquad\qquad\qquad\quad\;\; = 1$

Since L.S. = R.S., the solution is $x = 4$.

3. Solve and check.

a) $\dfrac{x}{3} + 1 = 4$

b) $\dfrac{x}{2} + \dfrac{1}{3} = \dfrac{5}{6}$

c) $\dfrac{x}{5} - \dfrac{1}{2} = \dfrac{3}{10}$

d) $\dfrac{x+3}{2} = x - 2$

e) $\dfrac{x-1}{2} = \dfrac{x+1}{3}$

f) $\dfrac{2x+1}{3} = \dfrac{x-6}{8}$

g) $\dfrac{x+4}{2} - \dfrac{x+10}{4} = -1$

h) $\dfrac{x+7}{5} - \dfrac{2x}{3} = 0$

i) $\dfrac{x+1}{8} + \dfrac{x+3}{5} = 3$

Solving proportions

Proportions can be solved using the cross-product rule, which states that, if $\dfrac{a}{b} = \dfrac{c}{d}$, then $a \times d = b \times c$.

To solve $2:5 = 3:x$, first write the proportion in fraction form, $\dfrac{2}{5} = \dfrac{3}{x}$.

Then, use the cross-product rule.

$$\frac{2}{5} = \frac{3}{x}$$
$$2x = 5 \times 3$$
$$2x = 15$$
$$x = \frac{15}{2} \text{ or } 7.5$$

1. Solve for x. Express each answer as a fraction in lowest terms.

a) $\dfrac{x}{6} = \dfrac{2}{5}$ **b)** $\dfrac{4}{5} = \dfrac{x}{3}$ **c)** $\dfrac{2}{x} = \dfrac{3}{7}$ **d)** $\dfrac{3}{2} = \dfrac{4}{x}$

e) $x:4 = 5:6$ **f)** $8:x = 6:7$ **g)** $4:9 = x:6$ **h)** $5:8 = 2:x$

2. Solve for x. Express each answer as a decimal. Round to the nearest hundredth, if necessary.

a) $\dfrac{x}{3.4} = 4.5$ **b)** $\dfrac{2.6}{x} = 5.8$ **c)** $3.2 = \dfrac{x}{4.3}$ **d)** $\dfrac{x}{1.5} = \dfrac{2.6}{3}$

e) $\dfrac{0.8}{x} = \dfrac{4.2}{1.4}$ **f)** $\dfrac{3.8}{1.7} = \dfrac{2.8}{x}$ **g)** $6.3:x = 7.5:8.3$ **h)** $1.4:0.5 = 2.9:x$

Subtracting polynomials

To subtract
$$\begin{aligned} 5x - 2y + 8 \\ 2x + 3y - 2 \end{aligned}$$

add the opposite of the polynomial that is being subtracted.
The opposite of $2x + 3y - 2$ is $-2x - 3y + 2$.

$$\begin{array}{r} 5x - 2y + 8 \\ -2x - 3y + 2 \\ \hline 3x - 5y + 10 \end{array}$$

1. Subtract.

a) $\begin{array}{l} 5x + 6y + 8 \\ 3x + 2y + 5 \end{array}$ **b)** $\begin{array}{l} 7x - 5y - 8 \\ 4x - 3y - 7 \end{array}$ **c)** $\begin{array}{l} 3x^2 - 6x - 4 \\ 4x^2 + 2x + 5 \end{array}$

d) $\begin{array}{l} 5a^2 - a + 3 \\ 2a^2 - 7a - 8 \end{array}$ **e)** $\begin{array}{l} -4a + 3b + 1 \\ 3a - 3b - 6 \end{array}$ **f)** $\begin{array}{l} 4y^2 + 2y - 3 \\ -3y^2 + 6y - 1 \end{array}$

Transformations

To translate △ABC 5 units to the left and 4 units up, translate each vertex of the triangle 5 units to the left and 4 units up. Join the new points to form the translation image, △A′B′C′. △ABC and its translation image, △A′B′C′, are congruent, since corresponding side lengths and angles are equal.

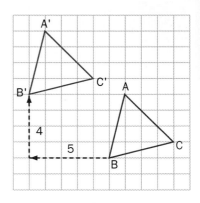

1. Draw each triangle on grid paper. Then, draw the translation image for the given translation.

a)

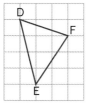

3 right, 3 down

b)

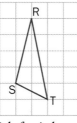

2 left, 4 down

c)

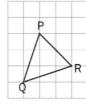

2 right, 4 up

To reflect △DEF in the reflection line *m*, reflect each vertex of △DEF in the line. Each vertex of △DEF and its reflection image are the same perpendicular distance from the line *m*. Join the new points to form the reflection image, △D′E′F′. △DEF and its reflection image, △D′E′F′, are congruent, since corresponding side lengths and angles are equal.

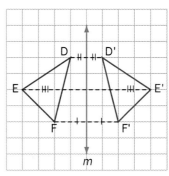

2. Draw each triangle on grid paper. Then, draw the reflection image in the given reflection line.

a)

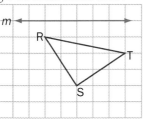

b)

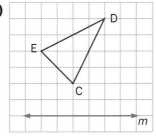

c)

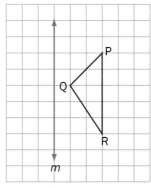

Graphing Calculator Keystrokes

Note: Unless otherwise stated, all keystrokes are for the TI-83 Plus or TI-83 graphing calculator.

Function or Instruction and Description	Keystroke(s), Menu, or Screen
Displaying a table A table of values can be calculated and displayed for any function.	**Example:** To display a table of values for the function $y = 2x^2 - 8$, enter the function into the **Y= editor**. If you wish the table of values to be generated automatically, press [2nd] [WINDOW] to define the initial value for the independent variable, x. Set TblStart to the initial value you want for your table of values, for example, –3. Set $\triangle$Tbl to the value of the desired increment for the independent variable, for example, 1. If you wish the values for both the independent variable, x, and the dependent variable, y, to be displayed automatically, select Indpnt: Auto and Depend: Auto. For this example, you will see: To display the table of values, press [2nd] [GRAPH]. For this example, you will see:

Function or Instruction and Description	Keystroke(s), Menu, or Screen
Expand function (TI-92 PLUS or TI-92) The expand function, on the TI-92 Plus or TI-92, expands and simplifies a product of polynomials.	To select the expand function from the Algebra menu, press [F2] 3. **Example:** To expand $(4x + 3y)(x - y)$, press [F2] 3 [(] 4 [×] X [+] 3 [×] Y [)] [(] X [−] Y [)] [)] [ENTER] You will see: 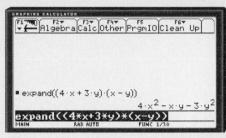
Factor function (TI-92 PLUS or TI-92) The factor function, on the TI-92 Plus or TI-92, factors a polynomial.	To select the factor function from the Algebra menu, press [F2] 2. **Example:** To factor $3x^2 - 5x + 2$, press [F2] 2 3 [×] X [^] 2 [−] 5 [×] X [+] 2 [)] [ENTER] You will see: 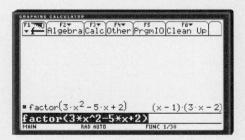

Function or Instruction and Description	Keystroke(s), Menu, or Screen

Format settings

Format settings define the appearance of a graph on the display. Format settings apply to all graphing modes.

To display the format settings, press (2nd) (ZOOM).
The default settings are shown here.

To change a format setting, press (▼), (▶), (▲), and (◀) as necessary, to move the cursor to the setting you want to select, and press (ENTER) to select it.

For example, the default setting GridOff means that no grid is displayed on a graph. If you wish to display a grid, press (▼), (▼), (▶), and (ENTER) to select GridOn.

▶Frac function

The ▶Frac function displays an answer as a fraction.

To display an answer as a fraction, press (MATH) to display the MATH menu. Press 1 to select ▶Frac to convert an answer to a fraction.

Example:
To find the exact point of intersection of $y = 5x + 3$ and $y = -2x - 5$, enter the functions into the Y= editor and graph them. Use the intersect operation to find the point of intersection, $x = -1.142857$ and $y = -2.714286$.

To find the exact value of x, press (2nd) (MODE) (X,T,θ,n) (MATH) 1 (ENTER).

To find the exact value of y, press (ALPHA) 1 (MATH) 1 (ENTER).

You will see:

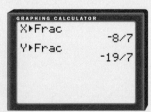

Function or Instruction and Description	Keystroke(s), Menu, or Screen
Intersect operation The intersect operation finds the coordinates of a point at which two or more functions intersect.	To find an intersection, display the graphs on the screen. The point of intersection must appear on the display to use the intersect operation. **Example:** To find the point of intersection of $y = 3x - 2$ and $y = -x + 6$, use the **Y= editor** to input both functions and graph them. Press ⟨2nd⟩ ⟨TRACE⟩, to display the CALCULATE menu. To select the intersect operation, press 5. You will see: 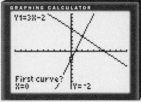 Press ⟨▼⟩ or ⟨▲⟩, if necessary, to move the cursor to the first function, and then press ⟨ENTER⟩. You will see: 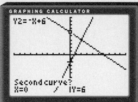 Press ⟨▼⟩ or ⟨▲⟩, if necessary, to move the cursor to the second function, and then press ⟨ENTER⟩. You will see: 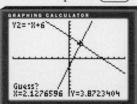 Press ⟨▶⟩ or ⟨◀⟩ to move the cursor to the point that is your guess for the point of intersection, and then press ⟨ENTER⟩. You will see: 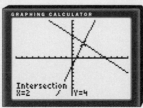 Notice that the cursor appears on the solution, and the coordinates of the solution are displayed.

Function or Instruction and Description	Keystroke(s), Menu, or Screen
LinReg (linear regression) instruction The linear regression instruction is used to fit the equation of a linear function to a given set of data. The values of a (slope) and b (y-intercept) are displayed for an equation of the form $y = ax + b$.	**Example:** Fit a linear equation to the following data points. L1 L2 2 0 3 12 4 24 5 36 To use the linear regression instruction, enter the data points as two lists using the STAT EDIT menu. Choose suitable window variables using the window editor, or adjust the window automatically using the ZoomStat instruction. Graph L2 versus L1 on a scatter plot using the STAT PLOTS menu. To select the linear regression instruction, press (STAT) (▶) to access the STAT CALC menu. You will see:  Select 4:LinReg(ax+b). You will see: 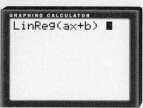 Press (2nd) 1 to specify the Xlist name, in this case L1. Press (,) (2nd) 2 to specify the Ylist name, in this case L2. Press (,) (VARS) (▶) 1 to list possible Y= variables. To store the regression equation in Y1, select 1:Y1 and press (ENTER). You will see:  Press (ENTER).

Function or Instruction and Description	Keystroke(s), Menu, or Screen
	You will see:  The regression equation is stored in the **Y= editor**. To view the line of best fit on your scatter plot, press GRAPH.
Maximum operation The maximum operation finds the maximum of a function within a specified interval.	**Example:** To find the maximum of $y = -2x^2 + 6x + 2$, input the function in the **Y= editor**. Press (2nd) (TRACE) to display the CALCULATE menu. Press 4 to select the maximum operation. You will see: 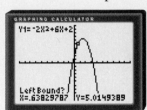 Press (▼) or (▲), if necessary, to move the cursor onto the function. Press (▶) or (◀) to move the cursor to the left of the maximum (or enter a value). Select the x-value for the left bound of the interval by pressing (ENTER). Press (▶) or (◀) to move the cursor to the right of the maximum (or enter a value). Select the x-value for the right bound of the interval by pressing (ENTER). Press (▶) or (◀) (or enter a value) to select an x-value for a guess at the maximum, and then press (ENTER). You will see: 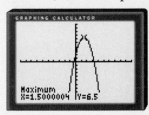 The vertex of $y = -2x^2 + 6x + 2$ is (1.5, 6.5). The maximum value of $y = -2x^2 + 6x + 2$ is 6.5 when $x = 1.5$.

Function or Instruction and Description	Keystroke(s), Menu, or Screen
Minimum operation The minimum operation finds the minimum of a function within a specified interval.	**Example:** To find the minimum of $y = 2x^2 + 5x - 4$, input the function in the Y= editor. Press ⌜2nd⌝ ⌜TRACE⌝ to display the CALCULATE menu. Press 3 to select the minimum operation. You will see:  Press ⌜▼⌝ or ⌜▲⌝, if necessary, to move the cursor onto the function. Press ⌜▶⌝ or ⌜◀⌝ to move the cursor to the left of the minimum (or enter a value). Select the x-value for the left bound of the interval by pressing ⌜ENTER⌝. Press ⌜▶⌝ or ⌜◀⌝ to move the cursor to the right of the minimum (or enter a value). Select the x-value for the right bound of the interval by pressing ⌜ENTER⌝. Press ⌜▶⌝ or ⌜◀⌝ (or enter a value) to select an x-value for a guess at the minimum, and then press ⌜ENTER⌝. You will see: 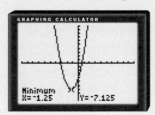 The vertex of $y = 2x^2 + 5x - 4$ is $(-1.25, -7.125)$. The minimum value of $y = 2x^2 + 5x - 4$ is -7.125 when $x = -1.25$.

Function or Instruction and Description	Keystroke(s), Menu, or Screen
Mode settings Mode settings control the way the calculator displays and interprets numbers and graphs.	To display the mode settings, press (MODE). The default settings are shown here. 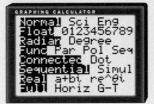 To change a mode setting, press (▼), (▶), (▲), and (◀) as necessary, to move the cursor to the setting you want to select, and press ENTER to select it. For example, the default setting Radian means that angles are measured in radians. If you wish angles to be measured in degrees, press (▼), (▼), (▶), and (ENTER) to select Degree.
PRGM key The PRGM key is used to access the programming menus.	To display the programming menus, press (PRGM). To exit the programming menus and return to the home screen, press (2nd) (MODE) to quit.
PRGM EXEC menu The PRGM EXEC menu is used to execute an existing program.	To display the PRGM EXEC menu, press (PRGM). Select a program name from the PRGM EXEC menu and press (ENTER) to execute the program. You will see a screen that resembles the one at the right, but the programs listed will vary. 

Function or Instruction and Description	Keystroke(s), Menu, or Screen
PRGM NEW menu The PRGM NEW menu is used when you want to create a new program.	To display the PRGM NEW menu, press (PRGM) (▶) (▶). To create a new program, press 1. You will see:   To name your program, type in the name of the program using the (ALPHA) key and appropriate letter keys shown in green on the calculator, and then press (ENTER). You can now enter your program. To use the operations found in the PRGM CTL menu, press the (PRGM) key. You will see:  To use the operations found in the PRGM I/O menu, press (PRGM) (▶). You will see:  If you need to input special characters such as =, ≠, >, ≥, <, ≤, press (2nd) (MATH) to display the TEST menu. You will see:  To choose the desired character, press the (▼) or (▲) keys to highlight the character and then press (ENTER), or type the number of the desired character.

Function or Instruction and Description	Keystroke(s), Menu, or Screen

QuadReg (quadratic regression) instruction

The quadratic regression instruction is used to fit the equation of a quadratic function to a given set of data. The values for *a*, *b*, and *c* are displayed for a function of the form $y = ax^2 + bc + c$.

To use the quadratic regression instruction, enter the data points as two lists using the STAT EDIT menu. Choose suitable window variables using the window editor, or adjust the window automatically using the ZoomStat instruction. Graph L2 versus L1 on a scatter plot using the STAT PLOTS menu.

To select the quadratic regression instruction, press [STAT] [▶] to access the STAT CALC menu.
Select 5:QuadReg.

You will see:

Specify the Xlist name, such as L1, by pressing [2nd] 1.
Specify the Ylist name, such as L2, by pressing [2nd] 2.
Press [,] [VARS] [▶] 1 to list possible Y= variables.
To store the regression equation in Y1, select 1:Y1 and press [ENTER].

You will see:

Press [ENTER].
You will see, for example:

The regression equation is stored in the Y= editor.
If you wish to view the curve of best fit on your scatter plot, press [GRAPH].

Function or Instruction and Description	Keystroke(s), Menu, or Screen
Solve function (TI-92 PLUS or TI-92) The solve function, on the TI-92 Plus or TI-92, solves an algebraic equation for an indicated variable.	To select the solve function from the Algebra menu, press F2 1. **Example:** To solve $3x - 4y = -12$ for y, press F2 1 3 × X − 4 × Y = (−) 12 , Y) ENTER You will see: 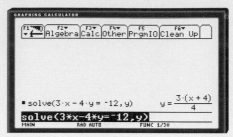
Standard viewing window The standard viewing window is the portion of the coordinate plane often used for graphs shown on the calculator screen.	Press MODE ▼ ▼ ▼ ENTER to ensure that the calculator is in Func graphing mode. To display a graph using the standard viewing window, press ZOOM 6. To display the current window variables, press WINDOW. You will see:  These are the window variables for the standard viewing window.

Function or Instruction and Description	Keystroke(s), Menu, or Screen
STAT EDIT menu The STAT EDIT menu is used when you wish to store, edit, and view lists of data in the stat list editor.	To display the STAT EDIT menu, press (STAT) You will see: 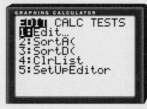

To display the stat list editor, press (STAT) 1:Edit
You will see:

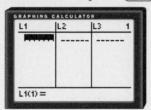

Lists of data can be stored in lists named L1 through L6.
To clear data from a specific list, for example L1,
press (STAT) 4:ClrList (2nd) 1 (ENTER)
To clear data from all lists, press (2nd) (+) 4:ClrAllLists

Example:
Enter the following table in lists L1 and L2.

L1	L2
2	0
3	12
4	24
5	36

Press (2nd) (+) 4:ClrAllLists (ENTER) to clear all data from lists L1 to L6.
Press (STAT) 1:Edit to display the stat list editor.
To enter the data in L1, press 2 (ENTER) 3 (ENTER) 4 (ENTER) 5 (ENTER).
To enter the data in L2, press (▶) 0 (ENTER) 12 (ENTER) 24 (ENTER) 36 (ENTER).

You will see:

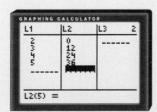

Function or Instruction and Description	Keystroke(s), Menu, or Screen
STAT PLOTS menu The STAT PLOTS menu allows you to plot data in a scatterplot, xyLine, histogram, modified box plot, regular box plot, or normal probability plot.	To display the STAT PLOTS menu, press (2nd) (Y=). **Example:** Plot the data in a scatter plot. | L1	L2
2	0
3	12
4	24
5	36 | Enter the data in lists L1 and L2 using the STAT EDIT menu. Press (2nd) (Y=) to display the STAT PLOTS menu. You will see:  Press (ENTER) to select Plot1 or use the (▼) key to select Plot2 or Plot3 and press (ENTER). To turn on a plot, press (ENTER). You will see:  To select a scatter plot, press (▼) (ENTER). If the Xlist is not already L1, press (▼) (2nd) 1 (ENTER). If the Ylist is not already L2, press (▼) (2nd) 2 (ENTER). Choose the type of mark for the data points, by pressing (▶) or (◀) to highlight the desired mark, and then press (ENTER). To display the plot, press (ZOOM) 9 to select the ZoomStat instruction. You will see: 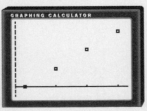

Function or Instruction and Description	Keystroke(s), Menu, or Screen
Trace instruction The TRACE instruction allows you to move the cursor along the graph of a function. The coordinates of points on the graph are displayed in the viewing window.	For a graph drawn using an equation in the **Y= editor**, press the TRACE key to display the cursor on the graph. Press ◄ or ► to move the cursor along the graph. The x- and y-coordinates of points on the graph will be displayed at the bottom of the screen. For a scatter plot drawn using the **STAT PLOTS menu**, press the TRACE key and ◄ or ► to move the cursor from one point to the next on the scatter plot. The coordinates of each point will be displayed.
Value Operation The value operation evaluates a function for a specified value of x.	**Example:** To evaluate the function $y = x^2 + 3x - 4$ for $x = -3$, input the function in the **Y= editor**. Press 2nd TRACE to display the CALCULATE menu. Press ENTER to select the value operation. You will see: 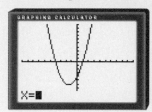 Enter the value −3 for x. Press ENTER . You will see: 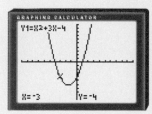 **Note:** The value for which you evaluate a function must lie between Xmin and Xmax of the viewing window used for the graph.

Function or Instruction and Description	Keystroke(s), Menu, or Screen
Window variables The window variables define the current viewing window.	To display the current window variable values, press [WINDOW]. To change a window variable value, press [▼] or [▲] to move the cursor to the window variable you want to change. Enter the new value and then press [ENTER].
With operator **(TI-92 Plus or TI-92)** The with operator (|) can be used to evaluate an expression or to solve an equation for one variable given the value of another variable.	To display the with operator, press [2nd] K. **Example:** To solve the equation $2x + 5y = -2$ for x when $y = 2$, press [F2] 1 2 [×] X [+] 5 [×] Y [=] [(-)] 2 [,] X [)] [2nd] K Y [=] 2 [ENTER] You will see: 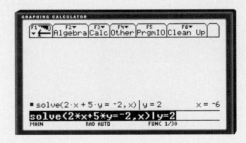

Function or Instruction and Description	Keystroke(s), Menu, or Screen
Y= editor The Y= editor is used to define or edit a function.	Press MODE ▼ ▼ ▼ ENTER to ensure that the calculator is in Func graphing mode. To display the Y= editor, press Y=. To move the cursor to the next function, press ENTER or ▼. To move the cursor from one function to another, press ▼ or ▲. To erase a function, highlight the function and press CLEAR. The independent variable is X. To input X, press X,T,θ,*n* or ALPHA STO. When you input the first character of a function, the = is highlighted. This indicates that the function is selected. To deselect a function, move the cursor to the = symbol of the function and press ENTER. **Example:** To input $y = 3x - 2$ using the Y= editor, press the Y= key. You will see:  Press 3 X,T,θ,*n* − 2 ENTER. You will see: 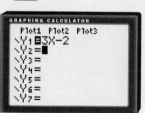

Function or Instruction and Description	Keystroke(s), Menu, or Screen

Zero operation

The zero operation finds the zeros or x-intercepts of functions. If a function has two or more x-intercepts, they must be found separately by repeated use of the zero operation.

Example

To find the x-intercepts of $y = x^2 + 2x - 8$, input the function in the **Y= editor**.

Press (2nd) (TRACE) to display the CALCULATE menu.

Press (▼) (ENTER) to select the zero operation.

You will see:

Press (▼) or (▲), if necessary, to move the cursor onto the function.

To find the left x-intercept, press (▶) or (◀) to move the cursor to the left of the left x-intercept (or enter a value). Select the x-value by pressing (ENTER).

Press (▶) or (◀) to move the cursor to a location between the left x-intercept and the right x-intercept (or enter a value). Select the x-value by pressing (ENTER).

Press (▶) or (◀) (or enter a value) to select an x-value for a guess at the left x-intercept, and then press (ENTER).

You will see:

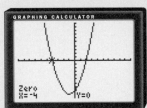

To find the right x-intercept, press (▶) or (◀) to move the cursor to a location between the left x-intercept and the right x-intercept (or enter a value). Select the x-value by pressing (ENTER).

Press (▶) or (◀) to move the cursor to the right of the right x-intercept (or enter a value). Select the x-value by pressing (ENTER).

Press (▶) or (◀) (or enter a value) to select an x-value for a guess at the right x-intercept, and then press (ENTER).

Function or Instruction and Description	Keystroke(s), Menu, or Screen
	You will see: 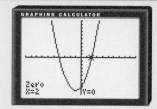
ZoomStat instruction The ZoomStat instruction redefines the window variables to display all statistical data points on the screen.	Press (ZOOM) to display the ZOOM menu. Press 9 to display all your data using the ZoomStat instruction.
ZSquare instruction The ZSquare instruction allow you to adjust the viewing window, so that graphs are plotted using equal-sized-scales on both the x- and y-axes.	Press (ZOOM) to access the ZOOM menu. Press 5 to display a graph using the ZSquare instruction. **Example:** To graph $y = x^2 - 4$ using the ZSquare instruction, input the function using the **Y= editor**. Press (ZOOM) to access the ZOOM menu. You will see: 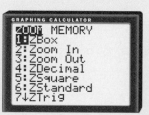 Press 5 to display the graph using the ZSquare instruction. You will see: 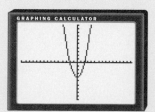

Using *The Geometer's Sketchpad*®

Preferences

Before you begin using *The Geometer's Sketchpad*®, you may need to change some of the default settings in the program. Click on the Display menu and choose Preferences.

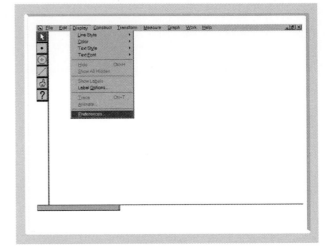

A window like the one shown will open up. Be sure that the Distance units are set to "cm" and not "inches." You should also change the Precision options to "tenths" instead of "units". If you are working with angle measures, make sure that the Angle Unit is "degrees," not "radians." Finally, click on the Autoshow Labels for Points button in the upper left corner of the window.

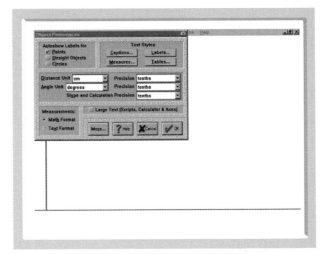

Tools and Menus

On the left side of the screen there is a set of features called a Toolbox. To select a tool from the Toolbox, click on the tool. The active tool will be highlighted.

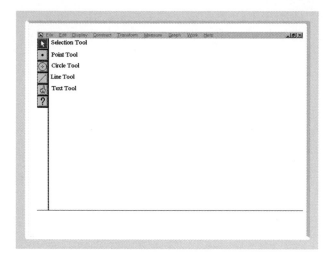

The **Selection Tool** is used to select objects on the screen. To select an object, click on the Selection Tool and then on the object, which will be highlighted. To highlight more than one object, press and hold the SHIFT key and click on the objects.

The **Point Tool** is used to create new points on the screen. Clicking anywhere on the screen creates a point.

The **Circle Tool** is used to create a circle on the screen. To use this tool, click on a point and hold the left mouse button. This creates the centre point of a circle. As you drag the mouse, the circle will be created. Release the mouse button to fix the size of the circle. A second method of creating a circle is given later in this appendix.

The **Line Tool** is used to create a line segment. Click on the first endpoint and drag out to the second endpoint. Later in this appendix, you will see that the Line Tool can also be used to create a ray or a line, and that a line segment can also be created using another method.

The **Text Tool** is used to show, hide, or change labels assigned to objects on the screen.

Across the top of the screen is a set of menus. A brief description of some of these menu items follows.

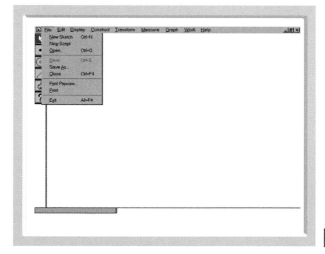

The File Menu

Click on New Sketch when you are ready to start a new drawing.
The Open command allows you to open a file saved on disk.
Save As allows you to save a drawing to disk.
The Print command sends a copy of your drawing to the printer.
Exit is used to quit *The Geometer's Sketchpad®*.

The Display Menu

At the start of every drawing, you can use the Display menu to set the Line Style to Thick and the "Color" to your choice.

The Preferences command at the bottom of the menu was referred to earlier. It is used to set up your preferences for *The Geometer's Sketchpad®*.

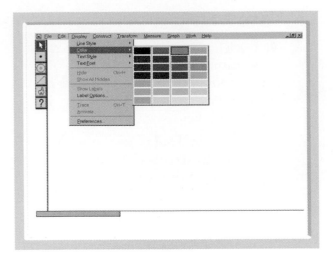

The Construct Menu

The Construct menu shows commands that apply to the object highlighted on the screen. In the graphic, a line segment is highlighted, so the menu gives you the choice of creating a point somewhere on the segment, or creating the midpoint of the segment, and so on. The commands will be explained as they are needed later in this appendix.

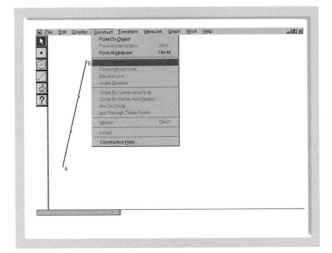

The Measure Menu

The Measure menu shows commands that apply to the object highlighted on the screen. The graphic shows the commands that apply to the same line segment as above. Other commands become available for other objects and will be explained as needed.

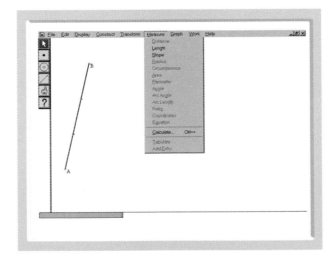

Constructions and Measurements

1 Constructing and Measuring a Line Segment

1. Click on the Point Tool on the left side of the screen. With this tool activated, clicking anywhere on the screen creates a point.

2. Create two points on the screen.

3. Highlight both points. To do this, click on one point, and then press SHIFT and click on the other point.

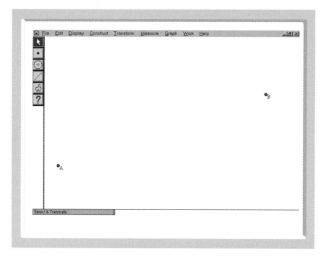

4. With both points highlighted, choose the Segment command from the Construct menu. You will create a line segment joining the points.

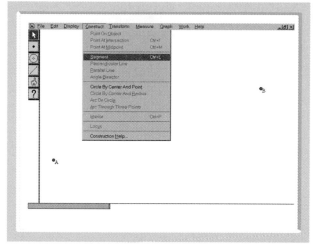

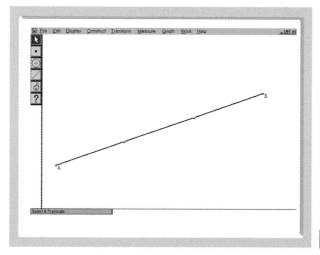

5. Using the Selection Tool, click on the line segment. You will see two small squares on the line segment to indicate that it is highlighted.

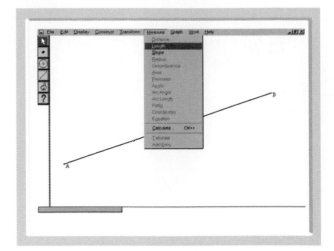

6. Choose the Length command from the Measure menu. The length of the segment will be displayed in the upper left corner of the screen.

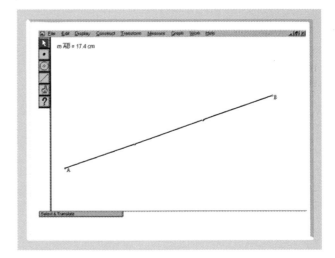

7. Drag one of the endpoints to make the line longer. To drag a point, move your cursor over the point and click on it with the left mouse button. While holding that button down, move the point to a different location on the screen. Notice that the measurement changes.

8. Experiment with using different colours for your line segment. To do this, choose "Color" from the Display menu.

9. To experiment with different line styles, choose Line Style from the Display menu. Choose a thin, thick, or dashed line style.

2 Measuring the Slope of a Line Segment

1. Construct a line segment. Choose the Slope command from the Measure menu to find the slope of your line segment. If the slope is positive, drag the line segment so that the slope is negative. If the slope is negative, drag the line segment so that the slope is positive.

2. Drag the line segment slowly so that it becomes horizontal. What happens to the slope as you move the line segment into the horizontal position?

3. Drag the line segment slowly into a vertical position. What happens to the slope as you move the line segment into the vertical position?

3 Constructing a Line

1. Click on the Line Tool on the left side of the screen and hold down the left mouse button. A window will pop up to the right. The first option is a line segment, the second is a ray, and the third is line. Select the line option.

2. Click on the Point Tool and create two points anywhere on the screen.

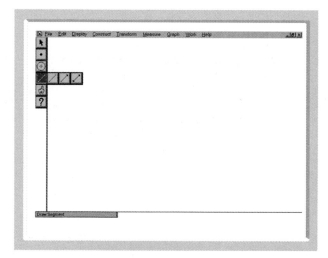

3. Click on the Construct menu and choose the Line command. A line through the two points will appear on the screen.

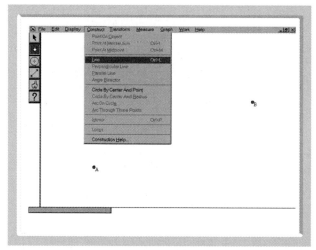

4 Constructing and Measuring an Angle

1. Construct a line segment AB anywhere on the screen. Construct a new point, C, and join it to A with a line segment. This creates an angle that is labelled ∠CAB. Point A is called the vertex of the angle.

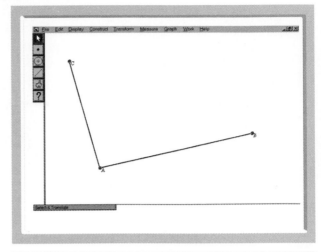

2. Highlight the three points in the order C, A, B.

3. Click on the Measure menu and choose the Angle command to find the measure of your angle.

4. Drag point B or point C to change the angle. Notice that the measurement changes.

5. Is it possible to drag one of the endpoints so that you construct a right angle? Describe what you would do to construct an obtuse angle.

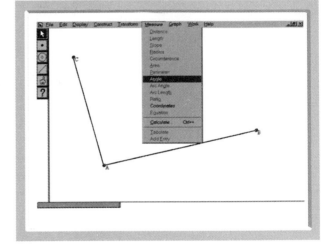

6. Drag one endpoint to create a straight angle.

7. Is it possible to drag one endpoint so that you construct a reflex angle?

5 Constructing and Measuring a Triangle

1. Construct and highlight three points on the screen. To create a triangle, △ABC, choose the Segment command from the Construct menu.

2. Highlight the three line segments that make up the triangle and click on the Length command from the Measure menu to find their lengths.

3. From the Measure menu, choose the Calculate command. A calculator will appear on the screen. The calculator can be used to highlight any measurement that is already on the screen and/or do any arithmetic operation. Click on the length of AB, and then click on the addition sign on the calculator. Click on the length of AC, followed by the addition sign on the calculator again. Finally, click on the length of BC, followed by the OK button. The perimeter of △ABC will be displayed on the screen.

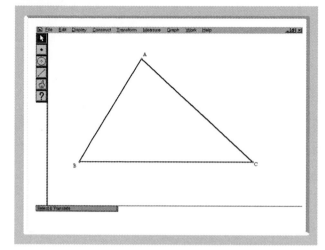

4. To calculate the area of the triangle, click on the three vertices and choose the Polygon Interior command from the Construct menu. Click on the Area command from the measure menu.

6 Constructing a Midpoint of a Line Segment

1. Construct a line segment, AB.

2. Choose the Point At Midpoint command from the Construct menu. You will create a new point, C, in the centre of the line segment.

3. Construct two new segments from A to C and from B to C.

4. Measure the lengths of AB, AC and BC. What do you notice about the lengths of AC and BC? How do the lengths of these segments compare to the length of AB?

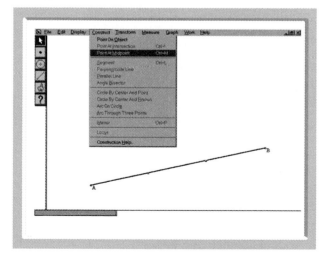

5. Are these properties preserved when you drag point A to a new location?

7 Constructing a Right Bisector of a Line Segment

The right bisector of a line segment is a line that intersects a line segment at its midpoint at a 90° angle.

1. Construct a line segment, AB.

2. To construct the midpoint, C, choose the Point at Midpoint command from the Construct menu.

3. Click on the midpoint and the line segment so that both are highlighted.

4. Click on the Construct menu and choose the Perpendicular Line command.

5. With this line highlighted, choose the Point on Object command from the Construct menu to create point D.

6. Measure the line segments AC and BC, and ∠DCA and ∠DCB.

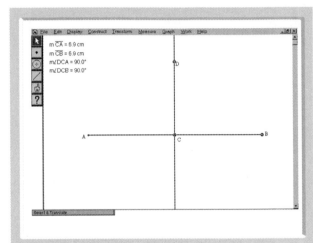

8 Constructing an Altitude of a Triangle

1. Construct and highlight three points on the screen. To create a triangle, △ABC, choose the Segment command from the Construct menu. This will create a triangle.

2. Highlight point A and side BC.

3. Click on the Construct menu and choose the Perpendicular Line command. This new line will be highlighted.

4. Hold down the shift key and click on side BC, so that it is also highlighted.

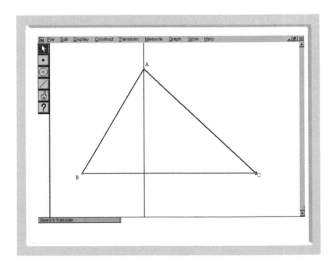

5. Click on the Construct menu and choose the Point At Intersection command. You will create a new point D on side BC.

6. Click on the line. Then, click on the Display menu and choose the Hide Line command.

7. Construct a line segment joining points A and D. This line segment is called an altitude.

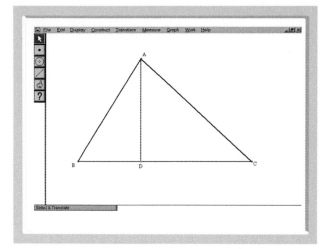

9 Constructing a Median of a Triangle

A median is a line segment drawn from a vertex of a triangle to the midpoint of the opposite side.

1. Construct a triangle labelled ABC.

2. Highlight side BC.

3. Construct the midpoint of BC at D.

4. Construct a line segment joining points A and D. Line segment AD is the median.

5. Measure the areas of △ADB and △ADC. How do the areas of these figures compare to each other? How do they compare to the area of △ABC?

6. Drag point A to a new location. Are the properties from question 5 preserved?

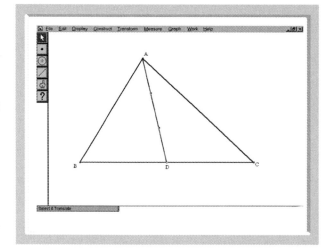

10 Constructing a Circle

Method 1

1. Construct two points anywhere on the screen.

2. Highlight the two points.

3. Click on the Construct menu and choose the "Circle By Center And Point" command.

4. Repeat steps 2 and 3, but click the points in the opposite order. How does this change affect your drawing?

Method 2

1. Click on the Circle Tool on the left side of the screen.

2. Click on any point in the centre of the screen. Keep the left mouse button pressed down and drag out to a new location on the screen. As you drag, a circle is constructed. When you let go, the circle is drawn in the colour you have selected.

11 Constructing a Square

1. Construct a horizontal line segment AB at the bottom of the screen.

2. Highlight point A and choose "Mark Center A" from the Transform menu. When you do this, point A will be accented briefly with circles.

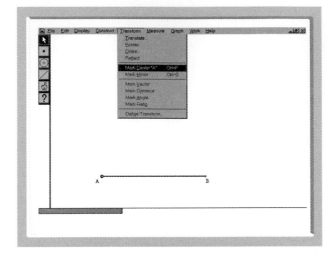

3. Highlight point B and the line segment AB. Choose Rotate from the Transform menu.

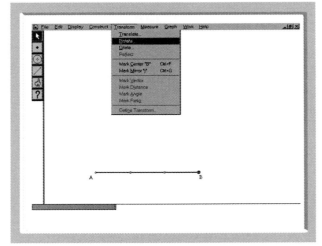

4. A window will open. Enter 90° for the angle and click on OK. You will now have two perpendicular line segments, AB and AB′, that are the same length.

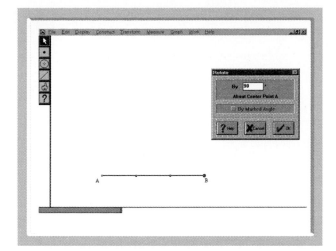

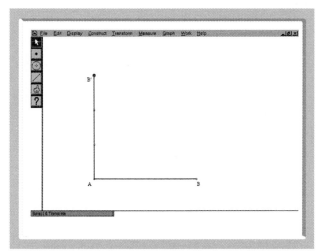

5. Click on the open area to remove highlighting.

6. Highlight the new point B′ and choose "Mark Center" from the Transform menu.

7. Highlight the new line segment AB′ and endpoint A.

8. Choose Rotate from the Transform menu. Enter 90° for the angle of rotation and click on OK. You will now have three sides of the square.

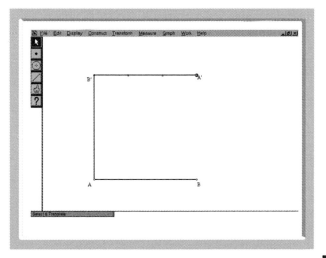

9. To complete the square, construct a line segment joining the points B and A'.

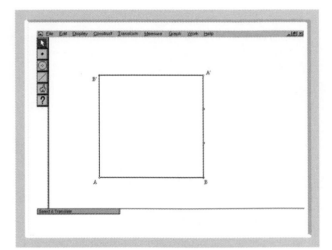

12 Using Scripts

A **script** is a small program that keeps a record of the steps in a construction. By saving a script, you can repeat the construction by drawing a minimum number of objects, running the script, and having the rest of the object drawn for you.

To construct a square using a script, follow the steps below.

1. Draw a horizontal line segment on the screen.

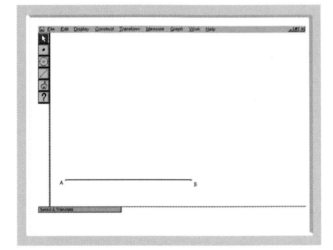

2. Click on the File menu and choose the New Script command. A window will open on the right side of the screen. This window will be used to record the steps in the construction.

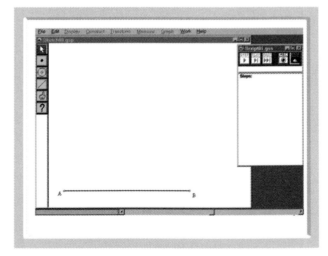

3. Refer to the list of steps in activity 11, Constructing a Square. You have already done the first step by drawing a horizontal line segment. Now begin recording instructions in your script by clicking on the "Rec" button in the script window. Repeat the construction of a square by starting at step 2 of activity 11.

4. When you have completed all of the steps and the square is finished, click on the Stop button in the script window. Note that the script lists not only your steps, but also the objects that you must create when you use the script in the future. This example lists Point B, Point A, and Object j (a line segment joining points A and B).

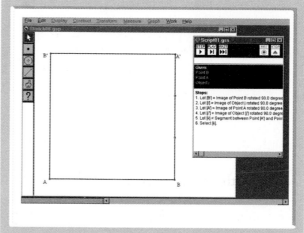

5. To save your script, click on the File menu and choose the Save As command.

6. To use your script, start a new construction, keeping the script window on the right side of the screen.

7. Construct a line segment on the screen.

8. Highlight one endpoint, followed by the second endpoint, and finally the line segment joining them. Be sure that all three are highlighted in that order. Click on Play in the script window. A square will be drawn, based upon the line segment that you provided.

Answers

Chapter 1

Getting Started p. 2
1. 10; The check digit will be 0. **2. a)** 9 **b)** 9 **c)** 2
d) 8 **3. a)** No, the check digit should be 6.
b) Yes, the check digit is correct. **c)** Yes, the check
digit is correct. **4.** Answers may vary. 123 456 717;
223 456 740 **5. a)** $10 - m$ **b)** 0 **c)** The check digit
is equal to $10 - m$ if $m \neq 0$ and 0 if $m = 0$.

Review of Prerequisite Skills p. 3
1. a) $x + 2$ **b)** $2x + 8$ **c)** $3y - 5$ **d)** $-5a + 3$ **e)** $6x + 14$
f) $5z - 8$ **g)** $7t + 41$ **h)** $2x - 9$ **2. a)** $6x$ **b)** $-2c$ **c)** x
d) $3n$ **e)** $x + 2y$ **f)** $3p - r$ **3. a)** 8 **b)** 2 **c)** -6 **d)** -5
4. a) 7 **b)** -3 **c)** 2 **d)** 12 **e)** $-\dfrac{1}{2}$ **f)** $\dfrac{3}{2}$ **g)** 4 **h)** -5 **i)** $-\dfrac{5}{2}$
j) -4 **k)** -1 **l)** 2 **5. a)** $x = 11 - 3y$ **b)** $x = 5y - 8$
c) $x = 2y - 4$ **d)** $x = \dfrac{5 - 3y}{2}$ **6. a)** $y = 3 - 2x$

b) $y = x - 2$ **c)** $y = \dfrac{-1 - 2x}{4}$ **d)** $y = \dfrac{3x - 4}{2}$
10. a) $(3, 1)$ **b)** $(5, -2)$ **c)** $(-1, 6)$ **d)** $(4, 8)$ **e)** $(-4, -5)$
f) $(2, -1)$ **11. a)** $9x - 4y + 1$ **b)** $13m^2 - 6m - 19$
c) $-a - 3b - 10$ **d)** $-e - 2$ **12. a)** $x - 8y + 10$
b) $-t^2 - 5t - 11$ **c)** $-9a + 3b + 1$ **d)** $12e - 1$

Section 1.1 pp. 4–5
1 Ordered Pairs and One Equation 1. a) $(1, 13)$,
$(24, -10)$ **b)** $(-2, -4)$, $(-12, 0)$ **c)** $(2, 3)$ **d)** $(0.5, -2.5)$
2. a) 3, 9, 10, -2 **b)** 2, -9, 11, -2 **c)** -1, 5, 13, 10
d) 5, 3, -4, -7
2 Ordered Pairs and Two Equations 1. a) $(1, 2)$
b) $(-3, 1)$ **c)** $(2, 3)$ **d)** $(6, -8)$ **e)** $(-2, -5)$ **f)** $(-4, 7)$
2. a) $(4, -3)$ **b)** $(6, 3)$ **c)** $(-1, 0)$ **d)** Answers may
vary. $(0, 0)$
3 Problem Solving 1. a) 55 **b)** 3 days **c)** \$55
2. a) The equations represent the same graph.
b) Answers may vary. $(-1, 2)$, $(-2, 3)$ **3.** The
equations represent parallel and distinct
lines. The lines never intersect.

Section 1.2 pp. 12–14
Practice   1. a) $(5, 4)$ **b)** $(-1, 2)$ **c)** $(-3, -5)$ **d)** $(2, -3)$
2. a) $(-2, 3)$ **b)** $(2, 0)$ **c)** $(2, -3)$ **d)** $(-3, -2)$
3. a) $(3, -1)$ **b)** $(-1, 6)$ **c)** $(4, -1)$ **d)** infinitely many
solutions **e)** $(6, 0)$ **f)** $(-3, 4)$ **g)** no solution
h) $(-2, -1)$ **i)** $(2, -1)$ **j)** $(-3, -2)$ **k)** $(4, 1)$ **l)** no
solution **m)** $(5, -1)$ **n)** infinitely many solutions
o) $(-1, -2)$ **p)** $(2, 2)$ **4. a)** $(0.5, 2)$ **b)** $(2, 1.5)$
c) $(-1, 0.5)$ **d)** $(1.5, -2.5)$ **5. a)** $(1.5, -0.8)$
b) $(6.7, 1.7)$ **c)** $(3.9, -0.3)$ **d)** $(-2.7, 0.3)$ **e)** $(2.3, 3)$
f) $(-2.6, 5.1)$ **6. a)** one solution **b)** no solution
c) infinitely many solutions **d)** one solution **e)** no
solution **f)** no solution **7.** Austria: 9, Germany: 16
8. a) $(20, 500)$ **b)** 20 months **c)** Champion **9.** $(-6, 3)$

10. $(2, 4)$, $(-1, -2)$, $(8, -2)$ **11.** $(3, -1)$, $(5, -\dfrac{1}{3})$, $(4, 0)$

12. parallelogram **13.** Answers may vary.
a) $x + y = 5$ **b)** $2x + 2y = 8$ **c)** $x + 2y = 4$ **14.** Answers
may vary. **a)** $x + y = 5$, $x - y = 1$ **b)** $x - y = 1$,
$2x - 2y = 2$ **15.** The system has infinitely many
solutions: all points on the line $x - 2y + 6 = 0$.
17. a) $(-12.5, 9)$; $(48, 24)$; $(-16, -18)$

Modelling Math p. 14
a) $(t, d) = (50, 1000)$ **b)** 50 **c)** less than 50
d) greater than 50

Career Connection p. 15
1. south: 5000, north: 125 000

Section 1.3 pp. 21–23
Practice   1. a) $x = 8 - 3y$ **b)** $x = -4y - 13$
c) $x = 7y + 7$ **d)** $x = 2y - 1$ **2. a)** $y = 11 - 6x$
b) $y = -5x - 9$ **c)** $y = x + 2$ **d)** $y = 3x + 4$ **3. a)** $(2, 2)$
b) $(-1, 1)$ **c)** $(2, -1)$ **d)** $(-2, -3)$ **e)** $(3, 0)$ **f)** $(3, 2)$
g) $(4, -5)$ **h)** $(5, 0)$ **i)** $(-2, 3)$ **j)** $(-2, -2)$ **k)** $(-1, 1)$
l) $(-3, -4)$ **m)** $(1, 0)$ **n)** $(1, 3)$ **o)** no solution **p)** $(3, -1)$
q) infinitely many solutions **r)** $(-1, -5)$
s) no solution **t)** $(1, 1)$ **u)** $(-1, 1)$ **4. a)** $(\dfrac{1}{2}, -1)$

b) $(\dfrac{7}{11}, -\dfrac{1}{11})$ **c)** $(3, -\dfrac{6}{5})$ **d)** $(1, -\dfrac{1}{3})$ **e)** $(-1, \dfrac{2}{7})$

f) $(\frac{4}{3}, \frac{11}{3})$ **g)** $(-\frac{32}{5}, -\frac{18}{5})$ **h)** $(-\frac{3}{4}, \frac{1}{2})$ **i)** $(\frac{1}{7}, -\frac{4}{5})$

Applications and Problem Solving   5. a) $(24, -18)$
b) $(-3, 2)$ **c)** $(\frac{3}{2}, 2)$ **d)** $(-\frac{5}{3}, \frac{1}{6})$ **6. a)** Fairweather
Mountain is 3970 m higher than Ishpatina
Ridge. Fairweather Mountain is 188 m less than
seven time higher than Ishpatina Ridge.
b) Fairweather Mountain: 4663 m, Ishpatina Ridge:
693 m **7. a)** The angles are complementary. Six
degrees less than $\angle y$ is three times $\angle x$. **b)** $\angle x = 21°$,
$\angle y = 69°$ **8. a)** The total number of tickets sold is
550. The total revenue from tickets is $9184.
b) adult tickets: 323, student tickets: 227 **9.** $(1, 2)$,
$(9, -14)$, $(-3, -2)$ **10. a)** $(5, 4)$ **b)** $(4, 5)$ **c)** $(-1, -5)$
d) $(\frac{1}{2}, -\frac{1}{2})$ **11.** A = 3, B = 2 **12. a)** $(1, 4, -2)$
b) $(2, -1, 3)$ **13.** $m = -1$ **14.** $n = \frac{1}{2}$

Modelling Math p. 23
a) $(h, C) = (4, 270)$ **b)** Quality is cheaper for less
than 4 h. ABC is cheaper for more than 4 h.
c) 10 h of work

Section 1.4 pp. 24–25
1 Equivalent Forms   1. Answers may vary. $(0, 6)$,
$(1, 5)$, $(2, 4)$ **2. a)** $2x + 2y = 12$ **b)** yes
3. a) $-3x - 3y = -18$ **b)** yes **4.** Yes, they all have the
same solution. **5.** Answers may vary. **a)** $2x + 2y = 4$,
$-x - y = -2$, $-2x - 2y = -4$ **b)** $2x - 2y = 8$,
$-x + y = -4$, $-2x + 2y = -8$ **c)** $-2x - y = -7$,
$-4x - 2y = -14$, $4x + 2y = 14$ **d)** $2y = 8x - 6$,
$3y = 12x - 9$, $4y = 16x - 12$
2 Equivalent Systems   1. $(5, 2)$ **2.** $(5, 2)$
3. a) $2x - 2y = 6, -x - y = -7$ **b)** $(5, 2)$ **4.** They all
have the same solution. **5.** Answers may vary.
$x + y = 3, x - y = 1$
3 Adding Equations   1. $(2, 1)$ **2. a)** $2x + y$ **b)** 5
c) $2x + y = 5$ **3.** They all pass through $(2, 1)$.
4. They are equivalent systems. They have the same
solution. **5.** They are equivalent systems. They
have the same solution.

Section 1.5 pp. 30–33
Practice   1. a) $(5, 2)$ **b)** $(3, 5)$ **c)** $(1, 7)$ **d)** $(1, 2)$
2. a) $(2, 6)$ **b)** $(-1, -3)$ **c)** $(-4, 1)$ **d)** $(3, -2)$ **e)** $(-2, 1)$
f) $(5, 3)$ **3. a)** $(1, 1)$ **b)** $(2, -1)$ **c)** $(-6, -3)$ **d)** $(-2, 0)$
4. a) $-4, 17$ **b)** $-20, 7$ **5. a)** $(1, -2)$ **b)** $(-2, -2)$
c) $(3, 1)$ **d)** no solution **e)** $(1, 0)$ **f)** infinitely many
solutions **g)** $(4, 2)$ **h)** $(-3, 2)$ **i)** $(-2, -3)$ **6. a)** $(9, -4)$

b) $(-3, 8)$ **c)** $(2, -1)$ **d)** $(\frac{1}{3}, 1)$ **e)** $(-2, \frac{1}{2})$ **f)** $(\frac{5}{9}, \frac{1}{9})$
g) infinitely many solutions **h)** $(\frac{4}{5}, \frac{3}{5})$ **i)** no solution
7. a) $(-1, -3)$ **b)** $(-0.2, 0.1)$ **c)** $(4, 3)$ **d)** $(3, 4)$
e) $(-0.5, 0.3)$ **f)** $(-0.4, -1.1)$ **8. a)** $(6, 10)$ **b)** $(3, 4)$
c) $(6, -4)$ **d)** $(3, -3)$ **e)** $(-6, -8)$ **f)** $(1, -1)$
Applications and Problem Solving   9. Answers
may vary. **a)** substitution **b)** elimination
c) substitution **d)** elimination **e)** elimination
f) elimination **10. a)** There are 10 provinces. Three
times the number of names with First Nations
origins is equal to twice the number of names with
other origins. **b)** 4 **11.** ham: $5, roast beef: $6
12. a) $(-1, -3)$ **b)** $(1, 6)$ **c)** $(-2, 3)$ **d)** $(2, 1)$
13. a) $x = a, y = -b$ **b)** $x = 3a, y = -b$ **14.** $(3, 2)$,
$(-2, 4)$, $(0, -2)$ **15.** $a = -2, b = 3$ **16.** $(4, 6)$ **17. a)** 10
b) 6 **18. a)** -2 **b** 3 **19.** $(2, 5)$ **20.** Answers may
vary. $2x + 3y = -3, x - 2y = 16$ **21.** Answers may
vary. **a)** $2x + 3y = 19, -2x + 3y = 11$ **b)** $3x + 2y = 2$,
$4x + 5y = 19$ **c)** $2x + 3y = 0, -3x - 6y = 1$

Technology Extension pp. 34–35
**1 Solving Systems Using a Graphing Calculator
Program   1. b)** Each of the following systems has
$AE - BD = 0$. In the system $ax + by = c$,
$kax + kby = kc$, one equation is a multiple of the
other. Thus, there are infinitely many solutions.
$CE - BF = ckb - bkc = 0$. In the system $ax + by = c$,
$ax + by = d$, the lines are parallel and distinct when
$c \neq d$. There is no solution, and
$CE - BF = cb - bd = b(c - d) \neq 0$, since $c \neq d$.
2. a) $(-1, -2)$ **b)** $(7, 10)$ **c)** infinitely many solutions
d) no solution
**2 Solving Systems Using Preprogrammed
Calculators   1. a)** $(2, 4)$ **b)** $(2, -3)$ **c)** $(\frac{1}{2}, -1)$
2. a) infinitely many solutions **b)** no solution

Section 1.6 pp. 36–37
1 Expressions in Two Variables   1. a) $x + y$
b) $x - y$ **c)** $5y - x$ **d)** $6x + 2y$ **2. a)** $x - y$ **b)** $x + y$
3. a) $x + 7y$ **b)** $x + 15y$ **4. a)** $x + y$ **b)** $10x$ **c)** $5y$
d) $10x + 5y$ **5. a)** $x + y$ **b)** $0.07x$ **c)** $0.06y$
d) $0.07x + 0.06y$
2 Equations in Two Variables   1. a) $x + y = 8$
b) $x - y = 5$ **c)** $y = 3x + 1$ **d)** $y = 2x - 1$
2. a) $l + w = 40$ **b)** $2b + 3t = 61$
3 Systems of Equations   1. a) $x + y = 7, x - y = 3$
b) $y = 2x, y = x - 4$ **2. a)** $x + y = 256$ **b)** $5x + 2y = 767$
3. a) $p + r = 295, p = r + 11$ **b)** $l = w + 6, l + w = 46$

c) $c = 2d$, $c - d = 17$ **d)** $b + f = 331$, $10b + 15f = 3915$
e) $x + y = 180$, $x + 4 = 3y$

Section 1.7 pp. 43–45
Practice 1. a) $140 **b)** $15 **c)** $210 **d)** $0.04x$
2. a) 30 kg **b)** 200 L **c)** $0.3x$ litres **d)** $0.09m$ kilograms

3. a) 240 km **b)** $40x$ kilometres **c)** 12 h **d)** $\dfrac{y}{90}$ hours

Applications and Problem Solving 4. 147, 108
5. $2000 at 6%, $6000 at 4% **6.** 200 km at 100 km/h,
270 km at 90 km/h **7.** 16 km/h, 4 km/h **8.** $6000 at
4%, $9000 at 5% **9.** $x = 34$, $y = 10$ **10.** 10 mL of the
5% solution, 40 mL of the 10% solution **11.** 25 mL
12. $x = 32$, $y = 20$ **13.** 495 km/h, 55 km/h **14.** 2.7 m
by 1.2 m **15.** 30 min **16.** 2.5 **17.** 400 km

18. $x = \dfrac{q+r}{2}$, $y = \dfrac{q-r}{2}$ **19. a)** 1.8 h **b)** 135 km

20. 8, 14, 31 **21.** No, since $a + b < c$. **22.** Answers
may vary. **23. a)** 24 m by 2 m **b)** not possible **c)** 24 m
by 2 m **d)** not possible

Career Connection p. 46
1. 100 g of 18-karat gold, 50 g of 9-karat gold

Modelling Math p. 46
a) Cost: $C = 2n + 2000$; Revenue: $C = 10n$ **b)** 250
c) 2250

Rich Problem pp. 48–49
1 Graphing and Interpreting Data 2. a) 95% **b)** 5%
3. 4 million years ago
2 Communication 3. a) (14, 50) **b)** Fourteen
million years ago, the populations were equal.
4. No, the graphs only show percents, not absolute
numbers. **5. a)** 5; −5
Technology Extension 1. $y = 5x - 20$; $y = -5x + 120$
2. (14, 50)

Review of Key Concepts pp. 50–53
1. a) (4, −1) **b)** (−4, 3) **c)** (3, 2) **d)** no solution
e) (1, −3) **f)** infinitely many solutions **g)** (−2, 1)

h) $(\dfrac{1}{2}, 5)$ **2. a)** (1.9, −2.2) **b)** (0.1, 0.7)

3. a) infinitely many solutions **b)** no solution **c)** one
solution **d)** no solution **4.** Sahara Desert: 9 million
square kilometres; Australian Desert: 4 million square
kilometres **5. a)** d represents the total cost or
revenue; p represents the number of paddles.
b) (62.5, 1125) **c)** greater than 62 **6. a)** (2, 2)
b) (1, −1) **c)** (4, −2) **d)** infinitely many solutions

e) (1, 3) **f)** no solution **g)** (−1, 5) **h)** $(1, \dfrac{1}{3})$ **7. a)** (3, −2)

b) (1, 1) **8.** Mount Pleasant: 16, Centreville: 15

9. a) (−1, 2) **b)** (−2, 1) **c)** (3, 2) **d)** (1, 0) **e)** no solution
f) infinitely many solutions **g)** (−2, −3) **h)** (4, 1)
10. Methods may vary. **a)** substitution: (−4, −5)

b) elimination: (1, 1) **c)** substitution: $(2, \dfrac{1}{2})$

d) elimination: (−1, 2) **11.** (−2, −3) **12. a)** (3, 4)
b) (0.6, −0.5) **13.** one night: $150, one meal: $15
14. 36 cars and 9 vans **15.** $5000 Canada Savings
Bond, $10 000 Provincial Government Bond
16. 75 kg of 24% nitrogen, 25 kg of 12% nitrogen
17. 40 km/h; 280 km/h **18.** 210 km

Chapter Test pp. 54–55
1. a) (4, 3) **b)** (−2, −3) **c)** (−1, 0) **d)** (1, −2)
2. a) (−0.7, 3.7) **b)** (2.4, 1.1) **3. a)** The lines
intersect at exactly one point. **b)** The lines are
parallel and distinct. **c)** The lines are coincident.

4. a) (2, 2) **b)** $(-3, \dfrac{1}{2})$ **5. a)** (−1, −1) **b)** (2, 1)

6. a) (3, 2) **b)** (2, −2) **c)** infinitely many solutions

d) no solution **e)** (−6, 4) **f)** $(\dfrac{2}{3}, \dfrac{1}{3})$ **g)** $(-\dfrac{4}{7}, -\dfrac{2}{7})$ **h)** (4, 1)

i) (5, 6) **j)** (3, −3) **7.** Mackenzie River: 4241 km,
Yukon River: 3185 km **8.** 240 g of 30% fruit, 360 g
of 15% fruit **9.** term deposit: $4000, municipal bond:
$9000 **10.** 50 km/h, 550 km/h

Problem Solving p. 57
Applications and Problem Solving 1. a) 8 h 29 min
b) 179 km/h **2.** Jupiter, Saturn **3. a)** Newfoundland
b) Prince Edward Island **4.** (information taken from
the web site of the Canadian Museum of Nature:
http:// www.nature.ca/english/eladback.htm)
a) extinct: a species that no longer exists; extirpated: a
species no longer existing in the wild, but existing
elsewhere; endangered: a species facing imminent
extirpation or extinction; threatened: a species likely
to become endangered if limiting factors are not
reversed; vulnerable: a species of special concern
because of characteristics that make it particularly
sensitive to human activities or natural events **b)** all
living things, including plants and animals
10. Alberta **11.** Answers may vary.

Problem Solving p. 60
1. 298 **2.** 50 **3.** 92 units **4.** infinitely many; they pass
through the centre of the rectangle **5.** 1, 3, 4, 5, 7, 8,
9, 11, 12, 13, 15, 16, 17, 19, 20, 21, 23, 24, 25, 27, 28,
29, 31, 32, 33, 35, 36, 37, 39, 40

Problem Solving p. 61
1. 253×14 **2. a)** 20 cm² **b)** 5 cm² **3.** 05:00 Wednesday
4. 321 cm² **5.** 16 **6.** 12 **7. a)** 94 **b)** 50 **8.** 31, 49

Chapter 2

Getting Started p. 64
1. a) 10; 9.1 **b)** 9; 8.1 **c)** 5; 5 **d)** 7; 7 **e)** 12; 8.6 **f)** 17; 12.2 **2.** when the two points are on a horizontal or vertical line **3. a)** square with side length $\sqrt{98}$ **b)** circle with radius 7

Review of Prerequisite Skills p. 65
1. a) 9 **b)** 13 **c)** 1.2 **d)** 0.7 **2. a)** 4.8 **b)** 2.7 **c)** 20.1 **d)** 35.4 **3. a)** 3.6 **b)** 7.1 **c)** 8.1 **d)** 9.4 **4. a)** 5 **b)** 7 **c)** 6 **d)** 11 **5. a)** 7 **b)** 11 **c)** 5 **d)** 8 **6. a)** 2 **b)** 3 **c)** 1 **d)** 4 **e)** −3 **f)** 1 **7. a)** $\frac{4}{3}$ **b)** 3 **c)** 2 **d)** $\frac{3}{2}$ **e)** $-\frac{5}{3}$ **f)** −2 **g)** 0 **h)** undefined **i)** $-\frac{5}{2}$ **j)** $\frac{3}{4}$ **8. a)** 3 **b)** 3 **c)** $-\frac{1}{3}$

Section 2.1 pp. 71–73
Practice 1. a) $\sqrt{17}$; 4.1 **b)** 15 **c)** $\sqrt{2}$; 1.4 **d)** $\sqrt{50}$; 7.1 **e)** 8 **f)** 7 **g)** $\sqrt{106.82}$; 10.3 **h)** $\sqrt{0.2}$; 0.4

2. a) $x^2 + y^2 = 9$ **b)** $x^2 + y^2 = 36$ **c)** $x^2 + y^2 = 100$ **d)** $x^2 + y^2 = 121$ **3. a)** 8 **b)** 2 **c)** 12 **d)** 1 **e)** 5.5 **f)** 1.1 **4. a)** 5 **b)** 7.3 **c)** 7.2 **d)** 11.4 **5. a)** isosceles; 22.4 **b)** scalene; 19.7 **c)** isosceles; 12.3 **d)** equilateral; 18 **Applications and Problem Solving 6. a)** 5 min 33 s **b)** 5 min 50 s **c)** 2 min 41 s **d)** 6 min 29 s **7.** PR = 9.2, QS = 11.4 **8.** 36 **9.** 14.6 km **10.** AB = $\sqrt{52}$, BC = $\sqrt{52}$, AC = $\sqrt{104}$; AB² + BC² = 52 + 52 = 104 = AC² **11.** AC = $\sqrt{45}$, BC = $\sqrt{45}$, AC = BC; slope AB = 2, slope AC = 2; so A, B, and C are collinear. Thus, C is the midpoint of AB.

12. a) $\sqrt{29} + \sqrt{40} + \sqrt{65} + \sqrt{10}$ **b)** 22.9 **13.** $\frac{\sqrt{80}}{2}$

14. KL = $\sqrt{17}$, LM = $\sqrt{29}$, MN = $\sqrt{29}$, NK = $\sqrt{17}$; $P = 19.0$ **15.** WX = $\sqrt{13}$, XY = $\sqrt{13}$, YZ = $\sqrt{13}$, ZW = $\sqrt{13}$; $P = 14.4$ **16. a)** $x^2 + y^2 = 25$ **b)** $x^2 + y^2 = 169$ **c)** $x^2 + y^2 = 40$ **17. a)** 330 km; 2990 km; 720 km **18. a)** $\sqrt{a^2 + b^2}$ **b)** $\sqrt{x^2 + 9y^2}$ **c)** $\sqrt{4 + n^2}$ **d)** $\sqrt{20p^2}$ **19.** −2, 8 **20. a)** (0, 5), (3, 4), (4, 3), (5, 0), (0, −5), (3, −4), (4, −3), (−3, 4), (−4, 3), (−5, 0), (−3, −4), (−4, −3) **b)** (2, 11), (8, 9), (10, 7), (12, 1), (−4, 9), (−6, 7), (−8, 1), (8, −7), (10, −5), (2, −9), (−4, −7), (−6, −5)

Modelling Math p. 73
1. a) 17.1 cm **b)** 48.3 cm **c)** 65.4 cm

Section 2.2 p. 74
1 Midpoints of Horizontal Line Segments 1. a) (5, 4) **b)** (2, 2) **c)** (3, −3) **d)** (−4, −2) **e)** (4, 0) **2.** The y-coordinates are the same. The x-coordinate of the midpoint is half the sum of the x-coordinates of the endpoints. **3. a)** (4, 3) **b)** (2, 1) **c)** (−5, 5) **d)** (4, −5) **4.** (4, 3), (6, 3), (8, 3)
2 Midpoints of Vertical Line Segments 1. a) (2, 5) **b)** (5, 2) **c)** (−3, −3) **d)** (−2, −2) **e)** (0, 3) **2.** The x-coordinates are the same. The y-coordinate of the midpoint is half the sum of the y-coordinates of the endpoints. **3. a)** (4, 4) **b)** (1, −1) **c)** (−2, 0) **d)** (0, 5) **4.** (3, 5), (3, 2), (3, −1)

Section 2.3 pp. 77–80
Practice 1. a) (4, 8) **b)** (5, 5) **c)** (0, −3) **d)** (−2, 2) **e)** (−2, −5) **f)** (1, 4) **g)** (1.9, 0.9) **h)** $\left(1, -\frac{1}{2}\right)$ **i)** (301.5, 149.5) **j)** $\left(\frac{a+c}{2}, \frac{b+d}{2}\right)$

Applications and Problem Solving 2. (−4, 3) **3.** Their midpoints coincide. **4.** (6, 9), (2, 2), (−2, −5) **5.** (2, −1) **6.** (8, 8) **7.** (−6, 8) **8.** (3, −2) **9.** 20.2 **10.** Their midpoints coincide. **11.** Their midpoints coincide. **12. a)** E(5, 2), F(3, 7), G(−1, 6), H(1, 1) **b)** EF = $\sqrt{29}$, GH = $\sqrt{29}$ **c)** FG = $\sqrt{17}$, EH = $\sqrt{17}$ **13.** T(0, −2), M(3, 0) **14.** $\sqrt{45}$, $\sqrt{18}$, 9 **15.** AM = $\sqrt{20}$, MB = $\sqrt{20}$ **16.** Let S be the midpoint of the hypotenuse QR. RS = QS = PS = $\sqrt{40}$. **17. a)** (9, 12.2) **b)** 5.81 km **c)** \$4 589 900 **d)** Find the length of the road and divide by 2. Then, multiply by the cost per kilometre. **18. a)** Try for the refuelling depot. **b)** Continue to the end. **19. a)** $\left(\frac{3x}{2}, \frac{3y}{2}\right)$ **b)** (6a, b) **c)** $\left(m, \frac{2n+1}{2}\right)$ **d)** (−t, t + 1) **20.** c = 10, d = 7 **21.** (2c − p, 2d − q) **22.** $\left(\frac{3x_1 + x_2}{4}, \frac{3y_1 + y_2}{4}\right)$, $\left(\frac{x_1 + x_2}{2}, \frac{y_1 + y_2}{2}\right)$, $\left(\frac{x_1 + 3x_2}{4}, \frac{y_1 + 3y_2}{4}\right)$ **23.** (−4, 0), (4, 0), (0, 6) **24. a)** (0, 5), (0, −3), (8, 1) **b)** (0, 1), (8, −3), (8, 5) **25. a)** sometimes true **b)** sometimes true **c)** always true **d)** sometimes true

Modelling Math p. 80
1. Their midpoints coincide at (30, 25). Thus, they bisect each other. **2.** No, the diagonals of quadrilaterals P and Q do not bisect each other.

Technology Extension p. 81

1 Length of a Line Segment 1. names the program; clears the memory; prompts user for x_1-data and reads it into variable P; prompts user for y_1-data and reads it into variable Q; prompts user for x_2-data and reads it into variable R; prompts user for y_2-data and reads it into variable S; assigns the difference R − P to the variable X; assigns the difference S − Q to the variable Y; assigns the square root of the sum of the squares of X and Y to the variable L; prints "LENGTH IS" and prints the value of L. **2. a)** 6.4 **b)** 17.1 **c)** 27.33

2 Midpoint of a Line Segment 1. Change line 6 to (R + P)/2 → X. Change line 7 to (S + Q)/2 → Y. Delete line 8. Change the last line to DISP"MIDPOINT IS". Add lines DISP"X=",X and DISP"Y=",Y. **2. a)** (−1, 6) **b)** (2.5, −3.5) **c)** (0.3, −3.45)

3 Collinear Points 2. a) collinear **b)** not collinear **3.** Answers may vary. **a)** (7, 6) **b)** (−7, 6)

Review: Equations of Lines pp. 85–87

1 Using the Point-Slope Form
1. a) $2x − y − 1 = 0$ **b)** $5x − y − 18 = 0$
c) $3x + y + 12 = 0$ **d)** $4x + y + 9 = 0$ **e)** $x − 2y − 18 = 0$
f) $x + 2y + 5 = 0$ **g)** $2x − 2y − 9 = 0$ **h)** $3x − 2y + 7 = 0$
i) $3x + 2y + 5 = 0$ **2. a)** $2x + y − 13 = 0$
b) $3x + y − 3 = 0$ **c)** $x − 2y − 9 = 0$ **d)** $2x − 5y − 11 = 0$
e) $5x − 4y + 22 = 0$ **f)** $4x − 3y + 12 = 0$ **3. a)** $y − 5 = 0$; $x − 4 = 0$ **b)** $y − 2 = 0$; $x + 3 = 0$ **c)** $y + 6 = 0$; $x + 5 = 0$
d) $y − 8 = 0$; $2x − 1 = 0$ **e)** $3y + 1 = 0$; $x − 9 = 0$
f) $y + 9 = 0$; $x = 0$ **g)** $y = 0$; $x + 1 = 0$ **h)** $y = 0$; $x = 0$

2 Using the Slope and y-Intercept Form

1. a) 3, 4 **b)** −4, 6 **c)** 1, 5 **d)** $\frac{1}{2}$, −4 **e)** $−\frac{1}{2}$, $\frac{4}{3}$ **f)** $\frac{1}{4}$, −1

g) $\frac{5}{2}$, −3 **h)** $−\frac{2}{3}$, 0 **i)** −20, 6 **2. a)** 1, 2 **b)** −1, 3 **c)** 2, 5

d) −3, 10 **e)** $\frac{1}{2}$, −1 **f)** $−\frac{1}{2}$, 1 **g)** 4, 7 **h)** $−\frac{1}{5}$, $\frac{13}{5}$ **i)** $\frac{1}{3}$, $\frac{5}{3}$

3 Parallel and Perpendicular Lines
1. a) $3x − y − 5 = 0$ **b)** $2x − y + 8 = 0$ **c)** $x + 2y + 1 = 0$
d) $x − 3y + 24 = 0$ **2. a)** $x − 2y + 8 = 0$ **b)** $3x + y − 2 = 0$
c) $2x − y + 2 = 0$ **d)** $x + 2y − 5 = 0$

Section 2.4 pp. 95–99

Practice 1. PQ and OR have slope $\frac{1}{5}$; OP and RQ

have slope $\frac{5}{3}$ **2.** XY has slope $\frac{2}{3}$; XZ has slope $−\frac{3}{2}$;

the slopes are negative reciprocals, so XY is perpendicular to XZ **3. a)** Both segments have

slope $−\frac{4}{3}$ and so are parallel. **b)** PQ = 5, KM = 10;

$PQ = \frac{1}{2}KM$ **4.** Opposite sides are parallel (two have

slope 0 and two have slope $−\frac{4}{3}$) and all sides have

length 5; so PQRS is a rhombus. **5. a)** KL and NM have slope −1; KN and LM have slope 1. Thus, opposite sides are parallel and adjacent sides are perpendicular. KLMN is a rectangle. **b)** KM and LN both have length $\sqrt{26}$ **6.** $x + y − 5 = 0$ **7. a)** The midpoint of BC is (4, 3). The line containing (4, 3) and A(3, 4) has slope −1. BC has slope 1. Thus, A(3, 4) is on the perpendicular bisector of BC.

b) The midpoint of QR is (0, 0). The line containing

(0, 0) and P(1, 3) has slope 3. QR has slope $−\frac{1}{3}$.

Thus, P(1, 3) is on the perpendicular bisector of QR. **c)** The midpoint of LM is (2, −2). The line

containing (2, −2) and K(−2, −4) has slope $\frac{1}{2}$. LM has

slope −2. Thus, K(−2, −4) is on the perpendicular bisector of LM. **8.** The midpoint of CD is (2, −1).

The line containing (2, −1) and O(0, 0) has slope $−\frac{1}{2}$.

CD has slope 2. Thus, O(0, 0) is on the right bisector

of CD. **9.** Slope AC is $\frac{1}{5}$ and slope BD is −5. The

slopes are negative reciprocals, so the diagonals AC and BD are perpendicular.

10. The opposite sides PQ and OR both have slope $\frac{1}{5}$

and so are parallel; the other two sides have different slopes, so are not parallel. OPRQ is a trapezoid.

11. PS and QR both have slope $\frac{2}{3}$; RS and QP are

both vertical. Thus, opposite sides are parallel and PQRS is a parallelogram. **12. a)** KL has slope 1, KM has slope −1. KL and KM are perpendicular. **b)** The midpoint of LM is a distance of $\sqrt{17}$ from each vertex. **13.** Opposite sides of the quadrilateral are

parallel (two sides have slope $\frac{2}{5}$ and two have

slope −5) and so the quadrilateral is a parallelogram.
14. a) $7x + 2y + 1 = 0$ **b)** $x − y + 1 = 0$ **c)** $x + 4y − 2 = 0$
15. a) $y = 0$, $x − 4 = 0$, $x + y − 4 = 0$ **b)** All three medians intersect at (4, 0). **16.** (4, 0) **17.** (2, 2)
Applications and Problem Solving 18. The vertices of the triangle are A(2, 0), B(−4, 3), and C(−1, −6).

$AB = AC = \sqrt{45}$; AC has slope 2 and AB has slope $−\frac{1}{2}$

and so they are perpendicular. The triangle is right isosceles. **19.** The equations of the diagonals are $x - y - 2 = 0$ and $2x + 3y - 9 = 0$. These lines intersect at $(3, 1)$. **20. a)** UV has slope 2; WV has slope $-\frac{1}{2}$; UV and WV are perpendicular. **b)** The median has length 5; the hypotenuse UW has length 10; the median is half the length of the hypotenuse.
21. a) Opposite sides are parallel (two sides have slope $\frac{3}{2}$ and two sides have slope $-\frac{2}{3}$). Adjacent sides are perpendicular and all sides have length $\sqrt{13}$. KLMN is a square. **b)** The midpoints of the diagonals coincide at $(-\frac{1}{2}, \frac{3}{2})$, so the diagonals bisect each other. One diagonal has slope $\frac{1}{5}$ and the other has slope -5. The diagonals are perpendicular. **c)** The diagonals both have length $\sqrt{26}$.

22. a) isosceles **b)** AC has slope $-\frac{1}{11}$ and the median from B to AC has slope 11; thus, they are perpendicular **23.** No, the perpendicular bisector of UV has equation $x + y - 2 = 0$, which does not contain the point $T(2, -1)$. **24.** One diagonal is vertical, and two segments joining midpoints of adjacent sides are also vertical; the other diagonal has slope $\frac{1}{10}$, and two segments joining midpoints of adjacent sides also have slope $\frac{1}{10}$. **25. a)** kite
b) Opposite sides are parallel (two sides have slope $-\frac{1}{3}$ and two have slope 3) and adjacent sides are perpendicular. Thus, it is a rectangle.
26. a) $(0, 0), (240, 0), (240, 120), (0, 120), (120, 60)$
b) One direction may be described by a line segment with slope $\frac{1}{2}$ and the other by a line segment with slope $-\frac{1}{2}$. These are not negative reciprocals, so the directions are not perpendicular.
27. a) $m\text{PS} = m\text{QR} = \frac{1}{2}$, $m\text{PQ} = -3$, $m\text{SR} = -\frac{1}{5}$
b) midpoint of PQ is A $(-2, -2)$, midpoint of SR is B$(6, 2)$; $m\text{AB} = \frac{1}{2}$ **c)** PS $= 2\sqrt{5}$, QR $= 6\sqrt{5}$, AB $= 4\sqrt{5}$; PS $+$ QR $=$ 2AB **28.** All sides have length 2.
29. a) The equations of the medians are $x = 6$, $y = 0$, and $2x + 3y - 12 = 0$; these lines intersect at $(6, 0)$.
b) The equations of the altitudes are $3x - y - 14 = 0$,

$3x - 4y = 0$, and $3x + 2y - 28 = 0$. These lines intersect at $\left(\frac{56}{9}, \frac{14}{3}\right)$. **c)** The equations of the perpendicular bisectors are $3x - y - 20 = 0$, $3x - 4y - 27 = 0$, and $3x + 2y - 13 = 0$. These lines intersect at $\left(\frac{53}{9}, -\frac{7}{3}\right)$. **d)** The slope of the line segment connecting the centroid and the orthocentre is 21. The slope of the line segment connecting the orthocentre and the circumcentre is 21. The three points are collinear.

Modelling Math p. 98
1. Two sides of the triangle have slopes -1 and 1, respectively. Thus they are perpendicular.
2. Opposite sides are parallel and adjacent sides are perpendicular (two sides have slope 1 and two have slope -1). **3.** Opposite sides are parallel (two have slope 0 and two have slope 1). **4.** For example, the line joining the midpoints $(15, 35)$ and $(25, 35)$ has length 10 and slope 0. The corresponding side of the triangle has length 20 and slope 0.

Career Connection p. 99
1. a) $(0, 0), (5, 0), (5, 3), (0, 3)$ **b)** $\sqrt{34}$ **c)** No, since $\sqrt{34}$ is an irrational number. A builder would probably round to the nearest millimetre.

Section 2.5 pp. 103–104
Practice 1. a) $\sqrt{8}$ **b)** $\sqrt{18}$ **c)** $\sqrt{10}$ **d)** $\sqrt{5}$ **e)** 2 **f)** 3
g) $\sqrt{117}$ **h)** $\sqrt{20}$ **2. a)** 2.1 **b)** 1.4 **c)** 1.8 **d)** 1.2 **e)** 0.5
f) 1.8 **g)** 2.5 **h)** 2.2 **3. a)** 0.7 **b)** 6.7 **c)** 4.2 **d)** 4.9 **e)** 4.5
f) 1.9 **g)** 0.2 **h)** 0.9 **4.** 6.01 **5.** 0; the point is on the line. **6.** $\sqrt{32}$ **7. a)** $\sqrt{45}$ **b)** 6.7
Applications and Problem Solving 8. 5 **9.** 5 **10.** 6.7
11. a) isosceles **b)** C lies on the perpendicular bisector of AB. **c)** 24 **12. a)** 5.58, 3.78, 3.94 **b)** 11.5
13. $\sqrt{2}$ **14.** 2.9 **15. a)** 0.38 **b)** 0.14 **16.** 60
17. a) $y = \frac{1}{2}x + \frac{\sqrt{65}}{2}$, $y = \frac{1}{2}x - \frac{\sqrt{65x}}{2}$
b) $y = -3x + \sqrt{50}$, $y = -3x - \sqrt{50}$

Modelling Math p. 105
1. $x + y - 40 = 0$ **2. a)** $\sqrt{450}$ **b)** $\sqrt{450}$ **3.** The points are the same distance from, and on opposite sides of, the diagonal. **4.** $(0, 10)$ and $(30, 40)$; $(10, 10)$ and $(30, 30)$; $(10, 20)$ and $(20, 30)$ The points in each pair are the same distance from, and on opposite sides of, the diagonal.

Technology Extension p. 106

1 Equations of Lines   5. a) $x + y = 7$ **b)** $3x + 4y = -6$
c) $5y = 4x + 4$ **d)** $y = x - 5$

Rich Problem p. 111

2. Five locations at $(6, 9)$, $(6, 8)$, $(7, 7)$, $(7, 8)$, and $(8, 7)$.

Review of Key Concepts pp. 112–115

1. a) 10 **b)** $\sqrt{40}$ **c)** $\sqrt{18}$ **d)** $\sqrt{232}$ **e)** $\sqrt{20}$
2. a) $x^2 + y^2 = 144$ **b)** $x^2 + y^2 = 400$ **3. a)** 11 **b)** 4.5
c) 20 **d)** 0.7 **4. a)** scalene **b)** 16.0 **5.** 23.6
6. $DE = \sqrt{82}$, $EF = \sqrt{41}$, $FD = \sqrt{41}$; $EF = FD$; so
$\triangle DEF$ is isosceles. **7. a)** $PQ = \sqrt{13}$, $QR = \sqrt{13}$,
$RS = \sqrt{13}$, $SP = \sqrt{13}$ **b)** $4\sqrt{13}$ **8. a)** $\left(-\frac{1}{2}, -1\right)$

b) $(4, 0)$ **c)** $\left(\frac{7}{2}, -3\right)$ **d)** $\left(-3, \frac{3}{2}\right)$ **e)** $(3, -0.5)$ **f)** $\left(\frac{1}{2}, 1\right)$

9. $(-3, 7)$ **10. a)** from A: $\sqrt{26}$, from B: $\sqrt{41}$, from
C: $\sqrt{17}$ **b)** $5.1, 6.4, 4.1$ **11.** Two sides have length
$\sqrt{17}$; two sides have length $\sqrt{20}$. **12.** Their midpoints
coincide at $\left(-\frac{1}{2}, -1\right)$. **13.** Opposite sides are parallel

(two sides have slope $\frac{2}{5}$ and two have slope $-\frac{7}{6}$).
14. Their midpoints coincide at $(1, 0)$, and one slope
is 3 and the other is $-\frac{1}{3}$. **15. a)** $ED = EF = \sqrt{80}$ and
so $\triangle DEF$ is isosceles. **b)** The line segment joining
the midpoints of the equal sides has slope -1 and
length $\sqrt{8}$ or about 2.83, and the third side has slope
-1 and length $\sqrt{32}$ or about 5.66. **16. a)** Opposite
sides are parallel and adjacent sides are perpendicular
(two sides have slope -2 and two have slope $\frac{1}{2}$).

b) Each diagonal has midpoint $(0.5, 2)$ and so they
bisect each other. Each diagonal has length 5.
17. a) Opposite sides of the quadrilateral formed
from the midpoints are parallel (two sides have slope $\frac{4}{3}$
and two have slope $-\frac{4}{3}$) and all sides have length 5.

b) One diagonal is vertical and the other is
horizontal; so they are perpendicular. Their
midpoints coincide at $(1, -1)$; so they bisect each
other. **18. a)** $x + 2y - 2 = 0$ **b)** $4x + y + 5 = 0$
c) $x - 2y = 0$ **19.** $\left(\frac{5}{7}, \frac{3}{7}\right)$ **20.** $\left(\frac{5}{3}, 1\right)$

21. $4x - 2y + 7 = 0$ **22.** The right bisector of PQ has
equation $x + 3y = 0$, which passes through the origin.
23. a) 3.5 **b)** 0.4 **c)** 3.8 **d)** 5.7 **e)** 4.5 **f)** 0.9 **24. a)** 5.7
b) 4.5 **c)** 6.0 **25.** 7 **26.** 5 **27. a)** $\sqrt{10}$ **b)** 10

Chapter Test pp. 116–117

1. a) 5 **b)** $\sqrt{29}$ **2. a)** $x^2 + y^2 = 9$ **b)** $x^2 + y^2 = 49$ **3. a)** 10
b) $\sqrt{15}$ **4.** 4.9 **5.** 17 **6. a)** scalene **b)** 13.7 **7.** $(-5, -1)$
8. $(-3, -9)$ **9.** The midpoint is $\sqrt{10}$ units from each
vertex. **10.** AB and DC both have slope $-\frac{3}{4}$, and the
slopes of BC and AD are different. **11. a)** Opposite
sides are parallel and adjacent sides are perpendicular
(two have slope $\frac{3}{2}$ and two have slope $-\frac{2}{3}$) and all sides
have length $\sqrt{13}$. **b)** The midpoints of the diagonals
coincide at $(\frac{1}{2}, \frac{3}{2})$; so they bisect each other. Their
slopes are -5 and $\frac{1}{5}$; so they are perpendicular. Each
diagonal has length $\sqrt{26}$. **12.** Opposite sides of the
quadrilateral formed by joining the midpoints are
parallel (two sides have slope 0 and two have
slope -3). **13.** $x - 4y + 5 = 0$ **14.** $(3, 2)$ **15. a)** 2.1
b) 3.1 **16.** 3.8 **17. b)** 4.5

Problem Solving p. 119

Applications and Problem Solving   1. a) 90 **b)** 160
c) 204 **d)** 385 **2.** 987 **3. a)** $y = x + 4$; $13, 16, 25$
b) $y = 2x + 1$; $17, 12, 101$ **c)** $x + y = 9$; $3, 8, 0$
d) $y = x - 7$; $5, 2, 7$ **e)** $y = x^2 + 1$; $6, 401, 10\ 001$
f) $y = 4x - 1$; $39, 16, 119$ **4. a)** 6 **b)** 3 **5. a)** 156
b) 1260 **6. a)** $41, 82, 81$ **b)** $42, 68, 110$ **c)** $37, 50, 65$
7. A: $p - q$, $-11, 5, 3$; B: $q - p$, $11, -5, -3$; C: $2p + q$,
$-4, -2, -12$; D: $p^2 - q^2$, $-11, -15, -27$; E: $pq + 1$, -29,
$-3, 19$ **8. a)** 146 **b)** $21\ 316$ **9. a)** 6 **b)** 4

Problem Solving p. 122

2. 32 **3.** G, P, W; R **4. a)** It is about 1.25 times the
surface area of Pluto, assuming both bodies are
spherical. **b)** about 540 times **5.** 43 **6. a)** 1 **b)** 2
8. L-shape or Z-shape **9. b)** The square is being
rotated 90° counterclockwise. **c)** same as square 3
d) same as square 1 **10.** $\frac{1}{57}$ **11. a)** 10 **b)** 10

Cumulative Review p. 123

Chapter 1   1. a) $(-14, -41)$ **b)** $(0.5, -3)$ **2. a)** $(-1, 1)$
b) $(1, 0)$ **3. a)** $(2, 2)$ **b)** infinitely many solutions
c) $(-3, -4)$ **d)** $\left(0, \frac{1}{2}\right)$ **4.** 600 g portobello, 400 g oyster

5. 20 km/h; 4 km/h **6.** $4000 in term deposit, $8000 in bonds **7.** 8 L of 30%, 12 L of 40%

Chapter 2 1. a) $\sqrt{20}$, 4.5 **b)** $\sqrt{89}$, 9.4 **2. a)** (5, 5)

b) $\left(\dfrac{5}{2}, -\dfrac{5}{2}\right)$ **3.** $x^2 + y^2 = 144$ **4.** 6 **5. a)** isosceles

b) 15.9 **6. a)** The diagonals have slopes 2 and $-\dfrac{1}{2}$;

so they are perpendicular. **b)** The midpoint of GI

is $\left(5, \dfrac{7}{2}\right)$. The midpoint of HJ is (6, 3). The

equations of the lines containing the diagonals are $x + 2y - 12 = 0$ and $2x - y - 9 = 0$. These lines intersect at (6, 3), the midpoint of GI. Thus, the diagonal HJ bisects GI, but the diagonal GI does not bisect HJ. **7.** Opposite sides have equal slopes

(two have slope $-\dfrac{1}{5}$ and two have slope $\dfrac{3}{2}$).

8. a) $x + 5y - 23 = 0$ **b)** $3x + y - 19 = 0$

c) $x - y - 1 = 0$ **9. a)** $\sqrt{8}$ **b)** 2.8

Chapter 3

Getting Started p. 126
1. a) 8, 12, 16, 20, 24 **b)** $4c + 4$ **c)** 44 **d)** 12, 20, 28, 36, 44 **e)** $8c + 4$ **f)** 84 **2. a)** 10, 14, 18, 22, 26 **b)** $2n + 6$
c) 50 **3. a)** 2, 5, 8, 11, 14 **b)** $3s - 1$ **c)** 44

Review of Prerequisite Skills p. 127
1. a) 15 **b)** 30 **c)** 30 **d)** 3 **e)** 0 **f)** 31 **g)** 93 **h)** 36
2. a) −7 **b)** −22 **c)** 48 **d)** 11 **e)** 17 **f)** −18 **g)** 144 **h)** 6
3. a) 2^7 **b)** 3^7 **c)** y^9 **d)** $8y^5$ **e)** $-8a^7$ **f)** $8x^6$ **g)** $12m^7$ **h)** 2^2
i) 3^0 **j)** m^3 **k)** y^6 **l)** $4a^2$ **4. a)** $6x$ **b)** $-3a + 5b$
c) $8a - 2b + 2$ **d)** $7x^2 + x - 11$ **5. a)** $2x - 10$
b) $8a + 12b - 8c$ **c)** $4 - 8x + 20y$ **d)** $-6x + 14$
e) $-3x^2 + 6x + 3$ **f)** $-2a + 4b + c$ **g)** $3x^2 + 6x$
h) $-2y^3 - 2y^2 + 6y$ **6. a)** $5x - 1$ **b)** $5y + 7$
c) $5m^2 + 3m + 1$ **d)** $x^2 + 9x + 10$ **e)** $3x^2 - 19x$
f) $17z^2 - 17z - 12$ **7. a)** $2y$ **b)** x **c)** $7b$ **d)** $10ab$ **e)** $6y^2$
f) $5cd$ **g)** rst **h)** $2x^2y$ **8. a)** $5x$ **b)** 4 **c)** $7xy$ **d)** $3m$ **e)** $5x$
f) $4m$ **g)** $11y$ **h)** 1 **i)** $9rs^2$ **9. a)** 2, 2 **b)** 2, 3 **c)** 1, 5
d) −4, 2 **e)** −4, −3 **f)** 2, 6 **g)** −5, 4 **h)** −8, −3 **i)** 4, 6
j) 2, 15 **k)** −1, −1 **l)** −2, 1 **m)** −5, 1 **n)** −3, 3 **o)** −2, 3
p) −2, 5 **q)** −7, −1 **r)** −4, −4 **s)** −8, −2 **t)** −5, 3

Section 3.1 pp. 131–133
Practice 1. a) degree 1, binomial
b) degree 2, binomial **c)** degree 3, trinomial
d) degree 3, polynomial **e)** degree 1, monomial

f) degree 0, monomial **2. a)** 0 **b)** 14 **c)** 18
3. a) $4x^3 + 6x^2 - 5x - 7$ **b)** $-3x^3 - 8x^2 + 1$
4. a) $11 + 2x - 6x^2 - 5x^3$ **b)** $-4 - 2x^2 + 3x^3 - 5x^4$
5. a) $8x + 6$ **b)** $9a + 3$ **c)** $9 + 3yz$ **d)** $6m - n$ **e)** $3x + 6$
f) $2a - 3b$ **g)** $2d$ **h)** $-m - 5n$ **6. a)** $7x^2 + x + 17$
b) $15x^2 + 2xy - 3y^2$ **c)** $a^2 + 4a + 4$ **d)** $-t^2 - 5t - 19$ **e)** −6
f) $x^2 - 6y^2$ **7. a)** $28x^3$ **b)** $-12a^2b^3$ **c)** $42m^3n^5$ **d)** $8x^4y^3z^3$
e) $32r^3s^5t^2$ **f)** $18x^5y^4$ **8. a)** $4x^3$ **b)** $2a$ **c)** $-9x$ **d)** $9ac^2$
e) $-5yz^2$ **f)** $3t^3$ **9. a)** $6x^2 - 8x$ **b)** $12a^2 - 9ab$
c) $-20st + 4t^2$ **d)** $-2x^2 + 7x$ **e)** $-3m^2 + 18$ **f)** $6x - 2$
g) $20a^2 + 15a$ **h)** $-3 + 18y$ **i)** $-4x^2 + 12x$ **10. a)** $7x + 7$
b) $-3m + 33$ **c)** $-12x - 73$ **d)** $11t - 36$ **e)** $-20x - 9$
f) $-10 - 8y$ **11. a)** $18a - 24b - 54$ **b)** $-12t^2 + 4t + 4$
c) $-4m^2 + m + 7$ **d)** $63y^2 - 21y - 49$
e) $-10x^2 - 15xy + 5y^2$ **f)** $8y^2 + 12y - 4$
g) $-18x^2 + 36xy + 54x$ **h)** $6a - 8ab + 10a^2$
i) $-3a^2 - 4ab + 2ac$ **12. a)** $-15x$
b) $4a^2 + 16ab - 2b^2 - 6a + 6b$ **c)** $-10x^2 - 3x - 23$
d) $-3y^2 + 9y - 3$ **e)** $6s^2 - st + 5s + 10$

Applications and Problem Solving 13. Answers may vary. **a)** $6x^3$ **b)** $2x + 1$ **c)** $x^2 - 2x + 3$ **14.** 291 m
15. a) $x^2 + 7x - 9$ **b)** $-x^2 - 7x + 9$ **c)** Reversing the order changes the sign of every term. **16.** x
17. a) $x(x + 10) = x^2 + 10x$ **b)** 21 000 m²
18. a) $18x^2y$ **b)** $30xy + 12x^2$ **19. a)** $\dfrac{\pi d^2}{4}$ **b)** d^2 **c)** $\dfrac{\pi}{4}$
d) 79% **20. a)** $3x(4x + 1) = 12x^2 + 3x$ **b)** 117 m²
21. Answers may vary. 3, 5 **22.** 30 cm by 20 cm

Section 3.2 pp. 137–139
Practice 1. a) $x^2 + 6x + 5$ **b)** $x^2 + 7x + 12$
c) $a^2 + 8a + 16$ **d)** $y^2 + 11y + 30$ **e)** $x^2 - 7x + 12$
f) $a^2 - 6a + 8$ **g)** $b^2 - 6b + 5$ **h)** $y^2 - 18y + 81$
i) $x^2 - 3x - 18$ **j)** $c^2 - 6c - 16$ **k)** $t^2 - 100$ **l)** $q^2 + 3q - 10$
2. a) $c^2 - c - 12$ **b)** $x^2 - 3x - 10$ **c)** $y^2 + 4y - 12$
d) $a^2 + 4a - 45$ **e)** $x^2 - 9$ **f)** $b^2 + 3b - 70$ **g)** $y^2 - 9y - 36$
h) $x^2 - 6x - 7$ **i)** $28 + 3x - x^2$ **j)** $6 - 5y + y^2$
k) $x^2 + 14x + 49$ **l)** $b^2 - 64$ **3. a)** $2x^2 + 11x + 5$
b) $3y^2 + 7y + 2$ **c)** $2x^2 - 3x + 1$ **d)** $2a^2 - 11a + 15$
e) $5y^2 + 8y - 21$ **f)** $4x^2 - 17x - 15$ **g)** $9x^2 - 24x + 16$
h) $4 - 19t - 30t^2$ **i)** $9a^2 - 25$ **4. a)** $2x^2 + 16x + 30$
b) $4x^2 - 16x - 180$ **c)** $-a^2 - a + 6$ **d)** $10x^2 + 20x - 350$
e) $18x^2 - 21x + 6$ **f)** $-8y^2 + 22y + 6$ **g)** $0.5x^2 + x - 1.5$
h) $1.8x^2 + 3.6x + 1.8$ **5. a)** $2x^2 + 15x + 30$ **b)** 15
c) $14x^2 + 26x - 11$ **d)** $2m^2 + 24m + 42$
e) $3x^2 - 11x - 34$ **f)** $30t^2 - 61t + 25$ **g)** $6x^2 + 36x + 5$
h) $-22y^2 - 20y - 5$

Applications and Problem Solving 6. a) L.S. = 21,

R.S. = 13 **b)** $x^2 + 8x + 12$ **7. a)** The length of the rectangle is $3x + 2y$. The width is $2x + y$. The area is $(3x + 2y)(2x + y)$. **b)** $6x^2 + 7xy + 2y^2$
8. a) $3x^2 + 13xy + 4y^2$ **b)** $8a^2 - 22ab + 5b^2$
c) $20m^2 - 7mn - 6n^2$ **d)** $20s^2 - 39st + 18t^2$
e) $7a^2 + ab - 8b^2$ **f)** $-6a^2 - ab + 12b^2$
9. a) $(x + 10)(x + 5)$ **b)** 750 m² **10. a)** $7x^2 - 72x + 20$
b) 29 280 cm²; 2.928 m² **11. a)** $x^2 + x - 2$
b) $x^2 + 3xy + 2y^2 + 3x - 3y$ **12.** $14x^2 + 17x - 3$
13. a) 42 cm² **b)** $(n + 2)(n + 3)$ **c)** $n^2 + 5n + 6$
d) 930 cm² **14. a)** $10x^2 + 10x - 10$ **b)** 290 cm²
15. No, the product of $(x - 1)$ and $(x + 1)$ is $x^2 - 1$, which is a binomial. The product of $(a + b)$ and $(c + d)$ is $ac + ad + bc + cd$, which has four terms. **16. a)** Take four consecutive numbers. Subtract the product of the outer numbers from the product of the inner numbers. **b)** 2, 2, 2, 2 **c)** $(x + 1)(x + 2) - (x)(x + 3) = 2$
d) The expression simplifies to 2.

Modelling Math p. 139
a) The product of three consecutive numbers plus the middle number. **b)** 8, 27, 64, 125 **c)** The answer is the cube of the middle number.
d) $(x - 1)(x)(x + 1) + x = x^3$ **e)** The expression simplifies to x^3.

Section 3.3 pp. 142–145
Practice 1. a) x^2 **b)** a^2 **c)** $4x^2$ **d)** $81t^2$ **e)** $9y^2$ **f)** $49p^2$
g) $16j^2$ **h)** $36q^2$ **2. a)** $-6x$ **b)** $+16y$ **c)** $+2xy$ **d)** $-2ab$
e) $+12x$ **f)** $-40a$ **g)** $+12xy$ **h)** $-84p$ **3. a)** $a + 7$ **b)** $x - 2$
c) $3m + 7$ **d)** $9x - 8$ **e)** $x + y$ **f)** $2a - 3b$
4. a) $x^2 + 10x + 25$ **b)** $y^2 + 2y + 1$ **c)** $x^2 - 12x + 36$
d) $m^2 - 6m + 9$ **e)** $x^2 - 9$ **f)** $y^2 - 36$ **g)** $m^2 - 49$ **h)** $t^2 - 64$
5. a) $9x^2 + 12x + 4$ **b)** $25x^2 - 10x + 1$ **c)** $4x^2 - 9$
d) $4m^2 + 28m + 49$ **e)** $9y^2 - 4$ **f)** $16y^2 - 24y + 9$
g) $1 - 25m^2$ **h)** $4 - 12t + 9t^2$ **6. a)** $4x^2 - 9y^2$
b) $4x^2 + 12xy + 9y^2$ **c)** $9a^2 - b^2$ **d)** $16t^2 - 40ts + 25s^2$
e) $16m^2 - 25n^2$ **f)** $9c^2 + 42cd + 49d^2$ **g)** $y^2 - 36x^2$
h) $a^2 - 16ab + 64b^2$ **7. a)** $2x^2 + 4x + 20$
b) $2y^2 + 14y + 13$ **c)** $-16m + 65$ **d)** $5a^2 + 12a - 6$
e) $-2x^2 + 100x - 94$ **f)** $-19t^2 - 30t + 105$
8. a) $-x^2 - 26x - 107$ **b)** $-8x^2 - 23x + 14$
c) $-7m^2 - 33m + 24$ **d)** $19t^2 + 12t - 14$
e) $-21y^2 + 13y + 28$ **f)** $54t^2 - 12t - 2$
g) $100s^2 - 22t^2 + 6t$ **h)** $12m^2 - 12mn + 2n^2 - 3m + 45$
i) $5x^2 + 4xy - 3y^2$ **j)** $-13a^2 - 28ab + 8b^2$
Applications and Problem Solving 9. a) L.S. = 16, R.S. = 10 **b)** $x^2 + 6x + 9$ **10. a)** $x + 10$ **b)** x^2, $(x + 10)^2 = x^2 + 20x + 100$ **c)** 625 cm²; 1225 cm²

11. $(20 + 4)(20 - 4) = 384$; $(50 - 3)(50 + 3) = 2491$; $(60 + 2)(60 - 2) = 3596$ **12. a)** 96 **b)** 216 **c)** 396 **d)** 84
e) 391 **f)** 896 **13. a)** $y^2 - 6y + 11$ **b)** $3y^2 - 7y - 7$
14. $2(x - 3)^2 + 4(x - 3)(x + 3) = 6x^2 - 12x - 18$
15. $6(2x - y)^2 = 24x^2 - 24xy + 6y^2$ **16. a)** $(x + 7)^2$
b) $(x - 8)^2$ **c)** $(2a + 3)^2$ **d)** $(3b - 4)^2$ **e)** $(8m - 2)^2$
f) $(9n + 5)^2$ **17. a)** $x^2 + 12x + 36$ **b)** $a^2 + 8a + 16$
c) $y^2 - 6y + 9$ **d)** $m^2 - 8m + 16$ **e)** $4x^2 - 4x + 1$
f) $9y^2 + 12y + 4$ **18. a)** $x^4 + 2x^2 + 1$ **b)** $y^4 - 2y^2 + 1$
c) $x^4 + 2x^2y^2 + y^4$ **d)** $x^4 - 2x^2y^2 + y^4$ **e)** $4x^4 + 12x^2 + 9$
f) $9y^4 - 24y^2 + 16$ **g)** $x^4 - 4x^2y^2 + 4y^4$
h) $16x^4 + 24x^2y^2 + 9y^4$ **19. a)** $x^4 - 1$ **b)** $y^4 - 4$ **c)** $x^4 - y^4$
d) $64a^4 - 9$ **e)** $9x^4 - 4y^4$ **f)** $16 - 9c^4$ **20.** The square, by 9 cm². **21.** The original garden is 25 m² larger than the new garden. **22. a)** $a^2 + b^2 + c^2 + 2ab + 2ac + 2bc$
b) $4x^2 + 9y^2 + 1 + 12xy + 4x + 6y$ **23.** 1 term, 5 terms
24. a) {7, 24, 25}; {9, 40, 41}, {9, 12, 15}; {12, 35, 37}, {12, 16, 20}, {9, 12, 15}, {5, 12, 13} **b)** Let a represent the given leg, $c + b$ represent one factor of a^2, and $c - b$ represent the other factor of a^2. Thus $(c + b)(c - b) = a^2$, or $c^2 - b^2 = a^2$, or $c^2 = a^2 + b^2$. So {a, b, c} is a Pythagorean triple, and represents the sides of a right triangle.

Technology Extension p. 146
1 Multiplying Binomials 1. a) $8x^2 + 42x + 27$
b) $6x^2 - 5x - 25$ **c)** $20y^2 - 52y + 33$
d) $32x^2 - 4xy - 21y^2$ **e)** $20x^2 + 7xy - 6y^2$ **f)** $9x - 14$
g) $7x^2 + 9x - 13$ **h)** $-6y^2 - 26y + 49$ **i)** $22x^2 + 12xy + y^2$
2 Special Products 1. a) $x^2 + 30x + 225$
b) $t^2 - 10t + 25$ **c)** $81 - 18y + y^2$ **d)** $16m^4 + 56m^2 + 49$
e) $36 - 60r + 25r^2$ **f)** $64x^2 + 48xy + 9y^2$
2. a) $4x^2 - 121$ **b)** $16 - 25x^2$ **c)** $9y^2 - 25x^2$ **3. a)** $4x$
b) $-4x - 13$ **c)** $44y^2 + 68y + 26$ **d)** $15 + 48m - 40m^2$

Section 3.4 p. 150–151
Practice 1. a) $5(x + 5)$ **b)** not possible **c)** $9(y - 1)$
d) $3(x - 5y)$ **e)** $5x(5x + 2)$ **f)** $2a(2x + 4y - 3z)$
g) $pq(5r - s - 10t)$ **h)** $2(x^2 - x - 3)$ **i)** not possible
2. a) $9(a^3 + 3b^2)$ **b)** $3x(x^4 - 2x^2 + 3)$ **c)** $4y(3 - 2y + 6y^2)$
d) $6w^3(4w^2 + 1)$ **e)** not possible **f)** $11b(3a + 2c - b)$
g) $8xy(3y + 2x)$ **h)** $5y(7x - 2y)$ **i)** not possible
j) $12xy(2y - 1 + 3x)$ **k)** $9a^2b^2(3b + 1 - 2a)$
l) $6mn^2(m^2 + 3mn - 2)$ **3. a)** $(a + b)(5x + 3)$
b) $(x - 1)(3m + 5)$ **c)** not possible **d)** $(p + q)(4y - x)$
e) $(m + 7)(4t + 1)$ **f)** not possible **4. a)** $(x + y)(w + z)$
b) $(x + 3)(y + 4)$ **c)** $(x + 1)(x - y)$ **d)** $(m + 4)(m - n)$
e) $(x + 2)(2x + 3y)$ **f)** $(t - 2)(5m^2 + t)$

Applications and Problem Solving   5. a) $20t - 5t^2$
b) 0 m, 15 m, 20 m, 15 m, 0 m, −25 m **c)** 20 m
d) The height is negative. Distance cannot be
negative. **e)** 0 s and 4 s **f)** $5t(4 - t)$ **g)** The height
of the ball is 0 m when $5t = 0$ and when $4 - t = 0$.
6. a) i) $4\pi x^2 - x^2$ **ii)** $x^2(4\pi - 1)$ **b) i)** $6xy - 3xz$
ii) $3x(2y - z)$ **c) i)** $\pi r^2 - 2r^2$ **ii)** $r^2(\pi - 2)$
d) i) $10x + 10y + 100$ **ii)** $10(x + y + 10)$
e) i) $6a + 3b + 3c + 6d + 36$ **ii)** $3(2a + b + c + 2d + 12)$
f) i) $4a + 4b - 16$ **ii)** $4(a + b - 4)$ **7.** k must be divisible
by 2, since the only common factor of $2x^2$ and 4 is 2.
8. Answers may vary. **a)** $s^3t^2 + s^2t^2 + st^2$ **b)** $st^2(s^2 + s + 1)$
9. Answers may vary. **a)** $12x^3y^2 + 9x^2y^3 + 6x^2y^2 + 3xy$
b) $3xy(4x^2y + 3xy^2 + 2xy + 1)$

Modelling Math p. 152
a) Number of Squares: 8, 14, 20, 26, 32; Perimeter:
18, 30, 42, 54, 66 **b)** $6n + 2$ **c)** $2(3n + 1)$ **d)** 452; 620
e) 28 **f)** $12n + 6$ **g)** $6(2n + 1)$ **h)** 822; 1254 **i)** 22
j) $2s + 2$ **k)** $2(s + 1)$ **l)** 186; 630 **m)** 152; 428

Section 3.5 pp. 156–158
Practice   1. a) 3, 5 **b)** 2, 9 **c)** −3, 10 **d)** 2, −10 **e)** 2, 5
f) −5, −2 **g)** −9, −4 **h)** −12, −3 **2. a)** $(x + 4)(x + 1)$
b) $(x + 5)(x + 3)$ **c)** not possible **d)** $(r - 6)(r - 7)$
e) $(n + 6)(n + 5)$ **f)** $(r - 2)(r - 5)$ **g)** $(w - 2)(w - 8)$
h) not possible **i)** $(m - 4)(m - 6)$ **3. a)** $(y + 4)(y - 5)$
b) $(x + 9)(x - 2)$ **c)** not possible **d)** $(n - 12)(n + 2)$
e) not possible **f)** $(x + 2)(x - 10)$ **4. a)** $(m + 10)(m + 8)$
b) $(m + 4)(m - 3)$ **c)** not possible **d)** $(r - 3)(r - 14)$
e) $(y - 9)(y - 8)$ **f)** $(x + 2)(x - 8)$ **g)** not possible
h) not possible **i)** $(x - 3)(x -7)$ **j)** $(w + 2)(w + 10)$
k) $(r + 5)(r - 6)$ **l)** $(y - 2)(y - 18)$ **m)** not possible
n) $(1 + y)(8 - y)$ **o)** $(8 + x)(2 - x)$ **5. a)** $(x + 7y)(x + 5y)$
b) $(a - 11b)(a + 7b)$ **c)** $(c - 2d)(c + d)$ **d)** $(x - 4y)(x + 9y)$
e) not possible **f)** $(p - 2q)(p + 16q)$
6. a) $3(x + 1)(x + 3)$ **b)** $5(y + 6)(y + 2)$ **c)** $4(t - 5)(t + 3)$
d) $6(x + 4)(x - 1)$ **e)** $a(x + 12)(x - 2)$ **f)** $x(x + 12)(x + 6)$
g) $2(x - 7)(x - 4)$ **h)** $5(w + 6)(w - 2)$ **i)** $x(3 + x)(1 - x)$
Applications and Problem Solving   7. a) $(x - 4)(x + 1)$
b) 18 m by 13 m **8. a)** $(x + 4)(x + 5)$ **b)** $(x + 3)(x + 4)$
c) $x^2 + 7x + 12$ **d)** $2x + 8$ **9. a)** $(x + 24)(x - 4)$;
$(x - 3)(x - 24)$; $(x + 4)(x - 20)$; $(x + 3)(x - 28)$;
$(x + 15)(x - 6)$; A = −4, C = −24, E = 4, K = −28,
M = 24, N = −3, O = −6, P = 15, S = 3, T = −20,
Y = 5 **b)** Mack Sennett, Keystone Kops
10. a) $x^2 + 6x + 5 = (x + 5)(x + 1)$,
$x^2 + 6x + 8 = (x + 4)(x + 2)$, $x^2 + 6x + 9 = (x + 3)(x + 3)$;
$x^2 - 5x + 4 = (x - 1)(x - 4)$, $x^2 - 5x + 6 = (x - 2)(x - 3)$;
$x^2 + 7x + 12 = (x + 3)(x + 4)$,

$x^2 + 8x + 12 = (x + 2)(x + 6)$,
$x^2 + 13x + 12 = (x + 1)(x + 12)$;
$x^2 - 6x + 5 = (x - 1)(x - 5)$;
$x^2 - 11x - 12 = (x - 12)(x + 1)$,
$x^2 - 4x - 12 = (x - 6)(x + 2)$,
$x^2 - x - 12 = (x - 4)(x + 3)$ **b)** All have more than one
except $x^2 - \blacksquare x + 5 = (x - \blacksquare)(x + \blacksquare)$. Because 5 is a
prime number, there is only one pair of negative
integers with a product of 5.   **11.** Answers may
vary. **a)** $k = -8, -3, 1$ **b)** $k = 12, 6, 10$ **12. a)** $(x^2 + 1)^2$
b) $(x^2 + 3)(x^2 - 2)$ **c)** $(x^2 - 5)(x^2 + 2)$ **d)** $(x^2 + 9y)(x^2 + y)$
13. a) $(x + a + 1)(x + a + 2)$ **b)** $(x - b + 5)(x - b - 1)$
14. a) $x^2 - 2x - 35 = (x - 7)(x + 5)$,
$t^2 + 3t - 40 = (t + 8)(t - 5)$ **b)** The trinomial has the
value zero when either factor is zero, or both factors
are zero.

Section 3.6 pp. 163–164
Practice   1. a) $(2y + 3)(y + 3)$ **b)** $(3m + 1)(m + 3)$
c) $(5t + 2)(t + 1)$ **d)** not possible **e)** $(x + 2)(2x + 7)$
f) $(3x + 1)(2x + 3)$ **2. a)** $(2x - 3)(x - 1)$
b) $(x - 1)(3x - 2)$ **c)** $(t - 2)(3t - 4)$ **d)** $(m - 2)(5m - 1)$
e) $(2m - 3)(3m - 2)$ **f)** not possible
3. a) $(x - 2)(2x + 3)$ **b)** $(3x - 4)(2x + 1)$
c) $(2t - 1)(t + 5)$ **d)** $(5n - 2)(3n + 1)$ **e)** $(x - 1)(3x + 4)$
f) $(y - 3)(5y + 1)$ **g)** $(2x - 3)(4x + 1)$ **h)** not possible
i) $(5t - 2)(2t + 3)$ **4. a)** $(2t + 1)(2t + 3)$
b) $(2x - 3)(5x - 1)$ **c)** not possible **d)** $(2y + 5)(y + 3)$
e) $2(4y - 3)(y - 2)$ **f)** not possible **g)** $3(2r + 3)(r + 1)$
h) $(3y - 2)(4y - 1)$ **i)** $2(x - 5)(2x + 1)$
j) $m(2m - 5)(m + 6)$ **k)** $t(2t + 1)(t + 4)$
l) $(2s - 1)(9s + 1)$ **m)** $3(r + 1)(4r + 5)$ **n)** $s(r - 1)(5r - 2)$
o) $(2 - y)(3 + 4y)$ **p)** $(2 - m)(1 - 3m)$ **q)** $2(6 + 9t + 4t^2)$
r) $(3 - 2y)(2 + 3y)$ **5. a)** $(2m - n)(3m + 2n)$
b) $(3x + y)(x + 2y)$ **c)** $(2u - b)(5a + b)$ **d)** $(x - 5y)(2x - y)$
e) $(6c + d)(c + 2d)$ **f)** $3(x - y)(2x - y)$
g) $2(m - 3n)(m + n)$ **h)** $4(y - x)(y + 2x)$
i) $2(3a - 2b)(a + 3b)$
Applications and Problem Solving
6. a) $(10x + 3)(x - 1)$ **b)** 503 m by 49 m
7. a) $10x^2 - 29x + 10 = (2x - 5)(5x - 2)$;
$4x^2 - 27x + 18 = (x - 6)(4x - 3)$;
$18x^2 - 27x + 4 = (3x - 4)(6x - 1)$;
$56x^2 + 15x + 1 = (7x + 1)(8x + 1)$;
$10x^2 - 91x + 9 = (x - 9)(10x - 1)$; A = 2, C = 5,
D = −2, E = 4, H = −3, I = −4, J = 3, L = −6, M = 6,
N = −1, O = 7, R = 8, S = −9, T = 10, U = −5, W = 1,
Y = −7 **b)** Joni Mitchell: folk singer; Ned Hanlan:
world champion rower; Marshall McLuhan: author,
communication theorist; Emily Stowe: first Canadian
woman to practise medicine in Canada **8. a)** ±8, ±16

b) $\pm13, \pm14, \pm22, \pm41$ **c)** $\pm5, \pm1$ **d)** $\pm35, \pm16, \pm9, \pm5, 0$
9. a) $(2x^2 + 1)(x^2 + 1)$ **b)** $(2x^2 - 1)(x^2 + 3)$
c) $(3x^2 - 4)(x^2 + 1)$ **d)** $(2x^2 - 3)(3x^2 - 2)$
e) $(2x^2 + y)(x^2 + 2y)$ **f)** $(3x^2 - y)(x^2 + 4y)$

Section 3.7 pp. 167–169
Practice 1. a) $(x + 3)(x - 3)$ **b)** $(y + 4)(y - 4)$ **c)** not
possible **d)** $(5a + 6)(5a - 6)$ **e)** $(1 + 8t)(1 - 8t)$
f) $(6 + 7a)(6 - 7a)$ **g)** not possible **h)** $(5x + 8y)(5x - 8y)$
i) $(2t + 3s)(2t - 3s)$ **j)** $(10p + 11q)(10p - 11q)$
k) $(16 + 9y)(16 - 9y)$ **l)** $(15b + a)(15b - a)$
2. a) yes, $(x + 3)^2$ **b)** yes, $(y - 5)^2$ **c)** no **d)** yes, $(2t + 1)^2$
e) yes, $(4t + 3)^2$ **f)** yes, $(7 + x)^2$ **g)** yes, $(1 - 8t)^2$ **h)** yes,
$(3x - 4)^2$ **i)** yes, $(2 + 7r)^2$ **j)** no **k)** yes, $(11m - 1)^2$ **l)** yes,
$(3a + 2b)^2$ **3. a)** $(y + 12)(y - 12)$ **b)** not possible
c) $(3a - 4)^2$ **d)** $2(x + 4)(x - 4)$ **e)** not possible
f) $3(x + 1)^2$ **g)** $(m - 7)^2$ **h)** $(2p + 5q)^2$
i) $(7x + 11y)(7x - 11y)$ **j)** $5(4a + 3b)(4a - 3b)$ **k)** not
possible **l)** $y(y + 6)(y - 6)$ **m)** $y(y - 9)^2$ **n)** $4(9x^2 + 25y^2)$
o) $3x(x + 4)(x - 4)$ **p)** $5m(m - 4)^2$ **q)** $(9x + 12)(9x - 12)$
r) $3(b + 10)(b - 10)$
Applications and Problem Solving 4. a) 600 **b)** 800
c) $640\ 000$ **5. a)** $2(x - 1)^2$ **b)** $2(x - 1)$, $x - 1$ **c)** 18 m by
9 m **6. a)** $(x - 1)(x + 5)$ **b)** $(1 + y)(7 - y)$ **c)** $-(2m + 3)$
d) $(x^2 + 11)^2$ **e)** $(t^3 - 9)^2$ **f)** $\left(\dfrac{x}{2} + \dfrac{1}{3}\right)\left(\dfrac{x}{2} - \dfrac{1}{3}\right)$
g) $(5x^2 + 9)(5x^2 - 9)$ **h)** $8xy$ **7. a)** ±8 **b)** ±42 **c)** 4 **d)** 9
e) 25 **f)** 16 **8. a)** $2x(x - 6)^2$ **b)** x, $(x - 6)$, $2(x - 6)$; $2x$,
$(x - 6)$, $(x - 6)$ **c)** 8 cm by 2 cm by 4 cm or 16 cm by
2 cm by 2 cm **d)** No, then two of the dimensions
would be negative. **9.** 5, 2; –5, 2; 5, –2; –5, –2; 11,
10; –11, 10; 11, –10; –11, –10 **10.** 20, 12, 4
11. a) $(x + 3 + y)(x + 3 - y)$ **b)** $(x - 2 + 3y)(x - 2 - 3y)$
c) $(2x + 3y + 2z)(2x + 3y - 2z)$ **d)** $(x^2 - y + z)(x^2 - y - z)$
12. 16 cm

Modelling Math p. 169
a) side length minus one all squared **b)** $(s - 1)^2$ **c)** 121;
8100 **d)** 24

Career Connection p. 170
1. a) $10\pi[(1.2)^2 - 10\pi(1)^2]$ **b)** $10\pi(1.2 + 1)(1.2 - 1)$;
4.4π **c)** The inner cylinder contains no concrete.
d) $13.8\ m^3$ **2.** Evaluate the expression in question 1a)
without factoring.

Technology Extension pp. 171
1 Factoring Polynomials 1. a) $3(2x^2 + 5x - 4)$
b) $7(2y^2 - 6y + 3)$ **c)** $5(4x - 3x^2 + 2)$

d) $2xy(2x + 3 - 4y)$ **e)** $3pq(p^2 + 6pq + 2q^2)$
f) $2b^2(6a^3 + 2a^2b + 4ab^2 - 3b^3)$ **2. a)** $(x + 2)(x + 17)$
b) $(x - 12)(x + 6)$ **c)** not possible **d)** $(5 - t)(3 - t)$
e) $(n + 1)(4n + 9)$ **f)** not possible **g)** $(x - 4)(5x + 3)$
h) $(3y - 2)(5y + 7)$ **i)** $(x + 2y)(x + 5y)$ **j)** $(x - 4y)(3x - 2y)$
k) $(3a - 2b)(5a + 3b)$ **l)** $(2x + 9y)(7x - 4y)$
m) $(x + a + 2)(x + a + 4)$ **n)** $(x - y - 2)(x - y - 3)$
o) $(x^2 + 5)(x^2 - 3)$ **3. a)** $3(x - 1)(x - 9)$
b) $2(2x - 3)(x + 4)$ **c)** $5(5y + 1)(3y + 8)$
d) $2(u - 2v)(u - v)$ **e)** $6(3x - y)(2x + 3y)$
f) $x(x + 1)(x + 2)$ **g)** $2t(t - 7)(2t + 1)$
h) $3(5x^2 + 2)(2x^2 + 5)$ **i)** $8(x + 1)(x - 1)(3x^2 + 1)$
2 Factoring Special Products 1. a) $(5x + 6)^2$
b) $(3y - 5)^2$ **c)** $(3n + 8)(3n - 8)$ **d)** $(5 + 13x)(5 - 13x)$
e) $(2x + 3y)(2x - 3y)$ **f)** $(7a - 4b)^2$
2. a) $16(m + 2)(m - 2)$ **b)** $4(3 + 2x)(3 - 2x)$
c) $5(5x^2 + 4)(5x^2 - 4)$ **d)** $2(6x + 7y^2)(6x - 7y^2)$
e) $2(x - 7)^2$ **f)** $3(2x + 5)^2$ **g)** $8w(2w - 5)^2$
h) $12(5 + 2x^2)(5 - 2x^2)$ **i)** $4(3y^2 + 5x^2)^2$

Rich Problem pp. 172–173
1 Writing Expressions for Areas 1. πr^2 **2.** r; $r + 1$
3. a) $\pi(r + 1)^2 - \pi r^2$ **b)** $\pi(2r + 1)$
4. a) $\pi(r + 2)^2 - \pi(r + 1)^2$; $\pi(2r + 3)$
b) $\pi(r + 3)^2 - \pi(r + 2)^2$; $\pi(2r + 5)$
c) $\pi(r + 4)^2 - \pi(r + 3)^2$; $\pi(2r + 7)$
d) $\pi(r + 5)^2 - \pi(r + 4)^2$; $\pi(2r + 9)$ **5. a)** The area is π
times the sum of twice the radius and one less than
twice the ring number. **b)** $\pi(2r + 2n - 1)$ **c)** $\pi(2r + 15)$
6. a) $44\ m^2$ **b)** $57\ m^2$ **c)** $75\ m^2$ **d)** $88\ m^2$
7. a) $13\pi(2r + 13)$ **b)** $740\ m^2$
2 Writing Expressions for Circumferences 1. $2\pi r$
2. a) $2\pi(r + 1)$ **b)** $2\pi(r + 2)$ **c)** $2\pi(r + 5)$ **d)** $2\pi(r + 12)$
3. a) $26\pi(r + 6)$ **b)** 690 m
3 Estimating Seating Capacities 1. Answers may
vary. Assume each person needs about 1 m of inner
circumference. **a)** 22 **b)** 41 **c)** 60 **d)** 690 **2.** 785 000

Review of Key Concepts pp. 174–179
1. a) $5x - 3y$ **b)** $8x^2 - 4x + 3$ **c)** $-a^2 - 6a - 8$
d) $m^2 + 3mn + n^2$ **2. a)** $-12x^4y^4$ **b)** $24r^2s^4t^6$ **3. a)** $-4a$
b) $4n^3p$ **4. a)** $8x + 18$ **b)** $4a + 28$ **c)** $8t^2 - 3t$ **d)** $y^2 - 7$
5. a) $x^2 + 2x - 8$ **b)** $a^2 - a - 30$ **c)** $6y^2 - y - 12$
d) $3x^2 - 11xy - 4y^2$ **6. a)** $2x^2 - 4x - 6$ **b)** $-2y^2 - 6y + 8$
c) $12m^2 - 28m + 8$ **d)** $12x^2 - 12x - 9$ **7. a)** $2y^2 - 4y - 6$
b) $-7x^2 - 12x + 6$ **c)** $8a^2 + 12a + 19$ **d)** $17x^2 - 10x + 12$
8. a) $x^2 + 8x + 16$ **b)** $y^2 - 16$ **c)** $a^2 - 10a + 25$ **d)** $9t^2 - 1$
e) $4x^2 - 12xy + 9y^2$ **f)** $25a^2 - 9b^2$ **g)** $18m^2 + 12m + 2$
h) $1 - 4x + 4x^2$ **i)** $48x^2 - 27$ **9. a)** $2m^2 - 8m + 7$
b) $-12x + 61$ **c)** $30t^2 + 12t + 1$ **d)** $-9x^2 + 18xy - 11y^2$

10. a) $(x + 1)(x - 1) = x^2 - 1$, and x is the average of the numbers. **b)** Square their average and subtract 4. **c)** $(x - 2)(x + 2) = x^2 - 4$, where x is the average of $x - 2$ and $x + 2$. **11. a)** $5(t - 7)$ **b)** $5y(y + 4)$ **c)** not possible **d)** $2xy(1 - 4y - 2xy^2)$
12. a) $(x + 4)(m - 3)$ **b)** not possible **c)** $(m + n)(2x - 1)$
13. a) $(m + 2)(x + y)$ **b)** $(x - y)(x - 1)$ **c)** $(m - 3)(2m + t)$
14. a) πr^2 **b)** $\pi r^2 + 6\pi r + 9\pi$ **c)** $3\pi(2r + 3)$ **d)** 122.5 cm^2
15. a) $(x - 4)(x + 3)$ **b)** $(y + 6)(y - 3)$ **c)** $(m + 3)(m + 8)$
d) $(t - 3)(t - 5)$ **e)** not possible **f)** $(n - 5)(n - 8)$
g) $(w - 6)(w + 5)$ **h)** $(7 - m)(2 + m)$ **i)** $(x + y)(x + 8y)$
j) $(c - 2d)(c - 8d)$ **16. a)** $2(x - 5)(x + 4)$
b) $a(y - 2)(y + 14)$ **c)** $3(x + 6)(x - 2)$ **d)** $5(x - 2)(x - 1)$
17. Answers may vary. $x^2 + 4x + 3$, $x^2 + 5x + 6$
18. Answers may vary. $x^2 - x - 2$, $x^2 + x - 6$
19. a) $(5m + 2)(m + 3)$ **b)** $(2x + 1)(3x + 2)$
c) $(2x - 5)(x - 1)$ **d)** $(t - 2)(3t + 10)$ **e)** not possible
f) $(3y - 1)(2y + 1)$ **g)** $(2x - 1)(3x + 1)$
h) $(3z - 2)(3z - 1)$ **i)** $(2x + y)(x + 5y)$ **j)** $(4p - 7q)(p + q)$
20. a) $2(2x + 1)(x + 1)$ **b)** $3(3t - 2)(t + 1)$
c) $4(m - 1)(5m + 3)$ **d)** $y(y - 2)(3y - 1)$
21. a) $(7x + 1)(11x - 7)$ **b)** 120 cm by 180 cm
22. a) $(x + 5)(x - 5)$ **b)** $(1 + 7m)(1 - 7m)$ **c)** not
possible **d)** $(7t + 9s)(7t - 9s)$ **e)** $4(a - 2b)(a + 2b)$
f) $(12p + q)(12p - q)$ **23. a)** yes, $(x + 5)^2$ **b)** yes, $(y - 6)^2$
c) yes, $(3t - 1)^2$ **d)** no **e)** yes, $(2x + 3)^2$ **f)** yes, $(5r - 2s)^2$
24. a) $5(x + 1)(x - 1)$ **b)** $4(2m + 3n)(2m - 3n)$
c) $2(3y + 5)^2$ **d)** $5(x - 2y)^2$ **25. a)** $(3x - 2)^2$; $3x - 2$
b) 220 m

Chapter Test pp. 180–181
1. a) $8y^2 - 3y - 3$ **b)** $-7x + 2$ **2. a)** $10a^4b^5$ **b)** $5xz^2$
3. a) $-6m - 14$ **b)** $5x^2 - 11x$ **c)** $-4a^3 - 7a^2 + 4a$
4. a) $y^2 + 2y - 15$ **b)** $6x^2 - 7x + 2$ **c)** $2a^2 - 5ab - 3b^2$
5. a) $m^2 - 12m - 3$ **b)** $6x^2 + 2x + 19$ **6. a)** $x^2 - 2x + 1$
b) $4y^2 - 9$ **c)** $x^2 + 4xy + 4y^2$ **d)** $30x^2 + 12x - 1$
7. a) $4m(m - 7)$ **b)** $3ab(1 - 3b + 2a)$ **c)** $(m - 2)(x - 4)$
d) $(y + 2)(y + x)$ **8. a)** $(x - 4)(x - 3)$ **b)** $(a + 7)(a - 3)$
c) $(y + 4)(y + 5)$ **d)** $(t - 9)(t + 3)$ **e)** $(x + 5y)(x + y)$
f) $(m - 2n)(m - 7n)$ **9. a)** $3(x - 2)(x + 1)$
b) $4(t - 2)(t - 5)$ **c)** $a(y + 4)(y - 3)$
10. a) $(t + 1)(3t + 5)$ **b)** $(m - 4)(2m - 1)$
c) $(3x - 2)(2x + 1)$ **d)** $(2y - 1)(2y + 3)$ **e)** $(r - 2s)(5r - s)$
f) $(2x - 5y)(2x + y)$ **11. a)** $(x + 2)(x - 2)$
b) $(1 + 6m)(1 - 6m)$ **c)** $(6t + 7s)(6t - 7s)$
d) $(11a + b)(11a - b)$ **e)** $(x + 4)^2$ **f)** $(y - 3)^2$ **g)** $(2t - 1)^2$
h) $(2m + 5)^2$ **12. a)** $3(y + 3)(y - 3)$ **b)** $t(3 + 2t)(3 - 2t)$
c) $2(2x + 3)^2$ **d)** $x(x - 2)^2$

13. a) $(5x + 3)^2 = 25x^2 + 30x + 9$ **b)** 1444 cm^2
14. a) $(5x - 8)(2x + 5)$ **b)** 152 mm by 69 mm

Problem Solving: Use Logic p. 183
Applications and Problem Solving **1.** 10 **2.** $25, 85$
3. Toronto and Calgary, Boston and Vancouver, Edmonton and Detroit, Chicago and Montréal
4. $h = 22$, $g = 3$ **5.** $6, 1, 10, 8$; $5, 9, 2$; $4, 7; 3$ **6. a)** one
thousand **b)** one billion **7.** Move 7 from the 11 pile to the 7 pile and you have 4, 14, 6. Move 6 from the 14 pile to the 6 pile and you have 4, 8, 12. Move 4 from the 12 pile to the 4 pile and you have 8, 8, 8.
8. Rohana **9.** Sharif **10.** Donna

Problem Solving: Guess and Check
p. 185–186
Applications and Problem Solving **1. a)** 7821 km
c) 17.7 h **e)** 5959 m **2.** Mary: 12, Sasha: 17, Paula:
19, Amandi: 21, Heather: 24 **3.** 118 and 119
4. $\{6, 3, 1\}$ and $\{6, 1, 3\}$ **5.** $2, 6, 10, 14, 18$ **6.** $2, 9, 4,$
$3; 5, 7, 6; 10, 8; 1$ **7.** 9 **8. a)** 8 m **b)** 16
9. a) $\dfrac{1}{2} + \dfrac{1}{3} + \dfrac{1}{6} = 1$ **b)** No, $\dfrac{1}{3}$ is the largest unit

fraction, and two of these are required to sum to 1.
10. front face, clockwise from lower left: 4, 7, 2, 5; rear face, clockwise from lower left: 6, 1, 8, 3

Problem Solving: Using the Strategies p. 187
2. 001 **4. b)** twice **5.** 120 **6.** 6 **7.** 4 cm by 8 cm by 18 cm **8.** $18, 20, 24$ **9.** Alexi: green, Kala: blue, Lisa: yellow, Jamal: red **10.** 68 **11.** 9 **12.** About 3.8 billion, assuming tiles are 8.5 cm by 8.5 cm. **13.** 10

Chapter 4

Getting Started p. 190
1. $d = 5t^2$ **2. a)** 245 m **b)** 320 m **c)** 55 m **3.** No, the graph is not a straight line.

Review of Prerequisite Skills p. 191
1. a) $11, 5, -4, -13, -19$ **b)** $16, 4, 0, 4, 16$ **c)** $5, -3, 0,$
$21, 45$ **d)** $23, 5, -5, -7, -1$ **2. a)** $7, 19, 7, 19$ **b)** $1, 1,$
$17, 17$ **c)** $2, 0, 6, 42$ **d)** $1, -3, -3, -24$ **e)** $4, 7, 15, 20$
f) $-3, 3, 3, 9$ **g)** $10, 2, 26, 5$ **h)** $-3, -4, 0, 5$ **3. a)** $x^2 + x$
b) $x^2 - 3x$ **c)** $x^2 + 2x$ **d)** $x^2 + 2x$ **e)** $x^2 - 4x$ **f)** $x^2 + 4x$
g) $x^2 - 6x$ **h)** $x^2 + 12x$ **4. a)** $(x + 2)^2$ **b)** $(x + 3)^2$
c) $(x - 1)^2$ **d)** $(x - 4)^2$ **e)** $(x + 10)^2$ **f)** $(x - 6)^2$ **g)** $(x - 9)^2$
h) $(x + 11)^2$ **5. a)** 1 **b)** 2 **c)** 2 **d)** 3 **e)** 2 **f)** 4 **6. a)** non-
linear **b)** linear **7. b)** Yes, a figure and its translation image are always congruent. **8. b)** Yes, a figure and its reflection image are always congruent.

Section 4.1 pp. 197–199

Practice 1. a) function **b)** function **c)** not a function **d)** function **e)** function **f)** not a function **2. a)** 3 **b)** 23 **c)** −5 **d)** −13 **e)** −21 **f)** 395 **g)** −3 **h)** −7 **i)** 3995 **3. a)** 6 **b)** 2 **c)** −2 **d)** 14 **e)** 8 **f)** −12 **g)** 7 **h)** 8.2 **i)** 0 **4. a)** 9 **b)** 5 **c)** 9 **d)** 105 **e)** 105 **f)** 5.25 **g)** 5.01 **5. a)** 3 **b)** 1 **c)** 19 **d)** 163 **e)** 243 **f)** 1.5 **g)** 1.5 **6. b)** yes **7. a)** function **b)** not a function **c)** function **d)** not a function **8. a)** domain: {3, 4, 5, 6}, range: {−2, 0, 1, 3} **b)** domain: {−3, −1, 1, 3, 5}, range: {2, 3, 4} **c)** domain: {−2, −1, 0, 1}, range: {3, 4} **d)** domain: {−1}, range: {1, 2, 3, 4} **9. a)** domain: {−2, −1, 0, 1, 2}, range: {1, 2, 5}; function **b)** domain: {0, 1, 2, 3}, range: {−2, −1, 0, 1}; not a function **10. a)** domain: {−2, 0, 2, 4, 6}, range: {0, 2, 4, 6, 8} **b)** domain: set of real numbers, range: set of real numbers **c)** domain: set of real numbers, range: $y \leq 2$ **d)** domain: {1}, range: set of real numbers **11.** {2, 3, 6}

Applications and Problem Solving 12. a) 2; 2.5 **b)** speed: independent, Mach number: dependent. The Mach number depends on the speed. **13. b)** 17.6 million **c)** 2039 **14. b)** No, the domain and range are both the set of real numbers. **c)** x does not have a minimum or maximum value. The domain is the set of real numbers. y has a minimum value of 0, but no maximum value. The range is the set of real numbers greater than 0. **15. a)** range: set of real numbers **b)** range: $y \geq -2$ **16. a)** ±2 **b)** ±4 **c)** 0 **d)** $\pm\sqrt{11}$ **17. a)** no **b)** Yes, there is only one name for every set of fingerprints. **18.** No, there are likely several people with the same first name. **19.** Since the x-coordinates of the points on a vertical line are all equal, if a vertical line passes through more than one point of the graph of a relation, then the relation contains two different points with the same x-coordinate, and so is not a function. **20. a)** $y = 8a + 3$ **b)** $y = -1 - 3n$ **c)** $y = m^2 - 2m + 2$ **d)** $y = 8k^2 + 8k - 1$ **e)** $y = 9t^2 + 6t - 4$ **f)** $y = 12w^2 - 32w + 25$ **21.** It is a vertical line. **22. a)** A closed dot is used to show the location of an ordered pair on a graph; an open dot is used to show that an ordered pair is omitted from the graph. **b)** It looks like steps. **c)** domain: $0 \leq t \leq 4$, range: {120, 200, 280, 360} **d)** (0.5, 120), (1, 120) **e)** (1, 120), (2, 200) **f)** No, the graph is a function.

Investigation pp. 200–203

1 Translations on a Coordinate Grid 1. a) D′(2, 4), E′(−2, 4), F′(−2, −2) **b)** P′(−1, 4), Q′(−5, 6), R′(−7, −3) **c)** U′(−3, −4), V′(−1, 3), W′(0, 0) **d)** F′(4, −1), G′(−2, 6), H′(1, −2) **e)** A′(1, −3), B′(7, −4), C′(5, −7)

f) J′(−1, −2), K′(−4, −1), L′(−6, −6) **2.** R(1, −4), S(−2, 3), T(−4, −5) **3. a)** A′(7, 3), B′(3, 8), C′(1, 4) **b)** A″(6, −2), B″(2, 3), C″(0, −1) **c)** 3 units to the right, 2 units downward

2 Reflections on a Coordinate Grid 1. a) A′(2, −4), B′(1, −1), C′(6, −2) **b)** D′(0, −3), E′(5, −4), F′(2, 0) **c)** P′(1, −2), Q′(−3, 2), R′(3, 1) **2. a)** A′(−1, 3), B′(−2, 1), C′(−6, 3) **b)** D′(−1, 2), E′(0, −2), F′(−3, 1) **c)** P′(2, 1), Q′(3, −3), R′(−1, −2) **3. a)** (2, −3), (−2, 3) **b)** (−1, 2), (1, −2) **c)** (−3, −2), (3, 2) **d)** (4, 0), (−4, 0) **4.** A′(−1, 1), B′(−5, 2), C′(−3, 6) **5.** R′(2, −5), S′(−2, −4), T′(−1, 2) **6. a)** y-axis **b)** x-axis

3 Dilatations on a Coordinate Grid 1. a) 2 **b)** $\dfrac{1}{3}$

2. a) A′(6, 4), B′(2, 8) **b)** C′(3, 2), D′(−1, 1) **c)** E′(−3, −3), F′(3, 6) **d)** G′(3, 1), H′(−2, 0) **3.** R′(6, 9), S′(−3, 12), T′(−9, −6) **4.** D′(3, 2), E′(−1, 3), F′(−2, −2), G′(2, −3) **5. b)** 8 **c)** P′(−6, 6), Q′(−6, −6), R′(6, −6) **d)** 72 **e)** P″(−1, 1), Q″(−1, −1), R″(1, −1) **f)** 2 **g)** 9:1; $\dfrac{1}{4}$:1 **h)** The first term is the square of the scale factor.

Section 4.2 pp. 213–216

Practice 1. a) up; (0, 5); $x = 0$; domain: set of real numbers, range: $y \geq 5$; minimum: 5 **b)** up; (0, −2); $x = 0$; domain: set of real numbers, range: $y \geq -2$; minimum: −2 **c)** down; (0, −1); $x = 0$; domain: set of real numbers, range: $y \leq -1$; maximum: −1 **d)** down; (0, 4); $x = 0$; domain: set of real numbers, range: $y \leq 4$; maximum: 4 **e)** up; (0, 0); $x = 0$; domain: set of real numbers, range: $y \geq 0$; minimum: 0 **f)** down; (0, 0); $x = 0$; domain: set of real numbers, range: $y \leq 0$; maximum: 0 **g)** up; (0, −1); $x = 0$; domain: set of real numbers, range: $y \geq -1$; minimum: −1 **h)** down; (0, 0); $x = 0$; domain: set of real numbers, range: $y \leq 0$; maximum: 0 **i)** down; (0, −3); $x = 0$; domain: set of real numbers, range: $y \leq -3$; maximum: −3 **j)** up; (0, 1); $x = 0$; domain: set of real numbers, range: $y \geq 1$; minimum: 1 **k)** down; (0, 7); $x = 0$; domain: set of real numbers, range: $y \leq 7$; maximum: 7 **l)** down; (0, −6); $x = 0$; domain: set of real numbers, range: $y \leq -6$; maximum: −6 **2. a)** The graph of $y = x^2 - 4$ is a translation of the graph of $y = x^2$ 4 units downward **b)** The graph of $y = -x^2 + 5$ is a translation of the graph of $y = -x^2$ 5 units upward. **c)** The graph of $y = 3x^2$ is a vertical stretch of the graph of $y = x^2$ by a factor of 3. **d)** The graph of $y = -\dfrac{1}{3}x^2$ is a vertical shrink of the graph of $y = -x^2$ by a factor of $\dfrac{1}{3}$ **e)** The graph of $y = 2x^2 - 2$ is a translation of the graph of $y = 2x^2 + 7$ 9 units downward. **f)** The graph of

$y = -0.25x^2$ is a reflection of the graph of $y = 0.25x^2$ in the x-axis. **3. a)** $y = -2x^2 + 3$ **b)** $y = 2x^2 - 3$ **c)** $y = 2x^2 + 3$ **d)** $y = -2x^2 - 3$ **4. a)** down; $(0, 0)$; domain: set of real numbers, range: $y \le 0$; maximum: 0 **b)** up; $(0, -11.4)$; domain: set of real numbers, range: $y \ge -11.4$; minimum: -11.4 **c)** down; $(0, 4.7)$; domain: set of real numbers, range: $y \le 4.7$; maximum: 4.7 **d)** up; $(0, -3)$; domain: set of real numbers, range: $y \ge -3$; minimum: -3 **e)** down; $(0, -8.3)$; domain: set of real numbers, range: $y \le -8.3$; maximum: -8.3 **f)** up; $(0, 9.9)$; domain: set of real numbers, range: $y \ge 9.9$; minimum: 9.9 **g)** up; $(0, 3.5)$; domain: set of real numbers, range: $y \ge 3.5$; minimum: 3.5 **h)** down; $(0, -0.5)$; domain: set of real numbers, range: $y \le -0.5$; maximum: -0.5 **5. a)** It becomes the point $(2, 13)$. **b)** It becomes the point $(2, -1)$. **c)** It becomes the point $(2, -2)$. **d)** It becomes the point $(2, -2)$. **6. a)** $(0, -9)$, x-intercepts: ± 3, y-intercept: -9 **b)** $(0, 1)$, x-intercepts: none, y-intercept: 1 **c)** $(0, 4)$, x-intercepts: ± 2, y-intercept: 4 **d)** $(0, -8)$, x-intercepts: ± 2, y-intercept: -8 **e)** $(0, 16)$, x-intercepts: none, y-intercept: 16 **f)** $(0, 18)$, x-intercepts: ± 3, y-intercept: 18 **g)** $(0, -3)$, x-intercepts: none, y-intercept: -3 **h)** $(0, 5)$, x-intercepts: ± 1, y-intercept: 5 **7. a)** ± 1.4 **b)** ± 1.7 **c)** no x-intercepts **d)** ± 2.2 **e)** ± 1.4 **f)** ± 2.4

Applications and Problem Solving **8.** -7.5; The graph is symmetric about the y-axis. **9. a)** $A = \frac{1}{2}h^2$ **c)** 0, 0 **d)** domain: $h \ge 0$, range: $A \ge 0$ **10. a)** $y = 5x^2$ **b)** $y = -6x^2$ **c)** $y = -8x^2 - 7$ **d)** $y = 0.2x^2 + 3$ **11.** $k = -15$ **12. b)** 2 m **c)** 150 m **d)** 17 m **13. a)** $(-3, 7)$, $(2, 2)$ **b)** Answers may vary. **14. a)** $y = x^2 + 2$ **b)** $y = -x^2 - 1$ **c)** $y = 2x^2 - 3$ **d)** $y = -\frac{1}{2}x^2 + 4$ **15. a)** $n = 2p^2 - 4$ **b)** $n = -2p^2 + 4$ **c)** They are reflections of each other in the n-axis. **16. a)** $A = \pi r^2$ **c)** No, the domain of the function is $r \ge 0$. **d)** domain: $r \ge 0$, range: $A \ge 0$ **17. a)** $A = 400 - s^2$ **b)** 16 **d)** domain: $0 \le s \le 16$, range: $144 \le A \le 400$ **Technology Extension** Answers may vary.

Modelling Math p. 216

b) 1st quadrant; d and t must be non-negative. **c)** 5.4 s **d)** 13.5 s

Section 4.3 pp. 222–227

Practice **1. a)** up; $(-5, 0)$; $x = -5$; domain: set of real numbers, range: $y \ge 0$; minimum: 0 **b)** down; $(-1, 0)$; $x = -1$; domain: set of real numbers, range: $y \le 0$; maximum: 0 **c)** up; $(3, 0)$; $x = 3$; domain: set of real

numbers, range: $y \ge 0$; minimum: 0 **d)** up; $(-2, 4)$; $x = -2$; domain: set of real numbers, range: $y \ge 4$; minimum: 4 **e)** down; $(2, -5)$; $x = 2$; domain: set of real numbers, range: $y \le -5$; maximum: -5 **f)** up; $(-3, -5)$; $x = -3$; domain: set of real numbers, range: $y \ge -5$; minimum: -5 **g)** up; $(-6, 2)$; $x = -6$; domain: set of real numbers, range: $y \ge 2$; minimum: 2 **h)** up; $(5, -4)$; $x = 5$; domain: set of real numbers, range: $y \ge -4$; minimum: -4 **i)** down; $(-4, 3)$; $x = -4$; domain: set of real numbers, range: $y \le 3$; maximum: 3 **2. a)** up; $(5, 0)$; $x = 5$; domain: set of real numbers, range: $y \ge 0$; minimum: 0 **b)** down; $(-4, 0)$; $x = -4$; domain: set of real numbers, range: $y \le 0$; maximum: 0 **c)** up; $(2, 1)$; $x = 2$; domain: set of real numbers, range: $y \ge 1$; minimum: 1 **d)** down; $(-1, -2)$; $x = -1$; domain: set of real numbers, range: $y \le -2$; maximum: -2 **3. a)** up; vertically stretched by a factor of 2; $(1, 0)$; $x = 1$; minimum: 0 **b)** down; vertically shrunk by a factor of 0.5; $(-7, 0)$; $x = -7$; maximum: 0 **c)** down; vertically stretched by a factor of 2; $(4, 7)$; $x = 4$; maximum: 7 **d)** up; vertically stretched by a factor of 4; $(-3, -4)$; $x = -3$; minimum: -4 **e)** down; vertically stretched by a factor of 3; $(5, 6)$; $x = 5$; maximum: 6 **f)** down; vertically shrunk by a factor of 0.4; $(8, -1)$; $x = 8$; maximum: -1 **g)** up; vertically shrunk by a factor of $\frac{1}{3}$; $(-6, -7)$; $x = -6$; minimum: -7 **h)** up; vertically shrunk by a factor of 0.5; $(-1, -5)$; $x = -1$; minimum: -5 **i)** up; vertically stretched by a factor of 2.5; $(-1.5, -9)$; $x = -1.5$; minimum: -9 **j)** down; vertically stretched by a factor of 1.2; $(2.6, 3.3)$; $x = 2.6$; maximum: 3.3 **4. a)** $y = -3(x + 1)^2 + 2$ **b)** $y = 3(x - 1)^2 + 2$ **c)** $y = 3(x + 1)^2 - 2$ **d)** $y = -3(x - 1)^2 - 2$ **6. a)** x-intercept: 2; y-intercept: 4 **b)** x-intercepts: -5, 1; y-intercept: -5 **c)** x-intercepts: 2, 4; y-intercept: 8 **d)** x-intercepts: -3, -1; y-intercept: -3 **7. a)** x-intercepts: -2.7, 0.7; y-intercept: -2 **b)** x-intercepts: -0.4, 2.4; y-intercept: -2 **c)** x-intercepts: $\frac{1}{2}$, $\frac{3}{2}$; y-intercept: -3 **d)** x-intercepts: none; y-intercept: -47 **e)** x-intercept: -4; y-intercept: 4 **f)** x-intercepts: -5, -1; y-intercept: -2.5

Applications and Problem Solving **8. a)** 83 m **b)** 6.0 s **9. a)** $y = (x - 7)^2$ **b)** $y = -(x + 5)^2$ **c)** $y = 2(x - 3)^2 - 5$ **d)** $y = -3(x - 6)^2 + 7$ **e)** $y = -0.5(x + 1)^2 - 1$ **f)** $y = 1.5(x + 8)^2 + 9$ **10. a)** $y = (x - 1)^2 + 5$ **b)** $y = -(x + 3)^2$ **c)** $y = 3(x - 4)^2 - 2$ **d)** $y = -2(x - 2)^2 - 3$ **e)** $y = 0.4(x + 3)^2 - 3$ **f)** $y = 5(x - 4.5)^2$ **g)** $y = -4(x - 3)^2$ **h)** $y = 2(x + 5)^2 - 6$ **11.** -11 **12.** $x = -1$; The axis of symmetry is halfway between the x-intercepts. It is the vertical line passing through

the midpoint of the line segment joining the
x-intercepts. **13.** $x = -3$ **14. a)** 38.5 m **b)** 1 m **c)** 5 s
d) 25 m **15. a)** 10 m **b)** 20 m **c)** 40 m **d)** 7.5 m **e)** No,
the ball would be at a height of 5.1 m, which is too
high to jump. **f)** $h = -0.025d^2$ **16. a)** 6 m **b)** 20 m
c) 2 m; 2 m **d)** 38 m **e)** 2.76 m **17. a)** The graphs in
each pair are identical. **b)** $(x - h)^2 = (h - x)^2$
18. b) $(-2, -3)$, $(1, 6)$ **c)** Answers may vary.
19. a) $m = n$ **b)** $m > n$ **c)** $m < n$ **20.** $k = 4$
21. a) $y = (x + 4)^2 - 5$ **b)** $y = -(x - 3)^2 + 2$
c) $y = -(x - 1)^2 + 6$ **d)** $y = 3(x + 2)^2 + 3$
e) $y = -2(x + 5)^2 - 3$ **f)** $y = \frac{1}{2}(x - 6)^2 + 4$
22. a) $y = 2(x - 1)^2 + 2$ **b)** $y = -(x + 2)^2 + 3$
c) $y = \frac{1}{2}(x - 2)^2 - 4$ **d)** $y = -\frac{1}{4}(x + 4)^2 - 1$
23. a) $a = 2$, $k = 4$ **b)** $a = -1$, $k = -4$ **c)** $a = -2$, $k = 5$
24. a) vertex on y-axis **b)** vertex on x-axis **c)** vertex
at $(0, 0)$ **25. a)** $A = (x - 2)^2 + 3$ **c)** $x = 2$ **d)** 0
26. a) $y = -3(x - 2)^2 - 1$ **b)** $y = 3(x + 2)^2 + 1$
c) $y = -3(x + 2)^2 - 1$ **27. a)** $(\pm30, 0.36)$ **b)** $y = 0.0004x^2$
c) $y = 0.0004(x + 30)^2 - 0.36$
d) $y = 0.0004(x - 30)^2 - 0.36$ **e)** 0.16 cm **Technology
Extension** Answers may vary.

Section 4.4 pp. 234–239
Practice 1. a) 49 **b)** 36 **c)** 1 **d)** 81 **e)** 25 **f)** 100
2. a) $y = (x + 3)^2 - 6$; $(-3, -6)$, $x = -3$; Points may
vary. $(0, 3)$, $(1, 10)$ **b)** $y = (x - 2)^2 - 5$; $(2, -5)$, $x = 2$;
Points may vary. $(0, -1)$, $(1, -4)$ **c)** $y = (x + 5)^2 + 5$;
$(-5, 5)$, $x = -5$; Points may vary. $(0, 30)$, $(1, 41)$
d) $y = (x - 1)^2 + 2$; $(1, 2)$, $x = 1$; Points may vary. $(0, 3)$,
$(2, 3)$ **e)** $y = (x + 6)^2 - 8$; $(-6, -8)$, $x = -6$; Points may
vary. $(0, 28)$, $(1, 41)$ **f)** $y = (x - 4)^2 - 4$; $(4, -4)$, $x = 4$;
Points may vary. $(0, 12)$, $(1, 5)$ **3. a)** $y = x^2 - 4$
b) $y = -x^2 + 4x$ **c)** $y = x^2 - 4x$ **d)** $y = x^2 + 4x$
e) $y = -x^2 + 4$ **f)** $y = -x^2 - 4x$ **4. a)** $(1, -9)$; $x = 1$;
x-intercepts: -2, 4; y-intercept: -8; $y \geq -9$ **b)** $(3, 1)$;
$x = 3$; x-intercepts: none; y-intercept: 10; $y \geq 1$
c) $(-2, -4)$; $x = -2$; x-intercepts: -4, 0; y-intercept: 0;
$y \geq -4$ **d)** $(6, 4)$; $x = 6$; x-intercepts: none; y-intercept:
40; $y \geq 4$ **5. a)** $y = -(x - 4)^2 + 5$; $(4, 5)$; $x = 4$. Points
may vary: $(0, -11)$, $(1, -4)$ **b)** $y = -(x + 4)^2 + 9$; $(-4, 9)$;
$x = -4$. Points may vary. $(0, -7)$, $(1, -16)$
c) $y = -(x + 2)^2 - 3$; $(-2, -3)$; $x = -2$. Points may vary.
$(0, -7)$, $(1, -12)$ **d)** $y = -(x + 1)^2 + 1$; $(-1, 1)$; $x = -1$;
Points may vary. $(0, 0)$, $(1, -3)$ **6. a)** $(-1, 4)$; $x = -1$;
x-intercepts: -3, 1; y-intercept: 3; $y \leq 4$ **b)** $(-2, -8)$;
$x = -2$; x-intercepts: none; y-intercept: -12; $y \leq -8$
c) $(4, 4)$; $x = 4$; x-intercepts: 2, 6; y-intercept: -12;
$y \leq 4$ **d)** $(5, 0)$; $x = 5$; x-intercept: 5; y-intercept: -25;
$y \leq 0$ **7. a)** minimum: -7 **b)** maximum: 5

c) maximum: 16 **d)** minimum: 0 **e)** minimum: -30
f) maximum: 13 **g)** minimum: -28 **h)** maximum: -3
8. a) $y = 3(x + 1)^2 - 11$; $(-1, -11)$; $x = -1$; $y \geq -11$
b) $y = -2(x + 3)^2 + 18$; $(-3, 18)$; $x = -3$; $y \leq 18$
c) $y = 2(x - 1)^2 + 3$; $(1, 3)$; $x = 1$; $y \geq 3$
d) $y = -4(x - 1)^2 - 3$; $(1, -3)$; $x = 1$; $y \leq -3$
e) $y = 4(x - 2)^2 - 16$; $(2, -16)$; $x = 2$; $y \geq -16$
f) $y = -3(x - 2)^2 - 2$; $(2, -2)$; $x = 2$; $y \leq -2$
9. a) minimum: 1 at $x = -1$ **b)** maximum: 6 at $x = 5$
c) maximum: 7 at $x = -3$ **d)** maximum: -1 at $x = 3$
e) minimum: -2 at $x = 2$ **f)** minimum: 2 at $x = 1$
g) maximum: 8 at $x = 2$ **h)** maximum: 0 at $x = 1$
Applications and Problem Solving 10. 5, -5 **11.** 17, 17
12. a) minimum: -14 at $x = -2$ **b)** minimum: -9 at
$x = -10$ **c)** maximum: 5 at $x = -5$ **d)** minimum: -5 at
$x = 2$ **e)** maximum: 5 at $x = 4$ **f)** maximum: 20 at
$x = 100$ **g)** minimum: 1.5 at $x = -1$ **h)** maximum: -0.5
at $x = 3$ **13. a)** $(-2, -1)$ **b)** $(1, -9)$ **c)** $\left(\frac{3}{4}, -\frac{25}{8}\right)$
d) $(-1, 12)$ **14. a)** 20 m **b)** 100 m **c)** 200 m
15. a) 4.25 m **b)** 5 m **c)** 2 m **16. a)** 46 m **b)** 480 m
c) 17 m **17. a)** 84 m **b)** 75 m **c)** 71 m **18. a)** 100 m
by 100 m **b)** 10 000 m^2 **19.** 15 m **20.** \$30
21. 12.5 cm^2 **22. a)** 123.6 m **b)** 7 s **23. a)** The
x-coordinates are both 0; the y-coordinates are
opposites. **b)** opposite **24. a)** The graph is a straight
line. **b)** The graph is a parabola with the y-axis as its
axis of symmetry. **25. a)** $k = 9$ **b)** $k < 9$ **c)** $k > 9$
26. a) $k = -8$ **b)** $k > -8$ **c)** $k < -8$ **Technology
Extension** Answers may vary.

Career Connection p. 239
1. a) $R = (2000 - 100x)(8 + x)$ **b)** $(6, 19\ 600)$ **c)** \$14
d) 1400 **2. a)** People will stop buying because of high
price. **b)** People will stop buying because of poor
quality.

Modelling Math p. 240
a) Earth: 22 m; Mars: 52 m; Pluto: 402 m
b) Earth: 2 s; Mars: 5 s; Pluto: 40 s

Section 4.5 p. 241
1. a) $y = x(x - 4) - 1$ **b)** $y = x(x - 8) + 6$
c) $y = 3x(x - 4) + 4$ **d)** $y = 2x(x - 2) + 3$
e) $y = x(x + 2) - 5$ **f)** $y = x(x + 6) + 7$
g) $y = 2x(x + 6) - 2$ **h)** $y = -x(x - 4) - 2$
i) $y = -4x(x - 2) + 1$ **j)** $y = -2x(x + 2) - 3$
2. Substituting $x = 0$ and $x = s$ into the equation
shows that $(0, t)$ and (s, t) are two points on the
parabola. Thus, the x-coordinate of the vertex is $\frac{s}{2}$.

Substituting $x = \frac{s}{2}$ into the equation and

simplifying yields $y = t - \dfrac{as^2}{4}$.

Section 4.6 pp. 242–245

1 Reviewing Linear Functions, $y = mx + b$ 1. a) y: 9, 11, 13; 1st Difference: 2, 2, 2 **b)** y: 2, 6, 10, 14; 1st Difference: 4, 4, 4, 4 **c)** y: 1, −2, −5, −8, −11; 1st Difference: −3, −3, −3, −3 **2.** It is a constant.

2 Investigating Quadratic Functions, $y = ax^2 + bx + c$
1. a) y: 13, 21; 1st Difference: 6, 8; 2nd Difference: 2, 2 **b)** y: 5, 6, 11, 20, 33; 1st Difference: 1, 5, 9, 13; 2nd difference: 4, 4, 4 **c)** y: −1, 4, 15, 32, 55; 1st Difference: 5, 11, 17, 23; 2nd Difference: 6, 6, 6 **2. a)** It increases by a constant amount. **b)** It is a constant. **4.** If the 1st difference is a constant, the function is linear. If the 1st difference is not a constant, but the 2nd difference is a constant, the function is quadratic. Otherwise, the function is neither linear nor quadratic.

3 Using Finite Differences 1. a) linear **b)** linear **c)** quadratic **d)** neither **e)** quadratic **f)** linear **g)** neither **h)** quadratic **i)** linear **j)** quadratic **k)** linear **l)** neither **2. a)** $y = x + 4$ **b)** $y = 2x − 1$ **f)** $y = 2x + 3$ **i)** $y = 3x − 4$ **k)** $y = −4x + 2$ **3. c)** $y = x^2 + 3$ **e)** $y = x^2 + x$ **h)** $y = x^2 − x − 2$ **j)** $y = x^2 + x − 12$ **4. a)** 11, 16, 21, 26 **b)** linear **c)** $a = 5d + 6$ **d)** 81; 111 **e)** 25th diagram **5. a)** 0, 5, 12, 21 **b)** quadratic **c)** $n = s^2 − 4$ **d)** 96; 621 **6. a)** 3, 8, 15, 24 **b)** quadratic **c)** $t = d^2 + 2d$ **d)** 255; 2600 **7. a)** P: 4, 8, 12, 16, 20; a: 1, 3, 6, 10, 15 **b)** linear; quadratic **c)** $P = 4b$; $a = \dfrac{1}{2}(b^2 + b)$ **d)** 60 units, 120 square units; 120 units, 465 square units **8. a)** 1, 7, 19, 37 **b)** quadratic **c)** $h = 3r^2 − 3r + 1$ **d)** 271

Section 4.7 pp. 246–247

1 Parabolas in the Form $y = ax^2 + k$ 1. c) $y = x^2 + 2$ **d)** $y = x^2 + 2$ **2. c)** $y = −x^2 − 3$ **d)** $y = −x^2 − 3$ **3. c)** Answers may vary. $y = x^2 − 5$ **d)** $y = x^2 + 0.23x − 5$ **4. c)** Answers may vary. $y = −x^2 + 4$ **d)** $y = −1.02x^2 − 0.11x + 4.43$ **5. c)** Answers may vary. $y = 2x^2$ **d)** $y = 1.94x^2 − 0.01x − 0.21$ **2 The Flight of a Cannonball 2.** $y = −5(x − 3)^2 + 45$ **3.** $y = −5x^2 + 30x$ **4.** 43.2 m, 32.2 m **3 Stopping Distance 2.** Answers may vary. $y = 0.008x^2$ **3.** Answers may vary with equation used. **a)** 29 m **b)** 80 m **4.** $y = 0.01x^2 − 0.3x + 13$ **5. a)** 31 m **c)** 83 m

Rich Problem p. 251

1. a) 30 **b)** $100 **c)** 18; 42 **d)** 26; 34 **2. a)** 60 **b)** $125 **c)** 36; 84 **d)** 49; 71

Review of Key Concepts pp. 252–257

1. a) function **b)** not a function **c)** not a function **d)** function **2. a)** 11 **b)** 19 **c)** 3 **d)** 1 **e)** −5 **f)** 4 **g)** 2.8 **h)** 203 **i)** 10 003 **3. a)** 7 **b)** 27 **c)** 7 **d)** −9 **e)** 27 **f)** −8 **g)** −8 **h)** 391 **i)** 1591 **4. a)** function **b)** not a function **5. a)** domain: {0, 1, 2, 3}, range: {4, 5, 6, 7} **b)** domain: {−3, −1, 1, 2}, range: {−1, 1, 3} **6. a)** domain: set of real numbers, range: set of real numbers **b)** domain: set of real numbers, range: $y \le 4$ **c)** domain: set of real numbers, range: {2} **7. a)** set of real numbers **b)** $y \ge −1$ **8. a)** The graph of $y = x^2 − 3$ is a translation of the graph of $y = x^2$ 3 units downward **b)** The graph of $y = −4x^2$ is a vertical stretch of the graph of $y = −x^2$ by a factor of 4. **9. a)** up; (0, 4); $x = 0$; domain: set of real numbers, range: $y \ge 4$; minimum: 4; **b)** down; (0, −2); $x = 0$; domain: set of real numbers, range: $y \le −2$; maximum:−2 **c)** up; (0, 0); $x = 0$; domain: set of real numbers, range: $y \ge 0$; minimum: 0 **d)** down; (0, 3); $x = 0$; domain: set of real numbers, range: $y \le 3$; maximum: 3 **10. a)** down; (0, 0); domain: set of real numbers, range: $y \le 0$; maximum: 0 **b)** down; (0, 3.5); domain: set of real numbers, range: $y \le 3.5$; maximum: 3.5 **c)** down; (0, −7); domain: set of real numbers, range: $y \le −7$; maximum: −7 **d)** up; (0, 3); domain: set of real numbers, range: $y \ge 3$; minimum: 3 **11. a)** ±2.6 **b)** ±1.4 **c)** none **d)** ±2.1 **12. a)** 2.13 m **b)** 12 m **c)** 1.2 m **13. a)** down; vertically stretched by a factor of 2; (3, 1); $x = 3$; domain: set of real numbers, range: $y \le 1$; maximum: 1 **b)** up; not stretched or shrunk; (−7, −2); $x = −7$; domain: set of real numbers, range: $y \ge −2$; minimum: −2 **c)** up; vertically shrunk by a factor of 0.5; (−1, 5); $x = −1$; domain: set of real numbers, range: $y \ge 5$; minimum: 5 **d)** down; not stretched or shrunk; (−3, −1); $x = −3$; domain: set of real numbers, range: $y \le −1$; maximum: −1 **14. a)** up; not stretched or shrunk; (−1, −1); $x = −1$; domain: set of real numbers, range: $y \ge −1$; minimum: −1 **b)** down; vertically stretched by a factor of 4; (1, 0); $x = 1$; domain: set of real numbers, range: $y \le 0$; maximum: 0 **c)** down; vertically stretched by a factor of 2; (4, −3); $x = 4$; domain: set of real numbers, range: $y \le −3$; maximum: −3 **d)** up; vertically shrunk by a factor of 0.25; (−2, 1); $x = −2$; domain: set of real numbers, range: $y \ge 1$; minimum: 1 **15. a)** (3, 0); minimum: 0; x-intercept: 3; y-intercept: 9; Points may vary. (1, 4), (2, 1) **b)** (−2, −4); minimum: −4; x-intercepts: −4, 0; y-intercept: 0; Points may vary. (1, 5), (2, 12) **c)** (3, −8); minimum: −8; x-intercepts: 1, 5; y-intercept: 10; Points may vary. (2, −6), (−1, 24) **d)** (−2, 9); maximum: 9; x-intercepts: −5, 1; y-intercept: 5; Points may vary. (2, −7), (−1, 8) **16. a)** −4.2, 0.2 **b)** −0.2, 2.2

17. a) 13 m **b)** 0.9 m **c)** 4.9 s **d)** 8.9 m **18. a)** 16 **b)** 49
19. a) $y = (x + 2)^2 - 3$; $(-2, -3)$; $x = -2$; Points may vary. $(0, 1)$, $(1, 6)$ **b)** $y = (x - 5)^2 - 10$; $(5, -10)$; $x = 5$; Points may vary. $(0, 15)$, $(1, 6)$ **c)** $y = -(x + 3)^2 + 4$; $(-3, 4)$; $x = -3$; Points may vary. $(0, -5)$, $(1, -12)$
d) $y = -(x + 2)^2 + 7$; $(-2, 7)$; $x = -2$; Points may vary. $(0, 3)$, $(1, -2)$ **20. a)** $(-3, -9)$; $x = -3$; $y \geq -9$ **b)** $(4, -4)$; $x = 4$; x-intercepts: 2, 6; y-intercept: 12; $y \geq -4$
c) $(-2, -5)$; $x = -2$; $y \leq -5$ **d)** $(-4, -1)$; $x = -4$; $y \geq -1$
21. a) $(1, 4)$ **b)** $(2, -5)$ **c)** $(-2, -3)$ **d)** $(-2, 3)$ **e)** $(-5, -2)$
f) $(3, 5)$ **22. a)** -3, 1 **b)** 2.7, 0.3 **23.** 6, -6
24. a) 150 m by 150 m **b)** 22 500 m^2
25. a) $y = x(x - 6) + 8$; points: $(0, 8)$, $(6, 8)$
b) $y = x(x + 8) + 12$; points: $(0, 12)$, $(-8, 12)$
c) $y = 2x(x - 2) - 6$; points: $(0, -6)$, $(2, -6)$
d) $y = -3x(x - 4) - 7$; points: $(0, -7)$, $(4, -7)$
26. a) linear **b)** quadratic **c)** neither **d)** quadratic
27. a) $n = 4d + 1$ **b)** 81 **c)** 50th diagram
28. a) $A = \frac{1}{2}(d^2 + 3d + 2)$ **b)** 136 **29. a)** $y = x^2 - 3$;
$y = x^2 - 3$ **b)** $y = -x^2 + 1$; $y = -1.05x^2 + 0.15x + 0.83$
c) $y = -2x^2$; $y = -2x^2 - 0.2x$

Chapter Test pp. 258–259
1. a) not a function **b)** function **c)** function **2. a)** up; $(0, -1)$; $x = 0$; domain: set of real numbers, range: $y \geq -1$; minimum: -1 **b)** down; $(0, 5)$; $x = 0$; domain: set of real numbers, range: $y \leq 5$; maximum: 5
3. a) none **b)** ± 3.2 **c)** ± 1.6 **4. a)** up; not stretched or shrunk; $(-3, -1)$; $x = -3$; domain: set of real numbers, range: $y \geq -1$; minimum: -1 **b)** down; vertically stretched by a factor of 2; $(5, -2)$; $x = 5$; domain: set of real numbers, range: $y \leq -2$; maximum: -2
c) down; vertically shrunk by a factor of 0.5; $(-2, 3)$; $x = -2$; domain: set of real numbers, range: $y \leq 3$; maximum: 3 **5. a)** -4.1, 0.1 **b)** 0.3, 3.7
6. a) $y = (x + 4)^2 - 8$; $(-4, -8)$; $x = -4$; Points may vary. $(0, 8)$, $(-1, 1)$ **b)** $y = -(x + 5)^2 + 21$; $(-5, 21)$; $x = -5$; Points may vary. $(0, -4)$, $(-1, 5)$ **7. a)** $(5, -25)$; $x = 5$; x-intercepts: 0, 10; y-intercept: 0; $y \geq -25$
b) $(-3, -1)$; $x = -3$; x-intercepts: none; y-intercept: -10; $y \leq -1$ **8. a)** $(-3, -5)$ **b)** $(4, -2)$
9. a) $y = x(x - 8) + 5$; points: $(0, 5)$, $(8, 5)$
b) $y = -2x(x - 2) - 3$; points: $(0, -3)$, $(2, -3)$
10. a) quadratic **b)** linear **c)** neither **11. a)** 86 m
b) 2 m **c)** 8 s **12.** $12 **13. a)** $A = w^2 + 2w$ **b)** 675
14. a) $y = x^2 - 2$; $y = x^2 - 2$ **b)** $y = -x^2 + 3$;
$y = -x^2 + 0.3x + 3$

Problem Solving: Use a Diagram p. 261
Applications and Problem Solving 1. Schedules may vary. 13:00–13:30: C and F; 13:40–14:10: A and D;

14:20–14:50: B, 15:00–15:30: E **2. a)** Alliston to Bevan to Gaston is 56 km. **b)** Clearwater to Flagstaff to Dunstan is 55 km. **c)** Gaston to Flagstaff to Clearwater to Bevan is 79 km. **d)** Flagstaff to Clearwater to Bevan to Alliston is 70 km. **3.** 276 m^2
4. 60 **5.** 300 **6.** 12 L (assuming paint may be purchased only in whole litres) **7.** 4 blocks east and 7 blocks south

Problem Solving: Work Backward p. 263
Applications and Problem Solving 1. Scott: 6, Ivan: 11, Enzo: 4 **2.** $3500 **3.** $(-2, 4)$ **4.** 6 cm by 4 cm
5. 256

Problem Solving: Using the Strategies p. 264
1. 38 cm **2.** 15 **3.** $(1, 15)$, $(2, 14)$, $(3, 13)$, $(4, 12)$, $(5, 11)$, $(6, 10)$, $(7, 18)$, $(8, 17)$, $(9, 16)$
4. 08:45 Saturday **5. a)** 10 **b)** 8 **6.** $143
7. $3 \times 54 = 162$ **8.** Tia: carpenter, turtle; Jane: lawyer, dog; Fran: police officer, parrot; Marta: teacher, cat

Cumulative Review, Chapters 3 and 4 p. 265
Chapter 3 1. a) $4x^2 - x + 2$ **b)** $-3y^2 - 2y + 9$
2. a) $4m - 9n$ **b)** $10p^2 - 7p$ **c)** $-4w^3 + 2w^2 - 9w$
d) $6x^2 + x - 1$ **e)** $13z^2 - 3z - 11$ **f)** $2y^3 + y^2 - 19y - 12$
3. a) $16x^2 - 1$ **b)** $4m^2 + 4mn + n^2$ **c)** $-8y + 20$
d) $12t^2 + 8t + 2$ **4. a)** $7x(2x - 1)$ **b)** $5yz(z - 7 + 2y)$
c) $(y - 3)(x - 4)$ **d)** $(2n + 3p)(m - 2)$
5. a) $(x - 2)(x - 10)$ **b)** $(y + 6)(y - 3)$ **c)** $(x + 9)(x - 9)$
d) $(2y + 1)(3y + 4)$ **e)** $(5a - b)(5a + b)$ **f)** $(n - 3)^2$
g) $(7b - 2)^2$ **6. a)** $2(s + 8)(s - 1)$ **b)** $3(x + 2)(3x + 2)$
c) $a(x + 3)^2$ **d)** $10(2c - d)(2c + d)$ **7. a)** $(4x - 5)(2x + 5)$
b) 63 mm by 39 mm
Chapter 4 1. a) down; vertically stretched by a factor of 2; $(0, 0)$; $x = 0$; domain: set of real numbers, range: $y \leq 0$; maximum: 0 **b)** up; not stretched or shrunk; $(0, -3)$; $x = 0$; domain: set of real numbers, range: $y \geq -3$; minimum: -3 **c)** up; not stretched or shrunk; $(-3, 0)$; $x = -3$; domain: set of real numbers, range: $y \geq 0$; minimum: 0 **d)** down; not stretched or shrunk; $(2, 1)$; $x = 2$; domain: set of real numbers, range: $y \leq 1$; maximum: 1 **e)** up; vertically shrunk by a factor of 0.5; $(4, 3)$; $x = 4$; domain: set of real numbers, range: $y \geq 3$; minimum: 3 **f)** down; vertically stretched by a factor of 3; $(-5, -2)$; $x = -5$; domain: set of real numbers, range: $y \leq -2$; maximum: -2 **2. a)** ± 2.2
b) -4.7, -1.3 **3. a)** $y = (x + 2)^2 - 6$; $(-2, -6)$; $x = -2$; Points may vary. $(0, -2)$, $(1, 3)$ **b)** $y = 3(x - 1)^2 + 4$; $(1, 4)$; $x = 1$; Points may vary. $(0, 7)$, $(2, 7)$
4. a) $(2, -4)$; x-intercepts: 0, 4; y-intercept: 0 **b)** $(1, 9)$; x-intercepts: -2, 4; y-intercept: 8 **5.** $y = x(x - 6) + 3$; points: $(0, 3)$, $(6, 3)$ **6. a)** quadratic **b)** neither
c) linear **7.** $22

Chapter 5

Getting Started p. 268

1. $s^2 = 16$ **2.** $s = \pm 4$ **3.** $s = -4$ because wave cannot have negative speed. **4.** $s = 4$ m/s **5. a)** $s = 2$ m/s **b)** $s = 6$ m/s **c)** $s = 1.2$ m/s

Review of Prerequisite Skills p. 269

1. a) 15 **b)** 30 **c)** 30 **d)** 3 **e)** 0 **f)** 31 **g)** 93 **h)** 36
2. a) −7 **b)** −22 **c)** 48 **d)** 11 **e)** 17 **f)** 6 **g)** 36 **h)** −39
3. a) $x = -16$ **b)** $y = -22$ **c)** $x = -3$ **d)** $w = 2$ **e)** $x = 1$
f) $t = 4$ **g)** $x = 2$ **h)** $x = \frac{1}{2}$ **i)** $x = -6$ **j)** $x = 6$
4. a) $4x(x + 2)$ **b)** $3x(x - 1)$ **c)** $2(3x^2 + 2x - 4)$
d) $5(x^2 - 4x + 2)$ **5. a)** $(x + 3)(x + 4)$ **b)** $(x - 5)(x - 2)$
c) $(y - 4)(y + 2)$ **d)** not possible **e)** $(r + 4)(r - 4)$
f) $(w + 5)(w - 5)$ **g)** $(z + 5)^2$ **h)** $(x - 7)^2$ **i)** $(t - 4)(t + 3)$
j) $(w + 6)(w - 4)$ **k)** not possible **l)** $(w + 11)(w - 8)$
m) $(x - 9)(x + 5)$ **n)** $(y - 1)^2$ **o)** $(z + 10)(z - 3)$
p) $(t + 7)(t + 4)$ **q)** $(w - 10)(w - 4)$ **r)** $(x + 9)(x - 3)$
s) $(y - 5)(y + 4)$ **6. a)** $(2x + 1)(x + 3)$
b) $(3t + 1)(2t - 3)$ **c)** $(2y - 5)(y - 1)$ **d)** $(5x + 2)(2x - 1)$
e) not possible **f)** $(2x + 3)(2x - 3)$ **g)** $(2x - 3)^2$
h) $(2w + 5)(w + 2)$ **i)** $(3t - 5)(t - 2)$ **j)** $(3x + 4)(x - 5)$
k) $(3y + 1)^2$ **l)** not possible **m)** $(3w - 1)(2w + 1)$
n) $(2x + 5)^2$ **o)** $(5n + 1)(5n - 1)$ **7. a)** ± 7 **b)** not
possible **c)** ± 11 **d)** ± 9 **e)** ± 4 **f)** ± 6 **g)** ± 8 **h)** ± 8 **i)** ± 9
j) ± 5 **k)** ± 10 **l)** ± 5

Section 5.1 pp. 275–277

Practice 1. a) $x = -3$ or $x = 2$ **b)** $x = 1$ or $x = 4$
c) $x = 2$ or $x = -2$ **d)** no real roots **e)** $x = 2$ or $x = -1$
f) $x = -4$ or $x = 1$ **g)** $x = -3$ **h)** $x = 0$ or $x = 5$
2. a) $x = 0$ or $x = -3$ **b)** $x = -4$ or $x = 1$ **c)** $x = 0$ or
$x = 3$ **d)** $x = 3$ or $x = -3$ **e)** no real roots **f)** $x = -5$ or
$x = 1$ **g)** $x = 2$ or $x = -1$ **h)** $x = 1$ or $x = 2$ **i)** no real
roots **j)** $x = 2$ **3. a)** $x = -1$ or $x = 1.5$ **b)** $x = -0.5$ or
$x = 3$ **c)** no real roots **d)** $x = -0.5$ **e)** $x = 0$ or $x = 2.5$
f) $x = -2.9$ or $x = 0.6$ **g)** $x = -0.5$ or $x = 1.3$ **h)** $a = 2.7$
i) $x = -0.6$ or $x = 0.4$ **j)** $x = -0.8$ or $x = 0.5$ **k)** $x = -1.6$
or $x = 3.6$ **l)** no real roots **m)** $x = 0$ or $x = -3.3$
n) $n = -1.7$

Applications and Problem Solving 4. $w = 8$ m, $l = 9$ m
5. 45 m **6.** $w = 3$ cm, $l = 11$ cm **7.** 6 m, 8 m **8.** 5 cm,
12 cm **9.** 5 m **10.** 35 m × 65 m **11.** $w = 14$ m,
$l = 26$ m **12.** $w = 4.8$ cm, $l = 6.4$ cm **13.** 14, 16 or
−16, −14 **14.** $w = 9.1$ m, $l = 18.2$ m **15.** 7, 8, 9
16. a) $x = 3$ or $x = 1$ **b)** $x = 1$ or $x = -3$ **c)** no real roots
d) $x = 3$ **e)** $x = 1$ **f)** $x = -\frac{1}{2}$ or $x = -\frac{3}{2}$ **g)** $p = 1$ **h)** $q = 1$
or $q = -7$ **17. a)** $x^2 - x - 12 = 0$ **b)** $x = 4$ or $x = -3$
c) The roots of the equation are the negatives of the

two numerical terms in the factored form of the
equation. **18. a)** $c < 0$ **b)** $c = 0$ **c)** $c > 0$ **19. a)** $c = 49$
b) $c < 49$ **c)** $c > 49$ **20. a)** $b = \pm 10$ **b)** $b > 10$ or $b < -10$
c) $-10 < b < 10$ **21. a)** $b = 0$ **b)** $x = 0$ always, $x = -b$
22. a) $x \geq 4$ or $x \leq -4$ **b)** $-5 \leq x \leq 5$

Modelling Math p. 277

20 m

Section 5.2 pp. 282–285

Practice 1. a) $x = -1$ or $x = -2$ **b)** $x = -3$ or $x = 1$
c) $x = 5$ **d)** $x = 2$ or $x = -3$ **e)** $x = -\frac{1}{2}$ or $x = 3$
f) $x = -\frac{4}{3}$ or $x = \frac{1}{2}$ **g)** $x = 0$ or $x = -9$ **h)** $x = 0$ or $x = 4$
2. a) $x^2 - 2x - 6 = 0$ **b)** $2y^2 - 3y + 2 = 0$
c) $3z^2 + 4z + 3 = 0$ **d)** $x^2 + 2x - 3 = 0$ **e)** $4m^2 - 3m = 0$
f) $2x^2 - x - 2 = 0$ **3. a)** $x^2 - 3x + 2 = 0$
b) $3x^2 + 2x - 6 = 0$ **c)** $x^2 + 10x + 16 = 0$ **4. a)** $n = -3$ or
$n = -4$ **b)** $y = 1$ or $y = 2$ **c)** $x = -2$ or $x = 3$ **d)** $a = 4$
e) $p = -7$ or $p = 5$ **f)** $m = -2$ or $m = 9$
5. a) $a = -2$ or $a = \frac{1}{2}$ **b)** $s = 1$ or $s = \frac{1}{3}$
c) $t = -5$ or $t = -\frac{1}{2}$ **d)** $x = \frac{2}{3}$ or $x = -3$
e) $m = -\frac{1}{2}$ or $m = \frac{3}{2}$ **f)** $y = 1$ or $y = \frac{3}{5}$
6. a) $x = 0$ or $x = -2$ **b)** $y = 0$ or $y = 3$
c) $m = 0$ or $m = -\frac{2}{3}$ **d)** $n = 0$ or $n = \frac{8}{5}$ **e)** $t = 0$ or $t = 4$
f) $x = 0$ or $x = -\frac{4}{3}$ **7. a)** $x = 5$ or $x = -5$
b) $y = 6$ or $y = -6$ **c)** $n = 4$ or $n = -4$
d) $m = 10$ or $m = -10$ **e)** $x = 1$ or $x = -1$
f) $z = 0.5$ or $z = -0.5$ **g)** $x = 4$ or $x = -4$
h) $x = 3$ or $x = -3$ **i)** $x = 2$ or $x = -2$ **j)** $y = 7$ or $y = -7$
8. a) $x = -3$ or $x = 5$ **b)** $w = 3$ or $w = 7$
c) $p = -3$ or $p = 1$ **d)** $t = \frac{3}{2}$ **e)** $r = 0$ or $r = \frac{2}{5}$
f) $x = 2$ or $x = 18$ **g)** $a = -2$ or $a = -6$ **h)** $b = 0$ or $b = 6$
9. a) $x = \frac{1}{2}$ or $x = -5$ **b)** $x = -2$ or $x = 6$
c) $x = -2$ or $x = -10$ **d)** $x = -3$ or $x = 6$
e) $x = 0$ or $x = -\frac{7}{2}$ **f)** $x = -\frac{2}{3}$ or $x = 2$
10. a) $z = 6$ or $z = -6$ **b)** $x = 4$ or $x = -4$
c) $y = 1$ or $y = -1$ **d)** $n = 5$ or $n = -5$
Applications and Problem Solving 11. 9 cm × 4 cm
12. 2 cm **13.** 11, 5 or −5, −11 **14.** 9, 10 or −10, −9
15. 16, 18 or −18, −16 **16.** 0 or −10 **17.** 12 or −12

18. 5 or –5 **19.** $w = 1$ m, $l = 18$ m **20.** 9 **21.** $w = \frac{8}{3}$ m, $l = 6$ m **22.** 8 cm, 15 cm **23.** 11 **24.** 8 cm

25. a) Outer: 8 cm × 8 cm, Inner: 4 cm × 4 cm
b) Outer: 9 cm × 9 cm, Inner: 3 cm × 3 cm **26.** 0.5 m
27. a) $w = 70$ mm, $l = 135$ mm **b)** The widths are the same but a Canadian $20 bill is longer with length 152 mm. **28. a)** $x = -3$; 1 root **b)** $x = -3$; there are two roots that are equal. **29. a)** $x = -\frac{1}{6}$ or $x = 1$

b) $x = -\frac{3}{4}$ or $x = 1$ **30. a)** $x = 0$ or $x = 1$ **b)** $x = -\frac{1}{2}$ or $x = 2$ **c)** $k = -4$ or $k = 2$ **d)** $z = \frac{1}{2}$ **e)** $x = -4$ or $x = 3$

f) $g = \frac{8}{3}$ or $g = 6$ **g)** $y = 3$ or $y = -3$ **h)** $n = 1$ or $n = -1$

i) $x = 0$ or $x = 7$ **31. a)** $x = -y$ or $x = -4y$ **b)** $x = -\frac{y}{2}$

or $x = 3y$ **c)** $x = \frac{y}{2}$ **d)** $x = \frac{y}{4}$ or $x = -2y$ **e)** $x = 0$ or

$x = -\frac{y}{5}$ **f)** $x = 0$ or $x = \frac{7y}{3}$ **32. a)** $x^2 - x - 6 = 0$
b) Yes, any constant multiple of $x^2 - x - 6 = 0$

33. a) $x^2 + (-p - q)x + pq = 0$ **34. a)** 10 **b)** $-\frac{1}{3}$

Career Connection p. 286
1. a) $16x^2 = 144$ m$^2 \Rightarrow x^2 = 9$ m$^2 \Rightarrow x = 3$m **b)** 2 m

Modelling Math p. 286
a) $-5t^2 + 9t + 2 = 0$ **b)** $(5t + 1)(-t + 2) = 0$; 2 s

Section 5.3 p. 287
1. $x = 4$ or $x = -2$ **2.** 4, –2 **4.** $x = 1$ **5.** $y = -9$
7. a) x–intercepts: 2, 6; vertex: (4, –4)
b) x–intercepts: –1, 3; vertex: (1, –4)
c) x–intercepts: –7, –3; vertex: (–5, –4)
d) x–intercepts: –4, 0; vertex: (–2, –4)
e) x–intercepts: 1, 5; vertex: (3, –4)
f) x–intercepts: –1, 7; vertex: (4, –15)
g) x–intercepts: 0, 8; vertex: (4, –16)
h) x–intercepts: –5, 7; vertex: (1, –36) **8.** No, because $ax^2 + bx + c$ is a perfect square, there is only one x – intercept, which is also the vertex. A point on each side of the vertex is needed to complete the sketch.

Section 5.4 pp. 292–295
Practice 1. a) $x = -1$ or $x = -5$ **b)** $x = -4$ or $x = 2$
c) $x = -1$ or $x = 3$ **d)** $x = 5$ or $x = 7$ **e)** $x = -2$ **f)** $y = 1$
2. a) $x = \frac{1}{2}$ or $x = 1$ **b)** $x = -\frac{1}{5}$ or $x = 3$ **c)** $x = -\frac{3}{2}$ or

$x = 4$ **d)** $x = \frac{1}{3}$ **e)** $x = -\frac{3}{2}$ or $x = \frac{3}{2}$ **f)** $x = -\frac{1}{2}$ or $x = \frac{2}{3}$

g) $x = \pm\frac{3}{2}$ **h)** $x = -\frac{3}{2}$ or $x = -\frac{5}{2}$ **i)** $x = 0$ or $x = \frac{5}{2}$ **j)** $x = -\frac{5}{3}$

or $x = -2$ **3. a)** $x = \frac{-5 \pm \sqrt{17}}{2}$; $x = -0.44$ or $x = -4.56$

b) $x = \frac{3 \pm \sqrt{13}}{2}$; $x = 3.30$ or $x = -0.30$ **c)** $x = \frac{1 \pm \sqrt{13}}{2}$;

$x = 2.30$ or $x = -1.30$ **d)** $x = \frac{-7 \pm \sqrt{41}}{2}$; $x = -0.30$ or

$x = -6.70$ **e)** $x = \frac{5 \pm \sqrt{33}}{2}$; $x = 5.37$ or $x = -0.37$

f) $z = \frac{1 \pm \sqrt{17}}{2}$; $z = 2.56$ or $z = -1.56$

g) $x = \frac{-1 \pm \sqrt{29}}{2}$; $x = 2.19$ or $x = -3.19$

h) $a = \frac{1 \pm \sqrt{21}}{2}$; $a = 2.79$ or $a = -1.79$ **i)** $x = \frac{-3 \pm \sqrt{65}}{4}$;

$x = 1.27$ or $x = -2.77$ **j)** $x = \frac{1 \pm \sqrt{13}}{6}$; $x = 0.77$ or

$x = -0.43$ **k)** $x = \frac{-1 \pm \sqrt{41}}{4}$; $x = 1.35$ or $x = -1.85$

l) $x = \frac{-3 \pm \sqrt{21}}{-6}$; $x = -0.26$ or $x = 1.26$

Applications and Problem Solving   4. a) 2.25 m **b)** 3.8 s
5. a) $x = 0$ or $x = 1.6$ **b)** $x = 1.3$ or $x = -0.3$ **c)** $x = 3.4$
or $x = -1.4$ **d)** $c = 3.9$ or $c = -0.9$ **e)** $n = 6.6$ or $n = -0.6$
f) $x = 2.8$ or $x = -1.3$ **g)** $x = -0.3$ or $x = -2$ **h)** $x = 10.7$
or $x = 1.3$ **i)** $d = 6.2$ or $d = 0.8$ **j)** $g = 0$ or $g = 1.9$
6. a) $x = 0.65$ or $x = -4.65$ **b)** $x = 5.16$ or $x = -1.16$
c) $y = 1.31$ or $y = -0.13$ **d)** $n = 1.67$ or $n = -0.5$
e) $x = -0.04$ or $x = -1.05$ **f)** $a = 9.94$ or $a = -12.44$
7. 82 m **8.** $w = 56$ m, $l = 116$ m **9.** 12 cm, 16 cm
10. a) 7.5 cm **b)** 6562.5 cm^3 **11.** $l = 8.1$ m, $w = 6.1$ m
12. 5.6 m **13.** $b = 7.4$ cm, $h = 5.4$ cm **14.** $h = 23.7$ cm, $w = 29.7$ cm **15.** 13 cm × 8 cm **16. a)** between 17 cm and 18 cm **b)** 17.72 cm **17. a)** $N = 110$ jackets; $P = \$160$ **b)** $N = 130$ jackets; $P = \$120$ **18.** 3.58 units

19. a) 6; 10 **b)** $s = \frac{p(p-1)}{2}$ **c)** $p = 11$ **d)** no

20. $b^2 - 4ac \geq 0$ **21.** $b^2 - 4ac = 0$ **22.** 3.2 cm

23. a) no real solutions **b)** two real, equal roots

c) two real, distinct roots **d)** two real, distinct,

irrational roots **24. a)** $x = -\dfrac{y}{2}$ or $x = -8y$

b) $x = (-1 \pm \sqrt{2})y$

Modelling Math p. 295
a) 4.0 s **b)** 2 s

Technology Extension: Solving Quadratic Equations pp. 296–297
1 Using a Graphing Calculator Program   1. Line
i) Displays "ENTER COEFFICIENTS".
ii) Prompts you to enter the values of A, B, C
iii) Calculates $B^2 - 4AC$ and assigns the value to D.
iv) Determines if $D \geq 0$. v) If $D \geq 0$, the program continues to line vi. vi) Displays

$\dfrac{-B + \sqrt{D}}{2A}$, $\dfrac{-B - \sqrt{D}}{2A}$. vii) If $D < 0$, the program

continues to line viii. viii) Displays "NO REAL

SOLUTIONS".   **2. a)** no real solutions **b)** $x = \dfrac{1}{4}$ or

$x = 2$ **c)** $x = -\dfrac{1}{2}$ or $x = -1$ **d)** $x = 0$ or $x = \dfrac{4}{5}$ **e)** $x = 0.1$

or $x = -3.5$ **f)** $x = -2$ or $x = 3$ **3. a)** $x = 1.65$ or
$x = -6.65$ **b)** no real solutions **c)** $x = 0$ or $x = 0.64$
2 Using Preprogrammed Calculators   1. a) $x = -1$ or
$x = 4$ **b)** $x = -5$ or $x = 2$ **c)** $x = -1$ or $x = -5$ **d)** $y = 1$ or

$y = 6$ **e)** $x = 8$ **f)** $n = 0.7$ or $n = -0.7$ **g)** $x = -1$ or $x = \dfrac{1}{2}$

h) $p = -\dfrac{2}{3}$ or $p = \dfrac{3}{2}$ **i)** $x = 0$ or $x = -\dfrac{3}{7}$ **j)** $x = -2$ or $x = -\dfrac{1}{3}$

k) $x = 3$ or $x = -5$ **l)** $s = 1$ or $s = -4$ **m)** $x = -\dfrac{4}{3}$ or $x = 2$

n) $x = -8$ or $x = \dfrac{1}{2}$ **o)** $z = -3.3$ or $z = 3$ **2. a)** $x = 1.32$

or $x = -5.32$ **b)** $a = 5.24$ or $a = 0.76$ **c)** $x = 4.56$ or
$x = 0.44$ **d)** $x = 1.26$ or $x = -4.76$ **e)** $t = -0.23$ or
$t = -1.43$ **f)** $x = 5.42$ or $x = -1.42$ **g)** $k = 1.34$ or
$k = -5.47$ **h)** $x = 3.85$ or $x = -2.85$ **i)** $x = 1.41$ or
$x = -1.21$ **j)** $w = 1.24$ or $w = -3.24$ **k)** $x = 2.65$ or
$x = 0.15$ **l)** $b = -5.88$ or $b = 1.21$ **3. a – b)** There are
no real roots since $(2)^2 - 4(1)(13) < 0$.

Rich Problem: The Golden Ratio pp. 298–300

1 Determining ϕ 1. a) $\phi = \dfrac{1 + \sqrt{5}}{2}$ **b)** $\phi = 1.618$

2 Geometry and ϕ 1. Given: AB = 2 and E bisects
AB. This gives AE = EB = 1. Also, ABCD is a
square. So, AB = BC = CD = AD = 2.
$(EC)^2 = (EB)^2 + (BC)^2$ by Pythagorean
theorem. Thus, $(EC)^2 = 1^2 + 2^2 = 5$. Therefore,

EC = $\sqrt{5}$ and EF = $\sqrt{5}$. AF = AE +EF = $1 + \sqrt{5}$.

Since AB = 2, $\dfrac{AF}{AB} = \dfrac{1 + \sqrt{5}}{2} = \phi$. **2.** The base of a

rectangle ABCD is bisected at E. Diagonals are
drawn from C to E and D to E, forming an isosceles

triangle EFD. If AB = 2 and AC = $\sqrt{2\sqrt{5} + 5}$, then

show $\dfrac{CE}{CD} = \phi$.

3 Fibonacci Numbers and ϕ 1. 377, 610 **2. a)** $\dfrac{5}{3}$ **b)** $\dfrac{13}{8}$

c) The Fibonacci Sequence is $a_1 = a_2 = 1$,

$a_{n+2} = a_n + a_{n+1}$. If $r_n = \dfrac{a_{n+1}}{a_n}$, then $r_{n+1} = 1 + \dfrac{1}{r_n}$

d) $\dfrac{34}{21} = 1 + \cfrac{1}{1 + \cfrac{1}{1 + \cfrac{1}{1 + \cfrac{1}{1 + \cfrac{1}{1+1}}}}}$

3. a) 2, 5, 7, 12, 19, 31, 50, 81, 131, 212 **b)** $\dfrac{5}{2} = 2.5$,

$\dfrac{7}{5} = 1.4$, $\dfrac{12}{7} = 1.714\ 285\ 714$, $\dfrac{19}{12} = 1.58\overline{3}$,

$\dfrac{31}{9} = 1.631\ 578\ 947$, $\dfrac{50}{31} = 1.612\ 903\ 226$, $\dfrac{81}{50} = 1.62$,

$\dfrac{131}{81} = 1.617\ 283\ 951$, $\dfrac{212}{131} = 1.618\ 320\ 611$. The

ratios converge to ϕ.
4 ϕ in Architecture, Design, and Nature   1. 18 m
2. slant height = 185.852 091 7 m;

$\dfrac{\text{slant height}}{115\ \text{m}} = 1.616\ 105\ 145 \doteq \phi$

3. AC = 167.343 957 2 mm, BC = 103.324 730 8 mm;

$\dfrac{AB}{BC} = 1.619\ 592\ 482 \doteq \phi$

Review of Key Concepts pp. 301–304
1. a) $x = -1$ or $x = 3$ **b)** $x = -2$ or $x = 1$ **c)** $x = -3$ or
$x = 3$ **d)** $x = -4$ or $x = 1$ **e)** $x = 1$ **f)** $x = -1$ or $x = -5$
g) $x = 0$ or $x = 5$ **2. a)** $x = -1.5$ or $x = 1$ **b)** $x = 0.3$ or
$x = 2$ **c)** $x = -3.6$ or $x = 0.6$ **3.** $w = 4$ cm, $l = 6$ cm
4. a) $x = -7$ or $x = 4$ **b)** $y = 2$ or $y = 3$ **c)** $g = -2$ or

$g = -5$ **d)** $x = -4$ **e)** $x = -\dfrac{5}{2}$ or $x = 6$ **f)** $x = -\dfrac{2}{3}$ or

$x = \dfrac{2}{3}$ **g)** $x = \dfrac{1}{2}$ or $x = -3$ **h)** $n = \dfrac{3}{2}$ or $n = -9$ **i)** $k = 0$ or

$k = \dfrac{3}{8}$ **j)** $m = -8$ or $m = 8$ **k)** $x = 2$ or $x = 4$ **l)** $x = \dfrac{1}{2}$

5. $l = 45$ m, $w = 5$ m **6. a)** x–intercepts: $-2, -4$; vertex $(-3, -1)$ **b)** x–intercepts: $5, -3$; vertex $(1, -16)$ **c)** x–intercepts: $0, 8$; vertex $(4, -16)$ **d)** x–intercepts: $-4, 2$; vertex $(-1, -9)$ **e)** x–intercepts: $5, -1$; vertex $(2, -9)$ **f)** x–intercepts: $1, 3$; vertex $(2, -1)$ **7. a)** $x = 4$ or $x = 3$ **b)** no real roots **c)** $n = 6$ or $n = -7$ **d)** $x = 1$ or $x = -1$ **e)** $x = 0$ or $x = -\dfrac{3}{2}$ **f)** $x = \dfrac{3}{2}$ **g)** $g = 1$ or $g = \dfrac{2}{7}$

h) $x = \dfrac{3}{2}$ or $x = -\dfrac{1}{2}$ **8. a)** $x = \dfrac{-5 \pm \sqrt{37}}{2}$; $x = 0.54$ or $x = -5.54$ **b)** $k = \dfrac{9 \pm \sqrt{85}}{2}$; $k = 9.11$ or $k = -0.11$

c) $w = \dfrac{-3 \pm \sqrt{73}}{16}$; $w = 0.35$ or $w = -0.72$

d) $x = \dfrac{-5 + \sqrt{61}}{6}$; $x = 0.47$ or $x = -2.14$

9. a) $x = 0.74$ or $x = -0.90$ **b)** $x = 0.33$ or $x = -0.75$ **10.** 8 cm $\times 15$ cm

Chapter Test p. 305

1. a) $x = -4$ or $x = 2$ **b)** $x = \pm 3$ **c)** $x = 2$ **d)** $x = 0$ or $x = -6$ **e)** no real roots **f)** $x = 1$ **2. a)** $q = -5$ or $q = 3$

b) $w = 3$ or $w = 8$ **c)** $k = \dfrac{1}{2}$ or $k = -4$ **d)** $x = -\dfrac{1}{3}$ or $x = \dfrac{2}{3}$

e) $x = 0$ or $x = \dfrac{3}{2}$ **f)** $x = \pm\dfrac{1}{2}$ **g)** $x = -1$ **h)** $x = \pm 12$ **i)** $x = \dfrac{1}{2}$ or $x = 1$ **3. a)** x – intercepts: $-1, -5$; vertex $(-3, -4)$ **b)** x – intercepts: $1, -5$; vertex $(-2, -9)$ **4. a)** $y = 6$ or $y = -3$ **b)** $x = 4$ **c)** $x = -2$ **d)** $x = \dfrac{17}{3}$ or $x = 0$ **e)** $x = \pm\dfrac{2}{3}$

f) no real roots **g)** $w = \dfrac{1}{6}$ or $w = -\dfrac{2}{3}$ **h)** $d = \dfrac{3}{4}$ or $d = -\dfrac{1}{3}$

i) $p = -\dfrac{2}{5}$ or $p = -1$ **5. a)** $x = \dfrac{-5 \pm \sqrt{53}}{2}$; $x = 1.14$ or $x = -6.14$ **b)** $t = \dfrac{-9 \pm \sqrt{33}}{8}$; $t = -0.41$ or $t = -1.84$

c) $x = \dfrac{1 \pm \sqrt{85}}{6}$; $x = 1.70$ or $x = -1.37$ **6.** $w = 13$ cm, $l = 21$ cm **7.** 3.5 m

Problem Solving: Solve a Simpler Problem
p. 307
Applications and Problem Solving 1. 70 **2.** 20 **3.** 32 square units **4.** 22.5 square units

5. 44.5 square units **6. a)** 253 square units **b)** 398 units **7. a)** 40 **b)** $n(n + 3)$ **c)** 2650 **d)** 15

e) $\dfrac{n(n+1)}{2}$ **f)** 1275

Problem Solving: Use a Table or Spreadsheet p. 310
Applications and Problem Solving 1. a)

Month	Profit ($)	Net Financial Position ($)
1	–2100	–2100
2	–1900	–4000
3	–1700	–5700
4	–1500	–7200
5	–1300	–8500
6	–1100	–9600
7	–900	–10 500
8	–700	–11 200
9	–500	–11 700
10	–300	–12 000
11	–100	–12 100
12	100	–12 000
13	300	–11 700
14	500	–11 200
15	700	–10 500
16	900	–9600
17	1100	–8500
18	1300	–7200
19	1500	–5700
20	1700	–4000
21	1900	–2100
22	2100	0
23	2300	2300
24	2500	4800

b) month 23 **c)** $n = 100(m - 11)^2 - 12\,100$
2. 5 months sooner **3.** 13 **4. a)** 276 **b)** 440
5. a)

Time (s)	Height (m)
1	44.1
2	78.4
3	102.9
4	117.6
5	122.5
6	117.6
7	102.9
8	78.4
9	44.1
10	0

b) 5 s **c)** 122.5 m **d)** $h = -4.9(t - 5)^2 + 122.5$
e) Domain: $0 \le t \le 10$; Range: $0 \le h \le 122.5$ **6.** 84
7. 10 **8.** No, he will not save more than $1000.

Problem Solving: Using the Strategies p. 311
1. 26 **2.** 14 m² **3.** Terry Bob Sand, Thomas Bill Stone, Tim Bevan Silver, Trip Brooks Sol **4.** 10
5. Paint on one face only: 22; paint on at least one face: 54 **6.** Answers will vary. **7. a)** 3 **b)** 1
8. Between 6 am and 8 am, Paris time. **9.** A = 6, B = 2, C = 5, D = 3; missing row sum = 21, missing column sum = 22 **11.** 8 **12.** If true, the average length of the bicycles must be $\dfrac{71 \text{ km}}{45000 \text{ m}} = 1.58 \text{ m}$.

Chapter 6

Getting Started p. 314
1. a) $a = \sqrt{2}$, $b = \sqrt{3}$, $c = \sqrt{4}$, $d = \sqrt{5}$, $e = \sqrt{6}$, $f = \sqrt{7}$, $g = \sqrt{8}$ **b)** $\sqrt{12}$ **2. a)** 8.6 cm **b)** 12.7 m **c)** 18.3 m
d) 5.1 cm **3. b)** $3 + \sqrt{3}$, $5 + \sqrt{3}$; 4, 8; $2 + 2\sqrt{2}$, $6 + 2\sqrt{2}$; $2 + \sqrt{2}$, $8 + \sqrt{2}$; $4 + \sqrt{2}$, $6 + \sqrt{2}$

Review of Prerequisite Skills p. 315
1. a) $\dfrac{11}{5}$ **b)** $\dfrac{21}{2}$ **c)** $\dfrac{9}{4}$ **d)** $\dfrac{5}{2}$ **e)** $\dfrac{2}{11}$ **f)** $\dfrac{2}{3}$ **g)** $\dfrac{24}{5}$ **h)** $\dfrac{3}{2}$ **i)** $\dfrac{28}{5}$
j) 15 **2. a)** 30.53 **b)** 27.66 **c)** 1.33 **d)** 0.37 **e)** 0.48
f) 0.12 **g)** 0.25 **h)** 2.52 **i)** 4.75 **j)** 1.2 **k)** 0.27 **l)** 6.56
3. a) AB = DE, BC = EF, AC = DF, ∠A = ∠D, ∠B = ∠E, ∠C = ∠F **b)** PQ = XY, QR = YZ, PR = XZ, ∠P = ∠X, ∠Q = ∠Y, ∠R = ∠Z
4. a) $x = 55°$ **b)** $a = 47°$, $b = 133°$, $c = 133°$, $d = 47°$, $e = 47°$, $f = 133°$, $g = 133°$ **c)** $a = 62°$, $b = 62°$, $c = 76°$
d) $a = 85°$, $b = 61°$, $c = 61°$, $d = 34°$ **e)** $a = 50°$, $b = 130°$, $c = 50°$ **f)** $a = 62°$, $b = 67°$

Section 6.2 pp. 322–325
Practice 1. a) $d = 14$ cm, $f = 8$ cm **b)** $r = 30$ cm, $s = 6$ cm **c)** $b = 7.5$ cm, $w = 6$ cm **d)** $p = 6.75$ cm, $r = 7.5$ cm **e)** $d = 12.5$ cm, $e = 15$ cm **2. a)** 8 cm
b) 9 cm **3.** 128 cm² **4. a)** ∠PQR = ∠STR, ∠PRQ = ∠SRT. Thus ∠QPR = ∠TSR and ΔPQR ~ ΔSTR. **b)** $x = 10$ cm, $y = 18$ cm
Applications and Problem Solving 5. 37.5 m **6.** 260 m
7. Compare corresponding angles or corresponding sides. **8.** 4.75 m **9.** 17.5 m **10.** 3:5 **11.** Only if the corresponding angles of the triangle are equal, are the triangles similar. For example, two isosceles triangles with angle measures 50°, 50°, 80° and 40°, 40°, 100° are not similar, but two isosceles triangles both with angle measures 30°, 30°, 120° are similar. **12.** Yes, corresponding angles are always equal, since they are always 60°. **13.** Yes, they are congruent if the ratio of their corresponding sides is 1:1. **14.** Yes, all congruent triangles are similar, since their corresponding angles are equal. **15.** 2:3

Modelling Math p. 325
233 m

Section 6.3 pp. 330–333
Practice 1. a) tan A = 0.333, tan C = 3
b) tan A = 0.714, tan C = 1.4 **2. a)** 0.268 **b)** 1.881
c) 0.087 **d)** 0.577 **e)** 7.115 **f)** 1 **3. a)** 31° **b)** 40° **c)** 72°
4. a) 39° **b)** 41° **c)** 60° **d)** 59° **5. a)** 0.4 **b)** 1
6. a) $\tan D = \dfrac{4}{3}$, ∠D = 53°, $\tan E = \dfrac{3}{4}$, ∠E = 37°
b) $\tan D = \dfrac{15}{8}$, ∠D = 62°, $\tan E = \dfrac{8}{15}$, ∠E = 28°
7. a) 11.0 m **b)** 6.0 m **c)** 11.2 m **d)** 11.3 m **e)** 5.1 m
f) 13.1 m **8. a)** 5.2 m **b)** 23.6 m
Applications and Problem Solving 9. 5.1 cm **10.** 3 cm
11. 2.1 m **12.** 93 m **13.** 12 m **14.** 35° **15.** 37°
16. 235 m **17.** $x = 7.0$ m, $y = 6.3$ m **18.** $x = 8.9$ cm, ∠y = 45° **19. a)** 45° **b)** 45° **c)** 45° **20.** 118 m

Section 6.4 pp. 338–339
Practice 1. a) sin A = 0.448, sin C = 0.896
b) sin A = 0.667, sin C = 0.742 **2. a)** 0.707 **b)** 0.866
c) 0.602 **d)** 0.423 **e)** 0 **f)** 1.000 **3. a)** 30° **b)** 72° **c)** 45°
d) 18° **e)** 86° **f)** 6° **4. a)** 42° **b)** 49° **c)** 30° **d)** 24°
e) 7° **f)** 51° **5. a)** $\dfrac{5}{11}$; 27° **b)** $\dfrac{1}{5}$; 12° **6. a)** 13.1 cm
b) 29.0 cm **c)** 48.1 cm **d)** 15.7 cm **e)** 18.3 cm
f) 27.4 cm
Applications and Problem Solving 7. 13.1 cm **8.** 56°
9. 16.2 cm **10.** 35 m **11.** 1.4 m **12.** 3.6 cm **13.** 4.1 m
14. a) 0.629 **b)** $\dfrac{a}{c}$ **c)** $a = 0.629c$ **d)** $c = \dfrac{a}{0.629}$
15. $x = 7.2$ cm, $y = 10.8$ cm **16.** $x = 7.4$ m, ∠y = 38°

Section 6.5 pp. 344–345
Practice 1. a) cos A = 0.894, cos C = 0.447
b) cos A = 0.371, cos C = 0.928 **2. a)** 0.866 **b)** 0.707
c) 0.5 **d)** 0.017 **e)** 1 **f)** 0.996 **g)** 0.946 **h)** 0.122
3. a) 70° **b)** 28° **c)** 52° **d)** 89° **e)** 43° **f)** 58° **4. a)** 80°
b) 63° **c)** 56° **d)** 29° **e)** 20° **f)** 78° **5. a)** $\dfrac{1}{2}$; 60°
b) $\dfrac{3}{10}$; 73° **6. a)** 7.6 cm **b)** 13.1 cm **c)** 8.2 cm
d) 12.2 cm **e)** 6.3 cm **f)** 28.6 cm
Applications and Problem Solving 7. 21.8 cm
8. 9.3 cm **9.** 4.7 m **10.** 225 m **11.** ∠W = 106°, ∠X = 37°, ∠Y = 37° **12. a)** 1
b) $(\sin x)^2 + (\cos x)^2 = 1$ for all values of x

c) $\left(\dfrac{\text{opposite}}{\text{hypotenuse}}\right)^2 + \left(\dfrac{\text{adjacent}}{\text{hypotenuse}}\right)^2 =$

$\dfrac{(\text{opposite})^2 + (\text{adjacent})^2}{(\text{hypotenuse})^2} = \dfrac{(\text{hypotenuse})^2}{(\text{hypotenuse})^2} = 1$

13. $x = 8.5$ m, $y = 9.5$ m **14.** $x = 17.1$ cm, $\angle y = 39°$

15. L.S. $= \dfrac{\text{opposite}}{\text{adjacent}}$,

R.S. $= \dfrac{\dfrac{\text{opposite}}{\text{hypotenuse}}}{\dfrac{\text{adjacent}}{\text{hypotenuse}}} = \dfrac{\text{opposite}}{\text{hypotenuse}} \times \dfrac{\text{hypotenuse}}{\text{adjacent}}$

$= \dfrac{\text{opposite}}{\text{adjacent}} = $ L.S.

Section 6.6 pp. 348–350

Practice   1. a) $\angle C = 57°$, CD $= 12.0$ m, DE $= 18.5$ m
b) $\angle B = 25°$, GF $= 13.5$ cm, GB $= 32.0$ cm
c) $\angle P = 61°$, PM $= 28.3$ m, PR $= 58.3$ m **d)** $\angle X = 60°$,
XZ $= 12$ cm, YZ $= 10.4$ cm **e)** $\angle S = 36°$,
NO $= 10.0$ km, OS $= 13.8$ km **f)** $\angle T = 77°$,
TX $= 2.9$ m, MX $= 12.7$ m **2. a)** BC $= 7.5$ cm,
$\angle A = 30°$, $\angle C = 60°$ **b)** GI $= 11.4$ cm, $\angle G = 52°$,
$\angle I = 38°$ **c)** JK $= 3.3$ cm, $\angle J = 56°$, $\angle L = 34°$
d) PR $= 14.9$ cm, $\angle P = 48°$, $\angle R = 42°$
e) RT $= 24.1$ m, $\angle R = 48°$, $\angle T = 42°$
f) WX $= 47.9$ mm, $\angle W = 28°$, $\angle Y = 62°$
Applications and Problem Solving   3. 190 m **4.** 51 m
5. 128 m **6.** 76° **7. a)** 13 m **b)** 12 m **8.** 23 m
9. a) 111 m **b)** 5 times as tall **c)** 135 storeys
10. a) 16.6 km **b)** 27° **11.** 5.1° **12. c)** greater than

13. a) ABC: $\dfrac{3}{4}, \dfrac{3}{5}, \dfrac{4}{5}, \dfrac{4}{3}, \dfrac{4}{5}, \dfrac{3}{5}$;

DEF: $\dfrac{5}{12}, \dfrac{5}{13}, \dfrac{12}{13}, \dfrac{12}{5}, \dfrac{12}{13}, \dfrac{5}{13}$

b) $(\tan x)(\tan(90° - x)) = 1$ **c)** $\sin x = \cos(90° - x)$

d) $\cos x = \sin(90° - x)$ **e)** In $\triangle$ABC, $\tan x = \dfrac{\text{BC}}{\text{AB}}$ and

$\tan(90° - x) = \dfrac{\text{AB}}{\text{BC}}$; $\sin x = \dfrac{\text{BC}}{\text{AC}}$ and

$\cos(90° - x) = \dfrac{\text{BC}}{\text{AC}}$; $\cos x = \dfrac{\text{AB}}{\text{AC}}$ and

$\sin(90° - x) = \dfrac{\text{AB}}{\text{AC}}$.

Career Connection p. 351
1. a) 1.1 m **b)** all of it

Section 6.7 pp. 355–358
Practice   1. 23.2 m **2.** 328.6 m **3.** 38.6 m **4.** 143 m
5. 80 m **6.** 49 m **7.** 45 m **8.** 24.4 m **9.** 10° **10.** 38.8°
Applications and Problem Solving   11. a) 126 m
b) 77 m **12.** 57.4 m **13.** 68 m **14. a)** 131.1 m
b) 132.7 m **15.** 150 cm **16. a)** 115 m **b)** 572 m
17. 50 m **18.** 706 km/h **19.** 31 cm **20. a)** 10.5 cm
b) 9.7 cm

Career Connection p. 359
1. a) 8483 km **b)** 1620 km **c)** Ignore the curvature of
Earth.

Section 6.9 pp. 366–368
Practice   1. a) 35 m **b)** 45 m **c)** 28 m **2. a)** 66° **b)** 45°
c) 52° **3. a)** 79.5 cm **b)** 7.6 m **c)** 11.0 cm **d)** 71.0°
e) 51.1° **f)** 86.2° **4. a)** $\angle A = 51°$, $a = 17$ m, $c = 20$ m
b) $\angle E = 54°$, $d = 17$ cm, $e = 14$ cm **c)** $\angle Y = 75°$,
$x = 9$ m, $z = 7$ m **5. a)** $\angle Q = 73°$, $\angle P = 46°$, $p = 9$ cm
b) $\angle K = 64°$, $\angle L = 84°$, $l = 19$ m **c)** $\angle C = 78°$,
$\angle E = 30°$, $c = 15$ cm
Applications and Problem Solving   6. 91 m **7.** 41 cm
8. 1809 m **9. a)** 78 m **c)** 61 m **d)** 2426 m^2 **10.** 47 cm,
35 cm **11.** In $\triangle$ABC, let $\angle A$ and $\angle B$ be the two
equal angles. Then, $\sin A = \sin B$. Since

$\dfrac{a}{\sin A} = \dfrac{b}{\sin B}$, then $a = b$. Thus, the equal sides are

opposite the equal angles. **12. a)** $x = 15.6$ cm
b) $x = 15.6$ cm **c)** The sine law yields

$\dfrac{x}{\sin 90°} = \dfrac{10}{\sin 40°}$. But $\sin 90° = 1$, so $x = \dfrac{10}{\sin 40°}$,

or $\sin 40° = \dfrac{10}{x}$, which is the sine ratio.

13. a) H_1: 344 m, H_2: 236 m **b)** 202 m

Modelling Math p. 368
3953 m

Section 6.10 pp. 373–376
Practice   1. a) 13.9 m **b)** 9.3 cm **2. a)** 50° **b)** 61°
3. a) 19.4 m **b)** 59.1° **c)** 28.3° **d)** 53.1 m
4. a) $\angle K = 58.4$, $\angle L = 48.2°$, $\angle M = 73.4°$
b) $g = 13.5$ m, $\angle H = 53.2°$, $\angle F = 46.8°$ **c)** $\angle I = 51.1°$,
$\angle J = 61.0°$, $\angle K = 67.9°$ **d)** $t = 23.4$ cm, $\angle U = 88.9°$,
$\angle W = 48.0°$
Applications and Problem Solving   5. 70.0° **6.** 24.2 km
7. a) 3330 m **b)** Athletes swim in a straight line.
8. 104 m^2 **9.** 339 m^3 **10.** 70° **11.** No, another angle

or side is needed. **12.** No, two sides and a contained angle are needed to find the other side. **13. a)** cosine law; $b = 10.5$ cm, $\angle A = 64°$, $\angle C = 46°$ **b)** sine law; $\angle E = 53°$, $\angle F = 64°$, $f = 10.1$ m **c)** sine law; $\angle P = 54°$, $p = 17.6$ m, $q = 18.6$ m **d)** cosine law; $\angle K = 59°$, $\angle L = 71°$, $\angle M = 50°$ **14.** $a = 6.1$, $b = 4.1$, $c = 5.8$, $\angle A = 73.1°$, $\angle B = 40.4°$, $\angle C = 66.5°$ **15.** The cosine law is $c^2 = a^2 + b^2 - 2ab\cos C$. In a right triangle, $\angle C = 90°$, and cos C = 0. Thus, $c^2 = a^2 + b^2 - 2ab(0)$, or $c^2 = a^2 + b^2$, which is the Pythagorean Theorem. **16.** Let $\triangle ABC$ be equilateral. Then

$$\cos A = \frac{b^2 + c^2 - a^2}{2bc} = \frac{a^2 + a^2 - a^2}{2a^2} = \frac{1}{2}.$$ Similarly,

$\cos B = \dfrac{1}{2}$ and $\cos C = \dfrac{1}{2}$. Thus, $\angle A = \angle B = \angle C = 60°$.

17. These side lengths cannot form a triangle, since $3 + 4 < 8$.

Technology Extension: Graphing Calculator Programs p. 377

1 The Sine Law 1. The first line clears the memory. The next line asks for B, the length of the side opposite the given angle, X. The next line asks for X. The next line asks for Y, the other given angle. The next line calculates the length of the unknown side, A. The last line displays the length of A. **2. a)** 8.9 cm **b)** 6.0 m

2 The Cosine Law 1. The first line clears the memory. The next three lines ask for B, C, and X, the given sides and contained angle. The next line calculates the length of the unknown side, A. The last line displays the length of A. **2. a)** 7.2 cm **b)** 12.6 m **3. a)** :ClrHome; Input "A=",A; Input "B=",B; Input "C=",C; cos⁻¹ ((B²+C²−A²)/(2BC))→X; Disp "X=",X **b)** 68.5°, 58.0°, 53.5°

Rich Problem p. 379

1 Discovery Harbour B(S42.64, 0), C(S51.48, 0), D(0, W47.55), E(N18.62, W72.44), F(N29.69, W24.04)
2 The Bayfield Complex G(N29.30, W42.84)

Review of Key Concepts pp. 380–389

1. a) $e = 10$ cm, $f = 6$ cm **b)** $q = 4$ cm, $w = 18$ cm **c)** $q = 6$ cm, $y = 10$ cm **2.** 44 m **3.** 27 cm² **4. a)** 53° **b)** 32° **5. a)** 10.5 cm **b)** 14.4 cm **6.** 244 m **7. a)** 23° **b)** 53° **8. a)** 14.8 m **b)** 97.6 m **9. a)** 65° **b)** 35° **10. a)** 18 mm **b)** 26 km **11. a)** $b = 5.8$ m, $\angle A = 31°$, $\angle C = 59°$ **b)** $e = 12$ cm, $\angle D = 23°$, $\angle E = 67°$ **c)** $\angle H = 40°$, $h = 2.6$ m, $g = 3.1$ m **d)** $k = 39.2$ mm, $\angle K = 59°$, $\angle M = 31°$ **e)** $\angle P = 32°$, $p = 30.0$ cm, $r = 56.6$ cm **f)** $\angle T = 35°$, $r = 29.6$ km, $s = 24.3$ km

12. 6° **13.** 32° **14.** 13 m **15.** 10° **16.** 30 cm **17. a)** 17.0 m **b)** 93.6 m **c)** 97.9 m **18.** 96 m **19.** 23 m **20.** 25.2 m **21.** 22.7 m **22. a)** $\angle Y = 75°$, $x = 11.2$ m, $y = 14.8$ m **b)** $\angle V = 43°$, $t = 16.6$ cm, $u = 16.1$ cm **c)** $\angle S = 74°$, $\angle R = 52°$, $r = 10.0$ m **d)** $\angle B = 44°$, $\angle C = 85°$, $c = 20.8$ cm **23.** 390 m **24.** 13 367 km **25.** 18.1 m **26.** 69° **27. a)** $b = 6.7$ m, $\angle A = 85°$, $\angle C = 38°$ **b)** $f = 9.6$ m, $\angle D = 51°$, $\angle E = 62°$ **28. a)** $\angle R = 70°$, $\angle S = 59°$, $\angle T = 51°$ **b)** $\angle X = 59°$, $\angle Y = 68°$, $\angle Z = 53°$ **29.** 294 m **30.** 4.0 km **31. a)** cosine law; $\angle R = 54°$, $\angle S = 79°$, $\angle T = 47°$ **b)** sine law; $\angle W = 50°$, $\angle Y = 58°$, $y = 4.5$ m **c)** cosine law; $b = 14.3$ m, $\angle A = 64°$, $\angle C = 50°$ **d)** sine law; $\angle D = 55°$, $e = 18.0$ cm, $f = 12.9$ cm

Chapter Test pp. 390–391

1. $w = 10.5$ cm, $r = 10$ cm **2.** 25.6 cm² **3.** 14.5 m **4.** 19.2 km **5.** 16.0 cm **6. a)** $\angle A = 53°$, $b = 7.5$ m, $c = 4.5$ m **b)** $d = 6.2$ cm, $\angle D = 51°$, $\angle F = 39°$ **7.** 77.0 m **8. a)** $\angle A = 74°$, $b = 3.3$ cm, $c = 4.8$ cm **b)** $\angle E = 47°$, $\angle F = 62°$, $f = 8.4$ m **c)** $q = 4.4$ cm, $\angle P = 41°$, $\angle R = 62°$ **d)** $\angle K = 41°$, $\angle L = 83°$, $\angle M = 56°$ **9.** 560 m **10.** 70 m

Problem Solving: Using the Strategies p. 392

1. 5 **2.** 32, 31 **3.** 60 cm² **4.** 1596 cm **5. a)** 16 m by 32 m **b)** 1600 m² **c)** 7° **6.** Weigh three coins against three other coins. If the scales balance, then the real coin is among the two not weighed and can be determined with another weighing. If the scales do not balance, weigh two of the three coins that tipped the scales most. If one side tips more, the real coin is found. If the scales balance, the real coin was the other of the three. **8.** Mr. Smith: farmer, Vancouver; Mr. Wong: accountant, London; Ms. Bevan: baker, Toronto; Ms. Lee: writer, Paris; Ms. Kostash: biologist, Melbourne **9. a)** 28 **b)** 168 **11. a)** Québec **b)** Manitoba

Cumulative Review: Chapters 5 and 6 p. 393

Chapter 5
1. a) -2, 4 **b)** ± 3 **c)** 3 **d)** -5, 0 **e)** no solution
2. a) -6, 3 **b)** 1, 7 **c)** -4, $\dfrac{3}{2}$ **d)** $-\dfrac{2}{3}$, 4
e) 0, $\dfrac{5}{2}$ **f)** ± 4 **g)** 1 **h)** $\pm\dfrac{1}{2}$ **3. a)** -3.2, 1.2 **b)** 0.4, 2.6
c) -1.5, 1 **d)** 0.3, 2.4 **e)** -1.8, 0 **f)** no solution
4. a) x-intercepts: 2, 4; vertex: $(3, -1)$ **b)** x-intercepts: 0, 6; vertex: $(3, -9)$ **c)** x-intercepts: -5, 1; vertex: $(-2, -9)$

d) x-intercepts: -5, 1; vertex: $(-2, -9)$ **5.** 8, 13 or -13, -8 **6.** base = 6 cm, height = 8 cm **7.** 5 m

Chapter 6
1. DE = 2.8 cm, DF = 2.4 cm **2.** 45.6 cm² **3. a)** $\angle P = 52°$, $r = 9.4$ cm, $q = 15.2$ cm **b)** $y = 7.1$ cm, $\angle W = 44°$, $\angle Y = 46°$ **4.** 62 m **5.** 18.0 m **6. a)** $\angle F = 69°$, $f = 8.8$ cm, $e = 7.5$ cm **b)** $\angle T = 46°$, $s = 7.3$ m, $\angle S = 61°$ **c)** $a = 6.9$ cm, $\angle B = 42°$, $\angle C = 70°$ **d)** $\angle W = 51°$, $\angle X = 45°$, $\angle Y = 84°$

Cumulative Review: Chapters 1–6 pp. 394–397

Chapter 1
1. a) $(1, 3)$ **b)** $(-2, 4)$ **c)** $(4, 7)$ **d)** $(-2, 5)$ **2. a)** one solution **b)** no solution **c)** one solution **d)** infinitely many solutions **3. a)** $(2, -1)$ **b)** $(-\frac{1}{2}, 2)$

4. a) $(-1, 0)$ **b)** $(2, 1)$ **c)** $(2, -1)$ **d)** $(-3, 2)$ **e)** $(6, -10)$ **f)** $(4, -2)$ **5.** 9 cm, 16 cm **6.** \$12 000 at 3%, \$8000 at 5% **7.** 24 mL of 20% solution, 36 mL of 40% solution

Chapter 2
8. a) 3.6 **b)** 6.7 **c)** 1.4 **d)** 4.5 **9. a)** $(1, 5)$ **b)** $(-3, 3)$ **10.** $(3, -1)$ **11.** $x^2 + y^2 = 225$ **12.** 10 **13. a)** 26 units **b)** 36 square units **14. a)** isosceles **b)** 15.3 **c)** midpoints: $(1, 4)$ and $(2, 2)$; slope of line connecting midpoints: -2, slope of BC: -2; length of line connecting midpoints: approximately 2.24, length of BC: approximately 4.47

15. a) slope WX = slope YZ = $\frac{1}{7}$;

slope WZ = slope XY = -6 **b)** The midpoints of the diagonals coincide at $(0, -\frac{1}{2})$. **16. a)** $4x + 5y = 12$

b) $x - 3y = 0$ **c)** $4x - y = 5$ **17.** 4.2

Chapter 3
18. a) $9x + 1$ **b)** $x^2 - 7x + 5$ **c)** $-8x^3$ **d)** $12x^4y^3z^3$ **e)** $-6ab^2$ **f)** $4ab^2c$ **19. a)** $7x + 3$ **b)** $-4t + 53$ **c)** $5x^2 - 17x$ **d)** $2x^2 - 11x + 22$ **20. a)** $x^2 + 2x - 35$ **b)** $12y^2 - 13y + 3$ **c)** $6m^2 - 7m - 3$ **d)** $6x^2 - 13x - 28$ **21. a)** $18x^2 - 8$ **b)** $8x^2 - 36x - 20$ **c)** $5y^2 - 9y - 26$ **d)** $x - 26$ **22. a)** $x^2 + 4x + 4$ **b)** $x^2 - 25$ **c)** $4y^2 - 9$ **d)** $16y^2 + 24y + 9$ **e)** $9x^2 - 6x + 1$ **f)** $25x^2 - 4y^2$ **23. a)** $3x^2 + 4x - 14$ **b)** $-6t + 58$ **c)** $-8x^2 + 8x + 11$ **24. a)** $7(x + 6)$ **b)** $4x(x - 7)$ **c)** not possible **d)** $7rt(2r - 1 + 3t)$ **e)** $(y + 4)(x - 2)$ **f)** $(m + n)(2x + 3)$ **g)** $(y + 4)(x - 3)$ **25. a)** $(x + 3)(x + 4)$ **b)** $(y + 3)(y - 2)$

c) not possible **d)** $(x - 5)(x + 3)$ **e)** $(y + 3)(y + 7)$ **f)** $(x - 2)(x - 9)$ **26. a)** $2(x - 4)(x + 1)$ **b)** $3(x + 1)(x + 3)$ **27. a)** $(3x - 1)(x + 2)$ **b)** $(2y + 3)(y + 4)$ **c)** not possible **d)** not possible **28. a)** $2(2x + 5)(x - 1)$ **b)** $6(3x - 2)(x - 1)$ **29. a)** $(x - 4)(x + 4)$ **b)** $(y + 5)^2$ **c)** not possible **d)** $(x - 3)^2$ **e)** $(2x - 1)^2$ **f)** $(3x - 4y)(3x + 4y)$ **30. a)** $7(x - 1)(x + 1)$ **b)** $5(x - 2)^2$

Chapter 4
31. a) yes **b)** yes **c)** no **32. a)** up; vertically stretched by a factor of 3; $(0, 0)$; $x = 0$; domain: set of real numbers, range: $y = 0$; minimum: 0 **b)** down; not stretched or shrunk; $(0, 5)$; $x = 0$; domain: set of real numbers, range: $y = 5$; maximum: 5 **c)** down; not stretched or shrunk; $(1, -3)$; $x = 1$; domain: set of real numbers, range: $y = -3$; maximum: -3 **d)** up; vertically stretched by a factor of 3; $(-4, 0)$; $x = -4$; domain: set of real numbers, range: $y = 0$; minimum: 0 **e)** up; vertically stretched by a factor of 2; $(-3, -4)$; $x = -3$; domain: set of real numbers, range: $y = -4$; minimum: -4 **f)** down; vertically shrunk by a factor of 0.5; $(-7, 2)$; $x = -7$; domain: set of real numbers, range: $y = 2$; maximum: 2 **33. a)** 8 m **b)** 10 m **c)** 1 m **d)** 1.7 m **e)** 20.7 m **34. a)** ±2.6 **b)** 0.2, -4.2 **35. a)** $y = (x - 4)^2 - 13$; $(4, -13)$; $x = 4$; Points may vary. $(0, 3)$, $(1, -4)$ **b)** $y = -2(x - 1)^2 - 3$; $(1, -3)$; $x = 1$; Points may vary. $(0, -5)$, $(2, -5)$ **36. a)** $(-3, -9)$; x-intercepts: 0, -6; y-intercept: 0 **b)** $(3, 1)$; x-intercepts: 2, 4; y-intercept: -8 **37. a)** $y = x(x - 6) + 3$; $(0, 3)$, $(6, 3)$; vertex: $(3, -6)$ **b)** $y = 2x(x - 4) + 7$; $(0, 7)$, $(4, 7)$; vertex: $(2, -1)$ **38. a)** 200 m by 200 m **b)** 40 000 m² **39. a)** linear **b)** neither **c)** quadratic **40. a)** $y = x^2 + 3$ **b)** Answers may vary. $y = 0.98x^2 + 0.08x - 3.69$ **c)** Answers may vary. $y = -0.98x^2 + 0.31x + 1.69$

Chapter 5
41. a) -4, 3 **b)** 3, 5 **c)** -2 **d)** 0, 7 **e)** ±1 **42. a)** -1, 9 **b)** -6, -1 **c)** ±11 **d)** 3 **e)** $0, -\frac{3}{2}$ **f)** $\pm \frac{3}{2}$ **g)** $\frac{5}{2}$, 4

h) $-3, \frac{1}{3}$ **43.** 7, 8, 9 or -9, -8, -7 **44.** 10 cm, 24 cm **45. a)** x-intercepts: -2, 6; vertex: $(2, -16)$ **b)** x-intercepts: 1, 9; vertex: $(5, -16)$ **46. a)** -3, 6 **b)** -3.3, 0 **c)** -1, 1.3 **d)** -3.4, -0.1 **e)** no solution **f)** ±2.1 **47.** 18.4 m

Chapter 6
48. a) $t = 4.375$ cm, $x = 9.6$ cm **b)** 10.7 cm² **49. a)** $\angle C = 43°$, $a = 11.0$ cm, $c = 10.2$ cm **b)** $\angle E = 34°$, $\angle F = 56°$, $d = 14.4$ mm **50.** 75 m

51. 72 m **52. a)** $\angle Y = 58°$, $x = 23.8$ cm, $y = 21.5$ cm
b) $\angle Q = 81°$, $\angle P = 31°$, $p = 8.2$ m **c)** $b = 11.8$ cm,
$\angle A = 50°$, $\angle C = 75°$ **d)** $\angle J = 48°$, $\angle K = 61°$, $\angle L = 71°$
53. a) 271 m **b)** 3412 m² **54.** 68°

Appendix A

Adding polynomials p. 398
1. a) $7x + 5y + 12$ **b)** $9x - 6y - 12$ **c)** $3x^2 + 2x + 4$
d) $5a^2 + 3a + 1$ **e)** $-y^2 - 1$ **f)** $-2a - b - 3$

Angle properties p. 399
1. a) $x = 41°$ **b)** $a = 115°$, $b = 65°$, $c = 65°$, $d = 115°$,
$e = 65°$, $f = 115°$, $g = 65°$ **c)** $w = 74°$, $x = 70°$, $y = 36°$,
$z = 70°$ **d)** $w = 79°$, $x = 101°$, $y = 101°$

Common factoring p. 399
1. a) $3x + 4y$ **b)** $2x - 5$ **c)** $2c + 5$ **d)** $2a - 3$ **e)** $ab + 2c$
f) $x - 2$ **2. a)** $5(y + 3)$ **b)** $8(3x - 2)$ **c)** $2a(2b + 3)$
d) $3x(x - 6)$ **e)** $2x(x^2 + 2x - 3)$ **f)** $3x(2x^2 - x + 3)$
g) $4ab(2b + 1 + 3a)$ **h)** $10(y^3 - 1)$

Congruent triangles p. 400
1. a) $\angle P = \angle S$, $\angle Q = \angle T$, $\angle R = \angle U$, PQ = ST,
PR = SU, QR = TU **b)** $\angle A = \angle K$, $\angle B = \angle L$,
$\angle C = \angle M$, AB = KL, AC = KM, BC = LM

Evaluating expressions pp. 400–401
1. a) 13 **b)** 11 **c)** 12 **d)** 6 **e)** 18 **f)** 11 **g)** 30 **h)** –2 **i)** –3
j) –21 **k)** 4 **l)** 0 **2. a)** 2 **b)** 1 **c)** –25 **d)** 12 **e)** –10 **f)** –11
g) 12 **h)** 0 **i)** 4 **j)** 216 **k)** –36 **l)** –41 **3. a)** 6, 5, 4, 3, 2
b) 1, –1, –3, –5, –7 **c)** 3, 4, 5, 6, 7 **d)** 5, 2, 1, 2, 5
e) 8, 3, 0, –1, 0 **f)** 4, 3, 4, 7, 12

Evaluating radicals p. 401
1. a) 2 **b)** 5 **c)** 0.9 **d)** 1.1 **e)** 0.3 **f)** 0.1 **g)** 15 **h)** 1.3
2. a) 6.6 **b)** 11.4 **c)** 58.5 **d)** 4.5 **e)** 9.5 **f)** 27.3 **g)** 256.5
h) 0.8

Expanding expressions p. 401
1. a) $2x + 6$ **b)** $3x + 3y - 21$ **c)** $5a - 5b + 5c$ **d)** $-10a + 8$
e) $-2x + y$ **f)** $x^2 + 6x$ **g)** $6x^2 + 14x$ **h)** $x^3 - x^2 + 5x$
i) $-3a^3 - 6a^2 + 3a$

Exponent rules p. 402
1. a) 2^7 **b)** 3^{10} **c)** 4^7 **d)** 5^6 **e)** 2^2 **f)** 3^3 **g)** 4^5 **h)** 2^6 **i)** 3^{12}
j) y^{11} **k)** z^6 **l)** y^1 **m)** z^6 **n)** x^{15} **o)** y^{16} **p)** $6x^7$ **q)** $8y^7$ **r)** $5m^4$
s) $9y^6$ **t)** $-8x^9$

First differences p. 402
1. a) linear **b)** linear **c)** non-linear **d)** linear
Graphing equations   2. a) x-intercept: 3, y-intercept: 3
b) x-intercept: 4, y-intercept: –4 **c)** x-intercept: 2,
y-intercept: 8 **d)** x-intercept: 5, y-intercept: –2

3. a) slope: 1, y-intercept: 3 **b)** slope: –1,
y-intercept: –4 **c)** slope: 2, y-intercept: 3 **d)** slope: 3,
y-intercept: –1 **4. a)** $(6, 2)$ **b)** $(2, 5)$ **c)** $(4, -2)$
d) $(-1, 4)$

Greatest common factors p. 404
1. a) $2x$ **b)** $4y$ **c)** $5z$ **d)** $10a$ **e)** $2x$ **f)** $7ab$ **g)** $6x^2$ **h)** abc
2. a) $2a$ **b)** $3y$ **c)** $4x^2$ **d)** $3mn$ **e)** $5rt^2$ **f)** 9

Lengths of line segments p. 405
1. a) 6 **b)** 4 **c)** 6 **d)** 8 **e)** 7 **f)** 13 **g)** 4 **h)** 12 **i)** 6 **j)** 7 **k)** 14
l) 6

Like terms p. 405
1. a) $6x$ **b)** $5y - 14$ **c)** $3x - y - 7$ **d)** $4a - 5b + 4c$
e) $-2x^2 - 9x - 3$ **f)** $-t^2 + t - 4$ **g)** $4x + 9y - 8$
h) $-y^2 - 18y + 3$ **i)** $-2t^2 - 10t + 15$

Polynomials p. 406
1. a) 1 **b)** 3 **c)** 2 **d)** 3 **e)** 4 **f)** 5

Pythagorean Theorem p. 406
1. a) 5.8 **b)** 7.2 **c)** 4.9 **d)** 6.7 **e)** 7.4 **f)** 8.1

Simplifying expressions p. 407
1. a) $7x + 14$ **b)** $9a - 21$ **c)** $2x - 12$ **d)** $-5y + 21$
e) $5t - 4$ **f)** $7y - 30$ **g)** $-6z - 8$ **h)** $17 - 2w$ **i)** $8x - 18$
2. a) $5x + 7y$ **b)** $5r + s$ **c)** $-p + 6q$ **d)** $20x - 9y$
e) $5a + 21b$ **f)** $-c + 19d$ **g)** $2a - 3b + 5c$
h) $10x + 3y - 6z - 5$ **i)** $14x + 17y - 4z$

Slope p. 407
1. a) 3 **b)** $\frac{1}{2}$ **c)** 2 **d)** 2 **e)** –2 **f)** $\frac{1}{5}$ **g)** 0 **h)** –2 **i)** $\frac{3}{2}$
2. a) $3, -\frac{1}{3}$ **b)** $-2, \frac{1}{2}$ **c)** $-1, 1$ **d)** $\frac{1}{4}, -4$ **e)** $-\frac{2}{3}, \frac{3}{2}$
f) $\frac{4}{5}, -\frac{5}{4}$

Solving equations pp. 408–409
1. a) 3 **b)** 6 **c)** –3 **d)** 4 **e)** –7 **f)** –2 **g)** 1 **h)** –8 **i)** –4
2. a) 1 **b)** 5 **c)** 4 **d)** –4 **e)** –9 **f)** 18 **g)** 1 **h)** 2 **i)** –6
3. a) 9 **b)** 1 **c)** 4 **d)** 7 **e)** 5 **f)** –2 **g)** –2 **h)** 3 **i)** 7

Solving proportions p. 410
1. a) $\frac{12}{5}$ **b)** $\frac{12}{5}$ **c)** $\frac{14}{3}$ **d)** $\frac{8}{3}$ **e)** $\frac{10}{3}$ **f)** $\frac{28}{3}$ **g)** $\frac{8}{3}$ **h)** $\frac{16}{5}$
2. a) 15.3 **b)** 0.45 **c)** 13.76 **d)** 1.3 **e)** 0.27 **f)** 1.25
g) 6.97 **h)** 1.04

Subtracting polynomials p. 410
1. a) $2x + 4y + 3$ **b)** $3x - 2y - 1$ **c)** $-x^2 - 8x - 9$
d) $3a^2 + 6a + 11$ **e)** $-7a + 6b + 7$ **f)** $7y^2 - 4y - 2$

Glossary

A

acute angle   An angle whose measure is less than 90°.

acute triangle   A triangle in which each of the three interior angles is acute.

addition property of equality   Adding the same quantity to both sides of an equation produces an equivalent equation. For any numbers a, b, and c, if $a = b$, then $a + c = b + c$.

algebraic expression   An expression that includes at least one variable.

$2x + 5$, $4y$, $8 - 3w$ are all algebraic expressions.

algebraic modelling   The process of representing a relationship by an equation or a formula, or representing a pattern of numbers by an algebraic expression.

algorithm   A specific set of instructions for carrying out a procedure.

alternate angles   Two angles formed on opposite sides of a transversal.

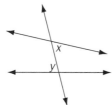

$\angle x$ and $\angle y$ are alternate angles.

altitude   The height of a geometric figure. In a triangle, an altitude is the perpendicular distance from a vertex to the opposite side.

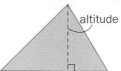

analytic geometry   The geometry that uses the xy-plane to determine equations that represent lines and curves. See also *coordinate geometry*.

angle bisector   A line that divides an angle into two equal parts.

angle of depression   The angle, measured downward, between the horizontal and the line of sight from an observer to an object.

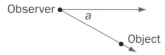

$\angle a$ is an angle of depression.

angle of elevation   The angle, measured upward, between the horizontal and the line of sight from an observer to an object.

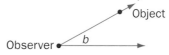

$\angle b$ is an angle of elevation.

application   The use of the concepts and skills of mathematics to solve real-world problems.

area   The number of square units contained in a region.

axis of symmetry   A line that is invariant under a reflection.

B

base (of a power)   The number used as a factor for repeated multiplication. In 6^3, the base is 6.

BEDMAS   An acronym that lists the order of operations. BEDMAS stands for **B**rackets, **E**xponents, **D**ivision, **M**ultiplication, **A**ddition, **S**ubtraction.

binomial   An algebraic expression with two terms.
$$3x - 4 \text{ is a binomial.}$$

broken-line graph   A graph that relates two variables as ordered pairs, with consecutive points joined by line segments.

C

capacity   The greatest volume that a container can hold, usually measured in litres, millilitres, or kilolitres.

Cartesian coordinate system   The system developed by René Descartes for graphing points as ordered pairs on a grid made up of two perpendicular number lines.

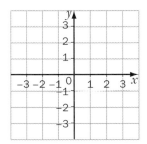

centroid of a triangle   The point of intersection of the three medians of a triangle. Also called the centre of gravity or balance point.

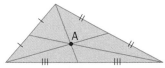

A is the centroid.

chord   A line segment joining two points on a curve.

circle   The set of all points in the plane that are equidistant from a fixed point called the centre.

circumcentre of a triangle   The point of intersection of the three perpendicular bisectors of the sides of a triangle.

circumcircle of a triangle   The circle with centre at the circumcentre of a triangle, and passing through the three vertices of the triangle.

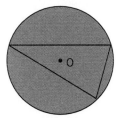

circumference   The perimeter of a circle.

coefficient   The factor by which a variable is multiplied. For example, in the term $8y$, the coefficient is 8; in the term ax, the coefficient is a.

co-interior angles   Two angles between two lines and on the same side of a transversal.

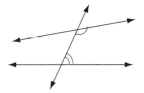

collecting like terms   Simplifying an expression containing like terms by adding their coefficients.

collinear points   Points that lie in the same straight line.

$(-3, -2)$, $(0, 1)$, and $(4, 5)$ are collinear points. They lie on the line $y = x + 1$.

complementary angles Angles whose sum is 90°.

composite figure A figure made up of two or more distinct figures.

concurrent lines Two or more lines that have one point in common.

cone A three-dimensional object with a circular base and a curved lateral surface that extends from the base to a point called the vertex.

congruence The property of being congruent. Two geometric figures are congruent if they are equal in all respects.

constant of variation In a direct variation, the ratio of corresponding values of the variables.

constant rate of change A relationship between two variables illustrates a constant rate of change when equal intervals of the first variable are associated with equal intervals of the second variable. For example, if a car travels at 80 km/h, in the first hour it travels 80 km, in the second hour it travels 80 km, and so on.

constant term A term that does not include a variable.

continuous graph A graph that consists of an unbroken line or curve.

convex polygon A polygon in which any line segment joining two points on the polygon has no part outside the polygon.

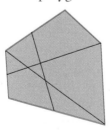

coordinate geometry The geometry in which geometrical points and figures are described in terms of their position in a coordinate system. See also *analytic geometry*.

coordinate plane A one-to-one pairing of all ordered pairs of real numbers with all points of a plane. Also called the Cartesian coordinate plane.

corresponding angles Four pairs of angles formed by two lines and a transversal. In the diagram, the pairs of corresponding angles are:

∠1 and ∠5

∠2 and ∠6

∠3 and ∠7

∠4 and ∠8

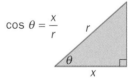

cosine law The relationship between the lengths of the three sides and the cosine of an angle in any triangle.

$$a^2 = b^2 + c^2 - 2bc \cos A$$

cosine ratio In a right triangle, for acute angle θ, the ratio of the length of the side adjacent to ∠θ and the length of the hypotenuse.

$$\cos \theta = \frac{x}{r}$$

cross-product rule If $\frac{a}{b} = \frac{c}{d}$, then $ad = bc$.

counterexample An example that demonstrates that a conjecture is false.

curve of best fit The curve that best describes the distribution of points in a scatter plot.

cylinder A three-dimensional object with two bases that are congruent circles, and a curved surface connecting the two bases.

D

degree of a polynomial in one variable
The greatest exponent of the variable in any one term.

The degree of $n^3 + 2n^2 - 8n$ is 3.

degree of a polynomial in two or more variables The greatest sum of the exponents in any one term.

The degree of $2a^4b^2 + 3a^2b^2 - ab^4$ is 6.

dependent variable In a function, the variable whose value depends on the value of the independent variable. On a coordinate grid, the values of the dependent variable are on the vertical axis.

diagonal A line segment joining two non-adjacent vertices of a polygon.

diameter of a circle A chord that passes through the centre of a circle.

difference of squares A technique of factoring applied to an expression of the form $a^2 - b^2$, which involves the subtraction of two perfect squares.

$$a^2 - b^2 = (a - b)(a + b)$$

dilatation A transformation that changes the size of an object. It involves a stretch or a shrink by a scale factor of k.

dilatation image The image of a figure in a plane after a dilatation.

direct variation A relationship between two variables in which one variable is a constant multiple of the other.

distributive property The property defined by $a(b + c) = ab + ac$.

division property of equality Dividing both sides of an equation by the same quantity produces an equivalent equation. For any numbers a, b, and c, where $c \neq 0$, if $a = b$, then $\frac{a}{c} = \frac{b}{c}$.

dodecagon A polygon with twelve sides.

domain The set of the first elements in a relation.

double root The solution of a quadratic equation where both roots are the same.

dynamic geometry software Computer software that allows the user to plot points on a coordinate system, measure line segments and angles, construct two-dimensional shapes, create two-dimensional representations of three-dimensional objects, and transform constructed figures by moving parts of them.

E

elements The individual members of a set.

enlargement A dilatation in which the image after the dilatation is larger than the original image, that is, $k > 1$.

equation An open sentence formed by two expressions related by an equal sign.

$2x - 7 = 3x + 2$ is an equation.

equilateral triangle A triangle with all sides equal.

equivalent equations Equations that have the same graph or solution.

equivalent expressions Algebraic expressions that are equal for all values of the variable.

$7a - 4a$ and $3a$ are equivalent expressions.

equivalent fractions Fractions such as $\frac{1}{3}$, $\frac{2}{6}$, and $\frac{3}{9}$ that represent the same part of a whole or group.

equivalent ratios Ratios such as $1:3$, $2:6$, and $3:9$ that represent the same fractional number or amount.

equivalent systems Systems of equations that have the same solution.

evaluate To determine a value for.

exponent The use of a raised number to denote repeated multiplication of a base. In $3x^4$, the exponent is 4, and $3x^4$ means $3 \times x \times x \times x \times x$.

exponential form A shorthand method for writing numbers expressed as repeated multiplications.

$$3^4 \text{ is the exponential form for } 3 \times 3 \times 3 \times 3 \text{ or } 81.$$

exponential notation The notation used by calculators to display numbers that are too large or too small to fit onto the screen of the calculator. For example, the number 135 000 000 000 might appear as "1.35 11" on a calculator screen. The number 11, to the right of the expression, indicates the number of places that the decimal point should be moved to express the number in standard form.

expression A mathematical phrase made up of numbers and variables, connected by operators.

exterior angle An angle contained between one side of a polygon and the extension of an adjacent side.

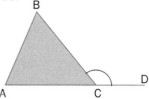

∠BCD is an exterior angle.

extrapolate Estimate values lying outside the range of given data. To extrapolate from a graph means to estimate coordinates of points beyond those that are plotted.

factor A number that is multiplied by another number to give a product.

$$3 \text{ is a factor of } 18.$$

factoring over the integers In factoring polynomials with integer coefficients, finding factors with integer coefficients.

family of lines Lines that share a common characteristic. For example, the family may have the same slope or the same y-intercept.

Fermi problem A rich estimation problem that requires the solver to make assumptions in order to solve the problem, and to check the reasonableness of the solution.

finite differences Differences between the y-values in tables with evenly spaced x-values.

first differences Differences between consecutive y-values in tables with evenly spaced x-coordinates. In a linear relation, the first differences are constant. For example:

x	y	First Difference
1	3	
2	5	$5 - 3 = 2$
3	7	$7 - 5 = 2$
4	9	$9 - 7 = 2$
5	11	$11 - 9 = 2$

first-degree equation An equation in which the variable has the exponent 1.

$$3(2x + 1) + 5 = 7x - 6 \text{ is a first-degree equation.}$$

first-degree inequality An inequality in which the variable has the exponent 1.

$$3x + 5 \geq 2x - 4 \text{ is a first-degree inequality.}$$

first-degree polynomial A polynomial in which the variable has the exponent 1.

   $6x + 5$ is a first-degree polynomial.

FOIL An aid in multiplying binomials where F refers to the product of the first terms, O, to the product of the outside terms, I, to the product of the inside terms, and L, to the product of the last terms.

function A relation in which, for each element in the domain, there is a single corresponding element in the range.

G

generalize Determine a general rule or conclusion from examples. Specifically, determine a general rule to represent a pattern or relationship between variables.

golden ratio A number, usually represented by Φ, that satisfies the proportion
$\dfrac{1}{\Phi} = \dfrac{\Phi}{1+\Phi}$.

golden rectangle A rectangle in which the ratio of length to width is the golden ratio, Φ.

graphing software Computer software that provides features similar to those of a graphing calculator.

greatest common factor (GCF) The monomial with the greatest numerical coefficient and greatest degree of the variables that is a factor of two or more terms.

   The GCF of $12ab$ and $8bc$ is $4b$.

H

Heron's formula A formula that can be used to calculate the area, A, of a triangle based on the lengths of the sides a, b, and c, and half the perimeter, s. $A = \sqrt{s(s-a)(s-b)(s-c)}$

hexagon A polygon with six sides.

hypotenuse The side opposite the right angle in a right triangle.

I

incentre The point at which the three angle bisectors of a triangle meet.

incircle of a triangle A circle, drawn inside a triangle, with centre at the incentre and radius, the perpendicular distance from the incentre to any side of the triangle.

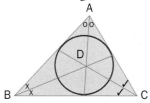

independent variable In a function, the variable whose value determines that of the dependent variable. On a coordinate grid, the values of the independent variable are on the horizontal axis.

integer A member of the set $\{..., -3, -2, -1, 0, 1, 2, 3, ...\}$.

intercept The distance from the origin of the xy-plane to the point at which a line or curve crosses a given axis.

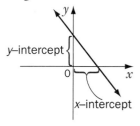

interior angle An angle that is inside a polygon.

interpolate To estimate values lying between elements of given data. To interpolate from a graph means to estimate coordinates of points between those that are plotted.

irrational number   A number that cannot be written as the ratio of two integers.

$\sqrt{2}$, $\sqrt{3}$, and π are irrational numbers.

isometric view   A two-dimensional representation of an object, showing the corner view.

isosceles trapezoid   A trapezoid in which the two non-parallel sides are equal in length.

isosceles triangle   A triangle with two equal sides.

kite   A quadrilateral with two pairs of adjacent sides of equal lengths.

lateral area   The area of the curved surface of a cone or cylinder. The sum of the areas of the lateral faces of a prism or pyramid.

lateral edge   The edge of a prism where two lateral faces meet.

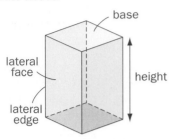

lateral faces   The faces of a prism or pyramid that are not bases.

length of a line segment   For a line segment with endpoints (x_1, y_1) and (x_2, y_2),

$$\sqrt{(x_2 - x_1)^2 + (y_2 - y_1)^2}\,.$$

length of the period (of a decimal)   The number of digits that repeat in a repeating decimal.

The length of the period of $0.\overline{27}$ is 2.

like terms   Terms that have exactly the same variable(s) raised to exactly the same exponent(s).

$3x^2$, $-x^2$, and $7x^2$ are like terms.

line of symmetry   A mirror line that reflects an object onto itself.

line segment   Two points on a line and the points between them.

linear equation   An equation in which each term is either a constant or has degree 1.

$y = 7x - 2$ is a linear equation.

linear relation   The relation between two values whose graph is or approximates a straight line.

lowest common denominator (LCD)   The least common multiple of the denominators of two or more rational expressions.

M

mass A measure of the quantity of matter in an object, measured in milligrams, grams, kilograms, or tonnes.

mathematical model A mathematical description of a real situation. The description may include a diagram, a graph, a table of values, an equation, a formula, a physical model, or a computer model.

mathematical modelling The process of describing a real situation in a mathematical form. See also *mathematical model*.

median (geometry) A line segment that joins a vertex of a triangle to the midpoint of the opposite side.

monomial A number, a variable, or a product of numbers and variables.

8, x, $-y^2$, and $3mn$ are monomials.

multiplication property of equality Multiplying both sides of an equation by the same quantity produces an equivalent equation. For any numbers a, b, and c, if $a = b$, then $ac = bc$.

N

natural number The set of numbers $\{1, 2, 3, 4, \ldots\}$.

net A pattern for constructing a three-dimensional object.

non-linear relation A relation whose graph is not a straight line.

numerical coefficient The number part of a monomial.

The numerical coefficient of $3m^2n$ is 3.

O

oblique triangle A triangle that is not right-angled.

obtuse angle An angle that measures more than 90° but less than 180°.

obtuse triangle A triangle with one obtuse angle.

octagon A polygon with eight sides.

ordered pair A pair of numbers used to name a point on a graph, such as $(-5, 3)$.

origin The intersection of the horizontal axis and the vertical axis on a Cartesian coordinate grid, described by the ordered pair $(0, 0)$.

orthocentre The point of intersection of the three altitudes of a triangle.

P

palindrome A number or word that reads the same forward and backward, such as 232.

parabola The graph of a quadratic function whose domain is the set of real numbers.

parallel lines Two lines in the same plane that do not intersect.

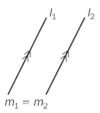

parallelogram A quadrilateral with opposite sides parallel.

partial variation A relation between two variables that involves a fixed amount plus a variable amount, such as $C = 3d + 15$.

pentagon A polygon with five sides.

percent A fraction (or ratio) in which the denominator is 100.

perfect square A number found by squaring an integer.

perfect square trinomial A trinomial that can be factored as the square of a binomial.

$$a^2x^2 + 2abx + b^2 = (ax + b)^2, \text{ where } a, b \neq 0.$$

perimeter The distance around a polygon.

period (of a decimal) The digits that repeat in a repeating decimal.

The period of $0.\overline{27}$ is 27.

perpendicular lines Two lines that intersect at 90°.

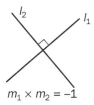

$$m_1 \times m_2 = -1$$

Platonic solids The five regular polyhedra: cube, regular tetrahedron, regular octahedron, regular dodecahedron, regular icosahedron

point of intersection The point that is common to two non-parallel lines.

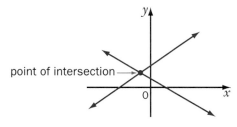

point of intersection

point-slope form of a linear equation For a line with a point (x_1, y_1), and slope m, the equation $y - y_1 = m(x - x_1)$.

polygon Closed figure formed by line segments.

polyhedron A three-dimensional object with faces that are polygons.

power A product obtained by using a base as a factor one or more times.

5^3 is a power.

principal square root The positive square root of a number.

prism A three-dimensional figure with two parallel, congruent polygonal bases. A prism is named by the shape of its bases, for example, rectangular prism, triangular prism.

proportion An equation that states that two ratios are equal.

proportional reasoning Reasoning or problem solving based on the examination of equal ratios.

pyramid A polyhedron with one base in the shape of a polygon and three or more triangular faces.

Pythagorean theorem The relation that expresses the area of the square drawn on the hypotenuse of a right triangle as equal to the sum of the areas of the squares drawn on the other two sides.

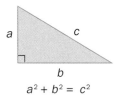

$$a^2 + b^2 = c^2$$

Q

quadrant One of the four regions formed by the intersection of the x-axis and the y-axis.

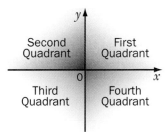

quadratic equation An equation in the form $ax^2 + bx + c = 0$, where a, b, and c are real numbers and $a \neq 0$.

quadratic function A function defined by a quadratic equation of the form $y = ax^2 + bx + c$.

quadrilateral A polygon with four sides.

R

radical sign The symbol $\sqrt{\ }$.

random number A number chosen from a set of numbers in such a way that each number has an equally-likely chance of being selected.

range of a relation The set of all the second coordinates of the ordered pairs in a relation.

rate A ratio of two measurements having different units.

> 100 km/h is a rate.

ratio A comparison of two numbers.

> 7:5 is a ratio.

rational number A number that can be expressed as the quotient of two integers where the divisor is not zero.

> $0.75, \dfrac{3}{8}$, and -2 are rational numbers.

ray Part of a line extending in one direction without end.

real numbers The set of all terminating decimals, all repeating decimals, and all non-terminating, non-repeating decimals.

> $0, -8, \dfrac{5}{6}$, and 0.4 are real numbers.

rectangle A parallelogram with four right angles.

rectangular solid A solid whose bases are congruent rectangles.

reduction A dilatation in which the image after the dilatation is smaller than the original image, that is, $0 < k < 1$.

reflection A transformation that maps an object onto an image by a reflection in a line.

reflection image The image of a plane figure after a reflection.

reflex angle An angle that measures more than 180° but less than 360°.

regression A method for determining the equation of a curve (not necessarily a straight line) that fits the distribution of points on a scatter plot.

regular polygon A polygon with all sides equal and all angles equal.

regular pyramid A polyhedron with a regular polygon as its base and lateral faces that are congruent triangles.

relation A set of ordered pairs.

repeating decimal A decimal in which one or more of the digits repeat without end.

rhombus A parallelogram in which the lengths of all four sides are equal.

right angle An angle that measures 90°.

right bisector of a line segment A line that is perpendicular to a line segment and divides the line segment into two equal parts.

right cone A cone in which the line segment joining the centre of the base to the vertex is perpendicualr to the base.

right cylinder A cylinder in which the line segment joining the centres of the bases is perpendicular to the bases.

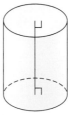

right prism A three-dimensional figure with two parallel, congruent polygonal bases and lateral faces that are perpendicular to the bases.

right triangle   A triangle containing a 90° angle.

rise   The vertical distance between two points.

roots   The solutions of an equation.

run   The horizontal distance between two points.

S

scale factor   The factor by which the coordinates of the points of a figure are multiplied to give the coordinates of the points on its dilatation image.

scalene triangle   A triangle with no sides equal.

scientific notation   Expressing a number as the product of a number, n, where $1 \leq n \leq 10$, and a power of ten.
$$2700 = 2.7 \times 10^3$$

scientific probe   A device that can be attached to a graphing calculator or to a computer in order to gather data involving measurement such as position, temperature, or force.

second-degree polynomial   A polynomial in at least one term of which the variable has the exponent 2, and no term has the exponent of the variable greater than 2.

$x^2 + 5x + 7$ is a second-degree polynomial.

second differences   The differences between consecutive first differences. In a quadratic function, the second differences are constant. For example:

x	y	First Difference	Second Difference
1	2		
2	5	$5 - 2 = 3$	$5 - 3 = 2$
3	10	$10 - 5 = 5$	$7 - 5 = 2$
4	17	$17 - 10 = 7$	$9 - 7 = 2$
5	26	$26 - 17 = 9$	

sector   A part of a circle bounded by two radii and an arc of the circumference.

sense   The orientation of a plane figure.

sequence   An ordered list of numbers.

similar   The relation of plane figures that have the same shape but not necessarily the same size.

simplest form of an algebraic expression   An expression with no like terms. For example,

$2x + 7$ is in simplest form.
$5x + 1 + 6 - 3x$ is not in simplest form.

sine law   The relationship between the sides and their opposite angles in any triangle.
$$\frac{\sin A}{a} = \frac{\sin B}{b} = \frac{\sin C}{c}$$

sine ratio   In a right triangle, for acute angle θ, the ratio of the length of the side opposite ∠θ and the length of the hypotenuse.

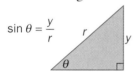

$$\sin \theta = \frac{y}{r}$$

slant height (of a cone)   The distance from the vertex to a point on the edge of the base.

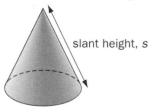

slant height, s

slant height (of a pyramid)   The height of each triangular face.

slope A measure of the steepness of a line. The slope of a line, m, containing the points $P(x_1, y_1)$ and $Q(x_2, y_2)$ is

$$m = \frac{\text{vertical change}}{\text{horizontal change}} \text{ or } \frac{\text{rise}}{\text{run}}$$

$$= \frac{\Delta y}{\Delta x}$$

$$= \frac{y_2 - y_1}{x_2 - x_1}, x_2 \neq x_1$$

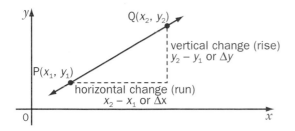

slope and y-intercept form of a linear equation The equation for the line through (x_1, y_1) with slope m and y-intercept b is given by $y = mx + b$.

solving a triangle Finding the values of all the unknown sides and unknown angles of a triangle.

spreadsheet A table used to manage data, including performing calculations with the data.

square A quadrilateral with four congruent sides and four right angles.

square root of a number A number that, when multiplied by itself, gives the original number.

straight angle An angle that measures 180°.

subtraction property of equality Subtracting the same quantity from both sides of an equation produces an equivalent equation. For any numbers a, b, and c, if $a = b$, then $a - c = b - c$.

supplementary angles Angles whose sum is 180°.

surface area The number of square units needed to cover the surface of a three-dimensional object.

system of equations Two or more equations studied together.

$$x + y = 3 \text{ and } 3x - y = 1$$
is a system of equations.

symmetry A quality of a plane figure that can be folded along a fold line so that the halves of the figure match exactly.

T

table of values A table used to record the coordinates of points in a relation. For example,

$$y = 2x + 1$$

x	y
−1	−1
0	1
1	3
2	5

tangent ratio In a right triangle, for acute angle θ, the ratio of the length of the side opposite $\angle\theta$ and the length of the adjacent side.

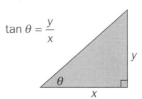

$$\tan \theta = \frac{y}{x}$$

term A number or a variable, or the product or quotient of numbers and variables.

The expression $x^2 + 5x$ has two terms: x^2 and $5x$.

terminating decimal A decimal whose digits terminate.

tetromino A polygon formed by joining three identical squares along whole sides.

transformation A mapping of points on a plane onto points on the same plane.

translation A slide transformation.

translation image The image of a plane figure after a translation.

transversal A line that crosses or intersects two or more lines.

trapezoid A quadrilateral with one pair of parallel sides.

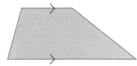

triangle A polygon with three sides.

triangular pyramid A polyhedron with a triangular base and three triangular lateral faces.

trigonometric ratio The ratio of the lengths of two sides in a right triangle.

trigonometry The branch of mathematics concerned with the measurement properties of triangles.

trinomial A polynomial with three terms.
$$x^2 + 3x - 1 \text{ is a trinomial.}$$

U

unit price The cost for one item, or for one unit of measurement.

unit rate A comparison of two numbers in which the second term is 1, such as $\dfrac{3 \text{ m}}{1 \text{ s}}$ or 3 m/s.

unlike terms Terms that have different variables, or the same variable but different exponents.
$$3x, 5y, -x^2, \text{ and } 2ab \text{ are unlike terms.}$$

V

variable A letter or symbol used to represent a number, such as x.

vertex A point at which two sides of a polygon meet.

vertex of a parabola The point of the parabola at which the graph intersects the axis of symmetry.

vertical line test A test for determining whether a given graph represents a function. If any vertical line intersects the graph in more than one point, then the relation is not a function.

volume The amount of space that an object occupies, measured in cubic units.

W

whole number A number in the set {0, 1, 2, 3, 4, 5, ...}.

X

x-axis The horizontal number line in the Cartesian coordinate system.

x-coordinate The first value in an ordered pair.

For the point P(4, 7), 4 is the x-coordinate.

x-intercept The x-coordinate of the point where a line or curve crosses the x-axis.

Y

y-axis The vertical line used as a scale for the dependent variable in the Cartesian coordinate system.

y-coordinate The second value in an ordered pair.

For the point A(5, −2), −2 is the y-coordinate.

y-intercept The y-coordinate of the point where a line or curve crosses the y-axis.

Z

zero of a function Any value of x for which the value of the function $f(x)$ is 0.

zero product property The property that, if the product of two real numbers is zero, then one or both of the numbers must be zero.

Technology Index

Index

Credits

Text Credits

106-110, 316-317, 360-361, Appendix C.
All References *The Geometer's Sketchpad*®
reprinted with permission.
248-250 (Material of CBL™ and CBR™)
Reprinted with permission of Texas
Instruments. Some material contained
in this text is adapted from
MATHPOWER™ 9, Western Edition,
author Knill, *MATHPOWER™ 11, Western
Edition,* author Knill; *MATHPOWER™ 10,
Western Edition,* author Knill;
MATHPOWER™ 9, National Edition,
author Knill. Reprinted by permission of
McGraw-Hill Ryerson Ltd.

Photo Credits

vii Corel Corporation/#761080; **viii** Corel
Corporation/#402056; **ix** Ian Crysler; **x** Ian
Crysler; **xii** Courtesy Terry W. Gintz e-mail:
terrywg@home.com. Homepage:
http://www.geocities.com/SoHo/Lofts/
5601/; **xiv** Canadian Press CP/Peter Bregg;
xv top Canapress Photo Service, bottom Ian
Crysler; **xviii** Canadian Tourism
Commission; **xx-1** T. Bonderund/First
Light; **5** Michael Newman/Photo Edit;
6 Canapress Photo Service; **16** top Jim
Brandenburg/First Light, bottom Thomas
Kitchin/First Light; **24-25** Ian Crysler;
26 Canapress/Associated Press AP; **34** Ian
Crysler; **37** Corel Corporation/#402056;
38 R.W. Ford; **48** K. Wothe/First Light;
49 Canapress/Bill Cooke/Associated Press
AP; **56** Canapress Photo Service;

58 Canadian Tourism Commission;
62-63 "Leaving Ontario" 1996 by Catherine
J. M. Rostron. Machine pieced, machine and
hand quilted, based on traditional pattern;
64 Dick Hemingway; **66** Natural Resources
Canada/National Air Library; **74** Ian
Crysler; **75** Ian Crysler; **82** Ian Crysler;
88 Courtesy Toronto Blue Jays Baseball
Club; **100** Hibernia Management and
Development Company Ltd.; **118** Royal
Ontario Museum # 922.17;
120 Canapress/Todd Korel;
124-125 Courtesy Terry W. Gintz e-mail:
terrywg@home.com. Homepage:
http://www.geocities.com/SoHo/Lofts/
5601/; **128** COMSTOCK PHOTOFILE
LTD; **134** Simon Fraser University/
Instructional Media Centre; **140** Courtesy
of the Royal British Columbia Museum,
Victoria B.C./# PN 10982; **147** Volvo Cars
of Canada Ltd.; **146** Ian Crysler;
153 SkyDome, Toronto, Canada;
159 Canadian Olympic Association/Claus
Anderson; **165** Courtesy of NASA;
172 Courtesy Cornwall Tourist Board;
182 Don Ford; **184** Canapress/David J.
Phillips/Associated Press AP;
188-189 Courtesy of NASA; **190** First
Light; **192** COMSTOCK PHOTOFILE
LTD/Russ Kinne; **204** David Clark/
Province; **217** Corel Corporation/#204064;
228 Canadian Space Agency; **247** Ian
Crysler; **248** Ian Crysler; **251** Corel
Corporation/#454047; **266-267** Canapress/
Ryan Remiorz; **268** Corel Corporation/
#204064; **270** Bob Torrez/Stone; **278** both

Canadian Olympic Association/Ted Grant;
287 Ian Crysler; **288** Canadian Sport
Images; **296** Ian Crysler; **300** John Winkley:
Ecoscene/CORBIS; **306** City of Hamilton;
308 Michael Newman/Photo Edit;
312-313 Don Ford; **314** Corel
Corporation/#761080; **318** Courtesy of the
Cochrane Area Community Development
Corporation; **326** Canadian Press CP/Peter
Bregg; **334** D. Lawrence/First Light;
346 CORBIS/#WTR042; **352** Don Ford;
362 Royal Observatory, Edinburgh/Science
Photo Library

Illustration Credits
2 Michael Herman; **75** Peter Cook;
111 Bernadette Lau; **133** Bernadette Lau;
187 Bernadette Lau; **214** Deborah Crowle;
236 Deborah Crowle; **237** Deborah Crowle;
262 Bernadette Lau; **313** Michael Herman;
340 Michael Herman; **357** Michael
Herman; **362** Michael Herman;
364 Michael Herman; **367** Michael
Herman; **368** Michael Herman; **369 center**
Michael Herman; **369 right** Peter Cook;
391 Michael Herman

Technical Art by Tom Dart, Bruce Krever,
Alana Perez, Claire Milne of First Folio
Resource Group, Inc.